Geography of
LATIN AMERICA

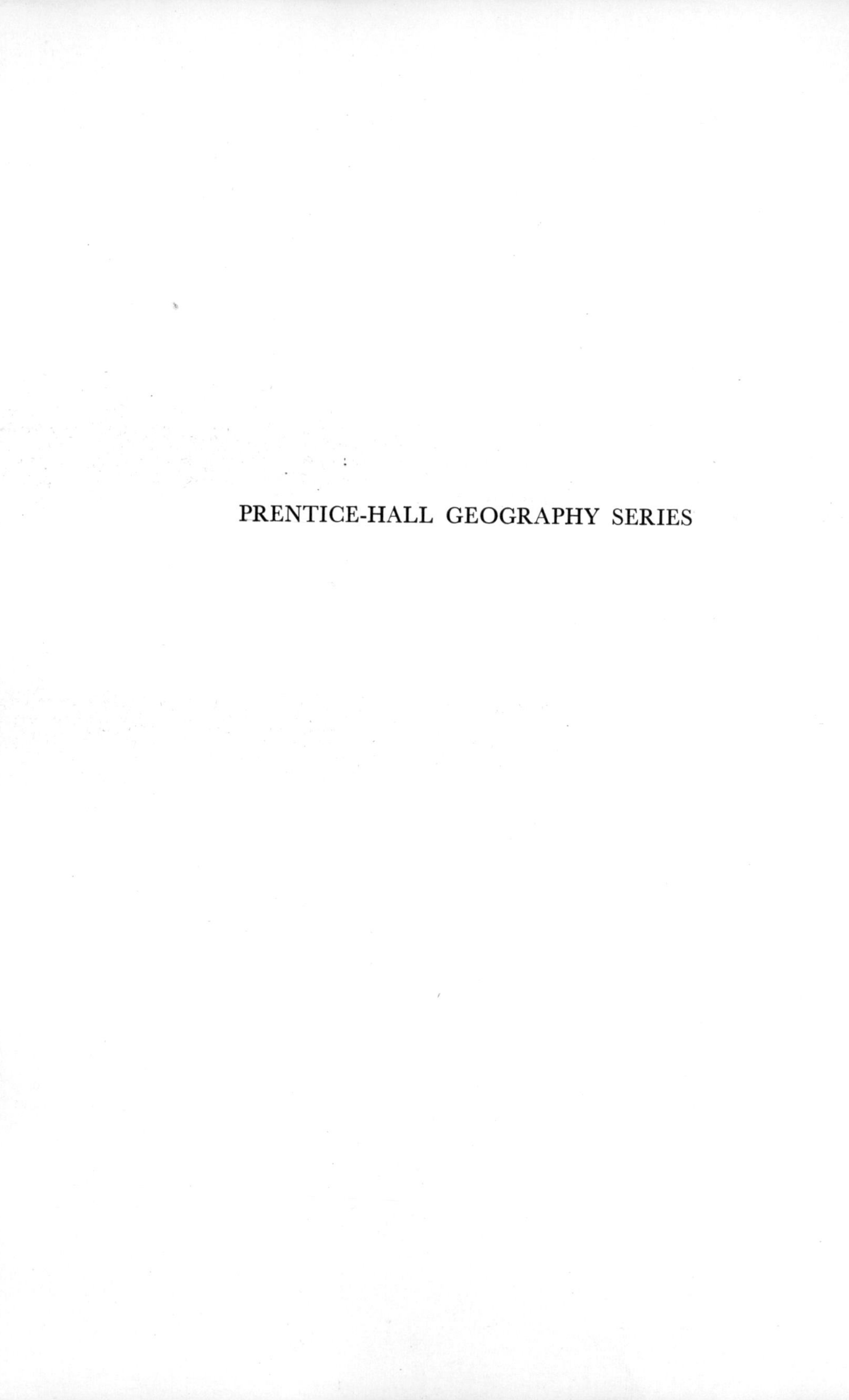

PRENTICE-HALL GEOGRAPHY SERIES

Geography of LATIN AMERICA

by FRED A. CARLSON

PROFESSOR OF GEOGRAPHY, THE OHIO STATE UNIVERSITY

THIRD EDITION

PRENTICE-HALL, INC.

Englewood Cliffs, N. J.

First Printing .... *January, 1952*
Second Printing .... *October, 1952*
Third Printing .... *October, 1953*
Fourth Printing .... *March, 1955*
Fifth Printing .... *January, 1957*
Sixth Printing .... *February, 1958*
Seventh Printing .... *January, 1959*
Eighth Printing .... *February, 1961*
Ninth Printing .... *March, 1964*
Tenth Printing .... *June, 1965*

PRINTED IN THE UNITED STATES OF AMERICA

35167-C

To My Grandson
"CHRIS." TURNER CARLSON, as
a testimony to my confidence
in the youth of the Americas.

PREFACE

SOUTH AMERICA, Central America, Mexico, and the West Indies are commonly known as Latin America or Hispanic America. Neither term is all-inclusive but merely represents dominant cultural influences. The Spanish forms, the noun *Hispania* and the adjective *Hispanic,* are derived from the Latin word *Hispanicus.* Hispania was the name of the Roman province of the Iberian Peninsula in which Lusitania, approximately the region of present Portugal, was a district. Thus, Hispanic refers not only to Spain but also to Portugal, and may rightly be applied to the Spanish-speaking and Portuguese-speaking countries of the Americas. But the Brazilians, of Portuguese heritage, object to the application of Hispanic to their country on the basis that the term is essentially Spanish. To meet this criticism the term *Ibero-America* has been proposed, the origin of Ibero being in the ancient Greek name for the homeland peninsula. The French-speaking Haitians, however, reject both Hispanic America and Ibero-America as terms for their republic. Apparently they maintain that the cultural attributes of other Latin or Roman lands, such as portions of France and Italy in addition to Spain and Portugal, should be recognized in the Americas. Similar opinions have been expressed by the Argentinians, in whose country there are potent evidences of Italian culture. To fulfill these broader demands there is the term Latin America. Everyone knows that the word Latin is used in connection with those countries of Europe which at one time were a part of the Roman Empire and whose languages were derived from Latin. However, the term Latin America, like Hispanic America and Ibero-America, is not free from objections and limitations. Probably a solution of this entangled nomenclature is found in the proposal that Hispanic America or Ibero-America should be used when one wishes to emphasize, primarily, Spanish and Portuguese influences. Hispanic has the priority of usage, but both terms are appropriate for this purpose. However, if there is a desire to recognize, as in this book, not only Spanish and Portuguese influences but also those of other Latin nations, then the term Latin America is more applicable.

Of course, the citizens of the individual countries do not wish to be known as Latin Americans, but as Brazilians, Argentinians, Mexicans, and so on, for the same logical reason that the inhabitants of the Anglo-American countries, the United States and Canada, want to be recognized, respectively, as Americans and Canadians. In fact, an attempt to interpret the affairs of a Latin American country in terms of Latin America as a whole can lead to nothing more than the evils of generalization and the fallacies of environmental determinism. While it is true that the political entities of Latin America have, in general, a common racial background, a culture of considerable similarity, and a natural landscape of striking likeness, these lands, nevertheless, do not possess geographical unity. In fact, Latin America, comprising 20 republics and important possessions of the United States, Great Britain, France, and the Netherlands, presents about as many different functionalities as there are major political divisions. For this reason the countries of Latin America are treated separately in this book.

The treatment of each country includes, for the most part, a brief review of the general characteristics, a description and interpretation of the natural-cultural regions, and a summation of the geography in relation to domestic and foreign affairs.

This book is an endeavor to establish a better understanding and appreciation of the countries of Latin America through the enumeration and interpretation of nature's conditions that have retarded or promoted their progress. Portions of the text have purposely been made factual and problematical to give students the task, with the assistance of the instructor, of determining the interpretation or solution not only for the educational value of stimulating an attitude of research but also to avoid undue indoctrination by the philosophy of the author.

One of the most difficult obstacles encountered in preparing this text was the inadequacy of data. Most of the available statistics on Latin America—particularly those on population, area, and trade—are subject to conjecture as to accuracy and completeness, and are probably not more than estimates. In fact, much of the area of Latin America has not been surveyed, and there are extensive regions that await rediscovery. This lack of available information made it impossible to complete regional studies of each country. However, while where is much need for further geographical research in Latin America, we must not be unmindful of the scholarly work of numerous organizations and individuals, so beautifully exemplified by the Map of Hispanic America prepared by the American Geographical Society.

Another serious problem was the spelling of Latin American geographical names. The profusion of languages and dialects in Latin America makes the standardization of word forms particularly difficult. The most progressive attempt toward unification is embodied in the work of the United States Geographic Board. The decisions of this worthy organization have been adopted in this book.

Selected references in geography and allied fields have been included for the purpose of encouraging extensive as well as intensive reading. The text is essentially a geographical index, with which additional references should be employed. Latin American geography, except in its basic form, is too "big" for inclusion in one book. In fact, the most striking change in Latin America during the past decade is its growth—its increasing population, greater agricultural and industrial development, and betterment of living conditions.

At the completion of this revision I am deeply conscious of my obligation to a host of contributors whose work has been a source of benefit and inspiration.

I again want to thank L. T. Hites, sometime Professor of Education in the Collegio Baptista, Rio de Janeiro, Brazil, for his generous and extremely effective cooperation. His service and interest in Latin America have made him a profound student and counselor of its land and people. For more than a decade he has given valuable suggestions, supplied important illustrations, and prepared manuscripts on Brazil, the West Coast countries of South America, and Central America—portions of which manuscripts I have adapted for this book. Dr. Hites' contributions have left their imprint on this book, but I alone assume full responsibility for any errors of facts or interpretations.

I also wish to recognize my indebtedness to my colleague, John H. Garland, for his assistance in the preparation of the subjects of the Guianas and the Maracaibo Basin. I am equally appreciative of the helpful suggestions and information received from B. H. Hunnicutt, President of Mackenzie College, São Paulo, Brazil, and Dr. Pedro C. Sánchez, Mexico, D. F. Many courtesies also, for which I wish to give cordial acknowledgment, were extended by various organizations—particularly by the American Geographical Society; the Library of Congress; the Pan American Union; the United States Bureau of Foreign and Domestic Commerce; the United States Weather Bureau; the Department of Meteorology, Mexico, D. F.; and the Pan American Institute of Geography and History, Mexico, D. F.

Since 1936, the date of the First Edition, *Geography of Latin America* has been adopted by many educational institutions. To their faculties and students I am indebted for constructive suggestions and valuable information employed in the preparation of this Third Edition. The late Doctor Clyde Cooper, Chairman of the Department of Geology and Geography, Ohio University, was most generous with his teaching experience and time in presenting a detailed record of suggested changes and additions. Doctor Ben. F. Lemert, Department of Economics and Business Administration, Duke University, has been equally helpful in making specific recommendations based upon his field experiences in Latin America. To Mr. George S. Mitchell, formerly of the United

States Weather Bureau, I am grateful for a compilation of climatological data. Ideas as well as photographs have been furnished by other geographers, also well known for their work in the field of Latin America, namely, Doctors C. Langdon White, Stanford University; Raymond E. Crist, University of Florida; and Edwin J. Foscue, Southern Methodist University. In the problems of orthography I received valuable assistance from Doctor Stanley M. Sapon, Department of Romance Languages, Ohio State University, for which I am most appreciative. The statistical data were supplied, primarily, by the Federal offices and related agencies, and every effort has been made to cite with credit the sources.

All three editions have been critically read by Nels A. Bengtson, a distinguished student of the geography of Latin America. For Dr. Bengtson's constructive suggestions and sympathetic interest, I wish to express my wholehearted appreciation and gratitude.

F. A. C.

CONTENTS

CENTRAL AMERICA, MEXICO, AND THE WEST INDIES

INTER-AMERICAN AFFAIRS

APPENDICES

MAPS AND ILLUSTRATIONS

[Maps and diagrams in *italics*]

MAPS IN FULL COLOR

INTRODUCTION

A new era. Mutual understanding and cooperation mark the beginning of a new era in inter-American and world relations. Now we know that each way of life is affected by the activities of others, and that individuals, groups, and nations cannot progress in isolation. We live in a world of interdependence and, ironical as it may seem, a world crisis was necessary to awaken us, the Americas, to a full realization of this fact. Heretofore our hemisphere has been the victim of misconceptions, not only between the United States and its southern neighbors, but also among all of the twenty-one American republics and Canada. How totally ignorant, and therefore unappreciative, we in the United States have been of the other Americas' greatness, as well as of their weaknesses in people, lands, and culture! We know now that great good can be obtained through friendly collaboration.

"Down there where they speak Spanish" is no longer a current Anglo-American pronouncement because we have learned that the south "Americas" and our own country have many things in common. All the American nations began as colonies from the Old World—including Spanish, Portuguese, French, Dutch, English, and African settlements. Each nation won its independence in the great American Revolution that took place during the period from 1776 to 1826. Washington established the freedom of thirteen English colonies; while Miranda, Bolívar, San Martín, Hidalgo, and others freed the Spanish colonies; and Pedro I gained independence for Portuguese America. The cultures of those early days are alive now in our country in New Mexico, Arizona, California, and Texas. In fact, certain portions of the United States are more Latin American than regions of the highlands of Peru and Bolivia or southern Brazil. Consequently, it is a mistake to think of the "border" as a line of abruption, dividing the Western Hemisphere into two distinct regions commonly known as Latin America and Anglo-America.

Our attention in this new era has been directed, not only to the correction of historical misconception, but also to a better understanding of the lands of Latin America. An examination of a map of the Western Hemisphere will re-establish, mentally, the position and land continuity of North America and South America. Note that Detroit, Michigan, is approximately due north of the most western point of South America; this fact shows that South America is not south but southeast of North

Courtesy The Columbus (Ohio) Gallery of Fine Arts.

Fig. 1. Portrait of George Washington by Gilbert Stuart, Frederick W. Schumacher collection.

"A slender acquaintance with the World must convince every man that actions and not words are the true criterion of the attachment of friends." . . . "Let us raise a standard to which the wise and honest can repair." In his Farewell Address, September 17, 1796, he said, " 'Tis our true policy to steer clear of permanent alliances with any portion of the foreign world."

Courtesy Pan American Union.

Fig. 2. Simón Bolívar.

"¡Qué bello sería que el Istmo de Panamá fuese para nosotros lo que el de Corinto para los griegos! Ojalá que algún día tengamos la fortuna de instalar allí un augusto congreso de los representantes de las repúblicas, reinos e imperios a tratar y discutir sobre los altos intereses de la paz y de la guerra, con las naciones de las otras tres partes del mundo. Esta especie de corporación podrá tener lugar en alguna época dichosa de nuestra generación."

America. So far east does it lie that the northeastern shores of Brazil are several hundred miles nearer than New York to the Mediterranean ports. The distance from the eastward bulge of Brazil to western Africa, at the nearest points, is about 1,600 miles, or one-half the distance from New York to London.

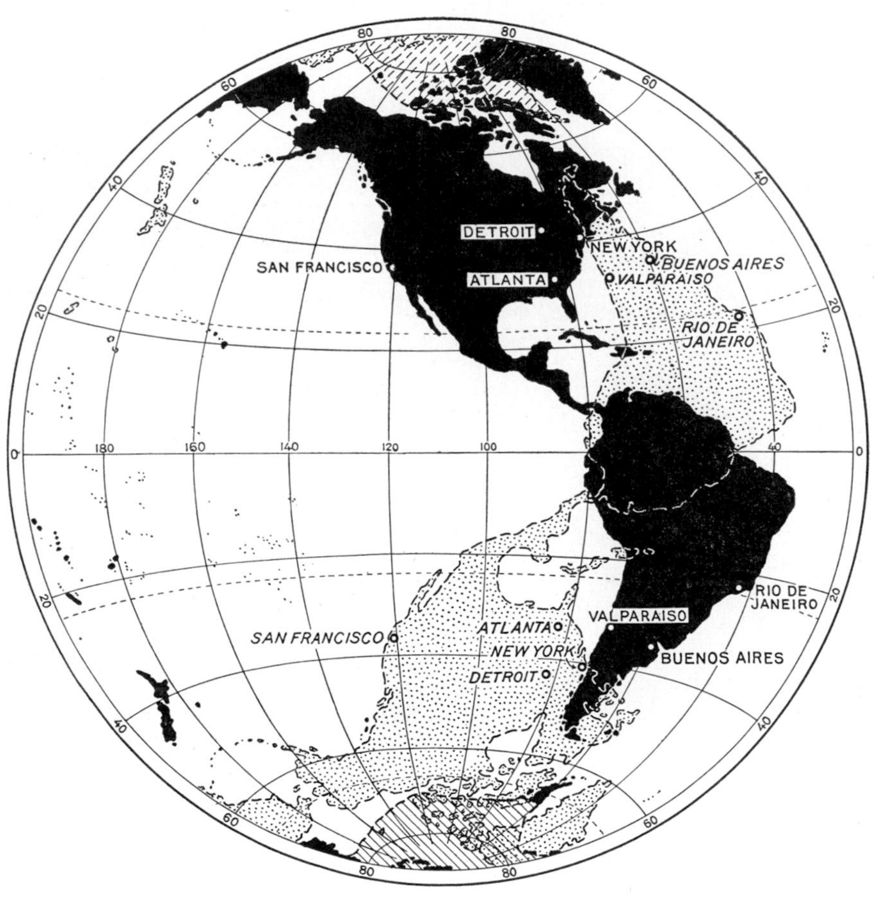

F. A. Carlson.

Fig. 3. North America and South America. More descriptive names for the two continents would be "Northwest America" and "Southeast America."

Are the Latin Americas "tropical"? It is true that the greater portion of their total area lies in the low latitudes, but it must be realized that the sun, or latitude, is not the only climatic control; other important factors are altitude, mountain barriers, land and water, ocean currents, air masses, and storms. In South America, Central America, and Mexico, extensive highlands in the low latitudes cause the climate range from tropical to polar temperatures. Furthermore, the "tropics" include deserts, regions of wet and dry seasons, and areas of heavy precipitation throughout the year. The white man's fear of the tropics has been only recently modified. The prevalent opinion that white people cannot live in the tropical regions has been qualified by evidence to prove that the white man can progress in the tropics through expert supervision of health, hygiene, sanitation, and nutrition. In later pages specific cases will be discussed.

With this era of better understanding among the Americas we have placed another milestone along the path of human progress—the spirit

Courtesy Moore-McCormack Lines.

Fig. 4. Nahuel Huapí National Park, Argentina. The higher mountains of the Nahuel Huapí region retain their snow cover even in summer. "Climates in Latin America range from tropical to polar."

of cooperation for the freedom of all peoples. In 1936, the Inter-American Conference for the Maintenance of Peace was held in Buenos Aires for the purpose of establishing a procedure of consultation to meet any emergency that might befall the relations of the Americas. Two years later, at the Eighth International Conference of the American States in Lima, Peru, the procedure of consultation was again emphasized. Then, at the outbreak of hostilities in Europe, the first meeting of the American Ministers of Foreign Affairs was held in Panama in 1939, for the specific purpose of discussing continental defense; a second consultation was held in Havana in 1940; this meeting was followed by the momentous sessions, the third meeting of Ministers of Foreign Affairs of the American Republics in Rio de Janeiro, Brazil, in 1942 and the fourth in Washington, D. C. in 1951. These conferences, and others of more recent date, have brought about active cultural, political, economic, commercial, and military cooperation among the Americas.

The plan of sympathetic understanding and fair collaboration, however, applies not to the Americas alone but to all freedom-loving lands worthy of respect and justice. This spirit of a world society of nations is found in the Eight-Point Pact, the Atlantic Charter. The essence of the plan is:

(1) no aggrandizement; (2) no territorial changes apart from the wishes of the people concerned; (3) each people shall choose its form of government; (4) equal access to trade and raw materials; (5) economic collaboration to provide for all improved labor, economic standards, and social security; (6) assurance of security against invasion; (7) freedom of the seas and oceans; and (8) abandonment of the use of force for realistic and spiritual reasons. Although the charter has not been universally accepted and has been grossly violated by some nations, its fundamental purpose has been generally respected by the Americas.

Courtesy American Geographical Society.

Fig. 5. The Isle of Pines, Cuba. A typical tropical savanna landscape.

To emphasize the futility of a policy of isolation and to restate the interdependence of the Americas and all other nations, and to establish the individuality or personality of each Latin American nation, this new edition of the *Geography of Latin America* presents three closely related units: (1) cultural and physical background, (2) political regions or countries, and (3) international relations.

CHAPTER I

CULTURAL HERITAGE

POPULATION ELEMENTS

THE PEOPLES OF THE AMERICAS total more than 309 million, and approximately half of this number live in Latin America—South America (109 million), Central America (9.6 million), Mexico (24 million), and the West Indies (17 million). With the exception of the Caribbean Islands, the regions are sparsely populated, and for the most part the inhabitants live in widely separated villages or cities. They include pure and mixed stocks of Indians, Europeans, and African Negroes. Since culture, the work of man, is in part an expression of racial and ethnic characteristics, let us examine each of the major groups.

Indo-America. Before the European conquest, the Indian population was spread here and there over the Americas. The population was more dense in the highlands than in the lowlands. Many opinions have been advanced to explain the origin of the occidental aborigines. Probably the most logical one, dealing with the dispersion of races, is that Asiatic peoples migrated to the Western Hemisphere across the region now known as the Bering Strait. They were people of the Mongoloid type. From them sprang the ancestors of the Mayas, the Incas, the Aztecs, and other great Indian groups of the early Americas. There are reasons for believing that waves of migration at different times extended across the Bering Strait and southward over the western lands of North and South Americas. Widely scattered focal centers of these early people were established in many places on the new continents. The search for food—better hunting, more abundant edible seeds, fruits, and fish—and the desire "to learn what is on the other side of the hill" led to the distribution of these original Americans to practically every part of the Western Hemisphere before the coming of the European settlers in the sixteenth century. Some groups may have become completely isolated from their companions and developed in the course of time into tribes of different characteristics. Furthermore, it is probable that originally they were not a homogeneous race of people, a fact which may in part explain why pure-bred Indians of today present widely different physical characteristics and traits.

When it became known that the seeds gathered for food could be cultivated and grown into desired plants, the science of agriculture was born in the New World. It meant permanent settlements, the congregation of peoples, and the development of power and supremacy. Finally, civic, religious, and ceremonial centers were established. They are typified by the Mayan ruins in Yucatán and Guatemala, the archaic pyramids of San Juan Teotihuacán in the Valley of Mexico, and many similar records of early culture. With continued progress, new foci were formed with carefully planned streets and an orderly arrangement of buildings, such as Tenochtítlan, the capital of the Aztec empire, the present site of Mexico, D. F.

The pre-Columbian Indian was nomadic, travelling from place to place. Archaeological excavations have revealed materials in Colombia, carried there from Mexico, the United States, and other distant lands. Even today the Indian seems to enjoy moving about. In Mexico, Guatemala, and other Latin American lands Indians may be seen with enormous packs of pottery, charcoal, and wood, trotting along roads and trails for unbelievable distances.

The Indian's contributions to the world are skills in weaving, basketry, and pottery and the development of many important plants, including maize, beans, potatoes, sweet potatoes, manioc, peanuts, squash, peppers, tomatoes, pineapples, and avocados. The Indian also made known the cacao bean, quinine, cocaine, tobacco, and rubber. Indian ingenuity is disclosed in pre-Columbian architecture, engineering, and the sciences of astronomy and mathematics. The hypothesis may be advanced that an Indian metallurgy which included the reduction of sulphides and oxides and the hardening, casting, and alloying of copper and silver was developed before the coming of the Spaniards.[1]

Among the Indian groups particularly worthy of mention are the Mayas of Guatemala and Yucatán; the Incas of Peru, Ecuador, Bolivia, and northern Chile; and the Aztecs in the Valley of Mexico. Of course many other groups, such as the Chibchas of Colombia and the Arawaks of the interior of South America and the Caribbean, have their own significance. Reference will be made to some of these groups later.

The Mayas. Sometime between 400 and 500 A. D. the Mayas entered Yucatán.[2] For many years prior to this period they had been living in

[1] C. O. Sauer: "The Personality of Mexico," *Geographical Review,* Vol. XXXI (1941), p. 360.

[2] Interesting descriptions of Mayan culture are found in the following books: G. C. Shattuck: *The Peninsula of Yucatán,* Carnegie Institution of Washington, Washington, D. C., 1933; Robert Redfield: *Chan Kom, A Maya Village,* Carnegie Institution of Washington, Washington, D. C., 1934; and T. A. Willard: *The Lost Empires of the Itzaes and Mayas,* A. H. Clark Co., Glendale, Cal., 1933.

the highlands of Guatemala and later in what are now the states of Tabasco and Chiapas of Mexico, and in the department of Petén of Guatemala. Part of this region, now a mass of dense tropical vegetation, had been cleared and put under intensive agriculture. Here great cities had been built, cities with spacious plazas and courts, lofty pyramid-temples, and monuments. It was probably one of the most densely populated areas of its size in the world at the time. In the realm of this old Mayan culture, wood carving, delicate molding in stucco, ceramics, painting, weaving, mosaics, and other arts were perfected. The Mayas

Courtesy Pan American Union.

Fig. 6. Yucatán, Mexico. Chichén Itzá: Temple of the Tigers, with Castillo in the background.

also excelled in the abstract sciences, such as arithmetic, chronology, and astronomy. Their chronology was more accurate than any other in the old world before the time of Pope Gregory XII, and in some respects more accurate than even our own Gregorian Calendar.

But, like many other great peoples, the Mayas suffered adversities that hampered their progress. They were forced to abandon the site of the old empire, and they migrated northward into the lands now known as the states of Yucatán and Campeche, Mexico. Reasons for this great Mayan exodus are not fully understood. Some of the causes cited are climatic changes that made the region unfit for human occupancy, internal strife, foreign invasion, disease, and the depletion of soil fertility. In the new Mayan region development was slow until about 1004 A. D., when the three largest city-states—Chichén Itzá, Uxmal, and Mayapan—formed a triple alliance under the name of the League of Mayapan.

Prosperity, brought about by this league, revived interest in art and architecture.

In the course of time tribes from other parts of Mexico, particularly from the Valley of Anahuac, entered Yucatán. Not only did they add to the social problems, but they also materially complicated the political situation. Civil wars followed, and by the time of the coming of the Spaniards, Yucatán was greatly reduced in importance.

The Incas. In a region of infinite contrasts, with intervening plateaus, valleys, and flanks of the lofty Andes, with a coastal desert on the west,

Courtesy Pan American Union.

Fig. 7. Incan Walls, Cuzco, Peru.

and rainy, tropical lands on the east, the Incas built a great empire. Students of ancient cultures have compared the renown of Inca civilization with that of the realms of Alexander, Caesar, Charlemagne, and Napoleon. Unlike the Mayas, the Incas were not a homogeneous people. It is recorded that in 1100 A. D. the Incas were a small tribe of Quechua-speaking llama herders, living near Cuzco. In the course of time, from 1100 A. D. to the middle of the fifteenth century, Incaland extended from Ecuador to central Chile. The golden age of this civilization is said to have been reached in 1450.

Inca ruins disclose material evidence of their culture, including knitting utensils, earthen jars, vicuña-wool fabric, and ornaments of gold, silver, or shells. Among the profusion of architectural structures still in existence stand the stupendous megolithic masonry of Fort Sacsahuaman above Cuzco and the walls of Machu Picchu. The Inca architecture in which balance and proportion seem to have been the main objectives is more massive and less ornate than the Mayan buildings. Of course all construction was done without machines, and the only tools were the inclined plane, the crowbar, probably the pulley, and stone and bronze hammers and knives. Reservoirs, irrigation forms, and roads are other lasting records of the Incas. Apparently roads or trails were given particular attention, for traces of them still exist throughout Incaland.

In the field the Inca farmer used plows of wood and a variety of tools for weeding and cultivating. Adobe for the walls and thatch for the roofs constituted the building materials for most of the houses. The knotted-string recorder, or *quipus,* was used for arithmetical calculations and narratives, and even today the llama herder may count his flock by means of this ancient recorder. The sundial was one of the methods used by the Incas to determine the position of the sun, the moon, the stars, and the seasons of the year. However, the hieroglyphic writings of the Mayans were not used by the Incas. The geographer should be interested to know that the Incas used relief maps made of clay, on which the natural features of their realms were represented. Not only does archaeological evidence index the early lands of the Incas, but their descendants give proof. For today the population in the Inca region of the past consists of 65 per cent Indian, 30 per cent mixed races, and the majority of the remainder of pure Spanish descent.

The Aztecs. The character and works of the Aztecs are better known than those of the Mayas or Incas. Elaborate collections of Aztec relics are on display in Mexico's National Museum of Archaeology, History, and Ethnology. Most impressive is the Aztec Calendar Stone or Stone of the Sun, a huge 24-ton monolith of basaltic porphyry with intricate markings, believed to have been used to determine the seasons and to tell the farmers when to sow and reap their corn. Mexico City contains other works of the Aztec period, including the so-called floating garden, or Zochimilco, located a few miles from the capital; and causeways, dikes, and irrigation forms. This ancient race excelled in agriculture, in gold- and silver-smith's art, in wood carving, and in the making of turquoise mosaics and featherwork. The Aztecs spun and wove cotton; made baskets, sandals, and pottery; and tanned skins. One of their many admirable traits, which has been handed down to modern Mexico, is their love for flowers. In addition, many of the present-day ornaments of gold, silver, wood, and feathers also reflect the influence of the artistic Aztec designs and symbols. The Aztec was truly a warrior, often referred to as the American Roman, but he was also a builder and a lover of the finer things of life.

From this discussion of the pre-Columbian Indian one might get the impression that all Indian works are superb and that all Indian qualities are good. Such a conclusion would be erroneous. One should not forget, however, that colonial domination subdued, and in many cases actually destroyed, a progressive Indian society, particularly in what are now the lands of Mexico and Peru. Every effort should be expended to preserve Indian traditions, Indian artistic individuality, Indian skills, and Indian patience and perseverance. Indians, like all other peoples, merit the rights of human beings.

Early immigration. In earlier days only Portuguese were admitted to Brazil. In fact, until the close of the colonial period, in 1808, vessels from other nations were forbidden to enter its harbors, except under special permit. Until the close of the nineteenth century, immigration to Brazil was almost exclusively Portuguese. In the last 50 years, however, several colonies of Germans, Russians, and Letts have arrived, and colonies of Japanese have been welcomed in the Amazon region and the state of São Paulo. During this period large numbers of Italians have made their homes in southern Brazil, as have numerous Spanish, German, Syrian, Greek, and Turkish colonists. At the close of the Civil War in the United States a few thousand North Americans found their way to the state of São Paulo. Their descendants have been almost entirely assimilated into the general population.

As in the Portuguese colony, only Spanish colonists entered the Spanish territories, though small numbers of persons of other nationalities participated as soldiers of fortune in the struggles for independence. During the past hundred years, however, there has been very little immigration into the west coast countries of Chile, Peru, Bolivia, Ecuador, and almost none to Colombia, Venezuela, and Mexico. Indigenous populations have developed in these countries, with relatively little infusion of fresh Spanish blood. On the eastern coast, in the south particularly, immigration has been steady and increasingly voluminous. Italians especially have entered this region in Argentina.

Immigration from Europe thus tends to avoid the tropics, finding its way principally to the southern ports on the Atlantic coast, and from there passing slowly into the interior. The large cities of the south Atlantic are distinctively European. Buenos Aires, Montevideo, and São Paulo are almost entirely white. Rio de Janeiro is largely white—more than half so, at any rate. The port cities of entry for immigrants normally retain great numbers of those who arrive, despite every encouragement by governmental authorities and by railroad companies, who have offered colonists free land, transportation, and financial backing if they would settle in the interior.

Of course, it is possible that the direction of immigration may change. A wave may some day flow toward the Bolivian Yungas, the Peruvian Montaña, or the interior of Brazil—no one knows.

African Negroes. The cultural and numerical strength of the Negro in the Americas to our south seems to have been ignored or not adequately recognized. While complete records are not available, probably there are not less than 23,000,000 Negroes in these southern lands, distributed as follows:

Mexico	300,000
Central America	638,000
West Indies	8,085,000
Brazil	12,870,000
Other regions	1,800,000

In the United States, the Negro population exceeds 12,000,000, and in Africa the members of the black race total more than 160,000,000. Early in the sixteenth century, the Spanish Crown was urged to legalize the importation of slaves as a substitute for the labor of Indians in mining and agriculture. The first slaves are said to have arrived in Española about 1502. Portuguese, Spanish, French, English, and Dutch companies —all shipped slaves to the West Indies, North America, parts of northern South America, the Guianas, and Brazil. From these coastal points the slaves were sent to the sugar, cotton, coffee, and tobacco plantations; to mining camps; and to domestic service in homes. Probably as many as 5,000,000 slaves reached the shore of northeastern Brazil, and it is reported that a far greater number landed in the West Indies—the two regions, at present, with a population dominantly Negro or mixed black and white.[3] African Negro culture is reflected in the fine arts, music, and sciences. In Brazil, Negro singers and musicians practically dominate the radio programs. They are justly recognized for their ability. Many have achieved fame as composers. Through the humid tropical lands of the Americas, the Negro and new ethnic groups of mixed races are growing in numbers, as well as in social, political, and economic power.

A century of immigration. Between 1820 and 1930, nearly 4½ million immigrants entered Brazil, more than were admitted by any other American nation except the United States and Argentina. The immigrants came from a number of European countries and, more recently, from Asia also. The 4½ million immigrants who landed in Brazil within the above period of 110 years were distributed by nationalities as follows: Italians, 34.5 per cent; Portuguese, 30.0 per cent; Spaniards, 12.2 per cent; Germans, 3.5 per cent; and others, 19.8 per cent. The number of German aliens and Brazilians of German birth or of German-born parents in Brazil today has been estimated to total 2 million. It was not until 1908 that the first Japanese colonists arrived in Brazil. In 1934, the Japanese statistics showed that some 873,000 Japanese were settled in foreign countries; Brazil, with 173,500 persons, held second place, pre-

---

[3] Arthur Ramos, *The Negro in Brazil* (translated from the Portuguese by Richard Pattee), The Associated Publishers, Washington, D. C., 1939, p. 9. The estimate of Negro immigrants—5,000,000—is probably too high.

ceded only by China. Since 1872 the total population of Brazil has increased from 10,112,000 to 52,000,000 in 1950.

During the colonial period, the growth of population in the lands of Argentina was slow, and few immigrants arrived. In 1810, at the beginning of the period of independence, the total population of Argentina amounted to about 405,000, almost entirely Spanish, and in 1950 the number was approximately 18,000,000. The difference between arrivals and departures of immigrants according to nationality from 1857 to 1939 is as follows: [4]

Nationality	*Numbers*	*Per Cent*
Italian	1,474,680	42.4
Spanish	1,143,339	32.9
Russian and Polish	265,836	7.6
German and Austro-Hungarian	132,739	3.8
Ottoman	108,353	3.1
French	105,468	3.0
British	14,685	0.4
Others	233,841	6.7
	3,478,941	100.0

In addition to Brazil and Argentina, the only other countries which have received a considerable number of immigrants are Cuba, 1,262,000 (1903–1932) and Uruguay, 510,000 (1900–1937).

It has been estimated that during the period 1821–1932 a total of 53.8 million immigrants reached the Western Hemisphere, of which Latin America received 14.4 million or about 27 per cent. If these statistics are approximately correct it can be said that relatively few immigrants migrated to Latin America and that the growth of population in the other Americas is primarily the result of the normal increase of births over deaths. Latin America has never attracted the pioneer or homesteader on a scale equal to that in the United States. One of the principal reasons was that land was difficult to obtain because most of the accessible land had been presented or acquired by members of the nobility or large land holding companies. By far the greater percentage of the immigrants supplied labor for the estates or urban centers.

Beginning with about 1900 and continuing for two or three decades, the Latin American countries, particularly Argentina and Brazil, attempted to encourage immigrants to come to their lands; elaborate publicity was circulated in Europe, advertising the proclaimed opportunities in the new Americas. In some instances greater privileges were extended to immigrants than to the nations' own citizens. Emphasis was placed primarily on the need for rural labor, and a considerable number

[4] Carlos Luzzetti Estevarena: "Ethnical Composition of the Population of Argentina," *Pan American Union Bulletin,* Vol. 75 (1941), p. 626.

of the immigrants took up residence in the farming regions; but in a relatively short time most of them migrated to the cities.

The extremely liberal open door policy of the early twenties, however, has become a policy of restrictions and selectivity. Latin America fully realizes that the call is not for untrained labor, but for skilled workmen in the building industry, highway construction, and manufacturing. Furthermore, Latin America needs capital, and that in part means immigrants with sufficient money and skill who will not become government charges. In fact the Latin American countries have become highly nationalistic in terms of their immigration policies, making it extremely difficult for the entrance of prospective citizens.

Growth of population. According to authoritative sources, "during the 1920–1940 period, Latin America added approximately 40 million, or about 41 per cent, to its population. In the same period the United States, starting with a larger population, added only 26 million, or roughly 25 per cent. The average annual rate of increase for the entire world between 1900 and 1940 is estimated to be 0.75 per cent, and this is the fastest rate the world has ever known; yet it is more than doubled by the recent pace in Latin America. This means that our southern neighbors are increasing their share of the world's population, and are doing it more rapidly than the people of any other region of equal area. . . . If the present growth rate continues, the population will be twice as large in 1986 as it is today, for it is doubling every 40 years; and by the year 2000 it will reach 373 million."[5] In all probability the present rate of increase in population in Latin America will not continue, due to economic and social changes now in evidence. It is generally accepted that as industrialization expands, the population increases, due to a reduction in the death rate caused by improvements in the economy and better living conditions. The birth rate, however, continues to increase or remain the same in the early stages of industrialization. But as the industrial activities develop and become more mature, the trend is toward a reduction in the birth rate with a consequent lowering in the rate of the growth of population. Of course it is obvious that the population pattern in form and size will vary in different Latin American regions.

The future. If one takes into consideration the natural increase in population, and also the fact that only limited numbers of immigrants are arriving each year in certain favored parts of Latin America, one may forecast the future racial complexion of the different areas with a fair degree of accuracy.

Argentina, Uruguay, southern Brazil, and the great central Brazilian

[5] Kingsley Davis: "Population Trends and Policies in Latin America," *Latin-American Studies,* The University of Texas Institute of Latin-American Studies, 1946.

plateau will become increasingly a white man's land; here the Indians will probably decrease in number and importance. The Pacific countries, Peru, Bolivia, Ecuador, and western Colombia, will become the home of an increasingly homogeneous amalgamation of the existing Spanish and Indian races, tending toward the predominance of the Indian. Chile, particularly its central valley, will remain largely white. The northern and northeastern coasts of Colombia, Venezuela, the Guianas, and far north Brazil will become areas of increasingly homogeneous combinations of the prevailing white and Indian races, with considerable proportions of Negro blood, unless the Negroes come in larger numbers from the Caribbean islands. The eastern coast of Brazil north of Rio de Janeiro will remain heavily Negro, and the far interior valleys and plateaus will remain predominantly Indian. There never has been, there is not now, and probably there never will be a homogeneous race of people on the South American continent. Middle America will become more and more a land of peoples of mixed races; Negro and white in the West Indies and white and Indian in Mexico and Central America.

What, now, about the industrial and economic efficiency of Latin America when examined in terms of races? If the Negro and the Indian races are not industrially proficient, we may anticipate that where they predominate in the population there will not be any great industrial advance. If European emigration brings to Latin America races that are not economically and industrially proficient in their homelands, we may expect that they will not become efficient in Latin America—unless climatic and other geographic factors stimulate them, and unless sufficiently pronounced social stimuli appear in their new environments to inspire such efficiency. At the present time the Italian and the German seem to be the industrial pioneers on the southern continent. They are locating primarily in Argentina and central and south Brazil. Will their influence and example be strong enough to carry along their less energetic brethren of Spanish and Portuguese extraction? Present tendencies seem to indicate that they will, and that this part of the continent, besides continuing its production of raw materials for exportation, will increasingly manufacture goods to supply its own needs and the needs of its neighbors. Central Chile also has an industrial and cultural future of promise. Within its borders are descendants of a Spanish ancestry drawn principally from the stronger races of northern Spain; descendants of the Araucanians, the fiercest Indians of primitive Americas; and thrifty Italian and German immigrants, with some British. Mexico likewise is in a position to expand her industrial activities. In all, however, Latin America will remain for many years essentially a producer of raw materials for foreign and domestic markets and limited industrial products for local consumption.

CULTURAL CHARACTERISTICS

The culture of a region may spring from one or several sources. It may be endogenous—that is, derived from within itself. On the other hand, it may be the result of diffusion, or importation, and thus be acquired. It could be the result of integration or fusion. In fact, culture could be the result of any one, or a combination, of these sources. Apparently, the environmentalist is concerned with endogenous or indigenous culture, which he may cite as the result of the relations between man and his environment. Undoubtedly he also recognizes that diffused or infused culture may likewise reflect environmental relationships.

In most regions a culture is dominantly of diffusion and infusion. In the Americas, the cultural patterns and functions are peculiarly variable and complex, and they clearly establish the above contention. In this respect let us first refer to the ancient Latins, whose culture had been carefully and logically elaborated until in imperial Rome it became exceedingly intricate. When the numbers of barbarians entering the Empire were too great to be controlled politically, they overthrew the Romans. But the culture of Rome dominated, and parts of central and southern Europe became culturally Latin. The penetrating power of this remarkable culture was so pronounced that it not only conquered Spain and Portugal, but through these peoples was transmitted to the New World. To this day we speak of *Latin* America.

Notice, now, what actually happened in Latin America. Three virile racial groups were involved—Indians, Europeans, Negroes. There was little objection to intermarriage among them, especially in the South Americas. Consequently fusion was rapid, although never complete in any locality. Each race possessed its own culture and traditions, differing from those of the other races. European culture was by far the most complex and highly organized of the three. In some respects it was exceedingly aggressive, as in politics, religion, system of government, and the ownership of the sources of wealth. Indian culture was passively resistant; Negro culture showed patience and sociability. Both Indian and Negro at times withstood the encroachments and demands of the European with show of armed force, but neither made any serious attempt to *convert* the European. The European made every effort to force certain aspects of his culture upon the others, notably his religion, his language, his system of government, and his tendency to congregate in urban centers.

Early efforts were made by Europeans to enslave the Indians. Workmen were needed for the sugar plantations, and the dominant Europeans wanted to be masters rather than to work with their hands. Slavery of African Negroes and aborigines from the Cape Verde and Canary Islands had existed in Spain and Portugal for a century before the discoveries of Columbus. Consequently raids were conducted, and Indians were captured and sold. When their missionary protectors finally secured an imperial order forbidding the enslavement of Indians, Negroes were imported to take their place, and the missionaries who dared oppose the dominant economic system were soon exiled from the scene.

But slavery in Latin America seldom became, after the first outburst of uncontrolled savagery, a brutal institution. Slaves were simply the humbler folk who worked for their food and shelter without wages. They were converted and became Christians. They attended the same churches their masters attended. They worshipped at the same altars. Fusion of culture among them was certain to be rapid. After the first orgy of destruction by the unprincipled Conquistadores had passed, laws were enacted for the protection of the Indians. Masters were in general as illiterate as their slaves. They were equals in many respects, and because they were equals there was very little restraint or hesitation about intermarriage. For these reasons the whole slave system was modified. Although it existed in Latin America long after it was abolished in the United States (slavery was ended in Greater Colombia in 1821, but was not abolished in Brazil until 1888), it existed in a quite modified form.

Language. In the fusion of language which occurred, the European was victor. Throughout Brazil Portuguese is the universal tongue, except among the Indian tribes in the far interior fastnesses, which have never really been touched by the white man's type of life. Throughout the remainder of the continent, except in the Guianas, Spanish is the official language. In the villages, far from civilization, large sections of the population are bilingual, using both Spanish and a native tongue.[6] The cities are primarily Portuguese or Spanish. Yet the language is not entirely that of the mother country. There are many important differences of pronunciation, of vocabulary, of word usage. Many Indian idioms have entered the local Portuguese and Spanish languages. Furthermore, in portions of the Andean countries, particularly in Ecuador and Bolivia, Indian dialects are spoken.

Agriculture. In agriculture, both climate and expediency forced a compromise. Some plants, like the sugar cane, the coffee tree, and some fruits of the intermediate latitudes, were brought in by the settlers, as also were some strains of European vegetables. But the banana, coconut, cacao, and any number of tropical fruits and nuts were indigenous, and culture of these plants was taken over eagerly by the Europeans, as also was the growing of numbers of vegetables, such as manioc, maize,

[6] In Paraguay, both Guarani, an Indian tongue, and Spanish are spoken by many of its inhabitants.

potatoes, pumpkins, beans, and tobacco. Wool and cotton fibers were known to the Indians for centuries and were widely used.

In the mode of agriculture, native and European methods were employed side by side. The invaders taught the natives; the natives taught the invaders. Among the Indians large plantations were absolutely unknown. Agriculture was carried forward in a very rudimentary manner, the work being done principally by women using primitive tools. Fruit trees in general grew wild, and what culture existed was elementary. Only on the Andean plateaus was there an established agriculture in which nearly everyone participated and where semi-scientific efforts were made to produce better strains of plants. Andean lands were often community owned and cultivated.

When the invaders settled down to make a business of agriculture, they planted huge fields of sugar cane, cotton, rice, and other field crops. They cleared immense areas for orange groves, bananas, cacao, and coffee. At the present time these huge plantations exist for the production of a single market crop, seldom diversified. They employ costly modern machinery, generally imported. Alongside the plantations are the small homes of the humble peasant workmen, mostly peons, who make no effort to till more than the very smallest plot of ground to produce absolutely necessary food. Moreover, in areas far away from the infrequent means of transportation, and back from the larger cities, there is no organized agriculture at all.

Mining. Mining is now carried forward in the larger centers, with the use of distinctively North American or European machinery and methods, and quantity production is the rule. Vast areas of mineral-producing lands are owned or leased by foreign capital, except where local laws restrict such ownership. But prospectors are numerous. Often they are scouts staked and paid by great companies. When a district is opened, as through the discovery of petroleum or gold, a new but not always permanent settlement is established.

Transportation and communication. Transportation has always been difficult. The Indians had their trails through the primeval forests and their canoes for use on the rivers. Throughout most of the length and breadth of the continent these are still important means of travel and transport. In most places the nature of the countryside is such that the construction and maintenance of any extensive railway or highway system would be economically prohibitive. The old Indian trail, with burdens carried on the backs of burros or men, is still the usual method of transport. Steamers and launches are found on many of the navigable rivers, but vast numbers of flat-bottomed boats, driven by paddles or by a single sail of the style employed by the Indians for centuries, are still in use.

Railways and improved roads are costly and depend upon a large population that wants to travel or has goods to dispatch. Throughout Latin

America public finances are for the most part low, and funds with which to purchase railway equipment are lacking, except in limited parts of the region. Personal incomes are in general small, and consequently railway fares have to be at a minimum. The result is that few railways have been constructed, except in the more highly populated and prosperous regions. In all of Latin America there are only 78,000 miles of tracks, as compared with 250,000 miles in the United States. Two-thirds of the continental mileage is concentrated in central Brazil and Argentina.

The cutting and maintenance of improved roads, wide enough for vehicles, through tropical vegetation is difficult. In many places trees

Courtesy Pan American Union.

Fig. 8. A rural scene in Uruguay. The new and the old means of transportation.

and brush grow profusely and will destroy any road that can be laid down unless constant maintenance is practiced. In other places the terrain is rocky and sparsely settled—or there is no rock at all with which to ballast roads. In still other places the mountainous nature of the countryside forbids the construction of anything but trails. Then, too, wide roads presuppose wheeled vehicles, and improved roads imply automobiles, neither of which are dominant. Where people ride muleback or horseback, and where animals are cheap and wagons or cars are costly, it is easy to use the primitive trails that have existed for centuries. Thus the primitive and the modern method of transportation are found side by side.

Regarding transportation there are two theories. One advocates waiting until population densities permit the systems to be opened, primarily at the cost of the local population. The other theory advocates building highways and railroads in advance of population, at the cost of the state, to open new areas to settlement and to stimulate the movement of population and goods. Throughout Latin America the tendency has been to construct in advance of needs. Today the increasing development of airplane service has effectively overcome some of the past obstacles encountered on land and water.

The postal service, the telegraph, and now the radio are, of course, the creations of modern civilization, as are also the steamship lines along the coast or on navigable rivers. These services are now almost universally available.

Courtesy C. Maxwell.

Fig. 9. Nambikura Indian huts near Cuiabá, Brazil.

The aboriginal cultures had none of the advantages of the machine age. However, today in most Latin American countries modern services are provided and thoughtfully administered. Except in populous areas, some of the transportation systems are operated at an annual deficit, which is absorbed by the government. Public utilities are owned and operated primarily by the government.

Architecture. In architecture the same imperfect fusion of three cultures that was detected in agriculture and transportation is to be seen. Some of the larger cities have buildings that are reminiscent of Paris or Madrid or Atlanta. A few larger places are tending toward the North American skyscraper city. In São Paulo, Rio de Janeiro, Lima, Montevideo, and other cities are department stores that remind one to some extent of the stores in medium-sized urban centers of the United States. There are municipal theaters and libraries and museums in some of the capital cities that are distinctly Parisian in their magnificence and interest. Factories operated usually by electricity remind one of the factories of Cleveland or prewar Turin. The architectural pattern for these larger buildings, of whatever type, is distinctly a European or American contribution, not aboriginal.

The architecture of the homes is somewhat different, for it is more adapted to climatic demands. When Portuguese or Spanish family groups began to arrive and settle in urban centers or in the country, they brought with them ideals of construction from the homeland. In the cities and towns, and even in the open country, one may see large numbers of these homes, adapted to tropical or subtropical conditions, but still reflecting the architectural ideals of the old country. The rooms are usually large, airy, and well shaded. The walls are thick and

Courtesy Moore-McCormack Lines.

Fig. 10. Palacio Salvo, Montevideo, facing Plaza Independencia.

plastered both inside and outside. Roofs are tiled; many windows are barred; gardens are cultivated and filled with beautiful flowers. A general air of aristocratic comfort pervades these homes. In the cities many modern conveniences have been introduced. Electricity, gas, running water, and sewage systems are features found in large cities, but not yet widely introduced in smaller towns or rural areas. Even in the best of the older homes the floor boards are usually wide and rough. Doors and windows are of simple hand construction, not milled. The architecture of these homes is distinctively Spanish or Portuguese.

Close to these attractive homes are the homes of the poorer classes—usually with adobe walls, of one or two rooms, frequently unplastered, with dirt floors, unglazed windows, and doors like those seen on sheds in the United States. These poorer-class homes are a compromise between the humbler Spanish home and the mud village of the Indian. In larger cities carefully planned building codes now make impossible the construction of any but sanitary and attractive homes, so that in the future these picturesque but unwholesome humbler constructions will finally disappear from the cities. In rural areas there is no code and consequently no control.

Courtesy American Geographical Society.

Fig. 11. A modern home in the Isle of Pines, Cuba.

Native simplicity and foreign style in dress. In dress there is the same tendency to compromise between native simplicity and foreign style. In the cities, among those who have come into contact with European models, the dress is the same as that of Europe or of the United States. Officialdom in Latin America dresses much more elaborately than do people of the same social scale in other places. Frock coats, canes, and other marks of the London or Parisian *gentleman* are in evidence in some urban centers. At the opera there is a blaze of colorful European dress, on the part of both men and women, that is very striking.

But the laboring man wears his cord sandals, his simple cotton trousers, and his shirt that does not tuck in. His wife is dressed modestly and comfortably in simple peasant style. In the upland areas the enveloping shawl of the Indian is the dominant aspect of many a street and market scene, as undoubtedly it has been for many centuries past.

Customs. In customs, folklore, and religion there has been a more complete and apparent fusion of cultures, with a disappearance of the main outlines of the simpler native modes and mores, and a dominance of the European system. That is, although the outlines are European, many of the details are native or Negro.

In the early colonial days many of the newcomers were dominated by an intense religious enthusiasm. They felt it a divine duty to convert the aborigines to the Christian faith. Later, when Negroes were imported, it was a feeling that slavery could be justified only when the slaves had an opportunity to receive the benefits of the Christian faith. Therefore, every effort was put forth by priests and other missionaries for their conversion, a process in which many slave owners wholeheartedly cooperated. The venerable "missions" of various places in both North and South America are standing testimonials to the zeal of these representatives of the Church.

Ideals of aristocracy. The prevalent ideals of aristocracy indicate an interesting fusion of cultures of the three races. Among the Indians there was never any antipathy to a community of work and a community of rewards of labor. All the Negroes were slaves and toilers. The European of the adventurer class never looked upon manual labor or the humbler callings of life with anything but disfavor. Now, in the United States, men of the professional classes will, after office hours, don their old clothes, and so will their wives. Together they will potter about the yard and the garden, dig in the dirt, build fences, paint, or do any number of tasks that bring them a sense of welcome relief from the mental strains of the day. Spanish or Portuguese professional men would seldom think of doing anything of the sort. It would be beneath their dignity. A professional gardener is employed to care for the lawns and flowerbeds of half a dozen families. Workmen of various sorts are called in for the other chores in which North American professional men would take delight.

White folk, or those predominantly white, of the upper class have always been the owners, the directors, the controllers, and they have been served by the humbler colored folk. White men have become the physicians, lawyers, government employees, university teachers, army officers, and merchant princes. (Of course, there has always been a large class of Portuguese and Spanish farmers and laborers in Latin America, but we are not here speaking of them.) The result of this uppercrust attitude has been the development of a very distinct class consciousness on the part of large numbers of people. Every family living in even moderate comfort keeps a servant or two. In the occupations also there are sharp lines of cleavage. The seamstress or elementary school teacher or the most humble office employee is socially far above the mechanic, the laborer, or those who serve in the homes.

In fact, one of the major problems in Latin America today is the result of class distinctions between the so-called aristocratic minority and the masses of poor people. The middle class, so prominent in the United States, does not exist in Latin America except in a few limited areas.

Education. The tradition of higher education has never profoundly influenced the mass of Latin American citizens. For that matter, it has never deeply influenced the Spanish or Portuguese people in their own countries. An ideal of university education and professional training has prevailed for the smaller group of the upper classes, and there have been many notable examples of brilliant authors and orators, artists and musicians, and some scientists. But among the rank and file of folk there has never been a thirst for knowledge or a deep desire to attend school or to send their children to school.

Most of the earlier colonists were illiterate folk, deeply interested in carving out a living, not in attending school. Until the time when the colonies attained their independence, there was a strict embargo on printing presses, and the importation of books was severely controlled. Perhaps the kings in Europe realized the danger of freedom of the press, for they effectually prevented the importation of printing machinery into the provinces except for the little that was smuggled in occasionally. Neither the Indians nor the Negroes had any educational ideals, as North Americans understand them. Consequently, in the fusion of cultures which followed the fusion of the races, there has never been any great demand for an elaborate educational system.

Citizens of Latin American nations, however, are deeply interested in public life and current events. Newspapers there carry numerous serious articles dealing with government activities and finances. Social questions are discussed on their merits, not only on editorial pages, but throughout the paper. Foreign trade, taxes, tariffs, industrial processes—all are given abundant space. The scent for "news" of a spectacular flavor that appears to dominate a large section of the press of the United States is strikingly absent from the leading papers of Latin America. Screaming headlines are almost unknown.

Groups of people meet on the street corners or in front of cafés to discuss political, social, or economic questions or even principles of education, philosophy, and religion. There is a solidity to the conversation of mature Latin Americans, particularly the whites, that is refreshing. Their interest in national and world affairs is strikingly like that of thoughtful English groups.

Many efforts have been made to establish and promote elementary schools for the masses, and they are becoming increasingly successful despite the cost and other difficulties, and notwithstanding the general disinterestedness of the common people in education. There have always been some private schools, and the governments have promoted secondary schools in all the principal cities, usually for the preparation of elementary school teachers. There have always been, from the earliest days, professional schools of medicine, law, theology, and military science, attended by sons of the aristocracy. Seldom have they been organized into a university or college in the North American sense of the word. In recent years there have appeared agricultural colleges and schools of mines that have made great strides. There are periodicals dealing with agricultural interests, agricultural educational institutions, experiment stations, and agricultural societies scattered throughout Latin America. The practical utility of this type of education is clear.

With the cultural heritage what it is (and this is no reflection upon it whatsoever), there probably will be no immediate wave of enthusiasm for popular education throughout all of Latin America. The *governments* have established schools and in some cases require children to attend. But the *people themselves* have not clamored for educational opportunities.[7]

Personalities. Visitors to our neighbors comment upon the politeness, courtesy, and gentility of many of the people they meet. The source of this almost universal characteristic is deep-seated and fundamental. It lies in the fusion of three cultures within a generally European frame of reference. The ideals of the Indian culture in Latin America included kindness, consideration, self-restraint, and hospitality; and many of these same values were stressed in the culture of the Negroes. Thus the European tradition of courtesy was brought into an atmosphere that favored easy adaptability and offered no great obstacles to the process of cultural diffusion for these patterns. The culture produced by the fusion retained all of these values in a coherent whole. To a North American, accustomed as he is to so much brusqueness, this Latin American consideration and quiet courtesy are refreshing. It is so surprising and so genuine that North American tourists and businessmen have sometimes taken advantage of it. Some are demanding and thoughtless in their expression toward native Latin Americans. Consequently they may leave behind them unpleasant feelings and an unwholesome attitude toward the United States and her citizens in general. Indeed, a good deal of the criticism which the Latin Americas level against so-called "Yankee Imperialism" would disappear if Americans visiting these southern nations would be personally more considerate.

[7] Ernesto Nelson: "A Problem for the Americas," *Points of View*, No. 5 (1942). Translated by Clarabel H. Wait, Division of Intellectual Cooperation, Pan American Union, Washington, D. C.

SELECTED REFERENCES [8]

Benedict, R. F.: *Patterns of Culture,* Houghton Mifflin Company, Boston, 1934.

Benedict, R. F.: *Race: Science and Politics,* Modern Age, New York, 1940.

Carlson, F. A.: "American Settlement in the Isla de Pinos, Cuba," *Geographical Review,* Vol. XXXII (1942), pp. 21–35.

Compton, George C.: "How many Americans?," *The Americas,* Vol. 1, No. 5 (July, 1949), p. 3.

Crist, R. E. and Chardón, Carlos: "Intercultural Colonial Politics in the Americas: Iberians and Britons in the New World." *The American Journal of Economics and Sociology,* Vol. 6, No. 3 (1947), pp. 371–385.

Davis, Kingsley: "Population Trends and Policies in Latin America." *Latin-American Studies II,* The University of Texas Institute of Latin-American Studies, The University of Texas Press, Austin, 1946, pp. 25–46.

Grubb, K. G.: *The Lowland Indians of Amazonia,* World Dominion Press, London, 1927.

Hill, Lawrence F.: "Confederate Exiles to Brazil," *Hispanic American Historical Review,* Vol. 7 (May, 1927), pp. 192–210.

Holdridge, Desmond: "Toledo: A Tropical Refugee Settlement in British Honduras," *Geographical Review,* Vol. 30 (1940), pp. 376–393.

Jefferson, Mark: "An American Colony in Brazil," *Geographical Review,* Vol. XVIII (1928), pp. 226–231.

Joyce, Thomas A.: *South American Archaeology,* G. P. Putnam's Sons, New York, 1912.

Joyce, Thomas A.: *Mexican Archaeology,* The Medici Society of America, Boston, 1920.

Joyce, Thomas A.: *Central American and West Indian Archaeology,* The Medici Society of America, Boston, 1916.

Karsten, Rafael: *The Civilization of the South American Indians,* Alfred A. Knopf, Inc., New York, 1926.

"Latin American Migration Statistics," *Commercial Pan America* (No. 87), Pan American Union, 1939.

Means, Philip A.: "The Incas: Empire Builders of the Andes," *National Geographic Magazine,* Vol 73 (February, 1938), pp. 225–264.

Morley, S. G.: "Yucatán, Home of the Gifted Maya," *National Geographic Magazine,* Vol. 70 (November, 1936), pp. 591–644.

Petrullo, Vincenzo: "Ancient Civilizations of America," *Bulletin of the Pan American Union,* Vol. LXIX (March, 1935), pp. 169–182.

"Pioneer Settlement," *Special Publication No. 14,* American Geographical Society, New York, 1932.

Price, A. Grenfell: "White Settlers in the Tropics," *Special Publication No. 23,* American Geographical Society, New York, 1939.

Price, A. Grenfell: "White Settlement in the Panama Canal Zone," *Geographical Review,* Vol. XXV (1935), pp. 1–11.

Radin, Paul: *Indians of South America,* Doubleday, Doran, New York, 1942.

Ramos, Arthur: *The Negro in Brazil* (translated from the Portuguese by Richard Pattee), The Associated Publishers, Washington, D. C., 1939.

Rippy, J. Fred: "The Japanese in Latin America," *Inter-American Economic Affairs,* Vol. 3, No. 1 (Summer 1949), pp. 50–65.

[8] For indexes and general references in associated fields see Appendix.

Rippy, J. Fred: "Italian Immigrants and Investments in Latin America," *Inter-American Economic Affairs,* Vol. III, No. 2 (1949), pp. 25–37.
Roberts, Frank H. H., Jr.: "In the Empire of the Aztecs," *National Geographic Magazine,* Vol. 71 (June, 1937), pp. 725–750.
Rosenblatt, Angel: *El desarrollo de la Población Indígena de América,* Tierra Firma, Madrid. No. 1 (1935), pp. 115–133; No. 2, pp. 117–148.
Schurz, W.: *Latin America,* E. P. Dutton & Co., Inc., New York, 1949.
Shattuck, G. C.: *The Peninsula of Yucatán,* Carnegie Institution of Washington, Washington, D. C., 1933.
"Some Educational and Anthropological Aspects of Latin America," *Latin-American Studies, V,* The University of Texas Institute of Latin-American Studies, The University of Texas Press, Austin, 1948.
Spinden, H. J.: *Ancient Civilizations of Mexico and Central America,* American Museum of Natural History, New York, 1928.
Stirling, Matthew W.: "America's First Settlers, The Indians," *National Geographic Magazine,* Vol. 72, (November, 1937), pp. 535–596.
Williams, M. W.: *The People and Politics of Latin America,* Ginn and Company, Boston, 1948.
Wissler, C.: *The American Indian,* Oxford University Press, New York, 1938.
Zelinsky, Wilbur: "Historical Geography of the Negro Population of Latin America." *Journal of Negro History,* Vol. 34, No. 2 (April, 1949), pp. 153–221.

CHAPTER II

POLITICAL EVOLUTION

ONE OF THE FUNDAMENTAL CHARACTERISTICS of "the nation," as of life itself, is its dynamic property of change—of constantly altering its expression and course. National position is due not only to inherent factors but also to the effects of exotic forces. One of the miseries of the doctrine of isolation is its blindness in not seeing the rest of the world. Knowing how life and regions differ and change from one part of the world to another is a primary principle of geography.

The rise and fall of empires in the old world is well known, and we have referred to similar changes in the pre-Columbian times of the new world, as in the realms of the Mayas, Incas, and Aztecs. Now let us examine in sequence the political patterns of Latin America since the beginning of the European conquest.

Colonial lands. In the fifteenth century when the discoveries by Columbus were made known, there was some fear of strife between Spain and Portugal because papal bulls had granted the Portuguese the rights to lands that might be found in the region of New Guinea and southward—probably the region that Columbus assumed he had discovered. In an attempt to prevent a clash between the Iberian rulers, the Pope, at the request of the Spanish sovereign, drew an imaginary line from north to south through the Atlantic Ocean and awarded to Portugal the lands on the African side of the line and to Spain the lands on the side toward the west. This line, drawn 100 leagues west of the Azores and Cape Verde Islands, included for Portugal, as was discovered later, only a small segment of the eastern coast of South America. But it did award the eastern Indian route to Portugal and the western route to Spain.

In a revision of the treaty made one year later, known as the Treaty of Tordesillas, the Line of Demarcation was changed from 100 leagues west of the Cape Verde Islands to 370 leagues west, Portugal to possess the lands to the east and Spain those to the west. This new provision added to Portugal's share a great deal of territory in the New World that had not yet been discovered, later to become known as Brazil; it left the

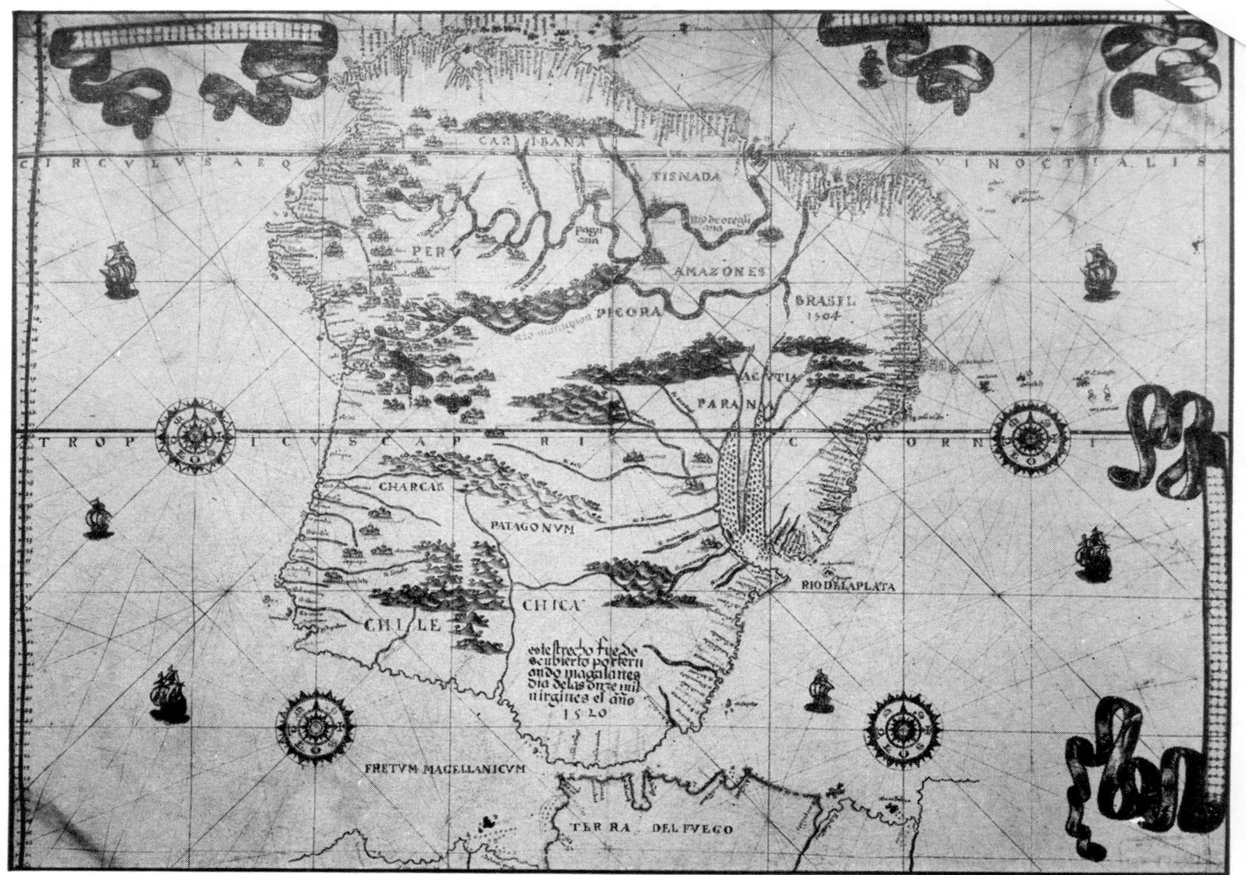

Fig. 12. A late sixteenth-century (1587) map of South America, from a manuscript atlas by Joan Martines, in the Biblioteca Nacional, Madrid. (From a copy in the Library of Congress.) "The world's a great book and they that never stir from home read only a page."—St. Austin.

remainder of the continent to Spain. This treaty, made in 1494, explains in part why South America is primarily divided into two clearly defined language groups: Brazil speaks the Portuguese tongue, and nearly all of the remainder of the continent speaks Spanish.

The lines of demarcation established by the Pope reached from north to south in a straight sweep, but as soon as man began his activities in the New World, the boundary between the Spanish and Portuguese lands became an irregular line. The theoretical boundaries represent the work of man without consideration of the nature of the landscape, while the actual boundary, the one now in existence, is the joint product of man and his environment.

Spain and Portugal apparently maintained in principle the obligations entailed by the treaty of 1494, but not without serious strife. Other nations, particularly the Protestant countries, the Netherlands and England, refused to recognize the right of the Pope thus to make presents of the new continent to Spain and Portugal and started explorations of their own to discover a passage through the new land mass toward India, working especially in the far north.

Later, when Aztec and Inca wealth began to flow toward Spain in huge but poorly defended vessels, buccaneers began the pleasant task of intercepting the galleons. Thus was initiated the reign of the freebooters. Even France did not like to see its neighbors to the southwest take all the New World to themselves, and began a clandestine commerce in the precious red dyewood, or *pau brazil*,[1] that existed abundantly in the forests of eastern South America. A century later it began to colonize the lower Mississippi and the St. Lawrence Valleys, thereby creating the Old French South of New Orleans and the New French Quebec, which have remained French to some extent in custom and language to this day.

Both the British and the Dutch established colonies on the North Atlantic seaboard, which undertakings gave to the future United States its predominantly Nordic complexion. The Netherlands attempted to establish a colony in what has become the state of Pernambuco, on the eastern coast of Brazil. The French made several desultory attempts to establish colonies on the Portuguese lands around Rio de Janeiro, but in every case they were unsuccessful. The island of Villegagnon, in the harbor of Rio de Janeiro, perpetuates the name of a famous French

[1] "A terra do pau brazil."—Early in the history of the New World a beautiful red dyewood was discovered, to which the Portuguese gave the name *pau brazil* because of its resemblance in color to red-hot coals. This wood brought a high price in European markets, especially in France, and consequently foreign vessels came expressly to procure it. These ships became known as visiting "a terra do pau brazil." Gradually the phrase was shortened to "a terra do brazil," and in 1530 this became officially the name of the new land.

soldier and gentleman who for a time directed the destinies of the region as a colony of France.

All three nations succeeded in establishing and holding colonies along the northern coast of South America. These have since come to be known as the Dutch, French, and British Guianas. And, in the course of time, certain of the smaller islands in the Caribbean Sea fell under the influence of these powers, notably Jamaica and Trinidad, which became British territory; Martinique and Guadeloupe, which became French; and Curaçao, Aruba, and Bonaire, which became Dutch. The larger islands of the West Indies were unequally divided between the great powers of France and Spain at the close of the colonial period. During the wars for independence in the first quarter of the nineteenth century, Portugal lost all its possessions in the New World and Spain all its continental possessions; and, as a result of the war with the United States in 1898, Spain lost the last of its island possessions in the Western Hemisphere.

After Columbus' initial voyage to the New World in 1492, other adventurers, mainly Spanish, immediately followed into the Indies and to the continent immediately beyond. Columbus himself made four trips to the New World and for a time was Spanish governor. Within a quarter century at least 25 Spanish colonies were established in the West Indies. In 1513 Balboa, with a large number of Spanish and Indians, crossed Panama and first viewed the Pacific Ocean, opening a new and intriguing field for further exploration. In 1519 Cortés reached the Valley of Mexico and stumbled upon the vast accumulated wealth of the Aztecs.

The sudden acquisition of this fabulous store of the precious metals electrified Europe. In the 40 years immediately following, parties of explorers reached Peru and central Chile to the south, establishing colonies along the way; passed north to San Francisco, travelling by way of the Pacific Ocean; mapped most of the coast of the Gulf of Mexico; explored a large part of the southern Mississippi Valley; and passed north from Mexico up the Colorado River to the interior of what is now Kansas. Several parties even entered Florida, some of them passing north as far as the Carolinas.

In 1516 Juan de Solis discovered the estuary of the La Plata system, but he was killed by hostile Indians. So deadly was the hostility of the Indian tribes that not until 20 years later was it possible to establish a colony sufficiently strong to become permanent.

In 1519 Fernão de Magalhães, a Portuguese in the employ of Spain, undertook to discover a passage he believed to exist through the unexplored land mass to the south. Late in 1520 he actually discovered such a passage, sailed through it, and continued on his way across the Pacific waters. Two years later the remnants of his little expedition, reduced to one small vessel, returned to Spain, having achieved the first circumnavigation of the earth. Magalhães himself was killed by savages in the Philippine Islands, which he named for King Philip of Spain. His name, in its English form of Magellan, was given to the strait he discovered.

Five years before Columbus made his epochal discovery, Portuguese navigators had made the first successful voyage to the Cape of Good Hope, at the southern point of Africa. During the years immediately following, the Portuguese continued intensively their search for a route to India around this cape, and were so completely convinced that it would be found that they paid little attention to the discoveries to the west. In 1497 Vasco da Gama completed the voyage around Africa, up its eastern side, and finally reached Calcutta. Portugal thus achieved in actuality what Spain thought it had attained, for at that time it had not yet dawned upon anyone that the new lands opened up to the west were not the outposts of the East Indies.

In 1500 a Portuguese expedition under the command of Pedro Alvares Cabral began another voyage to India by way of Africa. Sailing southward, they deliberately stood out at a distance from the shore line. They sought to avoid both the tropical calms experienced by previous expeditions and the fevers that had decimated other parties that had stopped for water and wood or to purchase slaves along the coast. Cabral planned to approach the continent of Africa farther to the south. Caught by the westward current along the equator, the party drifted unwittingly to the west, and to their amazement, on April 21, 1500, when six weeks out from Portugal, they discovered a new land. After a little further exploration to determine the character of the large island they believed had been found, Cabral sent a ship back to Portugal with the news, and continued on his way. Thus Portugal had, in addition to the Treaty of Tordesillas, the actual discovery of lands upon which to base its claim to territory in the New World.

Portuguese settlements. The Portuguese settlements on the eastern side of the new continent were different from those of the Spanish on the western side. In Europe the Portuguese nation had carved out its own destiny and had become permanently separated from the remainder of the Iberian peninsular peoples. The Portuguese were so separate that they developed a language and a distinct racial psychology all their own. In the new world they settled down to an agricultural type of civilization, while the Spanish newcomers continued feverishly their search for mineral wealth.

Owing in part to the fact that Brazil early became an agricultural colony rather than one of a mineral-seeking people, to fundamental differences between the Portuguese and Spanish peoples, to the different types of Indian races found on the eastern shores, to the lack of an early discovery of gold, to the nature of the landscape, and to its comparatively late monarchical type of government, Brazil has developed into a nation that shows marked differences from the other countries of South America in government, folklore, customs, and education.

Spanish domain. Spanish South America was too large a territory to

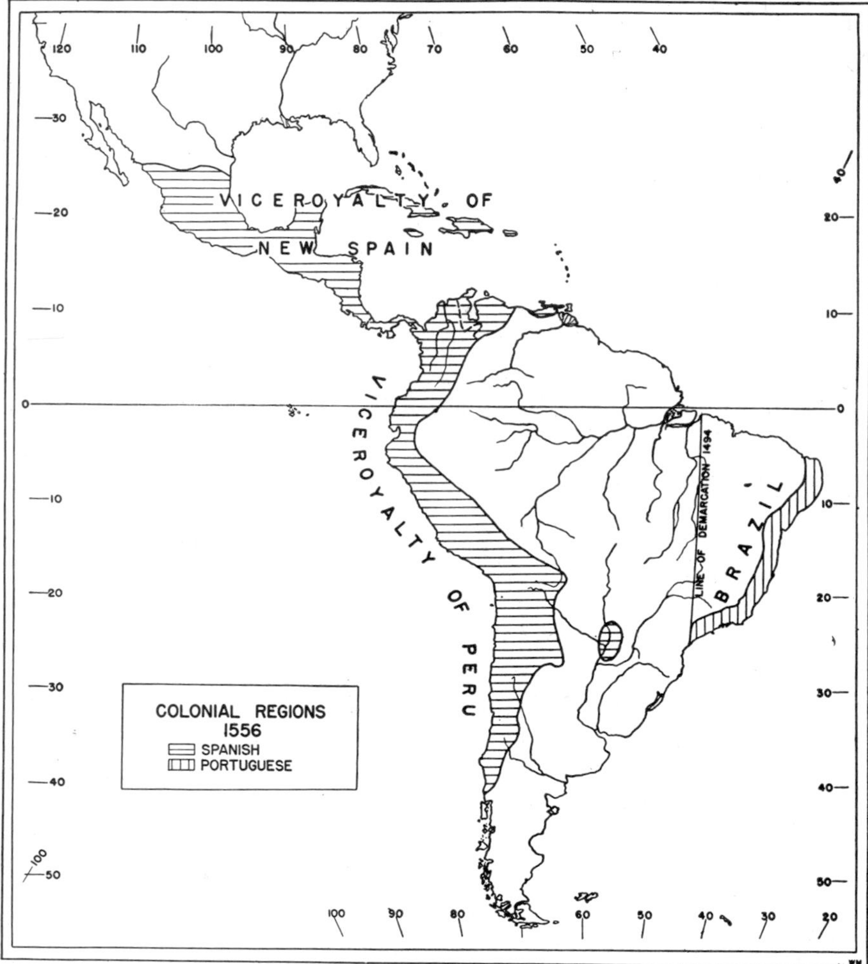

Goode's Homolosine Projection, by permission of the University of Chicago Press. Colonial pattern after Bolton-King Hispanic American Maps, by permission of Denoyer-Geppert Co.

Fig. 13. Colonial regions, 1556.

have a homogeneous population. The population was relatively small, perhaps not more than 3 or 4 million all told by 1800, and was scattered over immense areas with poor transportation facilities. Before freedom was attempted, Spain had divided its share of the New World into four administrative areas—La Plata, Peru, and New Granada, on the south, west, and north, respectively, of the southern continent; and New Spain in North America, which included Mexico, Central America, and a considerable portion of what is now southwestern United States.

The West Indies. For more than a century following the discoveries of Columbus, the West Indies were in the possession of Spain. It was

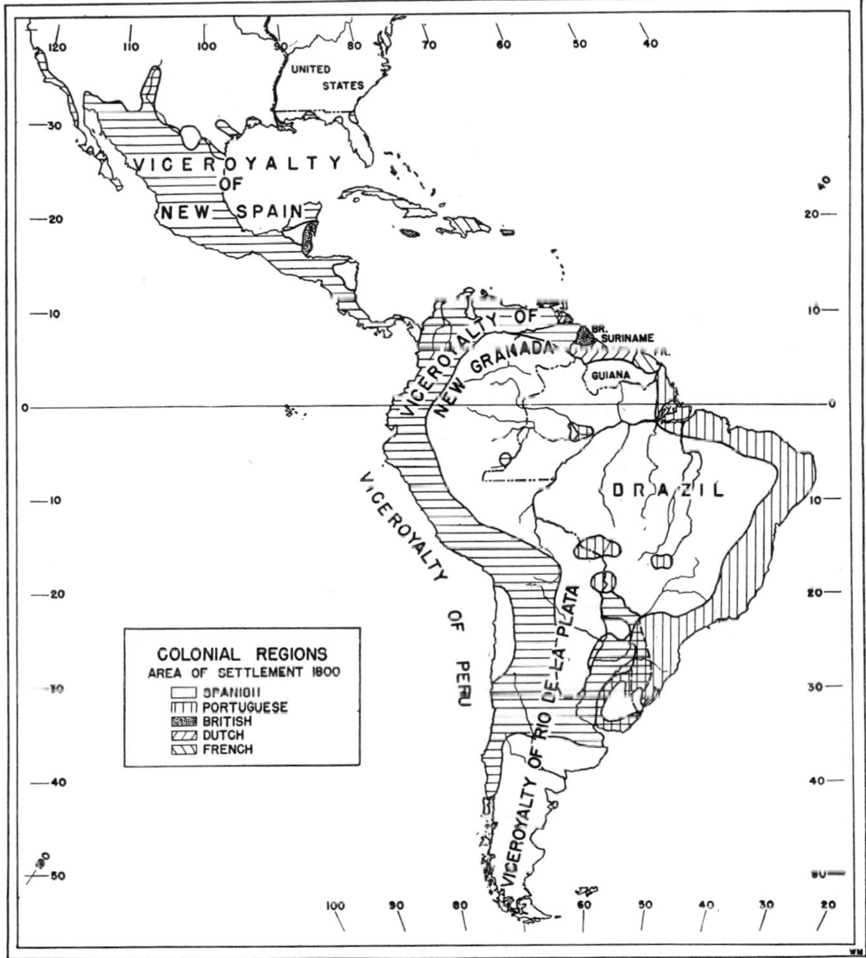

Goode's Homolosine Projection, by permission of the University of Chicago Press. Colonial pattern after Bolton-King Hispanic American Maps, by permission of Denoyer-Geppert Co.

Fig. 14. Colonial regions, 1800.

not until the period from 1600–1700 that the Spanish monopoly in the Caribbean was broken. In 1605 the English took possession of Barbados and in the years immediately following seized other small islands. By the middle of the seventeenth century (1655) Jamaica fell into English hands. This event represented what was up to that time the major break in the Spanish control of the West Indies. In the same century the French and Dutch also acquired possessions in the Caribbean. The French claims included a number of islands of the Antilles, from Grenada on the south to "Santo Domingo" on the north, while the Dutch took possession of a small group of islands off the coast of Venezuela.[2]

In the early colonial days some of the smaller islands, particularly those of the Lesser Antilles, passed from nation to nation; the transactors were the Spanish, Dutch, French, and English. During the latter half of the nineteenth century, up to 1898, the political pattern of the West Indies remained about the same: Cuba and Puerto Rico were Spanish; the Bahamas and Jamaica were English; two republics, Haiti and the Dominican Republic, occupied the island of Hispaniola; the Leeward Islands were divided about equally between France and Great Britain, with one small group, the Virgin Islands, belonging to Denmark; the Windward Islands were entirely British; and the Dutch held a small group of islands off the northern coast of Venezuela.

Since 1898, the political history of the West Indies shows some significant changes, with the entrance of a new nation, the United States of America, into its political pattern. Following the Spanish-American War, Spain lost Cuba and Puerto Rico to the United States. In 1902 Cuba was established as an independent country; Puerto Rico, however, remained a possession of the United States.[3] In 1917 the United States purchased the Danish Virgin Islands, including the islands of St. Thomas, St. John, and St. Croix.

The early days of independence. While the Spanish colonies cooperated somewhat in their struggles for freedom, final success was due largely to the personality of such outstanding military leaders as Bolívar, Miranda, and San Martín. The independence of each section was achieved separately. This movement led, inevitably, to the development of a number of separate nations. Each was to be regulated by its own constitution and governed by its own citizens, to have its own traditions and background, and to be related to the other nations on the continent through the same diplomatic channels that democratic nations employ. In general the relations with other nations on the continent would be friendly—identity of language, of racial heritage, of national problems would unite them into sentiments of friendship. A number of factors, however, would serve to pull them apart.

The most important of these factors was isolation. Immense distances separated the capitals. The roads were mere trails for pack animals or riders. There were no telegraphs or "Associated Press" service and few newspapers. Again, the very intensity of local problems of a frontier civilization tended to make less colorful the problems and happenings of other frontier states. In the development of a wholesome local and

[2] The Island called Santo Domingo is also known as Española and Hispaniola.
[3] Established as a Commonwealth in 1952.

regional society, the interests of most small-town whites were satisfied, while the Negro and Indian population, which was greatly in the majority, was interested merely in local village and agricultural life. Still further, the white population of each section had originated in Old Spain and looked to the mother country for its cultural contacts. Therefore, while contacts were maintained with Europe and were multiplied as time passed, and the bitterness of war was softened, *intimate contacts were not established with nations at home.*

Courtesy Pan American Union.

Fig. 15. Francisco de Miranda.

Two sources of international difficulty quickly arose. Disputes over intersectional boundaries were inevitable, and there were enough jingoes to make these disputes appear serious. Usually they were settled through arbitration and mediation, but in two or three especially bitter cases they led to serious wars. Military dictators secured the presidency of each nation occasionally, and these gentlemen provoked surrounding nations to war.

The new republics. After years of struggle and terrible hardships, alternating between victories and defeats, independence from Spain was finally secured by one country after another —approximately a third of a century after our American Revolution. Argentina declared her independence in 1816 and succeeded in maintaining it. Paraguay seceded in 1811, under the immediate influence of Argentina. Chile freed herself of royalist Spanish forces in 1818, Peru in 1824, and Bolivia in 1825.

Brazil was established as a monarchy in 1822 and in 1889 became a republic. Uruguay was declared a part of Brazil in 1825, but attained her independence from that country and became a separate republic in 1928.

Courtesy Pan American Union.

Fig. 16. José de San Martín.

Bolívar ended Spanish domination in the north of South America and in 1819 formed the Colombian Conferate, comprising roughly the provinces of Venezuela, New Granada, and Ecuador. Panama joined the union in 1821 and became known as its Department of the Isthmus. In 1831, the year following Bolívar's death, the union was dissolved, and out of it emerged the separate republics of Venezuela, Ecuador, and New Granada, the latter including Panama. In 1861 New Granada was renamed the United States of Colombia and later changed to the Republic of Colombia. Panama remained as a department of Colombia until 1903, the year Panama became an independent republic.[4]

In 1821, Guatemala and associated lands became a part of the empire of Mexico. In 1823, the year Iturbide was forced from the Mexican throne, Guatemala became a republic, and its congress declared that the country should form an independent nation under the title of Central American Federation, including the present republics of Guatemala, Honduras, El Salvador, Nicaragua, and Costa Rica. The union, however, did not hold, and one by one the states seceded, forming independent nations.

After a stormy period from 1813–1825, one of conquest, defeat, and reconquest, Mexico's independence was finally established. A war between the United States and Mexico, 1846–1848, resulted in the cession of New Mexico and part of Texas to the United States. A further adjustment in Mexico's northern boundary occurred in 1853, the year of the Gadsden Purchase. Only minor changes in Mexico's political boundaries have been made since 1853.

From nationalism to internationalism. From the day of independence to the beginning of the second World War in 1939, each American state pursued its own course. For each nation, like you or me, living and working in different lands, has its own objectives and problems. Consequently, contrasting as well as similar forms or personalities have developed, not only because of racial and cultural heritage and environment, but also as a result of extra-environmental factors. Unfortunately, the quest for security and greatness resulted in the formation of highly nationalistic entities which for the most part were totally unrelated. This ideology of self-sufficiency now has been correlated with one of interdependence or internationalism. "For each America is fully aware of its place in world affairs, and this realization will encourage each nation to not only break down its walls of isolation but also to preserve its own way of life."

SELECTED REFERENCES

Bannon, J., and Dunne, P. M.: *Latin America, An Historical Survey,* Bruce Publishing Company, Milwaukee, Wisconsin, 1947.

[4] Colombia's declaration of independence dates from 1811 (Cartagena) or 1813 (Bogotá); Venezuela's, 1811; that of Ecuador, 1820.

Chapman, C.: *Colonial Hispanic America,* The Macmillan Company, New York, 1947.

Chapman, C.: *Republican Hispanic America,* The Macmillan Company, New York, 1948.

Davis, H. E.: *Latin American Leaders,* H. W. Wilson Company, New York, 1949.

Hanke, Lewis V.: *The Spanish Struggle for Justice in the Conquest of America,* University of Pennsylvania Press, Philadelphia, 1949.

Haring, C. H.: *The Spanish Empire in America,* Oxford University Press, New York, 1947.

Humphreys, R. A.: *Study of Latin American History,* Lewis, London, 1949.

Humphreys, R. A.: *The Evolution of Modern Latin America,* Oxford University Press, London, 1946.

MacDonald, A. F.: *Latin American Politics and Government,* Thomas Y. Crowell Company, New York, 1949.

Madariaga, S. de: *The Rise of The Spanish American Empire,* The Macmillan Company, New York, 1947.

Madariaga, S. de: *The Fall of the Spanish American Empire,* The Macmillan Company, New York, 1948.

Moodie, A. E.: *Geography Behind Politics,* Hutchinson's University Library, Royal Institute of International Affairs, London.

Spykman, N. J.: *America's Strategy in World Politics,* Harcourt, Brace & Company, Inc., New York, 1942.

Wilgus, A. C.: *Latin America in Maps,* Barnes and Noble, New York, 1947.

Wilgus, A. C.: *The Development of Hispanic America,* Farrar & Rinehart, New York, 1941.

Wilson, W. J.: "The Spanish Discovery of the South American Mainland," *Geographical Review,* Vol. XXXI (1941), pp. 283–299.

MAPS

Bolton, H. E., and King, James, Maps: The Hispanic America Series, Denoyer-Geppert Co., Chicago, 1942.

Map of Hispanic America (Scale 1:1,000,000), American Geographic Society, New York.

Charts. Hydrographic Office, U. S. Navy Department.

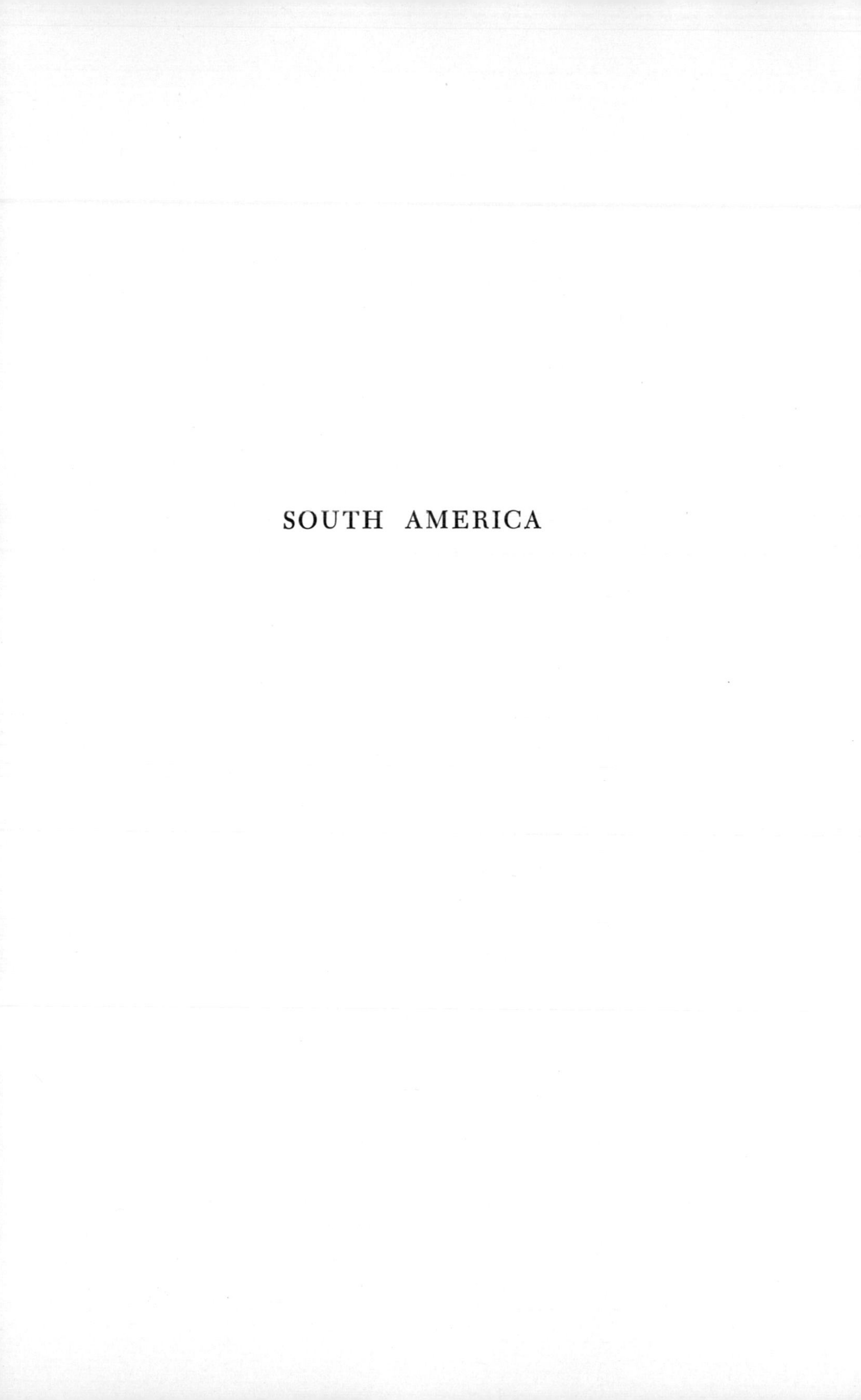

SOUTH AMERICA

CHAPTER III

PHYSICAL FEATURES

General survey. South America and North America are somewhat similar in their geological structure and physiographical pattern. The highland of eastern Brazil includes an extensive area of old formations, corresponding to the old rocks of the Appalachian Highland of eastern United States. On the western margin of both continents are recent formations, the Andes of South America and the Rocky Mountains of North America. Between the mountain systems of the two continents, the interior plains present a striking resemblance.

Climatically, South America resembles Africa more closely than it does North America. The larger portion of North America lies in the intermediate latitudes, while both South America and Africa have a broad expanse of territory within the low latitudes.

Because of the equatorial location, large areas of the coastal plains and interior lowlands of South America are too hot or humid to support an energetic population, while parallel sections of North America are climatically well suited to human habitation. The mountainous nature of that part of South America that is in low latitudes, however, provides a series of high river valleys and plateaus that are healthful and capable of sustaining a large population. For instance, Ecuador has three-fourths of her population on a partly enclosed plateau at an elevation of 8,000 to 10,000 feet above sea level; Bogotá, the capital of Colombia, is located on a plateau rising more than 8,000 feet above the sea; and in Bolivia 72 per cent of the total population lives at an elevation of 6,000 to 14,000 feet above sea level. The upper Cauca Valley in Colombia is the scene of thriving urban centers. The effect of altitude on climate and human activities is further illustrated in Brazil by striking contrasts between the coastal city, Santos, and the plateau city, São Paulo.

South of the Tropic of Capricorn, on the Atlantic Coastal Plain, lies the export city of Santos, with a population of about 190,000 persons. Except for that part of the population which is engaged in some aspect of the shipping business, the city is quiet, somnolent, and tropical. There is activity enough on the docks, in the warehouses, the shipping offices, the banks, and the customs houses. At certain times of the year and in some places the city takes on the appearance of a seaside resort. But aside from these aspects there is little activity.

Behind Santos rises a magnificent escarpment, the Serra do Mar—the Mountain of the Sea—to a height of some 2,500 feet. It is traversed by a splendid electric railway and a fine automobile road. On top of the escarpment, in an erosional basin, lies the industrial city of São Paulo, with about 2 million inhabitants, factories operated by hydroelectric power, and good schools and colleges, theaters, and stores—the seat of a thriving state government.

Why the difference? Santos lies in the tropical lowlands, while São Paulo is situated on the more temperate upland. An enervating climate pervades the one, a bracing climate the other.

Some North Americans are unhappily inclined to look upon South Americans as a lazy lot. It is true that South Americans, especially those living in the tropics, are more leisurely, more unhurried, than are the bustling citizens of the United States. They lack the energy, the push, the enthusiasm for active pursuits that characterize the conduct of the North American. "Tomorrow" is just as good as today for many purposes.

There are geographic reasons for this state of affairs. In the first place the climate in the tropics is enervating, in contrast with the more bracing climate of the intermediate latitudes. At the equator on the coast of Brazil, for instance, the mean average temperature at sea level is 80° F., with scarcely any variation. At Rio de Janeiro, situated some few miles north of the Tropic of Capricorn, the temperature seldom falls below 55° F., and nearly always ranges above 70°. Tropical vegetation is found almost as far south as Montevideo and Buenos Aires, close to the 35th parallel, about as far south as Memphis and Los Angeles are north.

The enervating property of the tropical climate, the depletion of human vitality, is due largely to the uniform high temperature, the direct or nearly direct rays of the sun, the nearly equal length of day and night at all times, and the high relative humidity.

Another reason for the loss of human energy lies in the uncontrolled prevalence of parasitic life. In the wet tropics there is no annual recurrence of winter frosts to regulate the life cycle of parasites and hold them in check. They may flourish at all times. Intestinal worms of a dozen virulent kinds, mosquitoes, and flies are found nearly everywhere. As a consequence, intestinal diseases, malaria, and tuberculosis destroy the lives of an amazingly large percentage of the population. Vast improvement will be experienced when the people awake to the dangers of these uncontrolled infections and apply scientific methods of screening, vaccination, isolation, purification of water supply, and adequate medical care. The prevailing good health of British colonists in north Australia shows that white men can live well in the tropics if they obey the laws of hygiene. The notable achievements of the American Government in the

Panama Canal Zone illustrate the same point. But generally such progress depends in a large measure upon education. In most of South America popular medical education has not yet been achieved.

Splendid results have followed sanitary measures in several notable instances. The larger cities have supplies of pure water and are relatively free from typhoid fever. They have cleaned out mosquitoes and almost eliminated malaria and yellow fever. They have compelled vaccination and virtually controlled smallpox. But away from the cities little protection has been afforded. The Rockefeller Foundation has attempted the control of hookworm with some success and has taught rural hygiene in many places. The Foundation's work in cleaning up and making sanitary the Ecuadorean port of Guayaquil aroused a continent-wide enthusiasm for similar hygienic activities. Institutes of agriculture have done some good. World-famous snake farms in a dozen South American cities have supplied thousands of people with serums—but these services are just a beginning toward what needs to be done, and there is still much to do.

TERRAIN

Physiographic divisions. South America may be divided into seven prominent regions—namely, the Andean System, the Brazilian Highland, the Guiana Highland, the Orinoco Plain, the Amazon Plain, the Paraná-Paraguay Plain (including the Pampa), and the Patagonia Plateau. Each of these major divisions exhibits a variety of minor configurations. An understanding of these lands will prove valuable in the interpretation of their cultural features and human activities. *The land, or natural environment, and man and his works, or economy, should not be thought of, geographically, as separate factors but in their whole dynamic relationship or association, expressing the compositiveness or entirety of a region.*

The Andes and associated lands. The Andean mountain system extends for a distance of some 4,400 miles. Rising from the Caribbean Sea in three distinct ranges, it continues, first as three separate ranges, then as a comparatively unbroken mass, to the southern shore of Tierra del Fuego, where it again plunges beneath the sea. At places in Chile its width is not greater than 20 miles; at other places, in central Bolivia, the Andean system and its associated plateaus extend more than 500 miles across. The average height is about 13,000 feet, although a score of majestic volcanic peaks rise to altitudes of more than 20,000 feet. The height of Mount Aconcagua in west-central Argentina, the highest mountain on the continent, has been measured variously at from 22,368 to 22,900 feet. Mount Tupungato, reaching some 21,480 feet, is close by. Many other mountain peaks and ranges rise above 18,000 feet.

One dominating western range is almost unbroken from farthest north to farthest south. This maritime chain is the true Andean cordillera. Parallel to this western range a second, and sometimes a third and a fourth range, is found to the east. Vast plateaus and high intermontane uplands, of which the Altiplano of Bolivia is an example, extend for hundreds of miles between these ranges at altitudes of 10,000 to 14,000 feet. In valleys associated with these plateaus nestle such populous cities as La Paz, Cuzco, Oruro, Quito, and Bogotá. The maritime chain reaches its greatest heights at 20 to 100 miles from the Pacific.

The Andes must not be thought of as a system of barren mountains. Dense forests flourish on many slopes, at altitudes up to 8,000 or 10,000 feet. Eucalyptus and Lombardy poplar trees have been introduced and have flourished in many places formerly barren. They furnish needed timber and fuel. In Cuzco, for instance, industries requiring fuel, such as the breweries and potteries, have planted groves of eucalyptus trees for that specific purpose. In rainless areas and above the timber line the ranges are, of course, largely barren.

In many sheltered valleys, even under the equator, glaciers have formed and still persist. In former times these glaciers extended to much lower levels than at present. In southern Chile and in Tierra del Fuego huge ice fields cover the Andes and make their way down numerous valleys to the sea. The abundant fjords and dendritic channels of southern Chile are nearly all glaciated valleys.

Passes traverse the ranges at frequent intervals; one of the lowest is Paso Pino Hachado, on the frontier between Chile and Argentina at an elevation of 6,000 feet. Because of its low altitude and ease of transit, this pass is widely used during the winter months of June, July, and August, when other passes are blocked with snow, although the Uspallata and Bermejo passes, each more than 10,000 feet high, are better known and more extensively employed as means of communication between the east and the west.

The young and vigorous Andean system stands in sharp contrast to the older ranges of Brazil on the eastern margin of the continent. These ranges paralleling the Atlantic show no recent volcanic activity, and erosion has worn them down to a mass of low-lying hills and plateaus, in part covered with verdant forests, punctured here and there by jagged projections where harder rock masses have successfully resisted the weathering effects of water and wind.

Geological structure.[1] The structure of the Andean region is complex. All of the geological systems from the pre-Cambrian to recent sediments are represented. The process of building has been recurrent and is still continuing actively. Overthrusting from east to west seems to have been

[1] See *Geologic Map of South America.* Published by The Geological Society of America, 1950.

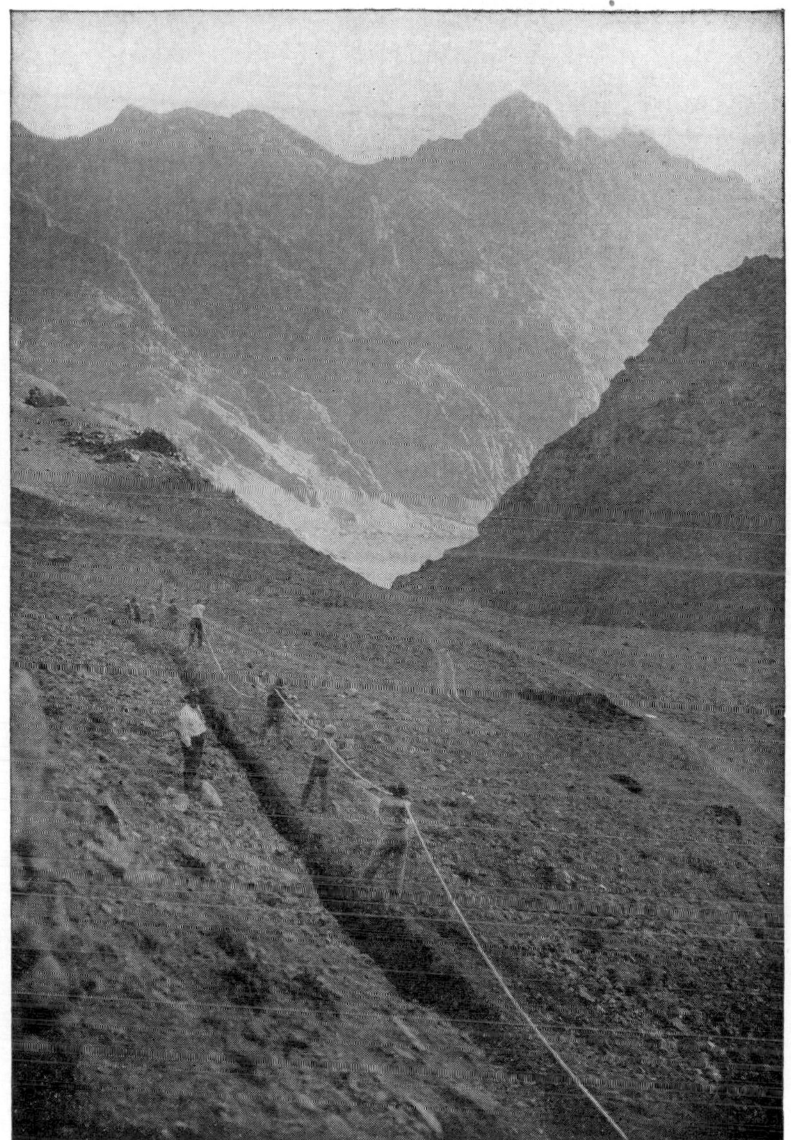

Courtesy International Telephone & Telegraph Corporation.

Fig. 17. Laying the trans-Andean telephone cable between Chile and Argentina, 1931. The complex Andean system extends for more than 4,000 miles and its lofty forms rise more than four miles above sea level.

responsible for the elevation of the eastern Peruvian ranges. Back of Santiago, in Chile, the primitive ranges consist of Jurassic and Cretaceous beds in relatively simple folds. The great central plateau region of Peru-Bolivia, the Altiplano, is formed largely of Archaean and Palaeozoic rocks. In Ecuador and Colombia great masses of gneiss and schist predominate in the inner ranges. Throughout the entire system volcanic activity has projected its intrusions.

Courtesy Moore-McCormack Lines.

Fig. 18. View from Sugar Loaf, Rio de Janeiro. Brazilian Highland outliers.

The structure is, therefore, the result of a long series of changes, some cataclysmic, others operating more slowly and persistently. After each cataclysmic folding a long process of adjustment and weathering seems to have intervened before another upheaval occurred. The result is a very complexly folded system, throughout which sedimentary rocks of varying ages alternate with granitic masses.

Along the entire range, from extreme north to extreme south, hundreds of towering volcanic cones arise, some extinct but many still active. In traveling in Ecuador between Riobamba and Quito, a distance of about 100 miles, one passes in view of at least seven volcanic cones: Chimborazo, Cotopaxi, Cayambe, and others. Sometimes they are smoking; at other times activity is not perceptible, but, presumably, gases are escaping. Mount Sangay, to the east of the "Avenida de los Volcanes," is said to be one of the most continuously active volcanoes in South America, rather regularly throwing out bombs and ash, but no longer pouring out the great lava flows that accompanied its eruptions in the past.

Brazilian Highland. The foundation of Brazil, with respect to agriculture and mining, is the prominent land division commonly known as the *Brazilian Highland.* This extensive upland, including more than half of the country, is the nation's most populous region. It is the scene of the world's largest coffee plantations and the site of rich mineral resources. *The future of the Brazilian upland is the future of Brazil.*

The Brazilian upland is underlain by the oldest rocks of the continent, probably pre-Cambrian in age. This ancient structure was once covered by more recent formations, but erosion has exposed the crystalline rocks in widespread areas. The most extensive belt of old rocks appears along the eastern margin, varying in width from 400 miles in northeastern Brazil to 50 miles in the state of São Paulo. In Santa Catarina and in northern Rio Grande do Sul a lava plateau projects eastward and the oldland practically disappears. In southern Rio Grande do Sul the oldland is exposed again and continues southward into Uruguay, where it passes under the coastal sediments. Westward the crystalline foundation slopes beneath more recent formations. But in places erosion has removed the sedimentary rocks from the crystalline basement and exposed great masses of igneous rocks surrounded by sedimentary formations.

The surface of the Brazilian Highland exhibits three well-defined types of features: (1) prominent seaward escarpments, (2) plateaus, and (3) rounded sierras, or mountain ranges. For the most part the relief is low, and some of the surface shows peneplanation.

Guiana Highland. The Guiana Highland is associated, not only with the three colonial possessions of Great Britain, the Netherlands, and France, but also with the republics of Venezuela, Colombia, and Brazil. It was once a portion of the ancient continent of northeastern South America, which included, in addition to the Guiana remnant, a similar old mountain area to the south, the Brazilian Highland. These two land masses were separated by a subterranean area that is now filled with recent sediments and forms the lower Amazon Plain.

nd geological disturbances have shaped the Guiana uplands coastal peneplain and a high inner peneplain. The low tends inland along the principal river courses, while the peneplain, apparently a more ancient land form that has been uplifted, occupies the upper interstream areas. Where the low peneplain passes under the coastal sediment it has an elevation of some 200 feet. The higher inner peneplain attains an elevation from 2,000 to 5,000 feet above sea level. The lower peneplain is further characterized by a

Courtesy John L. Rich and American Geographical Society.

Fig. 19. Brazilian Uplands 26 miles southwest of Vitória. Note mountain agriculture on slopes.

great number of isolated monadnocks. The Wilhelmina-Gebergte in the central part of Dutch Guiana, or Surinam, is an example of these rock islands. Similar groups of monadnocks are found in the French and British Guianas.

Along the international boundary between Brazil and the Guianas the uplands appear in the form of plateau ranges, such as Serra Acaraí or Acarí and Serra de Tumucumaque. Their southern exposure exhibits a series of steep escarpments facing Brazil, but northward the plateaus project like spurs between the streams and slope gradually seaward. These southern highlands carry the drainage of southward flowing tributaries of the Amazon and the northward flowing streams of the Guianas. Low divides between the headwaters offer routes of travel for the traders of Brazil and the Guianas.

Patagonian Plateau region. Southwestern South America is in part represented by a piedmont plateau, known generally as Patagonia.

In reality, the region comprises a series of plateaus. The altitude varies from a few hundred feet along the coast and rivers to 5,000 feet near the base of the Andes. The upper formations consist of sedimentary strata and sheets of lava that rest on a crystalline base. Streams and wind have dissected the terrain into a rugged landscape. The major features can be attributed to water erosion, the minor irregularities to the effects of wind. In the western portion of the plateau extensive evidences of glaciation are found in the form of drift, moraines, and outwash plains. Basin-like areas are found in places. In the north they are called *bajos* and in the south *mallins.* During the winter the bajos are partly filled with water that evaporates in the summer and leaves a crust of salt. These salt flats are called *salitrades.* The origin of such enclosed basins has not been clearly determined, but they are probably due largely to wind erosion.

The eastern margin of the plateau is really the coast line, as there is practically no coastal plain. A number of structural indentations are found, such as the Golfo San Matias, Golfo de San Jorge, and Bahía Grande. On the west a discontinuous pre-cordilleran or sub-Andine trough separates the plateau from the Andes. It is most prominent between Lago Nahuel Haupí and Estrecho de Magallanes (Strait of Magellan) and lies largely in the republic of Chile.

The Amazon Plain. The Amazon Plain is the largest and one of the most homogeneous natural regions of South America. Its area is greater than all of the United States east of the Mississippi River. Topographically, the land is low in elevation and low in relief; climatically it is hot and humid; and economically its resources are of the extractive kind.

The greater portion of the Amazon Plain falls within the political boundaries of Brazil. Its marginal areas embrace portions of Bolivia, Peru, Ecuador, Colombia, and Venezuela. It extends for more than 2,000 miles, from the Atlantic to the Andes, and varies in width from a maximum of 800 miles in western Brazil to less than 200 miles east of Manaus.

Early history reveals that the western portion of the lowland was once an embayment of the ancient Pacific which inundated the region now occupied by the Andes. This great gulf may have been connected with the Atlantic by a strait between the older land of the Guiana and Brazilian Highlands. When the mountain-building forces lifted the Andes far above sea level, this extensive gulf became an inland sea. Erosion of the associated uplands supplied great quantities of debris that filled this inland sea. As deposition continued, and some uplift of the area occurred, an extensive plain was built through which numerous

F. A. Carlson.

Fig. 20. Because South America lies mainly in the low latitudes, one is inclined to think of its climate as tropical; but we must observe that there are extensive uplands where temperature conditions range from temperate to polar. Altitude is South America's dominant climatic control.

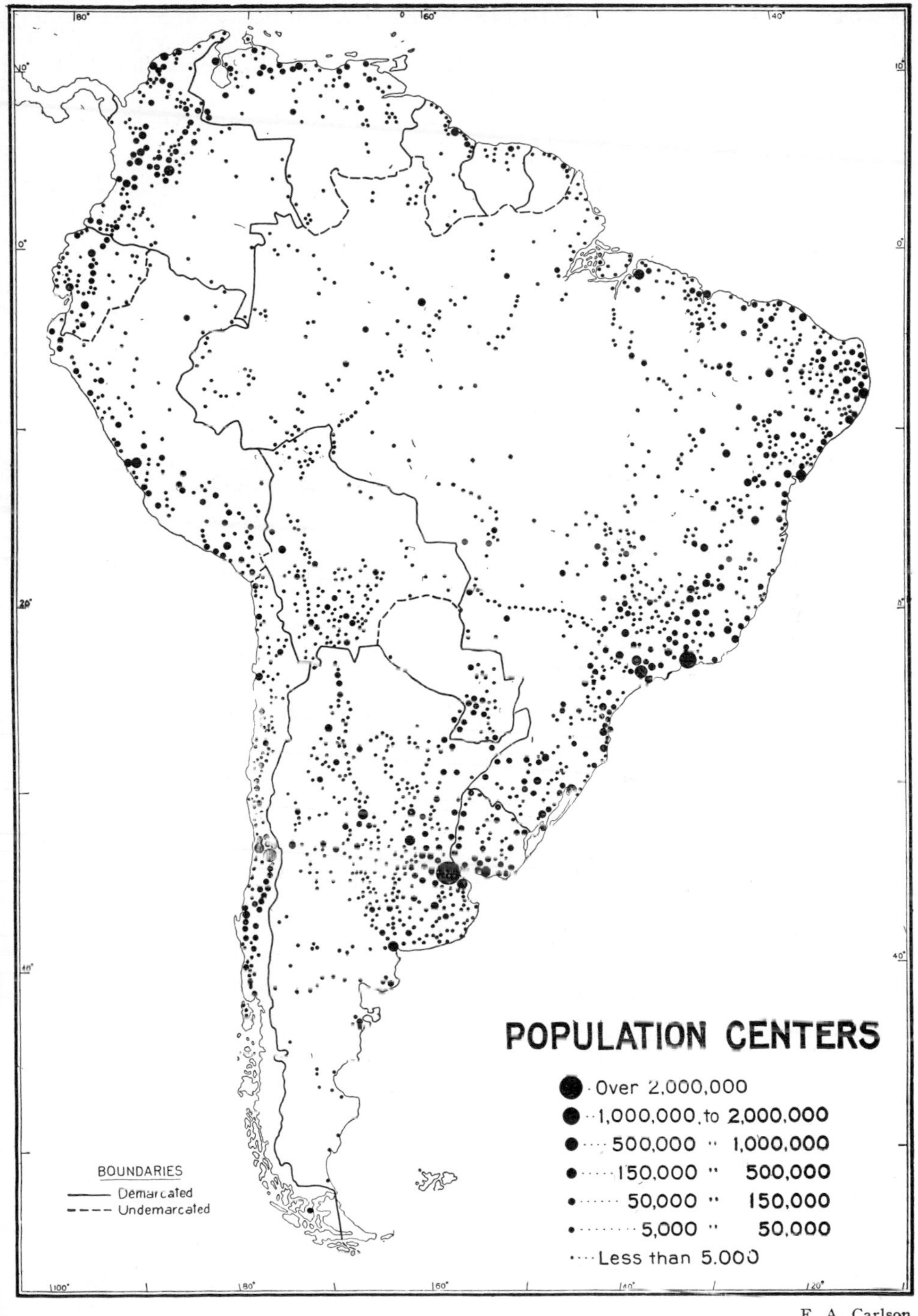

F. A. Carlson.

Fig. 21. The population of South America is about 109,000,000. By far the greater proportion of the inhabitants live within a few miles of the coast.

streams have integrated, forming the world's largest river system, the Rio Amazonas.

The Amazon region is not everywhere a flat plain but consists of broad swells and low hills and intervening vales. A rugged terrain occurs near the Andean border, where the more elevated portions of the plain have been maturely dissected. The major divisions of the plain are: (1) the level alluvial lowlands, or flood plain, and (2) the well-dissected undulating-to-rolling uplands.

The flood plain extends irregularly along the Amazon and its tributaries, known locally as the *varzea.* This alluvial terrain varies in width from 10 to 100 miles. It represents about 10 per cent of the entire area of the Amazon Plain, which totals some 2,000,000 square miles. Broad and disconnected swamps called *paranas* border the river within the flood plain. The surface is further diversified by channels or sloughs, known as *furos.* The deeper furos usually contain water even during the low-water stage. In most places the alluvial areas are separated from the major streambeds by well-developed terraces or natural levees. During floods, much of the varzea is inundated. The portion of the region above the flood waters is called *terra firma.*

Behind the alluvial plains are the upland plains, which may be classified into the upper and lower plains. The lower uplands lie along the alluvial areas, approximately in the axial belt of the river basin, while the upper plain occupies the rest of the upland region. About 90 per cent of the entire Amazon Plain is recognized as an upland plain. Only a small portion of its surface is permanently covered with water or imperfectly drained.

Orinoco Plain. Between the Venezuelan Andes and the Guiana Highland is an elongated plain, generally called the Orinoco Llanos. It is an alluvial lowland with interstream ridges, low hills, and extensive swells or basins. In the west it merges with the Andes through a system of well-defined terraces. Its lower portion projects seaward in the form of a delta.

Paraná-Paraguay region. The Paraná-Paraguay Plain includes a great agricultural region, the Pampa of Argentina and the Gran Chaco, embracing parts of Argentina, Paraguay, and Bolivia. It occupies the site of an early Atlantic embayment now filled with debris from adjacent highlands. Most of the material was apparently transported from the Andes on the west, judging from the position of the Paraguay River on its eastern border. The river has been literally pushed to one side. Only a few streams have made their way across the flat land to the Paraguay or Paraná Rivers. The Río Pilcomayo rises in the Bolivian Highland and reaches the Paraguay near Asunción, the capital of Paraguay. It forms a part of the northern boundary of Argentina. Southward is one other

Fig. 22. Two-thirds of South America's 60,000 miles of railways is concentrated in central Brazil and Argentina. Most of the lines were built in advance of traffic.

major river of the Chaco, the Río Bermejo, and many small streams, mostly intermittent.

Along the Paraguay and Paraná Rivers are broad swamps, or *malezais,* and lagoons, or *lagunas.* During the rainy summers the flood waters convert these features into great lakes and completely obscure the drainage lines. In places there are great depressions, called *banados,* that are filled with water during the time of flood but are baked mud flats in dry seasons. Some of the deeper banados contain water at all times. Such features are known as *esteros.*

Most of the Pampa, one of the world's leading agricultural regions, is a flat plain (Pampa is an Indian word signifying a flat country) with slight undulations, isolated depressions, and deep, fertile soil. The surface cover consists of sediments of alluvial and æolian origin transported by water and wind from the Andes Mountains and the Brazilian Highland. Below the unconsolidated material are horizontal strata resting on a granite base.

In the west the Pampa gives way to the *Monte,* a transitional zone of low mountain ranges and basins that lies between the Andes and the true Pampa. Northward there is also rising ground. In the south are two mountain masses, like islands in the sea, that break the monotony of the Pampa. North of Bahía Blanca is Sierra de la Ventana and more eastward is Sierra del Tandil. These highlands are the summits of buried mountain ranges.

On the Pampa there are few rivers. Some have their origin in the bordering Sierra de Córdoba and adjacent Sierra de San Luís, whereas other streams begin in the Pampa, some flowing to the sea and others ending in the Pampa. Underground drainage, however, is predominant because of the flatness of the surface, the presence of isolated basins, and the deep pervious soil.

CLIMATES

Temperature. Uniformity in temperature marks the climates of South America, primarily because most of the area lies in the low latitudes. The continental climates of North America, Europe, and Asia, with their extreme range in temperature, differ from those in South America. Nowhere in the continent, according to available records, is the range in temperature from summer to winter more than 30°. This slight variation is due to the narrowness of the land in the higher latitudes and to the adjacent oceans. For the same reasons the southern part of South America is much warmer in winter, freer from extremes, and cooler in summer than regions of the same latitude in North America. In the equatorial lowlands a high uniform temperature prevails throughout the year, but the highlands have temperate to polar temperatures even in regions of the equator. It is reported that in January the highest temperatures are found in the Gran Chaco region; in July the hottest part of the continent is in Venezuela and the Guianas.

Along the northern coast the mean annual temperature is about 80°.[2] and is probably the same on the western coast as far as 5° S. latitude. Southward the temperature of the coastal region decreases moderately. At this point it is interesting to note that the mean annual temperature

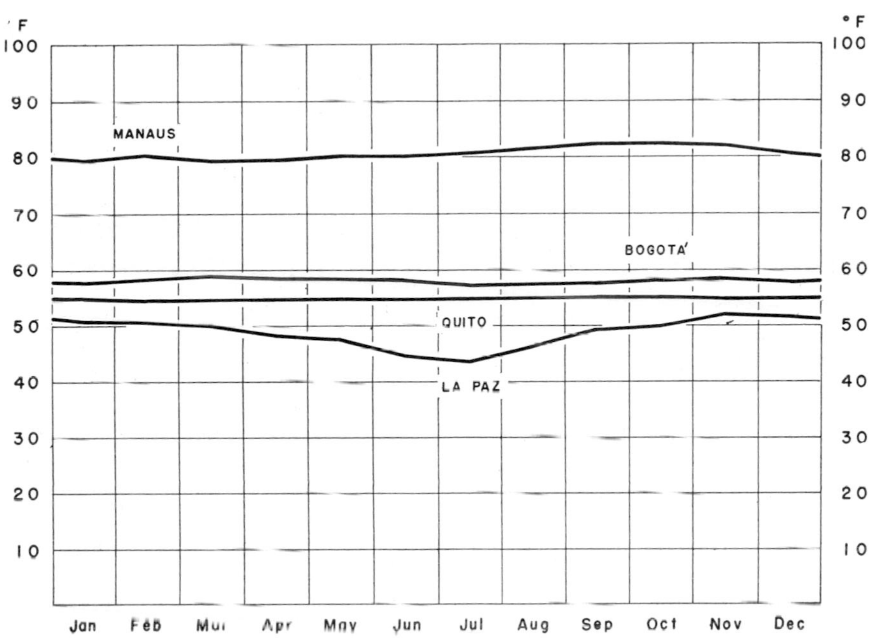

Fig. 23. Average temperature.

ELEVATION ABOVE SEA LEVEL

Manaus	133 feet
Bogotá	8,727 feet
Quito	9,248 feet
La Paz	12,002 feet

is lower along the western coast of tropical South America than along the eastern coast. At Trujillo, Peru (8° S.), the mean annual temperature is 69°, but at Recife, Brazil (also 8° S.), the yearly average is 80°. The lower air temperatures on the west coast are in part attributable to the cold Peruvian Current, a part of the great drift of the southern ocean that is deflected northward, whereas the higher temperature on the east coast is in part due to the warm southward flowing

---

[2] For more information on the climatic elements of the Andes and associated regions, see W. G. Kendrew, *The Climates of Continents;* Glenn T. Trewartha, *An Introduction to Weather and Climate;* T. A. Blair, *Climatology.*

Brazilian Current. Exceptions, however, are found, one in the southern part, where the ocean winds from the Pacific are warmer than the continental winds off the land on the east.

From the Tropic of Capricorn northward, the temperatures at interior stations with elevations of less than 250 feet are practically the same for the entire region, the mean annual temperature being about 82°. At elevations between 3,500 feet and 5,500 feet the range is from 70° to 65°;

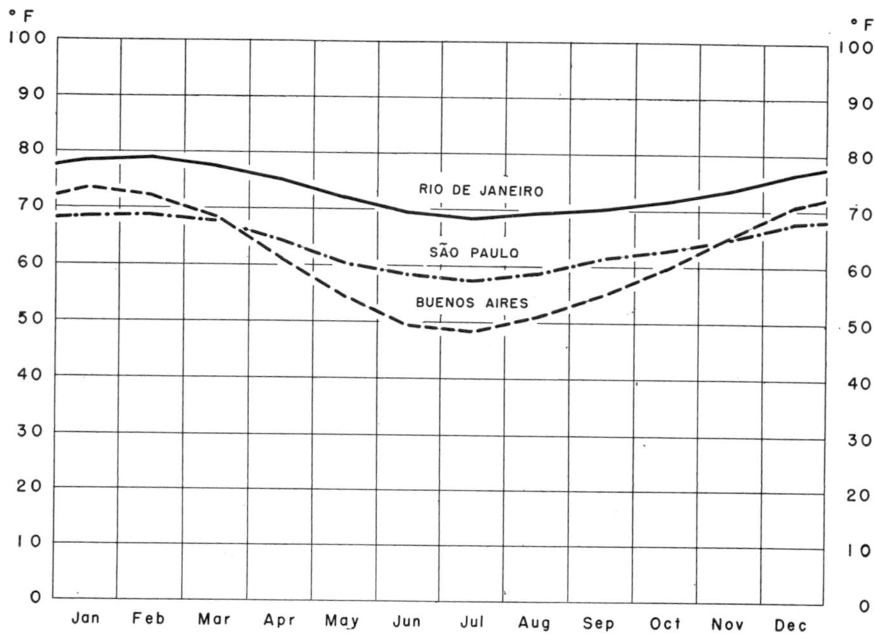

Fig. 24. Average temperature.

in the levels 7,500 to 9,500 feet the temperature seems to be remarkably uniform, from 60° to 57°; and in the high levels, 11,000 to 15,000 feet, the means appear to lie for the most part between 50° and 40°.

The effect of high elevations on air temperature is impressively shown in the case of La Quiaca, 11,358 feet, in latitude 22° S., which has the same mean annual temperature as Santa Cruz, 39 feet, in latitude 50° S. Another case is that of Puente del Inca, 8,948 feet, at latitude 33° S., with a mean annual temperature corresponding to that of Punta Arenas, 92 feet, at latitude 53° S. Near the equator the snow line is over 15,000 feet above sea level, while in the far south, in Tierra del Fuego, it is at 2,500 feet. The snow line, however, is governed, not only by temperature, but also by precipitation and several other factors. For example, the snow line on Chimborazo, near Quito, lies a little above 15,000 feet; it is at 16,000 feet in central Peru; and at the Tropic of Capricorn it is at

20,000 feet. But south of the tropical circle it declines rapidly as the degree of latitude increases.

Rainfall distribution. In the Andes and associated lands of northern South America the amount and seasonal distribution of rainfall are moderately variable. The upland region of Venezuela is well watered, with 40 to 70 inches a year, but there is a marked decrease along the coast and in its immediate vicinity, with the annual mean generally less

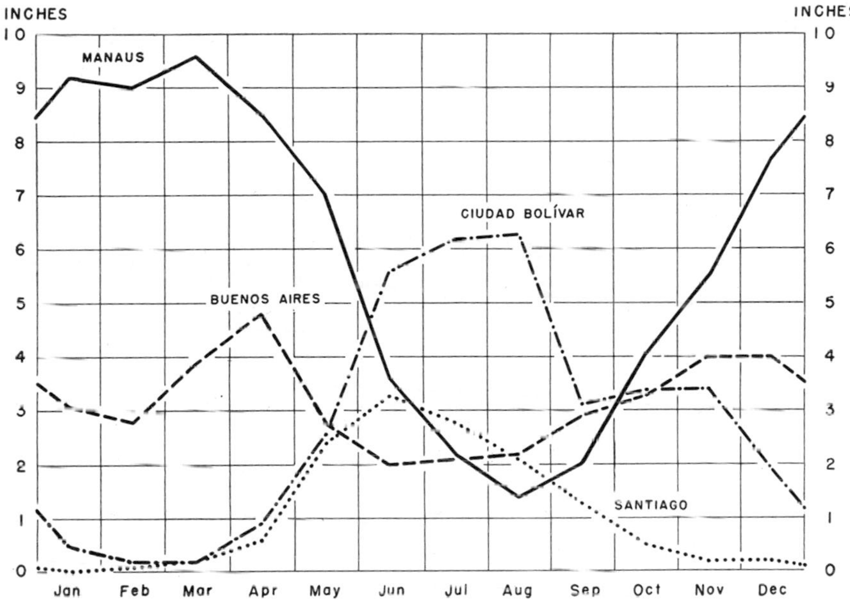

Fig. 25. Average precipitation.

than 30 inches and in some places below 12 inches. In northern Colombia the precipitation is less than 30 inches a year; it increases somewhat in the highland region, with some 40 inches annually at Bogotá, to excessive rainfall of more than 200 inches on or near the middle Pacific Coast region.[3]

Western South America is a region of extreme rainfall variations, the contrast being exceedingly great between the coastal region and the eastern slopes of the Andes. In northwestern Ecuador the mean annual precipitation is about 40 inches, but in the eastern region it is in excess of 100 inches. The so-called rainless region, the Atacama Desert, begins south of the Gulf of Guayaquil and extends along the entire Peruvian coast and into Chile through about latitude 28° S. The yearly precipitation of this arid region is generally less than two inches, a sig-

[3] Rainfall data for the west coast of Colombia are scarcely more than estimates, since few records are available.

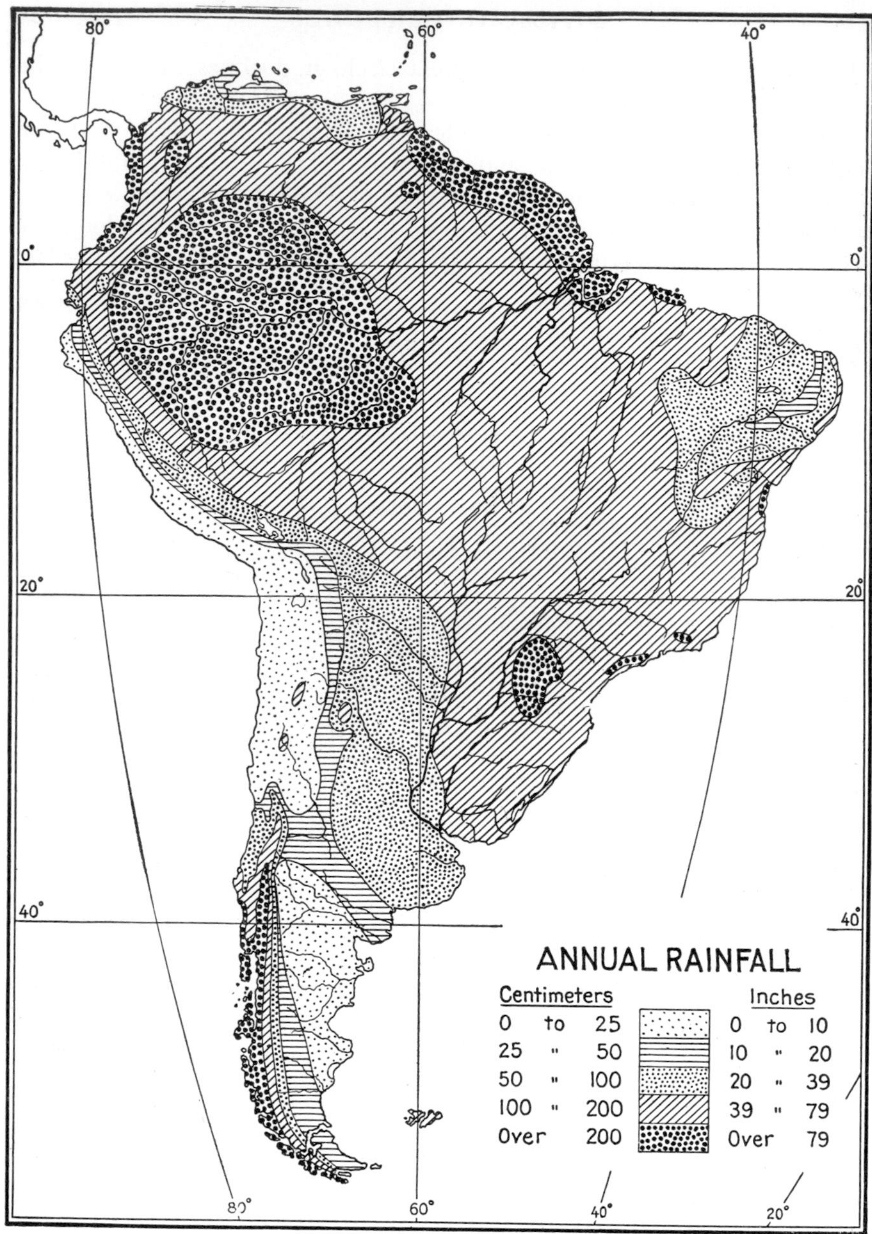

After K. Knoch, W. W. Reed, and others.

Fig. 26. Compare the maps showing annual rainfall, relief, and distribution of population in South America. Where precipitation is excessive and the temperature high, the climate is not healthful. On the lofty plateaus, altitude and lack of moisture combine to make climate unpleasant and life hard, but in some respects less enervating than the wet tropical lowlands.

nificant condition when it is noted that it embraces an area some 70 miles wide in northern Peru, more than 200 miles in the latitude of southwestern Bolivia, and extends north-south for some 2,000 miles. Inland from this dry region the mean annual precipitation increases eastward from 30 to over 80 inches.

From Copiapó, Chile, the approximate southern limit of the desert, begins a gradual increase in annual total of 30 to 50 inches around Concepción. Southward there is a marked increase to more than 80 inches over the remainder of the coast—for example, to 105 inches at Valdivia. In the highland region east of the area from Copiapó to Santiago the annual mean precipitation is not more than 10 inches. However, at El Teniente, elevation 6,800 feet, just south of this region, the annual total is more than 40 inches, and farther south it is as much as 140 inches.

Immediately east of the Andes in southern Argentina lies another extensive region of extreme aridity. This area and the northern Chilean and Peruvian coast warrant special discussion.

The arid condition of the coastal region of Peru and northern Chile is sometimes explained by stating that the Andes present an impassable barrier to the moist easterly winds. Forced ascent, such as air currents must undergo on the eastern slopes of the cordilleras, would deprive them of almost all of their water-vapor content. The moisture remaining cannot be great in view of the moderate to heavy rainfall precipitated from these currents over a vast area covering most of the eastern half of southern tropical South America. But this question arises: Why, with Pacific ocean winds, relatively high humidity, and cloudiness, does this coast and some of the adjacent interior remain one of the most extensive desiccated regions in the world?

The cause is to be found in the cold waters of the Peruvian Current. This cold ocean current flows from high latitudes to low latitudes, and, as a result, the moist air above it has a temperature lower than that in other corresponding latitudes. The effect of this condition increases as the current flows farther into lower latitudes because the temperature of the water rises but slowly. As a result, the air over the water is lower in temperature than that over the coastal land. Therefore, when south and southwest winds prevail over the coast, rain seldom occurs because the air has a greater saturation deficit and consequently absorbs moisture instead of precipitating it. This in part also explains why the aridity of this western region increases northward up to where the cold current is deflected away from the coast. It should also be made clear that the cold waters are associated with air movements in the same direction as the current. Such winds, blowing somewhat parallel with the coast line, tend to reduce rather than bring about precipitation.

East of the Andes, in southwestern Argentina, the aridity is largely due to the depletion of the water-vapor content of the westerly winds. During forced ascent to the crest of the southern Andes, the westerlies lose their moisture and descend as dry winds when they reach the eastern, leeward side. The Andes can, therefore, be looked upon as casting a great "rain shadow" over western Argentina.

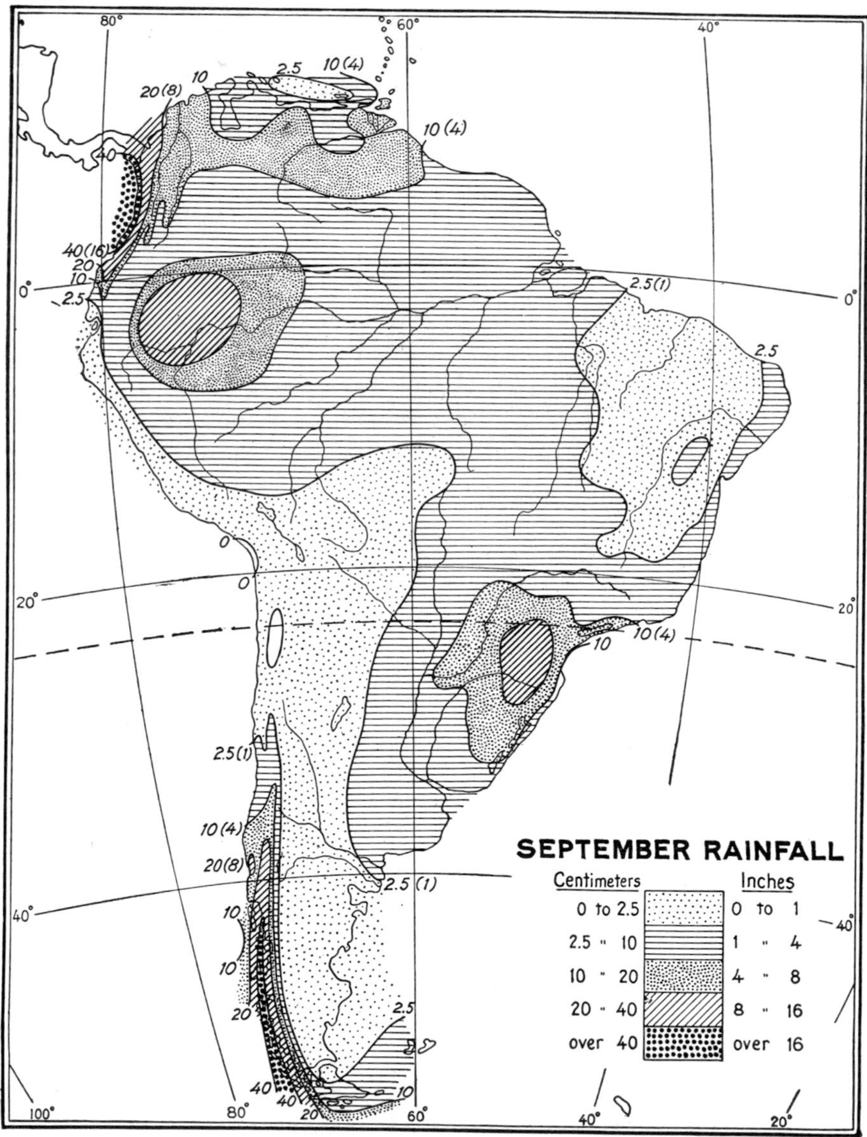

After K. Knoch, W. W. Reed, and others.

Fig. 27. The monthly rainfall of South America as a whole is at a minimum in September and at a maximum in January.

The greater part of eastern South America as far south as the Río de la Plata estuary has a summer rainfall. Beyond this point, most places receive rain in all seasons, with the greater percentage of the precipitation in autumn and winter.

The eastern slopes of the Andes in the equatorial region have the two

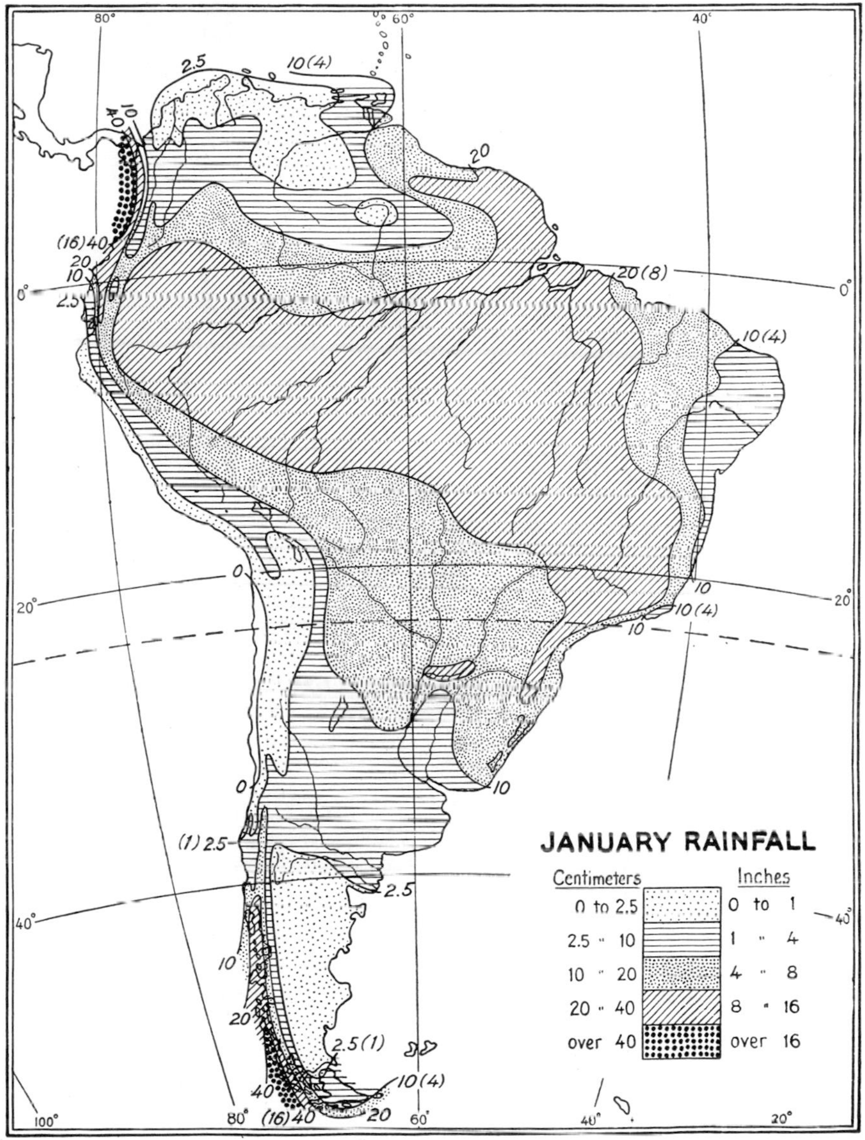

After K. Knoch, W. W. Reed, and others.

Fig. 28. Compare the January and the September precipitation maps of South America.

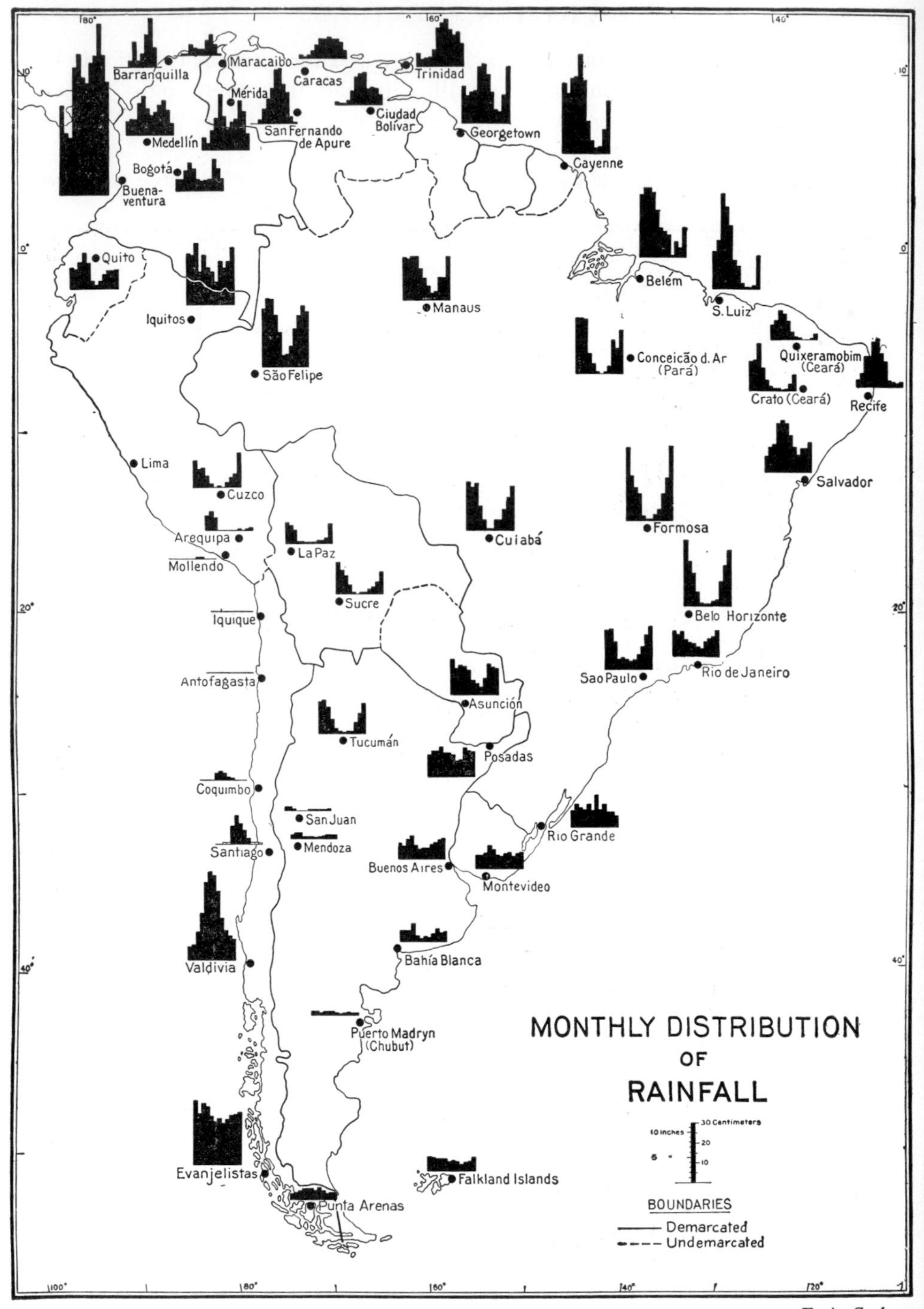

F. A. Carlson.

Fig. 29. Monthly distribution of rainfall in South America.

rainfall maxima at the time of, or shortly before, the overhead sun; while other parts of the tropics have for the most part one long rainy reason occurring in summer. Dry lands are primarily associated with the subtropical highs, about 30° south latitude, and with highland barriers.

Types of climates may be expressed in terms of the Köppen system.[4]

Courtesy John L. Rich and American Geographical Society.

Fig. 30. A typical narrow irrigated valley at the western base of the Andes, 18 miles east-southeast of Illapel.

Quantitative values of selected symbols are as follows:

A = Temperature of coolest month over 64.4° (18° C).
C = Temperature of coldest month between 64.4° (18° C) and 26.6° (−3° C).
E = Temperature of warmest month under 50° (10° C).
f = No month with less than 2.4 in. of rain.
w = Dry season in winter or low-sun period; at least one month with less than 2.4 in. of rain.
s = Dry season in summer; driest month of summer with less than 1.2 in. of rain.
a = Temperature of warmest month over 71.6° (22° C); hot summer.
b = Temperature of warmest month under 71.6° (22° C) but with at least 4 months over 50° (10° C); cool summer.
c = Temperature of not more than 3 months above 50° (10° C); cool, short summer.

[4] For detailed information see P. E. James, *A Geography of Man*, Ginn & Company, Boston, 1949; or V. C. Finch and Glenn T. Trewartha, *Elements of Geography*, McGraw-Hill Book Co., New York, 1949.

i = Annual range less than 9° (5° C).
B = Evaporation exceeds precipitation.
BW = Desert.
BS = Steppe.
h = Average annual temperature over 64.4° (18° C).
k = Average annual temperature under 64.4° (18° C).

Tropical Rainforest	Af–	Humid Subtropical	Cfa
Tropical Savanna	Aw–	Intermediate Latitude Steppe	BSk
Tropical Highland, Cwa, Cwb, others		Intermediate Latitude Desert	BWk
Tropical Steppe	BSh	West Coast Marine	Cfb
Tropical Desert	BWh	Mountain Climates	E– and others
Dry Subtropical	Cs–		

Political units. Having surveyed the broad and fundamental natural regions of South America our attention is now directed to its national entities or countries. As stated in the Preface to the First Edition—"an attempt to interpret the affairs of a Latin American country in terms of Latin America as a whole can lead to . . . the evils of generalization" and consequential misunderstanding. Each nation, regardless of size, economy, or any other factors calls for individual recognition. However, it is equally true that the affairs of a nation depend not only upon the physical and human factors within its political border but also upon factors adjacent or beyond its boundary. For example the place of the Rio Paraná in Argentina or the Amazon region in Brazil in terms of national and foreign affairs is clarified when these natural features are considered in their entirety as well as their national scope.

The order of presenting the countries in this text is somewhat academic and personal. Brazil, the largest Latin American country in area and population, a land of many contrasting regions, resources, and activities, is our next subject and the beginning of our study of the individual nations.

SELECTED REFERENCES

Boffi, Jorge Alberto: "Effect of the Andes Mountains on the General Circulation Over the Southern Part of South America," *Bulletin of the American Meteorological Society,* Vol. 30, No. 7 (1949), pp. 242–247.

Clayton, H. Helm: "World Weather Records," *Smithsonian Miscellaneous Collections,* Vol. 79 (1927), Vol. 90 (1934), and Vol. 105 (1947).

Hainsworth, R. S.: "The River Basins of Latin America," *Agriculture in the Americas,* Vol. IV, No. 9 (1944), pp. 163–167.

Holman, Eugene: "Petroleum and the Industrial Program of Latin America," *Latin American Studies II,* The University of Texas Institute of Latin-American Studies, 1946, pp. 75–81.

Hughlett, Lloyd J., Editor: *Industrialization of Latin America,* McGraw-Hill Book Company, New York, 1946.

Jefferson, M.: "Actual Temperatures of South America," *Geographical Review,* Vol XVI (1926), pp. 443–466.

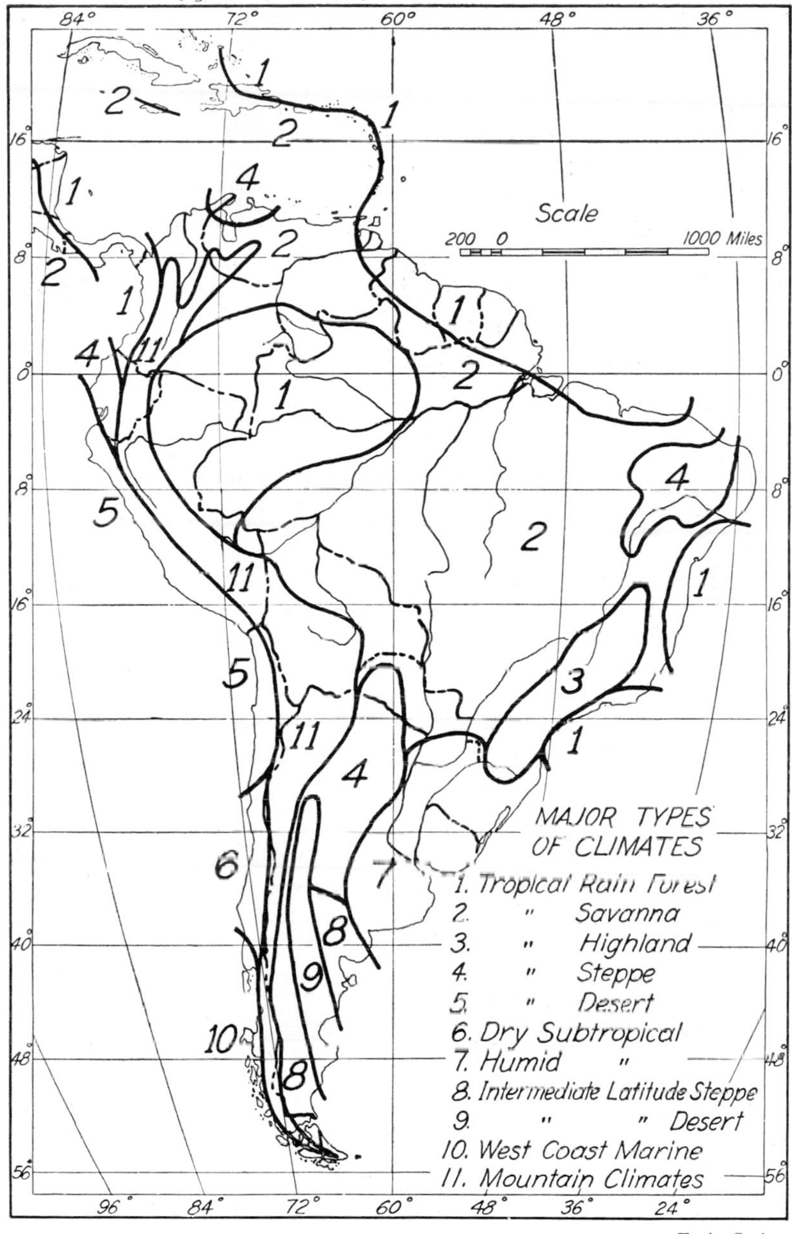

F. A. Carlson.

Fig. 31. Climates of South America. (Base map from the American Geographical Society, New York. Climatic data after W. Köppen, R. Geiger, and others.)

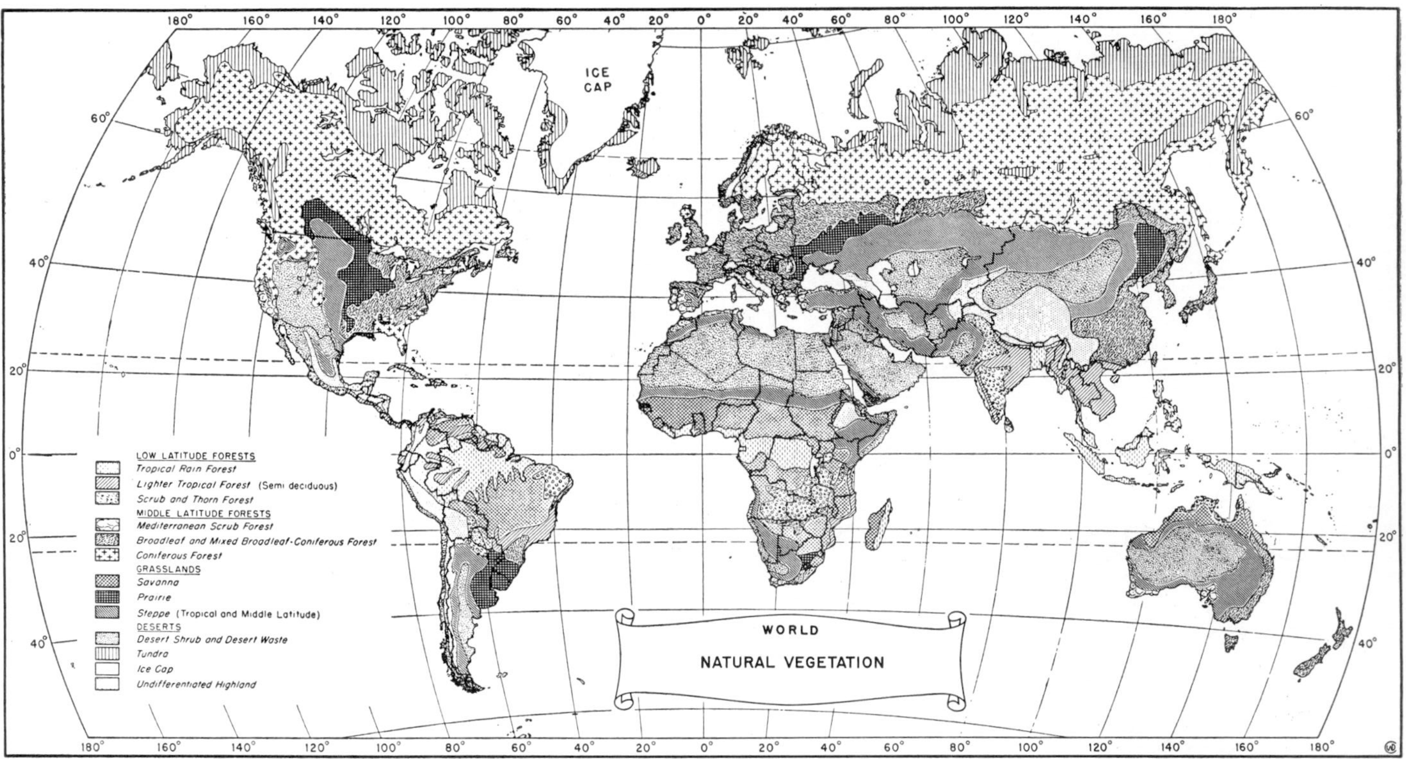
WORLD
NATURAL VEGETATION
ICE CAP
LOW LATITUDE FORESTS
Tropical Rain Forest
Lighter Tropical Forest (Semi deciduous)
Scrub and Thorn Forest
MIDDLE LATITUDE FORESTS
Mediterranean Scrub Forest
Broadleaf and Mixed Broadleaf-Coniferous Forest
Coniferous Forest
GRASSLANDS
Savanna
Prairie
Steppe (Tropical and Middle Latitude)
DESERTS
Desert Shrub and Desert Waste
Tundra
Ice Cap
Undifferentiated Highland

Fig. 32. Natural vegetation.

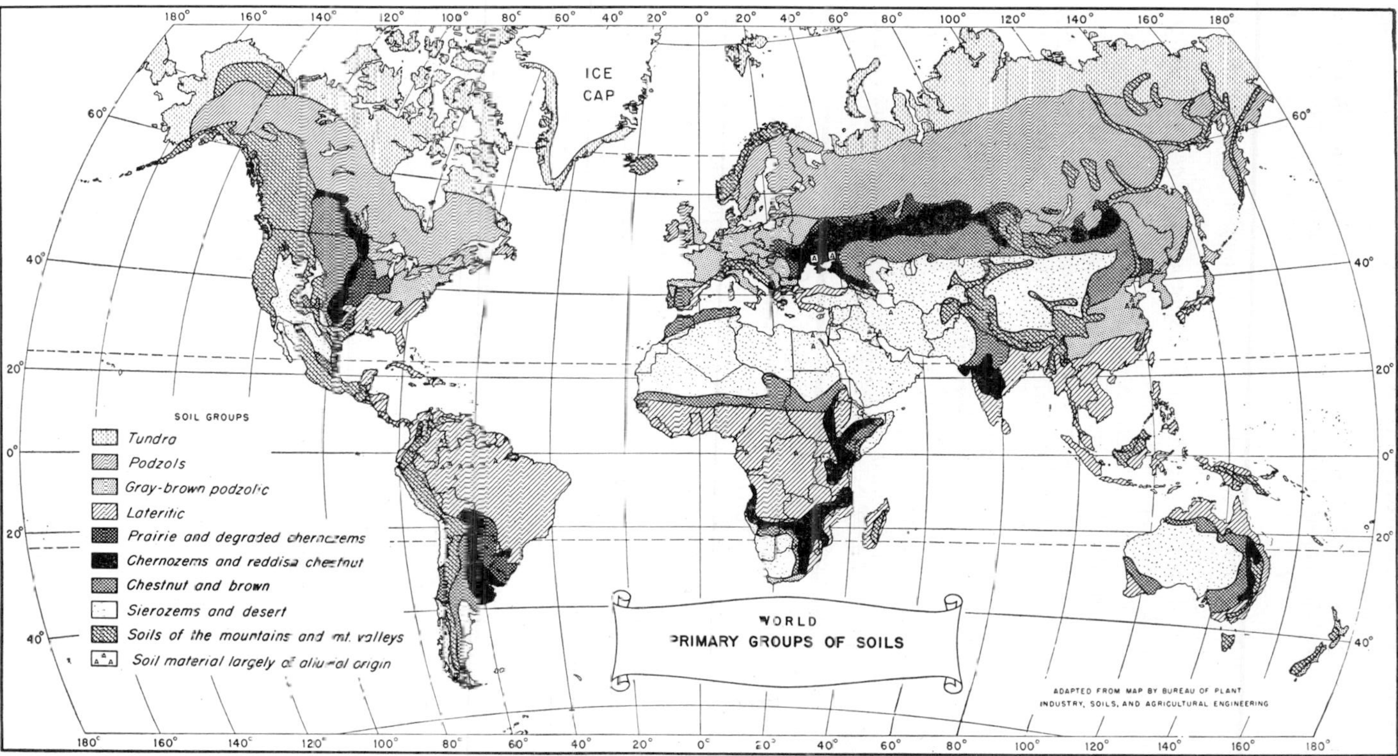

ICE
CAP
SOIL GROUPS
Tundra
Podzols
Gray-brown podzolic
Lateritic
Prairie and degraded chernozems
Chernozems and reddish chestnut
Chestnut and brown
Sierozems and desert
Soils of the mountains and mt. valleys
Soil material largely of alluvial origin
WORLD
PRIMARY GROUPS OF SOILS
ADAPTED FROM MAP BY BUREAU OF PLANT INDUSTRY, SOILS, AND AGRICULTURAL ENGINEERING

Fig. 33. Soil groups.

Jefferson, M.: "The Distribution of People in South America," *Bulletin of the Geographical Society of Philadelphia,* Vol. 5 (1907), pp. 182–192.

Kendrew, W. G.: *The Climates of the Continents,* Oxford University Press, New York, 1937.

Peterson, Lyall E.: "Forest Products from Latin America," *Journal of Forestry,* Vol. 45, No. 6 (1947), pp. 81–98.

Schley, J. L.: "Needs of Inter-American Transportation," *Economic Geography,* Vol. 21, No. 2 (1945), pp. 126–134.

Rich, John L.: "The Face of South America," *Special Publications No. 26,* American Geographical Society, New York, 1942.

Rich, John L.: "Oil Possibilities of South America in the light of regional geology." *Bulletin of the American Association of Petroleum Geologists,* Vol. 29 (1945), pp. 495–563.

Roseveare, G. M.: "The Grasslands of Latin America," *Bulletin 36,* Bureau of Pastures and Field Crops, Aberystwyth, Great Britain, 1948.

Schmieder, Oscar: "Landerkunde Sudamerikas," *Enzyklopädie der Erdkunde,* Leipzig and Wien, 1932.

Shanahan, E. W., *South America,* E. P. Dutton & Co., New York, 1929.

Shanahan, E. W.: *South America: An Economic and Regional Geography,* Methuen & Co., London, 1949.

Smith, Guy-Harold: *Physiographic Diagram of South America,* The Geographical Press, Columbia University, New York, 1935.

Stanislawski, Dan: "Early Spanish Town Planning in the New World," *Geographical Review,* Vol. XXXVII, No. 1 (1947), pp. 94–105.

Weeks, David: "European Antecedents of Land Tenures and Agrarian Organization of Hispanic America," *Journal of Land and Public Utility Economics,* Vol. 23, No. 1 (1947), pp. 60–67.

White, C. Langdon: "Is The Twentieth Century South America's?" *Economic Geography,* Vol. 21, No. 2 (1945), pp. 79–89.

Wythe, George: *Industry in Latin America,* Columbia University Press, New York, 1945.

Wythe, George: "Latin America's Vast Resources Spur Broadening Developments," *Foreign Commerce Weekly,* Vol. 35, No. 2 (1949), pp. 3–9.

CHAPTER IV

BRAZIL: NATIONAL DEVELOPMENT

Sectionalism. The cultural pattern of the United States of Brazil, as shown by its urban centers, highways, and railways, exhibits a striking degree of sectionalism. Vast areas, without the slightest evidence of man and his works, interposed between regions of modern and primitive civilization, depict the incompleteness and undeveloped structure of the Brazilian landscape. Three-fourths of the 52 million people of Brazil, representing about one-half of the total population of South America, live within a hundred miles of the coast. In fact, 10 of the nation's 25 largest cities are directly on the coastal plain. Another 10 lie within the hundred-mile band. But, even within this comparatively narrow margin of culture, there is a pronounced inadequacy of efficient means of human integration. Lines of culture, with few interconnections, project inland from widely separated coastal settlements in the shape of fans and dendrites. Each of the focal settlements is a separate unit, communication between them being much closer by ocean routes than by land routes. Until recently Brazil has faced eastward, and her development has been primarily along the coast, but now she is looking westward toward her vast interior of new land and new opportunities.

F. A. Carlson.

Fig. 34. The United States of Brazil.

Political structure. Brazil, embracing an area of some 3,286,170 square miles, has been carved into 20 states, 5 territories, and the Federal District. Sixteen of the states and the Federal District[1] border on the

[1] A number of years ago, under pressure of a wave of national enthusiasm, a

Atlantic Ocean. The four interior states have a total area greater than the entire 16 coastal states and a population less than one-fourth as large.

Urbanization. The average density of population is about 16 persons per square mile, as compared to 50 in the United States. In the vast interior of Brazil there are only 6 persons per square mile, and 70 per cent of this area has an even smaller population density than this figure.

Fig. 35. Political regions of Brazil.

Even more than do Americans, Brazil's people tend to concentrate in urban communities. According to most recent government estimates, Brazil has 488 cities of more than 5,000 inhabitants. Of these, 72 have between 20,000 and 50,000; 19 between 50,000 and 100,000; and 14 have

"Future Federal District" was set apart in a beautiful section of the highlands of Goiás, about 600 miles from the coast. The feeling was: (1) that the national capital should be placed in the geographical center of the nation; and (2) that it should be removed from the danger of attack to which Rio de Janeiro might be subject. At the present time there is no thought of removing the capital to the new location.

more than 100,000 population. Rio de Janeiro, the national capital, and São Paulo, an industrial city, each have about 2 million inhabitants.

POPULATION OF PRINCIPAL URBAN CENTERS OF BRAZIL

Rio de Janeiro	2,400,000
São Paulo	2,000,000
Recife	500,000
Salvador	384,000
Pôrto Alegre	380,000
Belém	235,500
Belo Horizonte	340,000
Fortaleza	205,700
Santos	190,000
Maceió	103,000
Niterói	175,000
Manaus	121,400
Curitiba	137,000
Pelotas	72,000
Maranhão	97,700

Regional integration. The nature and extent of highways and railways are an accurate index of national development. On this basis what is the situation in Brazil?

Railways. The nation shows a moderate concentration of railways in the northeast; a fairly good network in its central or southeastern region; a single line with short spurs in the far south; one railway extending west into the distant interior; and one short line in the Amazon region. Northern Brazil, equal to half the land area in the United States, is without overland transportation to central Brazil, the nation's social, political, and economic center. Commercially these northern lands are more closely related to Europe and the United States than to the southern part of their own country.

In central Brazil, however, the railways present a more nearly reticular pattern. One line extends from the port of Santos to São Paulo. Several lines radiate from São Paulo to important urban centers of the interior and along the coast. The principal line joins the cities of São Paulo and Rio de Janeiro and gives excellent passenger service at most hours of the day and night. This is the government-owned *Central do Brasil.* One artery runs west from São Paulo, 1,026 miles, to Pôrto Esperança, on the Paraguay River near the border of Bolivia.[2] One may travel northwest by rail from São Paulo to Anápolis, in the state of Goiás, a distance of approximately 600 miles; north to Pirapora, on the Rio São Francisco, passing Belo Horizonte on the way, approximately 700 miles; and northeast to Vitória, passing Rio de Janeiro, some 700 miles from São Paulo. Another line extends southward to the border of Uruguay, where railroad

[2] Construction is under way to join the Brazilian line with one projecting eastward from Bolivia via Cochabamba, Santa Cruz, and Puerto Suárez in Bolivia.

connection may be made for Montevideo. A branch of this line leads westward to the border of Argentina, where connection may be made to Asunción in Paraguay, and south to Buenos Aires, Argentina.

BRAZIL: AREA AND POPULATION

National Divisions[3] *and Regions*	*Area Sq. Miles (Approx.)*	*Population*			
		1940 Total	*Percentage*	*1950 Total*	*Percentage*
Amapá (Territory)	56,000	21,191			
Pará	471,000	923,453			
Rio Branco (Territory)	98,000	12,130			
Amazonas	595,000	416,011			
Acre (Territory)	57,000	79,768			
Guaporé (Territory)	97,000	21,297			
North Brazil	*1,374,000*	*1,473,850*	3.6		
Maranhão	133,000	1,235,169			
Piauí	95,000	817,601			
Ceará	58,000	2,091,032			
Rio Grande do Norte	20,000	768,018			
Paraíba	22,000	1,422,282			
Pernambuco	38,000	2,687,175			
Alagôas	11,000	951,300			
Fernando de Noronha (Territory)	7½	1,065			
Sergipe	8,000	542,326			
Bahia	204,000	3,918,112			
Northeast Brazil	*377,000*	*14,434,080*	35.0		
Minas Gerais	229,000	6,736,416			
Espírito Santo	18,000	750,107			
Rio de Janeiro	16,000	1,847,857			
Federal District	450	1,764,141			
São Paulo	95,000	7,180,316			
East-Central Brazil	*475,000*	*18,345,831*[4]	44.5		
Paraná	78,000	1,236,276			
Santa Catarina	37,000	1,178,340			
Rio Grande do Sul	109,000	3,320,689			
South Brazil	*224,000*	*5,735,305*	13.9		
Goiás	255,000	826,414			
Mato Grosso	486,000	420,835			
West-Central Brazil	*741,000*	*1,247,249*	3.0		
Brazil	*3,286,000*	*41,236,315*	100.0	52,445,500[5]	100.0

POPULATION OF BRAZIL 1872–1950

1872	10,112,061	1920	30,655,605
1890	14,333,915	1940	41,236,315
1900	17,318,556	1950	52,445,500

[3] In accordance with the Republican Constitution of 1891, Brazil was constituted by 20 States and the Federal District. Through the Treaty of Petrópolis, signed

Travellers, however, going from the cities of Rio de Janeiro and Santos to Rio Grande or to some other progressive city of southern Brazil, such as Pôrto Alegre and Pelotas, are far more likely to travel by steamer along the coast than to make the overland trip by rail. The numerous delays, the rough and tortuous roadbed, the fact that the trains run only in the daytime, and the lack of good hotels for overnight stops are reasons why the water route is more desirable. Steamship service is cheaper, cleaner, and altogether more pleasant. There is, likewise, very little overland travel between Uruguay and Brazil for the same reasons. It takes eight days by rail from São Paulo to Montevideo. The trip can be made comfortably by sea in half that time. From these facts one should not conclude that the Brazilian railways are entirely useless. They serve to connect the interior population centers with the coast and the principal industrial cities, and thus they are of great economic importance. During the war with Paraguay, Brazil had great difficulty in transporting troops and realized the strategic military importance of having railways to its principal borders. Its answer to the problem are the lines to the southern and western borders. A third strategic line is planned that will connect Belém, in Pará, on the Rio Pará, with Rio de Janeiro, 1,500 miles to the south, and to have laterals to the principal port cities. This projected line will open to settlement a vast area of fertile agricultural land with abundant mineral resources as well as link the Amazon region to central and south Brazil by rail.

Area, topography, climate, forests, jungles, and widely separated urban centers present difficult railway problems for Brazil. Distance alone prohibits the introduction of railways in many portions of the country. The diversified surface features, particularly near the coast, practically make extensive railway construction economically unsound. In the tropical regions, which include much of the nation's territory, railway building and maintenance are generally costly.

The natural landscape, however, is not the source of all railway transportation problems in Brazil. Many of the railways were built under contract at so much per kilometer. Some of them, as a consequence, are

---

with Bolivia in 1903, the Federal territory of Acre was incorporated. In 1937, six more Territories were created as follows: Fernando de Noronha, Amapá, Guaporé, Rio Branco, Iguaçu and Ponta Porã. However, in 1946, the Territories of Iguaçu and Ponta Porã were extinguished. Thus, the present political divisions of Brazil consist of 20 States, 5 Territories and 1 Federal District.

[1] The discrepancy in the total population of Central-East Brazil is due to the addition of some 70,000 inhabitants living in a region in dispute between Minas Cerais and Espírito Santo.

[5] Provisional data—subject to revision—based on the sixth national census (1950).

Source: Instituto Brasileiro de Geografia E. Estatística. Revista Brasileira de Geografia. Ano XI, No. 1 Janeiro—Março de 1949 and Ano XI, No. 4 Outubro–Dezembro de 1949. Brazil: Resources–Possibilities. Ministry of Foreign Affairs, 1946.

notoriously devious, ill placed, and poorly constructed. Gauges ranging from .6 to 1.6 meters add to the inconvenience of the traveller and shipper. Of the total mileage of railways in operation, about 22,000 miles, 91 per cent is 1 meter gauge; 3 per cent is narrower gauge, and 6 per cent is 1.6 meter gauge.

Approximately 68 per cent of the railways of Brazil is owned by the federal government, 25 per cent by the state governments, and 7 per cent by private interests. Some of the federal lines are leased to the states and some of both federal and state lines are leased to private companies. The lines have been built largely in advance of traffic. As a result, with few exceptions, they have been financially unprofitable. The former British-owned lines have fared better. Their favorable locations in areas of traffic density have made them valuable investments.

Despite difficult problems of construction and operation, the railways are becoming more efficient in handling both passengers and freight. They are offering more comfortable and more frequent service for passengers; trains are speedier than formerly; and service is more regular. Various types of cars to suit particular cargo requirements are now provided for shippers.

Highways. All-weather highways in Brazil are confined, primarily, to the areas adjacent to the larger cities, but the joining of important areas is increasing rapidly. The state of São Paulo and the Federal District account for over half of Brazil's automobile registration. Approximately 70 per cent of the roads suitable for motor traffic are located south of Vitória. The northeastern states have about 20 per cent. The sparsely settled interior states of Amazonas, Mato Grosso, and Goiás have not more than 10 per cent, and most of it is in the southern half of Mato Grosso.

Very few Brazilian roads have been paved. Most of them are simply graded dirt. During the dry season, therefore, the usable mileage is much greater than during the wet season, when highway travel in some areas practically ceases.

Several good automobile roads lead out from Rio de Janeiro and from São Paulo. It is possible to travel from Rio to Petrópolis, to São Paulo, or to Belo Horizonte at any time of the year. A splendid road extends from São Paulo down to Santos, beyond Campinas, and, in general, paved highways exist through the coffee regions of the state of São Paulo.

Much of the road-building work in Brazil is still done with pick and shovel, but there is a steady tendency toward increased use of machinery. The federal government and a few of the more progressive states are using modern road-building equipment. It is quite likely that road-building in Brazil as well as in all of South America will receive greater government support than railway construction in the immediate future. It should be borne in mind, however, that throughout South America, there is no extensive network of concrete highways as is found in the United States; most of the hard-surfaced highways are through arteries or within the cities or near their boundaries. "Good" roads means simply dirt roads that have been slightly graded and bridged to permit traffic to pass in good weather. "Bridges" over small streams in rural areas are usually the two flat sides of a split log, spaced to accommodate car or wagon wheels.

An agricultural nation. Brazil is now and probably for many years to come will be primarily an agricultural nation. The peculiar adaptability of its soil, topography, and climate, combined with the natural aptitudes of a very large portion of its population, make this fact almost certain. In its fields and forests lies the future greatness of Brazil.

With a population of 52 million people the production of food, the manufacture of clothing, and the construction of shelters are important functions, no matter how simple may be the tastes of the people or how low their purchasing power. The full significance of Brazil's agriculture is not revealed in its exports of coffee, cotton, cacao, and other commercial agricultural products. It is also necessary to take into consideration the vast amounts of animal and plant products used for food and for raw materials in manufacturing. More than 65 per cent of the persons employed in Brazil are engaged in agriculture and related occupations.

Brazil produces most of its staple food products. The diet of a Brazilian is heavy with starch, fruit, and fats. Rice, corn, manioc, and some wheat, together with a small proportion of potatoes, combine to form the starchy part of his diet. Rich, heavy, black beans, together with eggs, chickens, beef, and veal, supply his necessary proteins. Pork in abundance gives him plenty of fat, and fresh fruits of a wide variety give him vitamins. Relatively insignificant amounts of green vegetables are used, except among some of the later European immigrants. For his beverages the Brazilian uses large quantities of rich, black coffee, lesser amounts of Oriental tea, and very large quantities of yerba maté, or Paraguay tea. Few use milk except some of the children in the larger cities. The Brazilian drinks liberally of light wines and of a low-grade rum distilled from raw sugar. Whisky is imported from England for those who want it, but Brazilians use very little. Beer is produced in breweries in all the principal cities, and considerable quantities are consumed. A growing *União Brasileira Pro-Temperança* is attempting to create public sentiment in favor of limiting the use of alcohol as a beverage. Cigarette smoking seems to be a universal habit. For the most part the cigarettes used in South America are made of a heavier and darker tobacco than the American cigarettes. Some of the American factories use a different tobacco in cigarettes made for export to South America.

Foreign trade statistics, also, indicate that agriculture is the nation's major business. Approximately 80 per cent of the exports are vegetable and animal products and only 1 per cent are minerals. There are some exports of manufactured or finished products amounting to about 19 per cent of total export value during the latter part of the war period and dropping to less than 12 per cent in 1948.

The distribution of the agricultural activities of Brazil is related, not only to climate, soil, and topography, but also to social factors, including cheap land, cheap labor, and high cost of transportation. Cheap land and labor have tended to spread the agricultural industry over extensive areas, while the high cost of transportation governs the directions of expansion. With the introduction of more adequate facilities of transportation and lower freight rates, the agricultural pattern of Brazil will conform more closely to climate, relief, and soils.

The total acreage of Brazil is about 2 billion acres. Approximately 20.5 per cent of this area is in farms, so that 79.5 per cent is not as yet used for agricultural purposes. Of the percentage in farm lands only 3 per cent is under cultivation, 5.5 per cent in timber, and 12 per cent in pasture land. It has been estimated that 50 per cent of the undeveloped land, or land not used for farms, particularly in the great central interior, can be employed for agricultural purposes. However, official estimates indicate that 65 per cent of Brazilian labor is engaged in agriculture and animal husbandry.

In recent years the promotion of scientific agriculture has been the nation's chief objective. Many of the better *fazendas,* or farms, have modern Brazilian buildings and American farm equipment. There has been an increase in the number of small farms, indicating a greater number of landowners, which is one of the brightest signs of agricultural progress. There are well-directed and fairly well-equipped agricultural schools, colleges, and experimental stations. Agricultural societies have been organized to promote interest in such crops as cotton, sugar, rice, and corn, and to further the improvement of livestock.

Forest resources. Brazil's timber resources are extensive and varied. In the Amazon region lies the world's greatest expanse of tropical hardwoods. Other important timberlands lie along the coast, on the southern uplands, and in the far interior. A comparatively small amount of softwood is found in the drainage basin of the upper Paraná River. World statistics show that Brazil possesses 1,000 million acres of forest, or 13 per cent of the world's total, and is surpassed only by Russia and the British Commonwealth.

Mineral resources. Coal and petroleum are the minerals limiting the industrial expansion of Brazil. Coal deposits on a commercial scale have been discovered in several places, notably in south Brazil and in the western state of Mato Grosso. The southern deposits are being increasingly exploited, but those in Mato Grosso are entirely undeveloped. The coal is a low grade of bituminous, with high ash and sulphur content. Domestic production supplies only about 60 per cent of the nation's consumption. The three principal sources of coal imports in 1937 were Germany (47 per cent), United Kingdom (40 per cent), and the United States (9 per cent). By 1947, due to the effects of World War II, the pattern of coal trade with Brazil had changed in which the United States accounted for 90 per cent of the nation's foreign supply of coal. In all probability the United Kingdom will return in the near future as an important source of coal for the Brazilian market.

Petroleum. Petroleum has been eagerly sought, but only very small amounts have been discovered. The Bahia oil wells, the only ones in actual production in 1949, have a potential output of 10,000 barrels a day but the actual yield is less than 2,000 barrels daily. In 1948 the total domestic production of petroleum was 144,000 barrels. The federal and state governments have put such restrictions on the search for and the development of oil resources, that foreign oil companies are not deeply interested. Three areas possess potentialities for petroleum development in Brazil—(1) the coastal shelf (notably Bahia), (2) the Upper Amazon Basin, and (3) the Paraná Basin.

Water power. Far more important than the possibility of discovering petroleum or more coal, however, is the production of hydroelectric power. The principal centers of population are located within a relatively short distance of the high coastal escarpment. Behind this, or over its seaward slopes, pour numerous waterfalls. Within easy reach of these cities, therefore, is an abundance of potential electric power. Stimulated by the lack of coal for power and fuel, public service corporations have been organized, financed usually by foreign capital, to supply electricity. With the extension of this service to small population centers and with the normal increase of manufacturing, the importance of this natural resource is apparent.

The installed electric capacity of Brazil is reported to exceed 1,300,000 kilowatts of which 1,030,000 kilowatts are hydroelectric. Approximately 90 per cent of the total installed hydroelectric capacity is in São Paulo, Minas Gerais, Rio de Janeiro, and the Federal District. In northeastern Brazil where the rainfall is low and highly variable and in south Brazil, the only region of the nation where coal is mined, the production of electricity is, primarily, the output of thermally operated plants.

Electrification is progressing steadily throughout South America. In a number of regions, however, the lack of electric power is retarding industrial developments, particularly in such metropolitan areas as São Paulo, Buenos Aires, and Santiago. The potential hydroelectric power in South America is estimated at minimum stream flow from 46,400,000 kilowatts to 100,000,000 kilowatts. In the United States the potentiality of hydroelectric power is placed at 33,500,000 kilowatts. Although the United States has only 7 per cent of the world's population, it generates 45 per cent of the world's production of electricity in plants as follows: steam plants 39,234,257 kilowatts, hydroelectric plants 15,652,862 kilowatts, and internal combustion plants 1,576,390 or a total of 56,463,509 kilowatts. The installed electric capacity of the South American nations is as follows:

Argentina—1,400,000 kilowatts of which 45,000 are hydroelectric.
Brazil—1,300,000 kilowatts of which 1,030,000 are hydroelectric.
Chile—700,000 kilowatts, hydroelectric predominating.
Peru—294,000 kilowatts, hydroelectric predominating.
Colombia—250,000 kilowatts.
Uruguay—174,000 "
Venezuela—150,00 "
Bolivia—35,000 "
Ecuador—35,000 "
Paraguay—5,350 "

Iron and manganese. Iron ore and manganese compose Brazil's principal potential mineral wealth. The iron ore deposits are said to compare favorably in quantity and quality with similar resources of the United States. Because of the lack of available good coal and other industrial requisites, the iron ore of Brazil does not enter the channels of trade to any appreciable extent. Manganese, however, is mined for foreign markets, most of it being exported to the United States. Brazil is one of the five principal manganese-producing regions of the world. On the basis of output, Brazil ranks fifth, being surpassed by Russia, India, the Union of South Africa, and the African Gold Coast.

Industrialization. Some articles are manufactured or assembled in Brazil, but almost entirely for home consumption. For example, at the present time Brazil manufactures a large part of the cotton cloth used by its people and is increasingly producing its own woolens. For this industry it raises all its own cotton and most of its wool and has some cotton left over to export. It is true that many of its mills are owned by British capital, but nevertheless the product is made within the borders of Brazil and sold there. The iron and steel industry is another important development, particularly since the construction of the Volta Redonda plant. Cement production is sufficient to meet local demand and one of growing importance in the national economy of Brazil where there is a pressing need for new dams, bridges, and construction in general.

Brazil makes most of its clothing, hats, and shoes, practically all its cabinet work—and much of it is beautifully executed—and a large portion of its common utensils.

Reports show that there are some 60,000 manufacturing plants in

Brazil, employing over one million workers. In 1889, there were only 903 industrial establishments in all of Brazil.

A progressive policy. The school systems vary in different parts of Brazil. There are facilities for education from grade schools through colleges and universities. Strong emphasis is placed upon physical education and manual training. At least half the time the child spends in school is taken up with these physical activities.

The reasons behind this emphasis are two: First, Brazilian children tend to be physically a quiet lot. They have never learned the meaning of active play. They need all the stimulus that can be given toward the development of wholesome appreciation of an active, out-of-door life. Through carefully planned physical education and out-of-door play, it is hoped that the children's health will improve. The second reason is that Brazil needs skillful artisans. It is educating its children to perform effectively and skillfully the manual work of home and shop.

The education of girls is designed particularly with their future home life in view. They learn ideals of household management, cooking, the care of smaller children, and the making of clothing. They acquire ideals of cleanliness and neatness. Every effort is made to develop their interest in and appreciation of aesthetic values. Being by nature decidedly artistic, the girls profit enormously from this practical training. Their children and their homes will probably be cared for in a more intelligent, sanitary, and wholesome manner than that in which they themselves were reared. The education of boys includes these same fundamental ideals of cleanliness, personal hygiene, and sanitation, with the anticipation that intelligence will lead them to become in due time wiser fathers. They also learn the use of tools of various sorts.

If these children really learn to apply the laws of health and sanitation, if the girls learn to become good housekeepers and mothers, and the boys become wholesome fathers as well as good artisans, it will work wonders for their future well-being. As far as possible, a foundation for these ideals is laid in the first five years.

Brazil is not alone in this awakening to progressive rather than theoretical ideals in education. Throughout Latin America there is a spirit in elementary and secondary education moving toward the practical improvement of life and its ideals.

CHAPTER V

BRAZIL: REGIONAL ECONOMY AND SETTLEMENTS

EAST-CENTRAL BRAZIL [1]

Nation's economic center. In the early days, when all South America was aflame with a thirst for gold, several large bands of adventurers were organized on the coast of Brazil. These *bandeirantes* penetrated the far interior of Minas Gerais in search of gold and precious stones. They were tenacious and courageous men, and most of those who survived settled down in the interior. The descendants of those hardy pioneers form the nucleus of the population of Minas Gerais today. Their enterprise and enthusiasm, applied to the abundant natural resources, both agricultural and mineral, and under the stimulus of a bracing climate, have produced what its inhabitants proudly claim to be the finest state in the Brazilian Federation. Its population is estimated to be more than seven million people.

Bordering Minas Gerais on the southwest is São Paulo, the richest state of Brazil. Its early historical background is quite similar to that of Minas Gerais. Physiographically and economically they have much in common. Together they form the most powerful economic area in the nation.

São Paulo borders on the Atlantic. Between Minas Gerais and the ocean, north of São Paulo, lie the two small maritime states, Rio de Janeiro and Espírito Santo, each between 50 and 75 miles in width. Rio de Janeiro is a fertile plain, broken by numerous ranges, rising gradually toward the West. Espírito Santo is rugged with broken ranges almost throughout the southern half, but the mountains recede from the coast north of Vitória, leaving a broad, fertile plain.

The major cause of the present expansion and prosperity of the two upland states, Minas Gerais and São Paulo, is the agricultural development that originated some 75 years ago with the beginning of coffee exports. The enormous wealth annually brought to these two states through coffee alone—at least $150,000,000 to São Paulo and half that

[1] Known also as Southeastern Brazil, Mid-Eastern Brazil, and Central Brazil.

much to Minas Gerais—has stimulated all phases of economic life and brought an ever-expanding population.

In addition to agriculture and mining, a third factor, transportation, must be considered in the development of central Brazil. Two of the nation's finest harbors and the more accessible natural avenues of travel between the coast and the interior uplands are located in this region. An appreciation of these facts requires an examination of the surface features.

Surface configuration. Inland, from Santos to Rio de Janeiro, the forest-covered Serra do Mar rises above the narrow coastal plain. Behind this marginal escarpment lies the valley of the Rio Paraíba, which nearly parallels the coast for more than 200 miles. Bordering the Paraíba Valley on the west is the highest mountain range of the Brazilian Highland, known as the Serra da Mantiqueira. This range is the divide between the westward-flowing tributaries of the Paraná and the eastward-flowing Rio Paraíba. Only a few miles separate their headstreams. The highest peak in Brazil is Pico da Bandeira, towering 9,396 feet above sea level.

A natural break in the Serra da Mantiqueira, called the São Paulo Basin, is the site of the city São Paulo, the largest and most significant industrial center of Brazil. It is by means of this erosional basin, some 2,500 feet above sea level, that the principal routes of travel reach the upland city of São Paulo from the coastal cities Santos and Rio de Janeiro.

The distance of 50 miles, southeast from São Paulo on the highland to Santos on the coast, is traversed by a splendid electric railway and a magnificent automobile road. Because of the steep grade, an ascent of 2,000 feet in 50 miles, it is necessary to employ a cogwheel system for part of the way to pull trains over the steep escarpment.

Highly efficient railway and highway transportation exists also between São Paulo and Rio de Janeiro. The distance is about 300 miles. From Rio de Janeiro the route reaches the Paraíba Valley at Bara do Piraí. Then the route follows the valley and ascends to the São Paulo basin. From Guaratinguetá the rate of ascent is 500 feet in 25 miles.

Climatic relationships: temperature. In general, the coastal lowlands are uncomfortably hot and enervating during the summer and somewhat cooler during the winter. The average summer temperature is about 75° F. and the winter temperature about 65° F. However, the marginal highlands make it possible for one to escape the summer heat and depressing humidity of the coastal lands to a more pleasant climate within a few hours' time. Inland from Rio de Janeiro lies Petrópolis, a small mountain city to which, before the republic, the emperor and his court retired for the summer. It became actually the summer capital of the nation. It is now the summer home of large numbers of Brazilians and

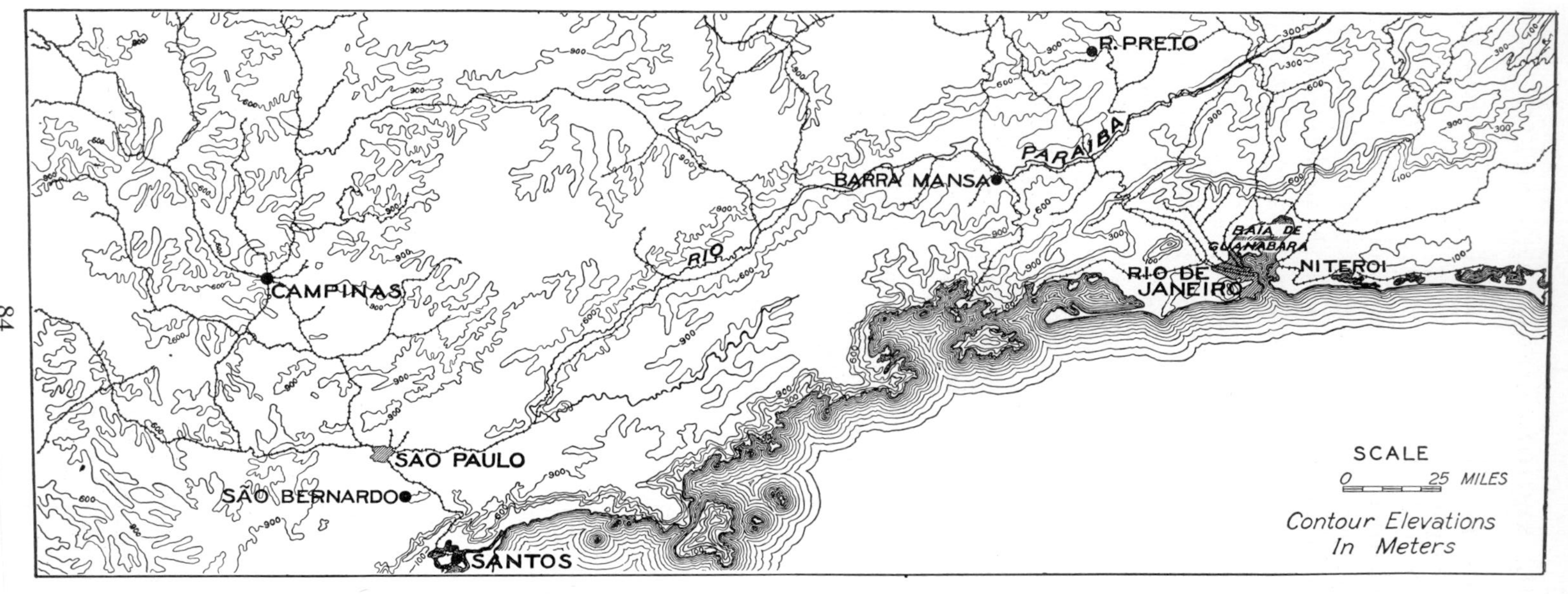

Fig. 36. *The "gateways" of central Brazil. The hinterland is rich in natural resources and is the nation's most highly developed economic region.*

foreigners alike. In a similar manner the upland city, São Paulo, serves the lowland city, Santos.

On the rolling uplands of central Brazil the summer temperature is high. A temperature of 95° F. is not uncommon in summer, while the winter temperature is 58° to 65° F. The mountain ranges are cool in the summer and cold in the winter. On these highlands frost occurs, but snow is unknown.

Precipitation. The coastal lowlands and seaward slopes of the marginal escarpment have an average annual rainfall ranging from 60 to 130 inches, with the maximum falling against the mountain slopes. The heavy rainfall on these seaward slopes supports a tropical rain forest cover. The maximum rainfall takes place in the summer months—December, January, and February. There is less seasonal distribution of rainfall in the lowlands.

The rainfall on nearly all of the upland region ranges from 40 to 80 inches a year. In general, the upland region as a whole has comparatively little rain during the winter months—June, July, and August. Most of the precipitation occurs in the summer months. On the plateau during December there is a daily downpour that usually comes without warning. The month of June is usually so dry that the vegetation is parched and subdued. The slightest breeze raises great clouds of dust. Since the drought is periodic, farmers and stockmen prepare for it, and serious effects seldom follow. Because of the dry seasons much of the native flora is of the savanna type. However, in places the original vegetation is principally a pattern of temperate forests and grasses.

Agricultural products. Central Brazil is the most highly developed agricultural region of the nation. It supplies a large part of the total production of coffee, cotton, sugar, tobacco, livestock, and fruits. Coffee, however, is the major crop.

Coffee production. Coffee is the traditional crop of Brazil, amounting to nearly one-half of the world's exportable production, except for seasonal fluctuations. For example, in 1940–1941 a drought in the São Paulo region reduced the nation's production to 21,000,000 bags. (Each bag contains 60 kilos, or about 132 pounds.) While production is distributed over most of the northern and central states, the largest number of coffee trees are found in the states of São Paulo and Minas Gerais.

COFFEE: ESTIMATED EXPORTABLE PRODUCTION
(*In 1,000 bags*)

	1935–39	*1947*	*1949*
Brazil	22,638	16,687	19,364
Colombia	4,202	6,000	5,410
El Salvador	1,011	1,035	1,260
Other South and North American Countries	3,699	3,405	.....
World	35,493	30,715	29,860

COFFEE: UNITED STATES IMPORTS
(In 132.3 pound bags)

From	*1946*	*1947*	*1949*
Brazil	11,647,827	10,004,172	12,763,683
Colombia	5,196,090	4,863,830	4,949,900
El Salvador	630,500	896,202	1,087,984
Venezuela	700,891	519,331	351,370
Others	....	....	....
Total	20,632,126	18,854,228	22,051,047

Brazil is the prime source of United States imports of coffee, furnishing in 1949 about 58 per cent.

The single state of São Paulo has more coffee trees than all the rest of Brazil combined. This is due to three factors: First, coffee grows best in a certain kind of deep fertile soil that is found most extensively in São Paulo. Second, the altitude of a portion of central Brazil is well suited for coffee production. Third, the wet and dry seasons of the uplands of this region are ideal for the coffee industry. Fourth, governmental and private capital have been turned very definitely toward the production of coffee rather than to any other one thing. Agriculturists are now beginning to diversify their crops, but as yet "Coffee is King." These same four reasons also explain why Minas Gerais is so rapidly increasing its production of coffee.

The coffee tree is a native of Abyssinia and was brought to Brazil in 1727. It was introduced first into what is now Belém, where it prospered.

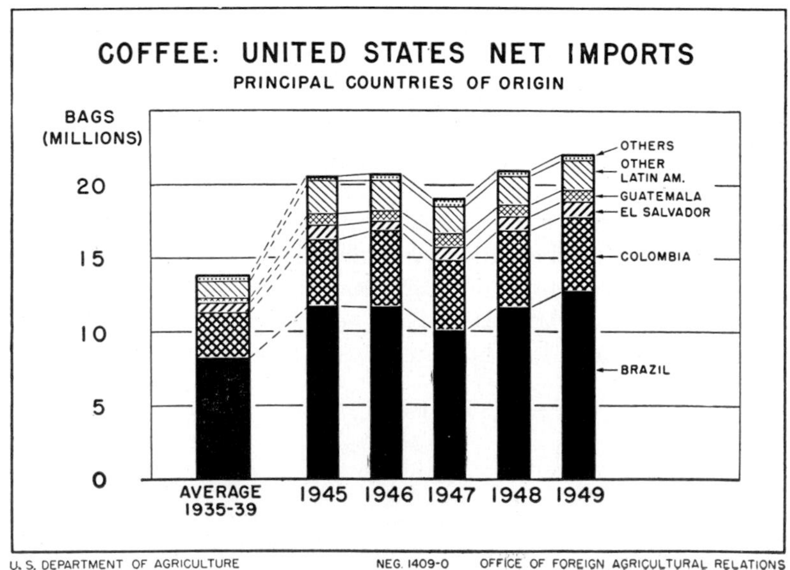

Fig. 37.

Station	Belém †	Manaus †	São Luís *	Natal *	Recife †	Ilhéus †	Cuiabá †	Corumbá †	Goiás *
Elevation (*Feet*)	42	133	65.6	9.8	97	147	541	476	1706.0
Average Temperature (°F)									
Period of Record	1923–1935	1931–1940	1912–1921	1904–1921		1924–1935	1911–1935	1931–1940	1912–1921
January	79	78.4	79.7	81.0		78.1	79.7	80.2	74.3
February	79	78.6	79.2	80.8		78.3	79.3	80.2	74.8
March	79	78.4	79.2	81.0		78.3	79.3	79.7	75.4
April	80	78.3	79.0	80.1		77.0	78.8	76.5	75.9
May	80	79.2	79.2	79.2		74.5	75.4	73.9	74.7
June	80	79.7	79.2	77.2		72.5	73.2	72.1	72.3
July	80	80.2	78.8	75.9		71.1	72.7	71.2	72.3
August	78	81.5	79.2	76.3		71.6	76.6	74.8	75.2
September	78	81.9	79.9	78.1		73.8	80.2	77.0	78.1
October	79	81.5	80.4	78.3		75.6	80.8	79.2	77.7
November	79	81.3	80.1	80.4		76.5	80.6	79.3	76.1
December	79	80.2	80.4	80.8		77.7	79.7	81.1	74.7
Annual	79	79.9	79.5	79.0		75.5	78.0	77.1	75.2
Range	2	3.6	1.6	5.1		7.7	8.1	9.9	5.8
Average Rainfall (*Inches*)									
Period of Record	1923–1935	1931–1940	1912–1919	1912–1920	1887–1922	1924–1935	1911–1935	1931–1940	1912–1919
January	13.8	10.9	7.4	2.8	2.1	4.6	8.7	6.3	11.9
February	17.3	9.9	10.4	5.2	3.3	6.8	7.7	5.6	11.7
March	18.0	12.5	18.5	5.9	6.5	11.2	8.1	3.8	11.4
April	13.1	11.3	16.6	8.9	8.5	12.5	4.0	3.5	5.0
May	12.0	8.7	12.4	7.8	11.0	6.7	1.8	2.5	0.4
June	6.8	3.7	5.8	12.3	11.0	5.1	0.5	1.1	0.5
July	5.4	2.1	4.4	6.7	10.5	8.0	0.4	1.0	0.1
August	5.1	1.8	1.1	3.5	6.4	4.5	1.2	0.9	0.4
September	5.0	2.5	0.5	2.4	2.6	3.9	1.9	2.0	1.8
October	3.4	4.4	0.4	1.1	1.0	5.4	4.7	3.8	4.8
November	3.4	6.4	0.7	0.3	1.1	7.2	6.4	4.2	8.7
December	7.0	8.6	6.5	0.7	1.2	7.2	8.6	7.1	10.2
Annual	110.3	82.8	84.6	57.5	65.2	83.1	54.0	41.8	66.5

Station	Belo Horizonte *	Petrópolis *	Rio de Janeiro †	Santos †	São Paulo †	Pôrto Alegre *	Rio Grande *	Uruguaiana *	Salvador †	Curitiba †
Elevation (*Feet*)	2811.7	2667.3	145	5	2,612	49.2	6.6	249.3	28	2,976
Average Temperature (°F)										
Period of Record	1910–1922	1915–1921	1882–1938	1923–1935	1931–1940	1909–1922	1912–1922	1912–1922	1931–1940	1931–1940
January	71.4	69.8	77.2	77.4	69.4	76.1	73.2	78.8	78.6	67.6
February	72.1	70.0	77.7	77.5	69.6	76.5	74.1	77.4	79.3	67.6
March	71.1	68.4	76.8	77.2	69.1	72.9	71.2	73.0	79.2	67.3
April	68.7	65.1	74.1	73.4	65.9	68.9	67.6	68.5	78.3	61.9
May	65.5	61.5	71.2	69.3	61.9	63.0	62.4	62.6	76.3	58.3
June	62.6	59.7	69.5	67.1	59.7	56.3	55.0	54.9	74.8	56.1
July	62.2	58.8	68.2	65.5	58.8	56.5	54.9	56.5	73.0	55.2
August	64.4	59.7	69.1	66.0	59.9	58.3	56.3	57.0	73.2	56.3
September	68.4	63.3	69.2	67.8	61.3	61.7	59.2	61.3	74.5	57.9
October	70.3	64.4	70.1	69.6	63.5	65.1	62.2	65.8	76.1	61.1
November	70.3	66.2	73.0	72.9	65.3	70.2	67.5	71.4	77.0	63.3
December	70.2	67.1	76.1	76.5	68.2	73.8	71.2	76.1	78.3	66.6
Annual	68.2	64.6	72.7	71.7	64.4	66.9	64.6	66.9	76.6	61.6
Range	9.9	11.2	9.5	12.0	10.8	20.2	19.2	23.9	6.3	12.4
Average Rainfall (*Inches*)										
Period of Record	1910–1919	1913–1919	1882–1938	1923–1935	1931–1940	1909–1922	1912–1922	1912–1922	1931–1940	1931–1940
January	12.8	11.3	5.0	11.3	8.5	4.3	3.5	3.7	3.4	7.1
February	9.5	9.6	4.6	11.5	6.9	3.7	5.7	3.9	3.4	6.1
March	6.3	11.9	5.1	13.5	6.4	3.6	3.5	6.9	7.0	4.1
April	2.9	6.3	3.6	6.9	3.1	4.8	3.0	5.8	10.5	3.6
May	0.6	3.3	2.6	5.7	2.6	4.1	3.2	4.5	11.9	3.2
June	0.5	2.7	2.3	5.4	1.6	5.0	4.5	5.0	7.3	3.1
July	0.4	2.4	1.7	3.4	1.0	4.3	5.2	2.8	8.8	2.4
August	0.9	2.6	1.6	3.5	1.9	5.1	3.6	3.0	4.5	3.6
September	1.5	2.9	2.5	6.3	3.6	4.6	4.8	3.9	3.5	4.9
October	4.9	7.3	3.3	6.0	4.8	3.1	3.3	3.8	4.0	5.7
November	8.3	12.9	3.7	8.1	5.5	3.3	3.4	3.7	4.6	5.2
December	10.7	10.6	5.0	8.5	7.4	4.1	2.9	4.4	3.4	5.8
Annual	59.1	83.7	41.0	90.1	53.3	49.8	46.5	5.15	72.3	54.8

Source: * K. Knoch: "Klimakunde von Südamerika," *Handbuch der Klimatologie*, Band II, Teil G, Berlin, 1930.
† Normais Climatológicas, Serviço Meteorologia, Ministério da Agricultura, Rio de Janeiro, Brasil, 1941.

Seeds were brought to Rio in 1774 and planted in the garden of an Englishman named Hoppman. From these trees were taken the seeds that established the great South American coffee industry.

The traveller in the state of São Paulo often rides for many miles with nothing in sight but coffee trees. Some of these are a century old and still producing well, although older trees require more careful attention and fertilizing than younger ones. Throughout the states of São Paulo and Minas Gerais many thousands of young trees are growing that will soon come into bearing and will augment the total produced. Trees begin bearing at about four years. "There is money in coffee," almost certain money, and both small farmers and large plantation owners are interested in the profits to be made.

F. A. Carlson.

Fig. 38. Coffee tree in fruit, Brazil.

Coffee grows in the form of a berry, with a somewhat thick pulp, inside of which the two halves of the coffee bean face each other. It ripens over a period of three months, but not all berries ripen at the same period. On a tree at a given time will be found fully ripe berries, partially ripened ones, and absolutely unripe ones. Late in the gathering season the blossoms and buds of the new crop appear.

The usual method of harvesting has been to wait until the latter part of the ripening period; then to clear the ground of all grass around the tree so that the fallen berries may easily be gathered; and finally to strip all berries from the branch at a single sweep of the hand. This process is cheap, rapid, and simple, but it is hard on the trees and produces a less desirable quality of coffee, since the green and partially ripe berries are astringent and not full flavored. A better method, which is somewhat more costly and more involved, is now coming into vogue. It is called the "natural harvest," for the fruit is gathered only when fully matured. The ground is cleared, and the gatherers shake or beat the trees lightly, to make the fully ripened berries fall. The unripe ones remain on the tree until they too become fully mature, and these are gathered in a second or third harvesting. This method is more costly, but the quality of the coffee is improved and consequently brings a higher price—and the trees live longer. Because of its ultimate economy, this "natural" process is rapidly taking the place of the older stripping. It is increasing the general quality of the Brazilian product, and thereby makes it possible for Brazil to compete more favorably with the product of the Caribbean areas.

After the berries have been swept up and stacked, they are washed in a tank of water, where stones, dirt, and other foreign matter are removed. The usual procedure is then to take the berries to the drying ground, where they are spread out on a concrete or brick floor and turned over and over until thoroughly dried, after which they are put through a

Courtesy National Coffee Department of Brazil.

Fig. 39. Coffee picking.

hulling machine. The drying takes from two days to two weeks, the time depending upon the coffee and on the weather. To avoid night rains or heavy dews, the coffee has to be hilled and covered with canvas each evening.

A method that is rapidly coming into use, because it improves the flavor of the coffee, is to carry the washed berries through a depulping machine that removes the outer skin. After twelve hours of fermenting, the inner pulp may be washed off. Then the coffee is dried, and the inner shells are removed. Recent experiments with kiln drying seem to show that this process improves the flavor of the coffee, and probably it will supersede sun drying on the more completely equipped plantations.

Until recently it was the custom to dump the total crop on the market at once, in somewhat the same way that farm produce is sold in the United States at the close of harvest. This meant great irregularity, confusion, and uncertainty with regard to prices, and glutted railway service to port cities. Under more recent government control warehouses for storing the crop have been constructed in the interior. Only a certain amount is shipped down to the port of exit each month, and the disposal of the crop is thereby distributed over the entire year. This makes for stability of prices, but it also makes necessary an adequate financing system to carry the producers.

The flavor of coffee depends on four main factors. Two of these are the responsibility of the grower, two of the consumer.

The *first* factor is the kind and quality of soil, the degree of exposure to direct sunlight, and the altitude in which the plant is grown. A very deep, rich, loamy soil is best. In Brazil coffee grown at altitudes of from 1,500 to 2,500 feet is apparently better than that grown at lower levels. The *second* factor is conditions and care under which the crop is prepared for export. Too much rain at the time of harvest is destructive. In the year 1927, for instance, Brazil suffered heavy harvest rains, and consequently 6,000,000 sacks of coffee produced at that time, nearly 40 per cent of the total crop, were badly damaged and ill flavored. Proper gathering, to insure only ripened berries, proper washing, drying, depulping, and cleaning and storing, all influence profoundly the flavor of the coffee. Coffee is known as *hard* or *mild,* the quality depending largely on the care in preparation for export.

Proper roasting liberates certain aromatic oils that have a decided bearing on flavor. This is the *third* factor. Overroasting or underroasting leaves an inferior taste. Likewise, if the coffee is prepared for drinking immediately after roasting, it tastes much better than after some time has elapsed. *Fourth,* and finally, flavor depends on the manner of preparation for the table. Brazilians say that coffee should steep but never boil. Any method of preparation that avoids boiling is effective.

A tremendous single crop of this sort requires an abundant supply of labor. In earlier days it was furnished by the Portuguese, but within the past 20 or 30 years Italian and Spanish immigrants have been attracted to the coffee-producing areas and have taken the place of the Portuguese or native Brazilians. About two decades ago a number of Japanese were encouraged to come to Brazil, and in some places they displaced the Italians. Although some of the Japanese have found their way into the Amazon Plain, most of them have settled in the agricultural lands of interior São Paulo. To date, there are probably 200,000 Japanese in Brazil.

The Japanese government cooperated with Brazil in the endeavor to permit only high-grade agricultural immigrants to make their homes in that country. Up to the present time these have formed their own colonies and have rarely intermarried with the Brazilian people. Since there is no racial antagonism or discrimination, at least among the farming classes, it is likely that these Japanese colonists will finally disappear into the great national body. There has always been opposition on the part

Courtesy L. Hites.

Fig. 40. One of the better farm houses, Brazil.

of some Brazilian leaders to Japanese penetration. The opposition has now become so powerful that immigration has ceased, for the present at least.

F. A. Carlson.

Fig. 41. Old and new farm laborer's houses.

In the coffee fields two plans for the employment of labor are in operation. The first plan settles the laborer's family on the land of the plantation owner, in a small workers' village. He is given a certain number of trees to care for, which he and his family work. During the larger part of the year the work is simple and not very hard. During the gathering season all members of the family must work early and late. For this labor the worker is guaranteed a modest living for himself and his family, and consequently he has a feeling of economic security. The second system employs laborers only when work is to be done. Additional hands from the cities are employed for the gathering and laid off again during the slack seasons. This system is not commonly in vogue in the coffee-growing regions. Workers object, and rightly, to the insecurity involved. Employers have frequently encountered serious difficulty in obtaining sufficient hands during the rush season.

Cotton ranks second. No longer is Brazil a one-crop export nation. Since 1900 coffee has accounted for about three-fifths of the total value of Brazil's exports. Today the value of Brazil's cotton exports is about one-half the value of her coffee exports. Coffee exports have dropped from 71 per cent of the nation's total exports in 1929 to less than 40 per cent in recent years. Cotton ranks second in the country not only in export value but also in value of production.

COTTON PRODUCTION
(*In 1,000 bales*)

	Av. 1935–39	*1947*	*1948*	*1950*[2]
Brazil	1,959	1,150	1,500	1,500
South America	2,716	1,882	2,318	2,587
United States	13,149	11,851	14,877	9,884
World	31,676	25,255	29,130	27,350

The Brazilian government has successfully encouraged the utilization of cotton within the country and has succeeded in establishing mills capable of manufacturing practically all of the domestic cloth. These mills are located principally in the city of Rio de Janeiro and in the states of São Paulo, and Minas Gerais. A number of mills are also located in the states of Pernambuco and Alagôas, in a good cotton-growing region.

Brazil produces two types of cotton: (1) a short staple, which is grown on the eastern lowlands, and (2) a fine-quality long staple, which grows on the uplands. The lowland plant is an annual, as in the United States, but the highland is a tree variety growing to a height of five or six feet and living for several years.[3] The earliest cotton plantations were laid

[2] Preliminary.

[3] The annual cotton plant is also grown on the uplands. Its quality and length of staple are comparable to the cotton grown in the United States.

out along the northeastern coast in the states of Rio Grande do Norte, Paraíba, Pernambuco, and Alagôas. Within recent years, however, São Paulo has been planting a constantly increasing acreage and has become the leading cotton region, producing about 65 per cent of the nation's total output. Because of the high quality of Brazilian long-staple cotton, it is likely that exports will increase in the future—unless overproduction occurs elsewhere. Efforts in the United States to limit the cotton crop of 1933–1934 encouraged larger plantings in Brazil. Although accurate statistics of cotton acreage and yield in Brazil are not available, it is not an exaggeration to say, on the basis of estimates, that Brazil has increased her cotton yield some 30 per cent in the past ten years, and that she is rapidly approaching an important place among the leading cotton-growing countries of the world.

Sugar. Sugar is produced in all states of Brazil. Three large areas are now extensively given over to its production: the eastern part of the plateau in Minas Gerais, the coast lands north and south of Rio de Janeiro, and the northeastern coast lands of Pernambuco and Alagôas. The Brazilian has such an appetite for sweets, however, that sugar is produced and consumed in large quantities near all the large centers of population. Fruit conserves are especially popular, as are fruit butters. The most common of these are made from oranges, bananas, and marmelos—respectively, *laranjada, bananada,* and *marmelada.* Considerable quantities of sugar are converted into alcohol, some of which is used for industrial purposes, while large amounts are converted into a low-grade rum called *cachaça,* and consumed as a beverage. In the early days exports of sugar from Brazil were a principal commodity in European markets. Brazil had virtually a world monopoly, and her planters became rich. Now, with increasing yields in many other parts of the world, exports have decreased, and practically the entire crop is consumed at home. Only 4 per cent of the annual yield is exported.

Tobacco. Tobacco is grown throughout the nation, and it is widely used. The government has taken particular interest in the improvement of qualities and in teaching farmers the proper care of the crop. Through these efforts, production and value have steadily increased. The state of Bahia leads in the production of this crop, followed by Rio Grande do Sul, and Minas Gerais. Nearly three-fourths of the entire amount grown is consumed in Brazil in the form of cigarettes.

Staple food products: Manioc. Manioc, known also as mandioca or cassava, is a tuber.[4] Two varieties are grown, one of which is non-poisonous, the other highly poisonous in its natural state. The latter is the more widely used. It is grown throughout Brazil, from the Amazon

---

[4] *Mandioca* is the Spanish form, but *manioc* is the preferred English term. The technical designation of the poisonous species is *Manihot utilissima.*

region to the state of Rio Grande do Sul. There are several varieties, some maturing in six months, others requiring 20 months. The tubers sometimes reach the astonishing length of 4 feet, growing entirely, of course, underground. When they are young, fresh, and tender, they are boiled and fried like potatoes and make a delicious and deservedly popular dish, although they require more flavoring than potatoes to make them highly palatable.

Courtesy Frank E. Williams.

Fig. 42. Mamão or papaya tree and fruit.

The mature plant is hard and fibrous and is utilized in a different manner. First, the poisonous juices are pressed from the tuber, after which it is thoroughly dried and ground into a fibrous, starchy grain that greatly resembles corn meal.[5] This meal is used in a variety of ways. On the table of every poor family (and many who are not poor) a dish of the raw meal is placed. A spoonful or two is scattered over the other food and eaten raw. Often the manioc meal is parched in a pan containing butter or chicken fat. Frequently it is boiled in meat liquor and becomes a gluey but tasty mush. Vast quantities of this meal are prepared and used throughout Brazil. When passed through a special process, it becomes the tapioca of the North American market. It is also used in the preparation of sizing materials and gum such as that used on the United States postage stamps.

Corn. Corn is grown on the eastern highland from Bahia south to Rio Grande do Sul. A considerable amount is used to fatten stock in the south, but a principal use is as a food for man. Prepared usually in the form of meal, it is made either into mush or bread, and in certain parts of the interior it forms an important item in the diet. Because of the height of the plant and the ease of cultivation, corn makes an excellent crop with which to break in new ground. It is frequently used as a filler between rows of young coffee trees. Corn is primarily a temperate crop and does not produce so well in the lush lowlands. While by far the larger part of the crop is consumed at home, Brazil exports a small quantity each year. The corn crop has been estimated at 200 millions of

[5] The starch grains and juices are squeezed out by means of a plaited "snake," and then the cyanic poisons are eliminated by several rinsings in clean water. The starch grains become pure white and as fine as flour.

bushels yearly, placing Brazil as third in known world production, surpassed only by the United States (over 3 billions) and China.

Rice. Rice of two varieties is grown: lowland and highland. South Americans in every country use vast quantities of rice, especially in the lowlands. In Brazil it is a staple starch food everywhere. Prepared in Spanish style, with tomatoes, fat, onions, and a touch of garlic, gorgeously colored with tumeric, it is a satisfying and attractive dish. No one knows how much is grown, but the fact that it is a universal dish throughout the land implies that the crop is large, probably as much as 2,500,000 tons. Small amounts are exported to Argentina and Uruguay.

Beans. Beans of many varieties are produced throughout nearly all of Brazil. The favorite type is a black bean of rich protein content and rather strong flavor. It is grown everywhere, but more intensively in the states of São Paulo, Minas Gerais, and Rio Grande do Sul, whence it is shipped in quantities to other easily reached parts of the country. These beans form the staple food of vast numbers of people and, when properly prepared, make a very tasty but heavy meal.

Potatoes. Potatoes form a minor item in the Brazilian diet. They do not grow well in Brazil, are usually small in size and watery, and do not keep. Statistics show that the southern states of Brazil produce annually some 235,000 tons. Each year about half a million dollars' worth of potatoes are imported, principally from the United States, and generally used as seed. The government's ministry of agriculture is working intensively in experimental stations in an effort to develop an "acclimatized" potato, and apparently is making progress.[6] One of the great problems of the department of agriculture is to persuade farmers, many of whom are provincial and opinionated, to employ profitable methods of agriculture and to use improved seeds after they have been developed. Yams and sweet potatoes are used to some extent in the south, but not extensively.

Fruits. Fruits of many kinds are produced in enormous quantities in Brazil and form a principal item in the diet. The names of the many Brazilian varieties are totally unfamiliar to the United States, for most tropical fruits cannot be transported because they spoil too readily. They cannot be described, for, as one American remarked after drinking a refreshing glass of *cajuada* (the juice of the fruit from which the cashew nut is obtained), "It reminds me of something I have never tasted before."

There is the *mamão* or *papaya,* a tree 8 to 15 feet high, leafless except for a crown at the top, producing a quantity of fruit shaped something like a pear and weighing from 2 to 10 pounds. In the center of the fruit is a cluster of small, round, black seeds exceedingly rich in pepsin.

---

[6] The Irish potato originated on the Andes highlands, where several varieties are grown at present.

The fruit is served peeled, sliced like a large cantaloupe would be, and eaten with knife and fork. The flesh is a pinkish orange color, and the taste is a cross between peach and cantaloupe. The mamão is a delicious fruit. It grows throughout the tropical regions. The *jaca* grows on an enormous wide-spreading tree. The fruit is shaped like a long watermelon and attains a weight of 10 to 20 pounds. It grows, of course, close to the trunk or on the stronger branches. The inside of the fruit is a white gluey mass, embedded in which are rows of seeds resembling small shelled Brazil nuts. Surrounding these seeds is the edible part of the fruit, a light orange in color, and resembling in texture and shape a seeded date. The fruit is sweet and delicious, but there is nothing in the dietary experience of a North American to which it can be likened. The jaca thrives in a moist, warm climate. The *mango,* similar to the mango produced in the West Indies and southern Florida, is a fruit with the shape of a flattened egg and the weight of a large pear. Its large flat and woody seed is the radiating center for a multitude of thick heavy fibers which extend to the skin, and among which the edible pulp of the fruit is produced.

The *banana* grows in wild profusion throughout the tropics. There are many varieties. The popular names are gold banana, the size of a man's thumb; apple banana, with a flavor suggestive of a winesap apple; plantains, a species of banana, used for cooking; and silver banana, resembling our current banana of commerce. There is no fruit more easily grown, more inexpensive, and more abundant in food values. Throughout Brazil enormous quantities are used.

Oranges likewise are found everywhere below the frost line, in a host of varieties. At one extreme is the "earth orange," or *laranja da terra,* the thick skin of which is made into preserve, while the bitter pulp is discarded. At the other extreme is the huge Bahia navel orange, which attains at times a diameter of more than four inches, and is deliciously sweet. Brazil not only grows enormous quantities of oranges for her own use, but exports large quantities to Argentina and Uruguay. Our own California navel orange is really a descendant of the Bahia orange. Some eighty years ago several of these trees were brought to Washington, D. C., where they were cared for and afterwards distributed. Those sent to California prospered. From them buds were grafted on the stock of seedling orange trees, and from this grafted stock developed our large navel-orange industry, with a $50,000,000 or more annual crop. California orange growers owe a debt of gratitude to the unknown orchardist of Bahia who recognized the value of the strange sport in his orchard and preserved it. Brazil's annual production of oranges totals more than 30,000,000 crates, and exports usually exceed 3,000,000 crates. The United Kingdom is the principal European market.

Grapefruit was unknown in Brazil until a few years ago, when it was introduced in São Paulo to meet the demands of Americans who were continually asking for it. Now it is becoming a little more plentiful. *Lemons* and *limes* are found nearly everywhere and are used in enormous quantities. Other fruits, a score of them, are widely used throughout Brazil. Peaches, pears, apples, and watermelons have been recently introduced from the United States and Europe, and they are rapidly finding a place on Brazilian tables.

Meat products. The diet of the Brazilian people includes great amounts of meat products. Consequently meat is produced near all the large population centers. It is also produced on many interior ranges

Courtesy B. H. Hunnicutt.

Fig. 43. Zebu or East Indian cattle. Brazil.

from which the cattle ready for market graze their way slowly toward the centers of use. It has been estimated that there are 46,000,000 head of cattle in Brazil. They are distributed pretty well over the entire country, for there is seldom any refrigeration except at the large packing plants, and animals used for food must be killed near the places where they are to be eaten. Cattle that are to be killed for export, however, are concentrated in the southern and east-central states, within easy access of the ports of embarkation, where the packing houses are located. At the present time, therefore, it is likely that Rio Grande do Sul has some 14,000,000 head of cattle; that Minas Gerais and São Paulo together have about 16,000,000; that Bahia and Goiás have some 6,000,000; that Mato Grosso has some 5,000,000; that the other northeastern states have some 3,000,000; and that the remainder is scattered in smaller districts along the coast, or in the Amazon region.

Brazil has three types of cattle. (1) In the very early days the Jesuit missionaries brought Spanish cattle up the interior rivers for their missions among the Indians. These animals formed the nucleus of cattle, now scattered throughout the interior—lean, wiry, and longhorned. They are used for jerked beef, and that part of their hides which has not been ruined by flies and ticks is employed in making leather. (2) In order to strengthen breeds and to develop a variety of domestic animal resistant to ticks, zebu (Brahma) bulls were brought from India. They have strengthened the stock, especially in the north and throughout Mato Grosso. (3) Other prize breeding stocks have been brought from the United States, Europe, and Argentina, varieties that produce better beef than the zebu. After much experimentation and careful selection of stock for survival, a variety has been produced that is resistant to ticks and to tropical diseases, and that gives excellent meat and leather.

In Rio Grande do Sul and in São Paulo, the principal packing houses are located to facilitate shipment abroad. Plants are also located on the upper Paraguay River in Mato Grosso. Beef goes to Europe. During an epidemic of hoof and mouth disease in Argentina a number of years ago, the United States placed an embargo on fresh beef from South America. The disease has not been completely eradicated; consequently the embargo is continued to the chagrin and bitterness of Brazilian and Argentine ranchers and statesmen, who refer to our "unfairness" and lack of cooperation. Much of the canned beef sold in American groceries comes from South America, as is shown by the labels on the containers.

Vast numbers of *swine* are found everywhere. They are easy to raise, and they offer the poor man an immediate food as well as a product that may always be sold for a little cash. Central Brazil is not a *sheep* country. The climate is too warm for them to prosper. In the more temperate South Brazil, however, there are more than 14,000,000 sheep, and in the northeastern dry sections of the country 5,000,000 *goats* are found, for these hardy animals can live and reproduce under the most difficult conditions. The dairy industry continues to grow, particularly in Southeastern Brazil. Fluid milk entering the cities of Rio de Janeiro and São Paulo is on a marked increase.

Mineral industry. The most important mineral state of all Brazil is Minas Gerais, which means, literally translated, "mines of all sorts." The great central plateau, of which the states of Minas, São Paulo, and contiguous parts of Bahia, Goiás, and Mato Grosso form a part, is rich in minerals of several kinds.

The belief that the interior contained large deposits of gold and emeralds led the *bandeirantes* (literally "standard bearers" or pioneers) in the early eighteenth century to undertake their famous penetrations of interior Brazil.

Gold. Gold was discovered, notably in Minas and Goiás. The Morro

Velho mine, in constant production since 1725, is one of the deepest mines in the world, more than 6,500 feet. Gold, in common with many of the mineral resources of Brazil, is owned by British capital. Of recent years, because of the scarcity of gold metal, the Brazilian government has purchased the entire product of these mines. An interesting fact about the Morro Velho mine is that the deeper the vein extends, the richer it becomes. Now, at 6,500 feet, it is much richer than when nearer the surface. How deep it may be possible to extend this mine before costs of production become prohibitive, it is impossible to say. Gold deposits have been discovered from western Mato Grosso to Paraná. Cuiabá, capital of Mato Grosso, is built upon the site of an ancient gold camp.

Diamonds. Diamonds were discovered at about the same time as gold, and they have been constantly mined ever since. Shortly after the rich mines were discovered, they were declared a monopoly of the crown. This, however, did not stop individual endeavor, but rather stimulated curiosity and prospecting. The most famous district surrounds Diamantina, a city of 10,000 inhabitants in Minas Gerais, and is known by the same name. Many tourists visit the place each year, and considerable numbers, many knowing little or nothing about diamonds, make unwise purchases. The stones are usually found either in the beds of streams or in deposits close by. Methods of working these deposits are most primitive; panfuls of loose earth are carried down to the stream and slowly washed out. In a few places, principally in the older fields, modern techniques and machines are employed.

In late years some 40,000 carats of diamonds have been extracted annually. Only a small percentage of Brazilian diamonds are fine gems. Most of them are used for industrial purposes, in abrasives, drills, and cutting tools.

Semiprecious stones, including the topaz, tourmaline, beryl, aquamarine, and sapphire, are also found. These semiprecious stones are sometimes very large.

IRON ORE PRODUCTION
(In metric tons)

	1937	*1946*	*1948*
Chile	1,489,637*	1,352,886	2,545,381
Brazil	209,715†	517,765	1,441,119
Mexico	136,018	275,445	229,077
Cuba	496,258‡	....	36,595
United States	73,250,649	71,980,145	102,854,886
World Total	213,700,000	154,000,000	211,000,000

* Chile—production of Tofo mine—1937.
† Brazil—exports 1937.
‡ Cuba—exports 1937.
Source: Bureau of Mines, Department of the Interior, Washington, D. C.

Iron and manganese. Iron and manganese compose Brazil's principal potential mineral wealth. The state of Minas Gerais alone is estimated to have total deposits of iron ore, averaging 45 to 60 per cent pure, of perhaps 15 billion tons. The principal deposit is known as the "Itabira," located about 325 railway miles from Vitória. Up to the present time not much iron has been taken out, because of the lack of fuel and the cost of transporting ore to the coast for export. There is no domestic coal in the state of Minas, and that used for smelting comes either long distances from the south, the states of Rio Grande do Sul and Santa Catarina, or it is imported. The cost of producing iron is so high that it is really cheaper to import pig iron. Nevertheless, the iron and steel industry in Brazil is growing. As early as 1806, iron was smelted in Minas Gerais, and since then a number of small furnaces have been erected. However, it was not until 1934 that the industry had its real beginning. The most recent progress is now in the form of a steel plant at Volta Redonda, located in the state of Rio de Janeiro in the valley of the Paraíba river about 90 miles from the federal capital. In 1950 it produced 420,000 tons of steel and 340,000 tons of pig iron. Among other iron and steel materials made in Brazil can be found such simple but essential products as nails, bolts, fencing, stoves, safes, and the simpler agricultural implements. The likelihood is that, more and more, Brazil will take care of its own needs for these fundamental iron manufactures, and also that it will gradually develop plants to produce rails and complex machines. It is not probable that Brazil will export iron or iron products in significant amounts. The peak exports of 421,000 metric tons occurred in 1941 but in 1948 the amount dropped to 350,000 tons.

Manganese deposits exist in the same general regions as the iron deposits. They are found mostly in Minas Gerais, south of Belo Horizonte, and near the town of Lafayette. More than 90 per cent of the manganese ore output of Brazil to date has been produced in this region. Other manganese deposits are found near Nazaré, Bahia, and in the state of Mato Grosso.

The annual output for the past five years has averaged about 200,000 tons, of which more than half has been exported to the United States. If adequate national transport were available, the production could be greatly increased.

The United States is almost completely dependent upon foreign sources of high grade manganese ore. The consumption of metallurgical-grade manganese ore in the United States was 1,200,000 long tons in 1948. Of this amount less than 110,000 long tons were produced domestically and the remainder was imported, mainly from Africa, U. S. S. R., India, and Brazil. Smaller amounts came from Mexico, Cuba, Chile, and the Philippine Republic. Every ton of steel produced has required approximately 12 to 14 pounds of manganese. It increases the strength of steel and acts as a purifier in the process of production.

Quartz crystals and other mineral resources. For many years Brazil has been practically the sole source of supply of quartz crystals for electrical and optical use. Most of the crystals are obtained from the northern part of the state of Minas Gerais. Other regions of production are Bahia, Goiás, and Mato Grosso. Mica, tungsten, chromium, nickel, lead, titanium, zirconium, and bauxite are mined in limited quantities. Further field work will be necessary to determine their potentialities.

MANGANESE ORE IMPORTED INTO THE UNITED STATES, BY COUNTRY OF ORIGIN 1938–1949

Year	Total	India	U.S.S.R.	Gold Coast	Brazil	Union of South Africa	Cuba	Chile	Mexico	Other
				In thousands of long tons						
1938	484	26	166	127	30		131			
1945	1,305	178	135	244	252	111	262	82	41	
1948	1,124	188	385	119	128	194	30	10	55	15
1949	1,379	383	73	332	135	316	55	7	53	25

MANGANESE ORE. PERCENTAGE DISTRIBUTION OF UNITED STATES IMPORTS

	1948 *	1949 †		1948 *	1949 †
India	16.7	27.3	Chile	0.9	0.5
U. S. S. R.	34.3	5.2	Mexico	4.9	3.8
Gold Coast	10.6	23.6	Philippines	0.8	0.9
Union of South Africa	17.3	24.3	Angola	0.2	0.5
Brazil	11.4	9.6	Belgian Congo	0.2	0.3
Cuba	2.7	3.0	French Morocco		0.1

* 1,124,000 long tons.
† 1,379,000 long tons.

Coastal settlements: Rio de Janeiro. Because of its security from storms, its relative ease of defense, its natural beauty, and its location about midway along the Brazilian coast line—and in part through an accident of history—Rio de Janeiro was selected in 1792 as the capital of Brazil. With 2,400,000 inhabitants, it is the largest city of the nation. It ranks as the second largest city on the southern continent, exceeded only by Buenos Aires. As the seat of the national government, it has attracted not only the families of multitudinous government officials but many of the elite of all nations. Just as Washington, D. C., has attracted many millionaires whose families "like to reside in the national capital," so Rio de Janeiro has become the center of wealth and aristocracy of Brazil.

The city lies on the coastal plain, on the flanks of dome-like hills, outliers of the Serra do Mar, and on the floors of bordering valleys. Its coastal border is the Bahia de Guanabara, a landlocked bay some 16 miles long from north to south and varying in width from one mile at the entrance to 15 miles at the broadest point. On the western shore of the bay stands Rio, on the eastern shore the city of Niterói, with a population of 175,000. Sugar Loaf Mountain, Pão de Assucar, 1,200 feet high, rises to the south of the entrance of the bay, and the summits of the Organ Mountains, their peaks rising like a series of organ pipes, range to the north. Corcovado, or the "Hunchback," another magnificent dome, rises some 2,200 feet above the sea and is encompassed on three sides by the city. On the far side, a narrow ridge permits a cog railway

Courtesy Pan American Union.

Fig. 44. View of the bay of Rio de Janeiro, showing Pão de Assucar (Sugar Loaf), Brazil.

to approach within a hundred feet of the summit. The face toward the city drops off a sheer thousand feet. A gigantic statue of the Christ, 40 meters (128 feet) high, was erected on the summit in 1930. A third beauty spot is O Bico da Jijuca, 3,300 feet high, the highest mountain within the city. An automobile road approaches its summit.

The urban morphology of Rio de Janeiro is an interesting combination of the ancient and the modern. Many streets in the older sections of the city are not more than 15 feet wide, with pavements three feet in width on either side. Shops, stores, and offices open directly on the sidewalk. Residences occupy the upper floors of the buildings. The streets, laid out in the early days of the empire, were made just wide enough for two ox-carts or carriages to pass. In modern days a narrow streetcar or bus passes close to the curb on one side, and just enough room is left on the other side for a cart or automobile. Other, newer streets, like Sete de Setembro and Rua Uruguaiana, are wider and more modern. They have a double streetcar line, a traffic lane on each side, and wide pavements. The Avenida Central, cut at enormous expense through the very heart of the city from north to south a few years ago, is a beautiful, wide boulevard. It is bordered with trees, flanked by curiously inlaid mosaic pavements, and lined with the city's most expensive business structures. On this avenue are also the Municipal Theater, one of the most magnificent in the world, the national library, the school of fine arts, and other public buildings. Facing its southern end is the Monroe Palace, constructed first for the St. Louis World's Fair as a memorial to inter-American friendship and later transported piece by piece to Rio.

Small public squares, richly adorned with statues of deceased statesmen, are scattered everywhere throughout the city. A number of extensive parks, beautifully landscaped, add to the city's charm. The newer sections do not have the quaintness of the older parts, but the streets are wider and well paved, and the residences are more beautiful and have wide lawns and yards.

New structures erected in Rio de Janeiro are closely supervised by a rigidly administered city department of buildings under a most severe building code. All constructions must be of brick, stone, or other fireproof material. Some of the older houses have walls two or three feet thick, ponderously constructed of unbaked brick. Modern buildings, with walls no thicker than those of buildings in this country, are solidly constructed of kiln-baked bricks. Exterior walls of residences are covered with a waterproof plaster, the outer coat of which is usually tinted some attractive pastel shade. The roofs are of durable tile, usually red in color. The façades are ornamented with attractive designs in plaster or stone. The aesthetic quality of the designs must be approved by the city authorities.

Modern residences are usually set back from the sidewalk and surrounded by a high brick wall on three sides. A high iron grill with a gate separates the yard in front from the street. In the newer homes an electric bell on the gatepost summons a servant; in older homes one stands at the gate and claps his hands, a summons which is always recognized as a "knock at the door."

The building code of Rio, as in other principal South American cities, is very strict. Residences have no underground basements. The ground beneath the house must be surfaced with a four-inch layer of concrete to keep out rats and termites. Each room must have a certain window surface commensurate with its cubic area, and space outside the window must be unobstructed for at least one meter. Strict construction laws are operating to produce a sanitary and healthful city as well as a beautiful one.

In common with most South American cities of any size, Rio de Janeiro is clean. No heating systems are required for residences or other buildings; consequently no smoke or grime pollutes the atmosphere. The fuel used for cooking is either gas or charcoal. In more modern homes electricity is being increasingly employed for household tasks, including cooking. The homes are not heated for two reasons. In the first place, except in the more southerly parts of Brazil, or in the mountains, the climate is such that heating is not needed. Temperatures are seldom below 55° F. On rainy days in the cool season the humidity becomes penetrating, but there are few rainy days at that time of the year. Secondly, until very recently all the coal used was imported from Great Britain or the United States, and the price was prohibitive for use as a heating fuel. Imported coal is used to make gas, and the coke is used in industrial processes, but this is in relatively small amounts. Furthermore, houses are constructed with the Venetian type of window, for more effective ventilation. Such open construction would make heating more difficult, even if coal were available. A few of the residences built by Americans or Englishmen have wood-burning fireplaces.

The lack of an abundant native fuel makes coal-burning factories scarce in Brazil—and in all South America, for that matter. This very lack, however, has compelled progress along another line. Within easy reach of most principal coast cities, and of most interior cities, there is available abundant water power that can be readily converted into hydroelectric power. Not far from Rio de Janeiro is a power site at which is produced practically all the current necessary to operate the streetcars, telephones, and factories of the city. It also supplies illumination for homes and streets, as well as the smaller amounts of current needed for cooking and other household uses.

Capital for the development of these public utilities has come largely from England, Canada, and the United States. Today, however, the railways, most of the streetcar systems, many of the telephone lines, and most of the power production and distribution companies are owned by the federal government. The streetcars in Rio are called *bondes.* It is related that when the present electric system was being developed, a high-pressure bond selling campaign was conducted to raise funds locally for the improvement. The populace began in a joking way to refer to each of the new cars as a *bonde.* The name stuck and is now the accepted designation used both by the public and by the company in its advertising.

In earlier days the water supply for the city was brought from the hills over an aqueduct from which pipes radiated to distribution centers. The terminus of the aqueduct still stands in a small square in the center of the city. The aqueduct itself is now used as a bridge over which streetcars pass from the lower city to a beautiful residential section upon the sides of a series of hills. The modern water supply still comes from the hills behind the city as formerly, but it is regulated by a different system. Many small streams and springs arise in these hills. From the best and cleanest of these the water is caught and impounded in reservoirs high above the city, and modern mains lead down to the homes below.

Besides streetcars and busses, two principal railway systems whose terminals are in the city serve large suburban areas. These are the Central do Brasil, and the Leopoldina Railway. Each of these railways serves a populous suburban community and has a multiple-track system. At certain hours of the day their local and express trains operate on a very close schedule. The Central railway serves the regions west, southwest, and northwest. The Leopoldina serves the entire state of Rio de Janeiro north and east of the city. It continues on to the state of Espírito Santo. It also extends to Vitória and beyond, and to parts of eastern Minas Gerais.

A system of modern ferryboats serves the many populous islands in the harbor and the city of Niterói across the bay. These ferries transport thousands of persons to and from their work in the capital every day.

Taxicabs are ubiquitous on all the principal streets of the city. The rates are very reasonable—if the cabs are metered, or if one bargains for the ride in advance. Seldom does one wait for a taxi on a principal traffic artery more than two or three minutes. In Brazil traffic passes on the right, as in the United States. By contrast, in Argentina traffic passes to the left, following the English custom.

The people of Rio are of many different types. The city was the seat of the old monarchy. It was here that the Portuguese nobility tended to settle and to establish homes. Because of commercial advantages, merchants from all nations have made the city their headquarters. The numerous government bureaus have attracted a large clerical class. Rio is the military headquarters for the nation, and therefore many soldiers are always on hand. It is the principal port of entry for immigrants, and for this reason these newcomers tend to settle in the city. There is the inevitably large laboring class; the artisans are usually white, and the servant classes and unskilled laborers are usually Negro. Exceptional educational advantages offered in the city have brought from all parts of the nation a growing student class.

The leaders among the people are those of European ancestry—Portuguese, Italian, and Spanish, or, in smaller proportion, German, Syrian, or Turkish. A few of the nation's outstanding leaders have been either Negro or Indian. The number of Mohammedan Turks is becoming increasingly large.

Splendid harbor facilities have contributed to making Rio de Janeiro the nation's principal center of import and export and to fostering the banking and commercial activities that such importance involves. It is true, of course, that local products are shipped from local ports—rubber from Belém or Manaus, coffee largely from Santos, meat from Rio Grande, tobacco from Bahia—yet Rio de Janeiro remains Brazil's principal port. Whether the coffee port of Santos will ever surpass Rio in value of business transacted is a matter of conjecture. In Rio are located the headquarters of the Brazilian National Bank and of all the foreign banks which have branches in that country. Some have sub-branches in other cities, such as São Paulo, Santos, Recife, Bahia, and Belém. The principal networks of railways extending into the central interior ramify from either Rio de Janeiro or São Paulo.

F. A. Carlson.

Fig. 45. Avenue of royal palms, Botanical Garden, Rio de Janeiro.

Because of Rio's strategic location, large numbers of factories are established in the city. Rio is exceeded in this respect, however, by São Paulo, which employs nearly twice as many workers. All of the factories operate on electric power, and they are therefore clean. Their construction, especially the exteriors, must harmonize with the city's aesthetic standards; consequently they add to the architectural charm of the community.

The immigration service centers at Rio. While immigrants are permitted to enter through some other ports, the great majority are brought to Rio. Adequate facilities are provided for their reception, examination, orientation, and distribution.

What New York City is to the United States, Rio de Janeiro is to Brazil. There are other ports and harbors and important cities, but Rio ranks first.

Vitória. Vitória, a city of 51,600, located 268 miles north of Rio de Janeiro, is a natural port that may experience rapid development. It may some day serve as the outlet for the mineral wealth of that section of the state of Minas Gerais which lies at its back door. Plans have been drawn to improve harbor facilities by loading manganese and iron ore from bins, and with the growing emphasis on mineral exports, Vitória may become a leading port. The immediate hinterland is a rich agricultural region with sugar as the chief crop. The city proper is on an island in a beautiful landlocked harbor. The entrance of large steamers is somewhat impeded by a narrow, tortuous passage.

Santos. Some 225 miles south of Rio de Janeiro lies the world's greatest coffee port, Santos. The city is located on the island of São Vicente, which is sheltered from the sea by another island, Santo Amaro. These two islands are so located and so shaped that they outline what is known as the Gulf of Santos. The port is equipped to handle coffee in the most efficient manner. Although coffee is loaded at nearly all steamship berths, there is special equipment at several of them. These are fitted with large warehouses, and there are railway lines on both the water side and the street side of each warehouse. Several travelling electric elevators load bags of coffee at a very rapid rate. Often three or

Courtesy Moore-McCormack Lines.

Fig. 16. São Paulo, Brazil.

four vessels taking on coffee lie abreast. The larger warehouses have space for two to four million sacks of coffee. Santos is the Atlantic terminal of the Santos to São Paulo railway, which serves as a carrier for the rich upland hinterland.

Upland cities: São Paulo. São Paulo, the capital of the state of São Paulo, is the second largest city of Brazil with a population of about two million. It is the most important manufacturing center of the country, with some 300,000 industrial workers. Located in the São Paulo Basin, on the eastern margin of the interior upland, it functions as an inland entrepôt. Its rich hinterland supplies coffee, animal products, and other important agricultural commodities, while its adjacent coastal region offers international contacts.

The city pattern is arranged concentrically around a compact commercial core. Retail stores and workshops partly surround the core, or hub, of the city. Within this area, however, are a number of decadent residential sections built up during the nineteenth century. The local retail stores line the various avenues extending star-shaped outward from the core. Beyond this inner structure lie the factory districts. The distribution of residential sections is typical of most large industrial cities. The poorer houses either cluster around the factories near the center of the city or are grouped in more isolated districts. The superior residences occupy the high-class suburban districts and the high-level ridges overlooking the city.

The population of São Paulo is primarily white. A large portion of the population is Italian and German. There are probably more American and English residents in São Paulo than in all the remainder of Brazil—

Courtesy B. H. Hunnicutt.

Fig. 47. The 99 royal palms, Carlos Gomes Square, Campinas, Brazil.

probably eight or ten thousand altogether. The number fluctuates, and very few are permanent residents.

São Paulo, like most large South American cities in transition between the old regime and the new, has the same combination of wide and narrow streets, the same general type of architecture, the same careful supervision over sanitation, the same adequate streetcar system and automobile service, the same progressive education, and the same experimental attitude toward innovations.

Belo Horizonte. The capital of the state of Minas Gerais, Belo Horizonte, deserves special mention. It is one of the few important cities of the world planned in advance, with specific provisions made for its needs as a state capital. It was once the center of a very old settlement that dated back to 1750. The state selected the site as its new capital in 1897. The government had the entire area surveyed, and a city plan was prepared. All street intersections were to be at right angles, and blocks to be equal in length. Intersecting the regular streets at 45-degree angles a series of avenues was projected, each avenue having twice the width of an ordinary street. One glorious boulevard was to surround the entire urban area. Public squares were planned at the intersections of the avenues, and at two points in the city were to be larger public parks. One park was reserved for landscaping and flowers; the other was laid out as a zoölogical garden. Government buildings were strategically grouped between two large squares, facing the larger public park. Four squares were set apart as sites for schools of higher learning. Sites were reserved for an adequate public hospital and for a modern hotel. A large hippodrome was projected and a municipal cemetery planned to be placed just outside the city. The railway station was located in a convenient but not obtrusive place. A special plot of ground in the lowest part of the area was set apart for an abattoir and such services as sewage disposal, railway shops, and so forth (a hygienic misplacement of the abattoir!).

The city was divided into three zones. In the center was the urban area, immediately surrounded by a suburban zone. This in turn was bordered on one side by a large area reserved for large estates. Within the urban area itself the right-angle plan was rigidly enforced, and this gave to Belo Horizonte an excellent geometrical layout. The same plan was followed wherever possible in the suburbs, although natural obstacles prevented its complete adoption. The city has grown to a population of 340,000 inhabitants. Fortunately it was planned in advance!

WEST-CENTRAL BRAZIL [7]

A frontier. The undeveloped territory of the states of Goiás and Mato Grosso reflect conditions prevalent in the southwestern portions of the United States a century or more ago. Much of the land is unexplored, and only a small portion has been accurately surveyed. Goiás is 1,000 miles long, from north to south, and 300 miles broad. Mato Grosso stretches 1,200 miles from north to south and is from 400 to 1,000 miles broad. Goiás lies immediately west of Minas Gerais; Mato Grosso lies still farther to the west, and borders on the neighboring countries of Bolivia and Paraguay.

The region harbors a sparse population of less than two persons per square mile. Most of the white inhabitants live in the southern and eastern portions, where they are engaged in pastoral and mining activities. In the more distant interior are found an indeterminable number of nomadic Indians.

Brazil is not ready to develop this vast interior. At the present time its social and economic affairs do not warrant further expansion but demand, rather, a more intensive utilization of lands already under development. In accord with the present degree of progress, the region

[7] Examine political map of Brazil for location of interior States and Territories.

is accessible. One railroad extends from the populous south-central part of Brazil to Pôrto Esperança, in southern Mato Grosso. The distance is about a thousand miles. Pôrto Esperança is near Corumbá, a city of 13,000, the second largest population center of this far interior, being surpassed by Cuiabá with 19,000 inhabitants. The principal route of travel to Goiás is by rail through Minas Gerais to Ipamerí, or Anápolis, and then by a dirt road to Goiânia, the state capital. For travel to the interior the Paraná, Paraguay, and associated rivers may be used. This route, however, is tedious and slow: it requires a journey of more than 1,800 miles. In the northern portion are headstreams and tributaries of the Amazon River, but they are difficult to navigate because of the great number of waterfalls and rapids. However, canoes on the smaller streams and launches on the larger ones are the common means of travel, except where overland trails are necessary.

Courtesy C. Maxwell.

Fig. 48. Coconut grove near Cuiabá, Brazil.

Physical landscape. One of the first needs in the study of the surface features of the far interior of Brazil is to examine carefully the drainage pattern. Within the states of Mato Grosso and Goiás, the great western lands of Brazil, are found some of the major headstreams of the Rio Amazonas, the Rio Paraguay, and the Rio Paraná. These major rivers of South America have carved great valleys, radiating outward, like the spokes in a wheel, from the more central uplands or hub of Mato Grosso and Goiás. Two major land forms are in command: the Goiás Plateau, a dissected peneplain; and the Mato Grosso Plateau, a highland with a more definite plateau character than the Goiás upland. The most distinctive difference between the two is that the Goiás Plateau or Massif is a part of the oldland of the Brazilian Highland, the crystalline formations being exposed, while the Mato Grosso Plateau retains its covering of sedimentary rocks. The surface areas of the Mato Grosso Plateau are tabular or tablelands, while the Goiás is a rolling peneplain. Both have a rather complex physiognomy, and each minor section bears locally a different name.

Goiás Plateau. The surface of the Goiás upland may be described as a rolling peneplain. The sedimentary rocks that once covered its surface have been denuded, and now the old crystalline basement appears. Two important rivers drain the region, the Rio Tocantins and the Rio Alto Paraná. The former flows to the Amazon; the latter to the Rio Paraná. The headstreams of these rivers have not only removed the more recent sediments, but also have carved deep valleys into the oldland. From the northeast a high sedimentary area invades the east-central portion of the Goiás upland. Near the western border of the upland is the city of Goiânia, located on one of the principal overland routes from southeast Brazil to Mato Grosso.

Courtesy C. Maxwell.

Fig. 10. Nambikura Indian hut.

Mato Grosso Plateau. A large part of the Mato Grosso Plateau lies in the state of Mato Grosso, but its broad northern portion spreads into the states of Amazonas, Pará, Goiás, and Maranhão. To the south it is narrow, and the general outline of the plateau is in the shape of a triangle. Its northern slopes have been reduced by the southern tributaries of the Amazon to the stage of late maturity or old age. Here the rainfall is heavy and uniform throughout most of the year and supports a dense forest in places, particularly on the low divides and slopes of the valleys. Southward the plateau is higher, and the rainfall is seasonal. The summer months are rainy, while the winters are dry—conditions that favor the savanna, or grassland. In this region are the great cattle ranges of the State.

The higher portions of the Mato Grosso Plateau are largely in the form of mesa-like tablelands, or *chapadas*. The term *chapada* is generally used in Brazil to denote tableland area, and for the most part the chapada is associated with the savanna vegetation that gives it a geographic distinction.

One of the most prominent portions or sections of the plateau is found east of Cuiabá, the capital of the state, and is known as the Planalto de Mato Grosso. It is about 300 miles across. On most maps of Brazil it is labelled "Plateau of Mato Grosso." This high, unexplored tableland and its several linear remnants are literally the nucleus of the drainage systems of the entire plateau. The Planalto de Mato Grosso may be likened to the palm of one's hand from which extend finger-like plateaus. Between these linear uplands, or fingers, flow the southern headstreams and tributaries of important branches of the Amazon River.

The southwestern portion of the state of Mato Grosso is a part of the Paraná-Paraguay Plain. This lowland extends from the Andes to the southern extension of the Brazilian Highland and continues southward as the Argentine Pampa. The Mato Grosso portion, commonly called the *Pantanal,* includes the population centers of Corumbá and Cuiabá, the outposts of Brazilian culture. Following the summer rains, parts of this great morass is inundated.

The natural forage of the plains adjacent to the Paraguay River and the uplands of southern Goiás and Mato Grosso is the most important resource. Today it supports some eight million head of cattle. The herds are pastured on great grassy fields that know no fences and often no owners. For the most part the cattle are of poor quality, better suited for jerked beef and hides than for fresh beef. Although great expanses of nutritious grasses and surface water for the stock exist throughout the year, there are also extensive savannas where vegetation is harsh and desiccated, and where droughts are frequent. These adversities, accompanied with ticks, cattle diseases, and the great distance to consuming markets, will keep the cattle industry of the far interior in a state of questionable importance, at least for the immediate future.

The northern portion of this interior region has a dependable rainfall that favors the growth of forests. The best growth of forests occurs in the river valleys and the more moist portions of the elevated sections. However, isolation and inadequate means of transportation prevent the utilization of these timber resources at present.

There is comparatively little available information concerning the mineral resources of this distant region. Coal has been discovered in Mato Grosso. In the alluvial sands in the river beds and flood plains of southeastern Goiás, black diamonds constitute an important resource. Gem diamonds and gold are also found in the region.

A far interior town. The typical town of 5,000 inhabitants in the interior is not inspiring. In all probability there is no railway within 50 miles. Transportation is by mule train—not an automobile road—through the forest or the savanna. With a dozen exceptions, the houses of this typical small town rest flat on the ground. They are one story high, have brick floors and unglazed windows, open directly on the narrow sidewalk, and have no front yards. The town is constructed around a public square, which is frequently an attractive little park with a bandstand, fountain, walks, and flowers. On the most prominent corner is a Catholic church (Brazil, in common with other Latin American countries, is predominantly of the Roman Catholic faith), the most imposing structure in town. A small public school (usually a converted residence building), a row of small shops, and a public market place complete the civic center. A few families may be prosperous enough to have attractive two-story houses, and the town may have two or three really excellent residences surrounded by flower gardens and trimmed lawns. Electric

F. A. Carlson.

Fig. 50. A typical scene in a small interior Brazilian town.

lights, waterworks, and sewer systems, often owned and managed by foreign capital, are being increasingly introduced in the smaller cities with a population of 20,000 or more; but in the town of 5,000, few of these conveniences are found. Within the past five years a movement to erect public school buildings really adequate for educational purposes has been gaining ground, but any public demand for education, even the most elementary, is very slight.

The economic life of such a small town depends upon the rural areas surrounding it. It is, of course, the center of trade, where country folk sell their produce and make their purchases. Here or near by will be found the manioc and sugar mill and a distillery for making a low grade of potable alcohol. Exports from the surrounding district pass through the city, where they are frequently reconditioned for transport. There may be a pottery or some other small manufacturing industry. A score or more tailors are busy, for most clothing, for men and women alike, is made by hand. Medical services and government offices are located here. Since everybody of consequence keeps a servant or two, there is a large number of cooks, washers, house-girls, and gardeners. Prosperous farmers whose fields lie near by may reside in town. Many retired farmers and ranchers are here. Life moves on placidly and uneventfully from one year's end to the other. Recreation is centered either in the plaza, with its band, or in the church, with its many festivals and celebrations and processions. Crimes and public disturbances are low in number. Birth and death rates are high. Perhaps one-tenth of the population is literate or learning; the other nine-tenths is frankly indifferent to the arts of education.

SOUTH BRAZIL

Regional characteristics. Pastoral and forest resources constitute the bases of the major human activities of south Brazil, a region including the states of Paraná, Santa Catarina, and Rio Grande do Sul. More than one-third of all the cattle and three-fourths of the total sheep of Brazil are found in this southern region. The forests have the largest reserve of softwood in all of South America and also supply a major portion of the beverage plant, *yerba maté*.

South Brazil is the nation's only known source of commercial coal. It is further distinctive in being the sole producer of Brazil's limited supply of wheat.

Natural landscape. A dissected upland, an extension of the Paraná Plateau, occupies nearly all of the states of Paraná and Santa Catarina and the northern portion of Rio Grande do Sul. In southern Rio Grande do Sul the oldland of the Brazilian Highland appears. The average elevation of the upland is 2,000 feet above sea level, while some of the mountain peaks exceed 5,000 feet. Along the coast a narrow plain extends south to Pôrto Alegre, where it widens out to include the broad lagoons, Lagôa dos Patos, Lagôa Mirim, and Lagôa da Mangueira.

The region has a generally healthful climate. High temperatures prevail on the eastern lowlands, but the uplands are cool and have a wider daily range in temperature. The seasonal changes in temperature are also much greater than in the adjacent regions to the north. Snow is not uncommon on the highland of south Brazil. In contrast to other parts of the country, the seasonal distribution of rainfall is uniform. For the most part, the warm season has a slight maximum, but each of the four seasons receives between 14 and 20 inches. Nearly all of south Brazil has an annual precipitation of about 60 inches, the southeast and southwest portions having slightly less than the northern portion.

Temperature, soils, and the slight variations in rainfall govern the native flora of south Brazil. A dense tropical rain forest, consisting primarily of hardwoods, occupies the northeast; a more open stand of softwood, the Paraná pine, the northwest; and savanna, the south. The

Paraná pine is the chief source of wealth from these forests. It grows in all three states, but principally in the Rio Alto Paraná valley in western Paraná and Santa Catarina. *Yerba maté,* another valuable forest product, is widely distributed throughout the uplands. The grasslands are regions of thriving pastoral activities.

People of south Brazil. The white people of south Brazil consist mostly of Germans, Italians, and Poles. There are relatively few inhabitants of Portuguese descent and no Negroes. This situation is in striking contrast to that in northeast Brazil, where a large proportion of the population is descended from the early Portuguese or the African Negro. In Pôrto Alegre, a city of 380,000, the largest population center of south Brazil,

Fig. 51. Paraná pine, south Brazil.

more than one-quarter of the inhabitants are of German descent. Both Germans and Italians have settled in the states of Rio Grande do Sul and Santa Catarina, while Paraná seems to have attracted predominantly Polish immigrants. There are at least 500,000 Germans or persons of German descent in Rio Grande do Sul, out of the state's total population of 3,321,000. In all of South Brazil the German element totals more than 1,000,000.

Regional associations. The Paraná pine, a splendid softwood, grows in pure stands and covers considerable areas in Paraná and Santa Catarina. The tree is tall and straight, with few branches, and has a diameter up to six feet. Although this is a softwood extremely susceptible to attack by white termites—and there are myriads of termites in Brazil—it may be impregnated by chemicals that render it immune to attack.

Yerba maté,[8] or Paraguay tea, is a brush that grows wild over a certain large area in eastern Paraguay, northern Argentina, and in the Brazilian states of Paraná, Santa Catarina, and Mato Grosso. The leaves and very fine twigs of the plant are broken into small pieces, and from these is brewed a pleasant-tasting beverage similar in appearance to China tea. Brazilians, especially in the south, use quantities of hot maté as an afternoon or evening refreshment. The effect of the hot drink is refreshing and stimulating, but it does not induce wakefulness, as China tea is said to affect some persons, nor is it habit-forming. Practically all of the 100,000 tons of Brazilian maté exported goes to Argentina, Uruguay, and Paraguay. Small quantities are finding their way to Europe and the United States. There is now an institute for the development of the maté market. It is not impossible that the advertising campaign of this institute may result in considerably increasing the demand in the United States. The tea may be purchased now in any American city in stores specializing in imported foods.

Brazil's coal resources are located primarily in the southern states. The chief coal belt extends discontinuously from southern São Paulo, through the states of Santa Catarina, Paraná, and Rio Grande do Sul. The mines in operation produce annually slightly more than 2 million tons, or approximately 60 per cent of Brazil's total consumption. During 1948 domestic coal totaled 2,016,000 metric tons and imports 1,052,000 metric tons. All of the coal produced in Brazil is bituminous. The ash and sulphur content are high, and consequently the quality is low.

The inaccessible location, the great distance between producing centers, and the low quality hinder the development of the Brazilian coal industry. The São Jerônimo and Butia mines in Rio Grande do Sul supply about 80 per cent of the nation's total output. The coal reserves at the Jerônimo and Butia mines are estimated at 25 million tons. In the Santa Catarina fields the output is low, but it is reported that the coal can be reduced to the coke that is necessary in the iron and steel industry being developed in Brazil. Of course, throughout most of Brazil wood and charcoal are used as fuel in the homes.

Urban centers. Pôrto Alegre, Pelotas, and Rio Grande, the largest urban centers of the state of Rio Grande do Sul,[9] are located on the

[8] *Yerba maté* is the Spanish name; in Portuguese it is known as *herva matté.*

[9] The *state* of São Paulo and the *city* of São Paulo have been mentioned. Several Brazilian states contain cities of the same name. The reader will need to observe the distinction between the two. Thus Rio de Janeiro, the capital city of Brazil, is also the name of a prosperous state 200 miles long and 50 wide that surrounds the capital. São Paulo city is the capital of São Paulo state. The deep-water seaport of the state of Rio Grande do Sul is the city of Rio Grande. Goiás city is the capital of Goiás state. The capital of the state of Bahia is Salvador, but the city is almost universally called Bahia. The capital of the state of Pernambuco is Recife, but it is often called Pernambuco. The capital of Pará is Belém, but the city is frequently called Pará. There is a state of Rio Grande de Norte and another state of Rio Grande do Sul.

Lagôa dos Patos. On the west shore, nine miles from the entrance to the sea, stands Rio Grande, a city of 60,000 people. Pelotas, a city of 72,000 inhabitants, is a little farther north, on the São Gonçalo River. Pôrto Alegre (380,000 population), is located on the Guaíba River at the north end of the lagoon.

Rio Grande do Sul is accessible to large steamers. Freight carriers

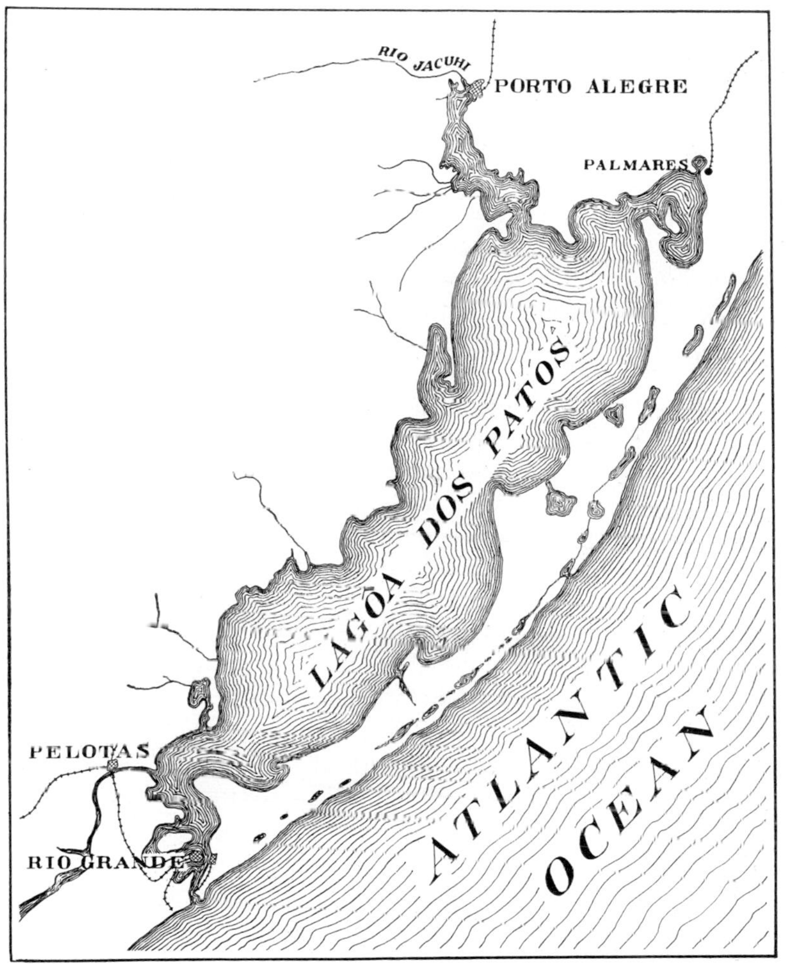

Fig. 52. Principal ports of the state of Rio Grande do Sul, south Brazil.

from the United States and Europe call at irregular intervals. The lagoon is not deep, but coastal vessels regularly ascend its length, 120 miles, to Pôrto Alegre. Railroads join the lagoon cities with the interior. Pôrto Alegre is connected by rail with Uruguaiana near the Argentine border, a distance of 480 miles west by rail. It is also joined to the south with Livramento on the border of Uruguay. Other lines from Pôrto Alegre reach Rio Grande do Sul and Pelotas. The longest railroad of south Brazil leads north to São Paulo.

The principal city of Paraná is Curitiba, a plateau settlement of 137,000. Santa Catarina does not have any large cities. Its largest urban center is Florianópolis (50,000), located on an island off the coast.

NORTHEAST BRAZIL

Regional characteristics. Northeast Brazil includes the states of Bahia, Sergipe, Alagôas, Pernambuco, Paraíba, Rio Grande do Norte, Ceará, Piauí, Maranhão and the insular Territory Fernando de Noronha. Until near the end of the eighteenth century, including most of the colonial period, the northeast was the political and economic center of Brazil. Salvador (Bahia) was the capital of Brazil until 1792, when Rio de Janeiro became the political center. During the early days an important sugar industry, the first in South America, developed on the coastal lowlands of the northeast. It may be considered the first major industry of Brazil, preceding rubber, gold, and coffee. This enterprise—the production of sugar—led to the importation of Negro slaves, the foundation of the present large black population of these coastal lands.

Today, northeast Brazil produces about 30 per cent of the tobacco and 95 per cent of the cacao grown in the nation. It supports nearly 36 per cent of the total Brazilian population.

As a whole, this is the driest geographic division of Brazil. In a number of places, 50 miles or more from the ocean, the region receives less than 20 inches of rainfall a year. Furthermore, there is a pronounced seasonal irregularity in the distribution of precipitation. As a result, droughts are frequent and often bring problems of famine to the inhabitants. This region has been referred to as one of the notorious famine zones of the world. The interior of Ceará is especially subject to devastating droughts. Almost no rain fell there from 1928 to 1931. The most terrible famine conditions prevailed. At great cost the federal government is now constructing a series of impounding dams to save the region in periods of future calamity.

The aridity of the climate is reflected in its goat industry. Here more than two-thirds of the nation's five million goats are raised. The goat is better suited for dry and hot lands than are cattle and sheep and is able to thrive and reproduce under the most adverse situations. Contrast this division with the lands of south Brazil, where there is adequate rainfall, a moderate temperature, a flourishing cattle industry, and a large white population.

Surface features. The extreme northeastern projection of Brazil includes the Borborema Plateau. This upland has been developed upon granite, gneiss, mica schist, and other igneous and metamorphic rocks. Its surface is, primarily, a peneplain. Numerous mountain ranges, or serras, representing residual granite monadnocks, rise several hundred feet above the surface of the plateau. The elevation of this upland varies between 1,500 and 3,000 feet. The higher elevations are represented by the serras rising above the general peneplained surface. In places young valleys have been carved into the rolling upland.

São Francisco Valley. One of the potentially great regions of Brazil is the São Francisco river valley. It includes the states of Sergipe and Alagôas and parts of Bahia, Pernambuco, and Minas Gerais with an estimated area of 230,000 square miles. The São Francisco Hydroelectric Company reports that when the São Francisco river is harnessed water will be available for extensive irrigation on farms now suffering from periodic drought, and power for mining, industries, and electrification of urban and rural areas. It is estimated that the São Francisco river represents about 10 per cent of Brazil's potential hydroelectric power—a total of 15 million kilowatts. The chief center of water-power will be the Paulo Afonso Falls located near the boundaries of Bahia, Pernambuco, and Alagôas. Within the plans of the project are the establishment of fertilizer plants, other chemical plants, cement factories, canning factories, and other industrial activities along with expansion and improvement in farming, and an over-all betterment of living conditions in a region of extreme rainfall variability and its resultant uncertainties.

Climatic conditions. Northeast Brazil may be classified in three zones: (1) the wet coastal lands; (2) the dry uplands; and (3) the moist serras. By far the greater portion of the area is semiarid. On the Borborema Plateau and associated uplands westward the annual rainfall varies between 10 and 20 inches. The region to the south, including the oldland upland, and the tablelands of the upper São Francisco River, has a moderate rainfall, between 30 and 60 inches. Practically all the land along the coast has a heavy annual rainfall. The precipitation along the coastal margin of Bahia is 80 inches or more per year. The rainfall is heaviest south of Salvador and is uniform in its seasonal distribution, while north of the capital less rain falls between September and February. Recife shows a heavy rainfall during the months from March to August and a drier season from October to February. At São Luís the rainy season extends from December to July, while little rain falls from June to November.

Northeastern Brazil exhibits an interesting correlation between vegetation on the one hand and elevation and rainfall on the other. Three zones are to be observed: (1) the *mata;* (2) the *sertão;* and (3) the *serra.* The mata represents the coastal margin where the abundant rainfall supports a tropical rain forest cover. The sertão includes the upland surfaces where the scant rainfall permits the growth of only drought-resistant brushwood and grasses. The serra is the area of mountain ranges that rises above the sertão and induces sufficient rainfall to maintain a luxuriant growth of vegetation.

Cultural relationships. The hot and humid mata zone is the scene of the principal sugar plantations, the cacao groves, the lowland cotton fields, and plots of the numerous subsistence crops. It is the site of greatest density of population and principal cities. The inhabitants are largely Negroes or mulattoes.

The chief agricultural activities of the sertão are the production of upland cotton, some sugar, and the raising of cattle and goats. The sertão is a region of moderate density of population and periodic droughts. The lack of rainfall has brought misery to the inhabitants, the death of animals, and the destruction of crops. Because of drought it is frequently necessary to drive the cattle to the more succulent fields of the serra or mata. Occasionally whole villages have emigrated as the population sought more desirable regions.

In contrast to the sertão, the serra supports primarily cultivated crops. Here the rainfall is sufficient, in most cases without irrigation, to raise coffee on the slopes and sugar in the valley bottoms, and to carry on an active grazing industry at the higher elevations. Both the serra and sertão differ from the mata in racial characteristics. The inhabitants of these uplands are descendants of Portuguese or native Indians. There are few Negroes, the predominant people of the mata region.

Cotton, sugar, and cacao. The chief cultivated crops of northeast Brazil are *cotton, sugar,* and *cacao.* Cotton is grown primarily in the dry west and north, while sugar is produced in the wet zone near the coast. Pernambuco and Paraíba are the principal cotton- and sugar-producing states of the northeast. Both cotton and sugar are important cash crops, but sugar is the more significant in the lives of the inhabitants, since it is extensively used in their daily diet.

Two distinct varieties of cotton are grown: the lowland cotton and the upland cotton. The lowland, or mata, cotton is an annual. The yield per acre is high, but the quality is low. The upland cotton is a perennial. It yields less than the lowland cotton, but it is a long-fiber plant and its quality is superior.

Because of the facility with which the cacao tree may be grown in the excellent climate of eastern Brazil, particularly along the rainy coast of Bahia, it would be a simple matter to increase production and thereby to take a larger part of the world's market. The cacao tree is subject to blights and rots of various kinds, including the devastating *witches'-broom* and *monilia,* and the fruit is attacked by various insect pests. Brazilian farmers in general give inadequate care to the harvest, and their plantations are untidy. This militates against a high-quality fruit. All these things if not controlled make it possible that the industry may be destroyed at some period of rapid deterioration. In 1924 it was seriously injured in Ecuador, although it has since been reëstablished. In Venezuela the tree is less susceptible to these two blights.

CACAO BEAN EXPORTS
(In 1,000 pounds)

	Av. 1935–39	1947	1949
Brazil	263,980	218,350	291,545
Ecuador	42,372	43,324	....
Venezuela	36,934	22,900	29,802
America's Total	471,579	385,607	....
Africa	1,065,749	949,975 [1]	....
Grand Total	1,554,849	1,397,553 [1]	....

[1] For year 1946.

CACAO: UNITED STATES IMPORTS
(In 1,000 pounds)

	1947	1949	195–
Brazil	130,010	200,117	......
Gold Coast, Africa	168,260	192,554	......
Nigeria, Africa	119,005	100,051	......
Dominican Republic	64,151	44,786	......
Venezuela	23,999	23,197	......
Ecuador	30,952	26,251	......
Others	......	......	......
Total	598,240	628,787	......

The cacao is an indigenous South American plant. It was well known among the aborigines, but its development has been grossly neglected until recently. In 1940 Africa accounted for two-thirds of the world production: the Gold Coast, Nigeria, and the Ivory Coast were the principal producers. Brazil was second to the Gold Coast as a producer of the cacao bean, and evidence of greater production in this great agricultural land is in sight. Other important Western Hemisphere producers are the Dominican Republic, Venezuela, Ecuador, and Panama.

Other agricultural products. Tobacco occupies an important place in the agricultural activities of northeast Brazil. It is grown throughout the coastal lands, with a pronounced concentration in northeastern Bahia, where the dry period between September and February excludes the cultivation of the moisture- and heat-requiring cacao. The 14,000,000 cattle and 5,000,000 goats of the northeast are of no small significance; nor are the corn, beans, manioc, and other products that are grown for local consumption.

Carnaúba palm. In the dry regions of the northeast, the carnaúba palm is an exceedingly valuable tree, perhaps the most completely usable tree in all Brazil. The root is a depurative and is widely used in the treatment of blood diseases. From the bark is prepared a meal that is highly prized. The trunk furnishes a wood employed in rough timbering. The fruit is an excellent food for animals, and, when ripe, has a soft, dark, lustrous, sweet pulp that is delicious either raw or made into a conserve. Around the fruit is a shell five inches in diameter, which, when roasted, is made into a drink resembling coffee, and which also yields an illuminating oil. From the surface of the young leaves comes the famous carnaúba wax, which is widely used in the phonograph disks, in cinema films, in insulation for cables, in candles, and in floor wax and polishing compounds.

Courtesy Silva, Jr., Brazilian Information Bureau.

Fig. 53. Carnaúba palms near Fortaleza, Ceará, Brazil.

Trade centers: Recife. One of the foremost Atlantic ports of northeastern Brazil is Recife, capital of the state of Pernambuco. This port is located at the confluence of the Capibaribe and Beberibe Rivers, and consists of four parts: Recife, São Antonio, São José, and Boa Vista. Recife, the business part of the city, is built on the south end of the Olinda Peninsula. Boa Vista lies opposite it on the mainland. Between the two lie São Antonio and São José, on a small sand island.

Recife has an estimated population of 500,000. The city is the principal tidewater terminal of the lines of the Great Western Railway, the most important line of northern Brazil. The chief exports consist of cotton, sugar, rum, hides, and dyewoods. The strategic location of Recife, nearer to Europe than any other leading port, is of considerable importance.

Salvador. Salvador is the capital of Bahia. It is a city with a population of 384,000, and lies at the entrance to the Bahia de Todos os Santos. It is one of the oldest settlements in the Western Hemisphere, established in 1510. Numerous steamers call there from various parts of the world. The harbor is deep and is well protected from the sea. The state of Bahia produces the finest tobacco in Brazil, and the city of Bahia is her most famous tobacco port. In Bahia there are many cotton, cloth, jute, candle, match, and boot and shoe factories, sawmills, soap works, and tannery plants. The central sugar factories are the most productive in the country. Cocoa also is made from the native cacao beans that are produced in the southern part of the state.

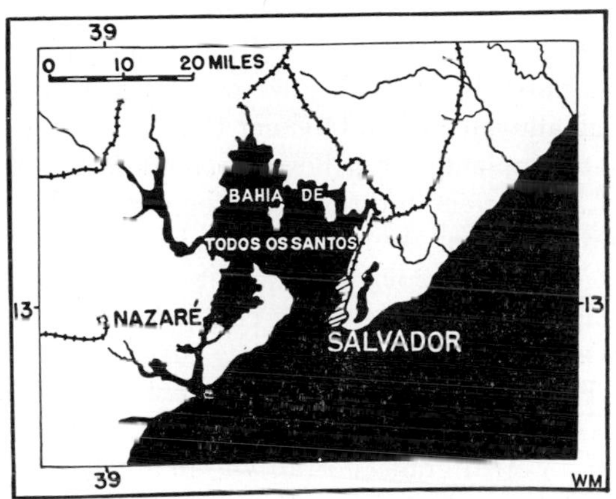

Fig. 54. Salvador's physical setting.

Ilhéus, Maceió, and Natal. Ilhéus, a city of 50,000 inhabitants, at the mouth of two rivers, is Brazil's chief cacao port. Maceió and Natal are other important ports of northeastern Brazil. Maceió is a city of 103,000, capital of the thriving sugar and cotton state of Alagôas. Some of the sugar is made into *aguardiente*—literally "fire water"—and sold along the coast from the Amazon River to Argentina. A considerable part of the cotton is made into cloth in the highly efficient mills near Maceió. Natal, a thriving city of 104,000 people, located at the northeastern point of Brazil, is the capital of Rio Grande do Norte. In the future Natal may greatly strengthen its economic position because of its proximity to Africa. During World War II, Natal was an important air base for planes en route to northwest Africa and Europe.[10]

[10] Examine *Observations on the Physical Geography of Northeast Brazil* by Preston E. James. Annals of the Association of American Geographers. Vol. 42, No. 2, 1952. Pages 153–176.

CHAPTER VI

NORTH BRAZIL: AMAZON REGION

Beyond the frontier. "That indescribable realm," the Amazon region, is the world's greatest expanse of *terra incognita.*[1] Much of the area has not been surveyed or even explored, and only limited records are available of its known portions. Probably we can say with accuracy that the terrain consists of alluvial lowlands along the rivers and that the interfluves are undulating uplands. Furthermore, records show that the region includes areas of heavy rainfall throughout the year and areas of seasonal distribution of precipitation. In addition, we have learned that the floral landscape is not one vast tropical forest but that the region consists of forests and grasslands. In fact, striking contrasts occur within comparatively small areas. For example, the Marajó island situated at the mouth of the Amazon River presents two distinct regions. The southwestern portion is covered with a dense tropical forest, and the northeastern region consists of an open grassland—all within an area only about twice the size of the state of Massachusetts. While vastness of land and vegetation adds to the magnitude of the Amazon region, the dominant feature of this great area is the sea of rivers, the Rio Amazonas.

Rio Amazonas. The Amazon is really a labyrinth of rivers. Someone has compared it with a vast inland sea emptying itself into another sea by flowing around a multitude of low-lying islands. The tributaries are really the important part of the system. More than half of them rise in the Andean mountains or foothills. Several large streams drain the marshes of lower Bolivia. Four principal rivers take their rise in the highlands of two far interior states of Brazil, Goiás and Mato Grosso.[2] Several other important rivers drain the lower interior of Colombia or rise in the mountain ranges of Venezuela or the Guianas. In general, the tributaries of the Amazon lie parallel to one another, separated by low ranges of hills or low-lying plateaus.

In several places tributaries of the Amazon and the La Plata systems

[1] The political divisions of North Brazil, or Amazon Region, are listed in the chapter on National Development of Brazil.

[2] On the outer fringe of Brazil's Amazon are a number of Territories. See political map of Brazil.

rise within a few miles of each other. In one place a tributary of the Orinoco and one of the Amazon rise in the same deep jungle swamp. They are joined by an intervening channel broad enough for small vessels to pass through. This passage occurs between the Rio Negro, a branch of the Amazon, and the Casiquiare, essentially a headstream of the Orinoco. It is said to be 20 feet deep and 50 feet or more wide in seasons of high water.

The tributaries of the Amazon are wide and remarkably deep, making possible steamship navigation for great distances. Estimates of the navigable distances vary, and none of them are, in the nature of the case, accurate. It is reported that light ocean-going steamers may navigate more than 10,000 miles on these great inland waterways; that vessels whose draft is not more than six feet may safely traverse twice that distance; and that still smaller boats, whose draft would not exceed two feet, could safely navigate 100,000 miles of waterways. By means of the river system, therefore, the country may be penetrated almost everywhere. The channels of even the smaller streams are usually deep, although many of them are rendered impassable by trees that have fallen across them. The ever-present creepers that swing above the streams often drop in loops to the water's edge. The excellence of most of the waterways makes unnecessary, at least for the present, the construction of highways and railways.

The Amazon itself has a length of 3,460 miles, of which 1,495 lie in Peru and 1,965 in Brazil. It traverses almost the entire breadth of the continent, one source being near Cuenca, in the Andes of Ecuador, a distance approximately 50 miles from the tidal waters of the Pacific Ocean. A source of confusion to foreigners is the fact that the great river is frequently known by different names in its different reaches. In Peru it is called the Marañón; in the upper reaches of Brazil, the Solimões; from Manaus to the island of Marajó, the Amazon; and from there to the ocean it is frequently known as the Pará River. Brazilian geographers are attempting to rename the entire stream, from its source in the mountains of Peru to its mouth in the ocean, the Rio Amazonas.

For a distance of more than 700 miles from its mouth, to Manaus, the main channel of the river is more than 200 feet deep, and up to Iquitos in Peru, nearly 2,000 miles, the channel is 30 feet deep. Ocean-going vessels of 7,000 tons ascend to Manaus, while vessels of half that tonnage regularly make the trip to Iquitos, an inland port of 40,000 inhabitants.

The waters of the Amazon are turgid with mud. It has been estimated that more than 160 million tons of solid matter, principally rich loam, are carried down to the ocean each year. In times of flood the waters rise from 15 to 20 feet and have been known to rise 40 feet above low-water levels. Not only do these flood waters inundate vast areas of lower-lying territory, but they eat at the soft earth that comprises the banks in most places, washing away literally mile after mile of forest land. These *terras cahidas*, or "fallen lands," result in huge bays, or *furos*, that frequently become large lakes. In the explored areas of the state of Amazonas alone there are more than a thousand known lakes and lagoons.

A fluvial island, the largest in the world, divides the Amazon into two arms. The northern channel exceeds 100 miles at its widest point and is thickly studded with islands. The southern channel, the more open of the two, and the one frequented by ocean-going vessels, is from 20 to

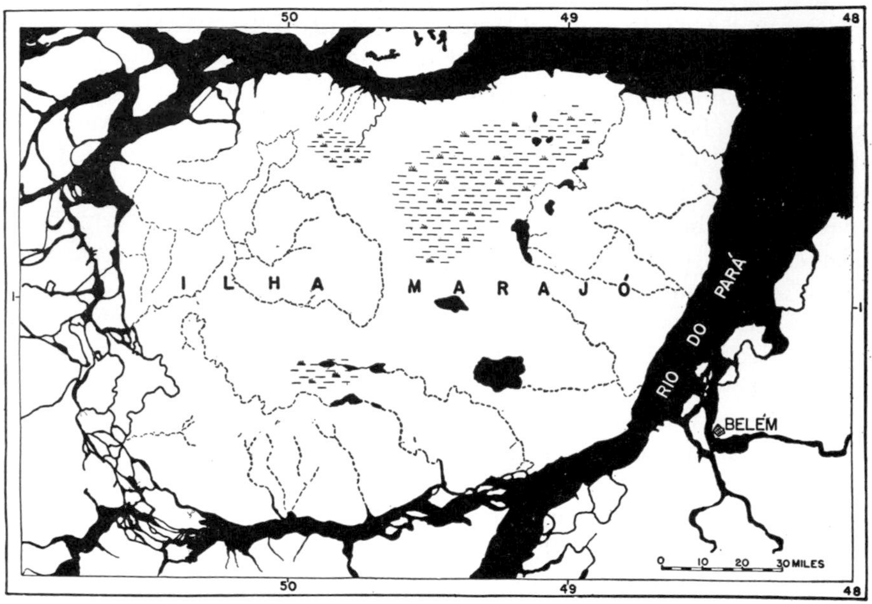

Fig. 55. Island of Marajó.

40 miles broad. The island of Marajó, lying between the two channels, is over 100 miles across, north-south and 180 miles east-west.

High waters occur at different times along the river, owing in part to the seasonal distribution of the rainfall and in part to the slow movement of the high waters downstream. There are two periods of high water each year. In February floods begin high up the river in Peru; in April the waters are high in the middle reaches about Manaus; and in June they are high near the ocean. It requires about four months for the waters to recede from the high stage to low, and approximately two months of rains are required to flood the channels again. Thus at Belém, in Pará, high water occurs in July and January, low water in October and April. The reason for this slow, ponderous movement of high water is simple: the banks of the river are low, and high waters not only overflow the banks but inundate perhaps 200,000 square miles of land. It requires time for the waters to fill the vast reservoirs of lowland. It requires time for them to drain out again.

An interesting phenomenon is known as the *pororoco*, which refers to the roaring noise made by the Amazon River on certain occasions. Because of the very wide entrance to the river and its slight declivity, the tide is forced up the channel in the form of a huge bore, often 2 feet or more in height, rushing up-river at an amazing speed and churning everything before it. Following the first rush of the bore, there is a rapid rise of the river, until sometimes it attains a total height of 5 feet. The effect of this movement is felt powerfully for more than 400 miles upstream, and with diminishing momentum far beyond that. The roaring noise made by the rushing waters, the *pororoco*, can easily be heard a mile from the river's edge. When the conjunction of sun and moon is perfect and the tides are at their strongest, and when a strong on-shore wind is blowing, the rise of the waters is sufficiently violent to cause great damage. Small boats at the banks of the river may be swamped or lifted and hurled into the bush. Larger vessels must be securely moored in quiet waters, or they too may be seriously damaged. Because of the waves and floods, all houses near the water's edge are built upon hillocks or on timber sufficiently strong to withstand heavy pressure.

Climatic relationships. Rainfall is heavy in portions of the Amazon Basin, heavier in some places and at certain seasons of the year than at other times and places. In the western portion of the region the precipitation is more than 125 inches annually; rainfall decreases slightly to the east but is greater on the coast than in the central portion. At Manaus the maximum rainfall occurs from December to June and at Belém from January to May.

After sundown in the Amazon Lowland the air temperature drops rapidly. In many places, especially during the hours between midnight and dawn, the "cold," or low sensible temperature, is so penetrating as to be positively uncomfortable. Night temperatures of around 60° F. are by no means uncommon. In the daytime the temperature rises to 80° or 90° F. It might be said that the night is the winter of these tropical regions. Belém, the Amazon entrepôt, illustrates the slight annual range in temperature. One of the coolest months is September and one of the hottest months is July, the average temperatures being 78° and 80° F., respectively. There is a difference of only about 2 degrees in temperature between the coolest and the hottest months. Manaus, in the heart of the Amazon region, shows practically the same conditions as those at Belém. At both of these stations the diurnal range of temperature is more than 27° F. At the former place September shows the highest average monthly temperature of about 82°, while March shows the lowest, at approximately 78°.

As a consequence of these climatic conditions, respiratory and rheumatic ailments are common. The anopheles mosquito is prevalent in the region, with resultant malaria. These causes, added to improper food and the widespread but moderate use of alcohol, further weaken the people. The result is a population that is not very resistant to disease. Fevers of various kinds are common, as are ulcerations due to unhealthy blood. And yet there are many primitive Indian tribes that seem to enjoy perfect health. Others, eating proper food and living according to simple laws of sanitation, maintain themselves in good health. After three or four years in the region, however, most foreigners from temperate climates find it advisable to spend a winter where the climate is cold, because of the enervating influence of the constant warmth.

POPULATION CENTERS

Cities: Belém. The traveller enters the great interior nearly always through the city of Belém, capital of the Brazilian state of Pará.[3] This is a modern city of 235,500 population, located on the Rio Pará, about 100 miles from the ocean. The city has broad avenues lined with mango trees, extensive parks and public gardens, one of the most beautiful cathedrals in all Brazil, a good normal school, a large municipal theater, good hospitals, and public schools. It is the point of transshipment for much of the traffic of the Amazon region. Here are located the customs house and the army and navy arsenals. Excellent hotels await the traveller. Department stores, similar to those of European or American cities of similar size, await his patronage. Many ocean-going freight vessels ascend the river to Manaus, some even to Iquitos. The larger passenger-carrying vessels, however, stop at Belém, and passengers transfer to picturesque, flat-bottomed, side- or stern-paddle river steamers.

There are no great cities in the interior. Above Belém only twelve Brazilian cities of any size are found on the Amazon River or its tributaries. Eleven of these have between 12,000 and 20,000 inhabitants, and the only city of real importance is Manaus, a center of some 121,400 people.

Manaus. Manaus owes its importance partly to the fact that it is the capital of the state of Amazonas. Located at a strategic position on the Rio Negro near its junction with the Amazon, it is the port from which quantities of exports are shipped abroad. It is the administrative center of a great state and the cultural center of the interior. Manaus is one of the most attractive small cities of all Brazil. Although it is situated only 120 feet above sea level, the efforts of the department of public sanitation have made it healthful. As in most nations, culture is drawn to centers of commercial wealth and to cities of administrative importance. Manaus is thus the cultural center for the Amazon interior, the

[3] Refer to map on page 126.

center of its aristocracy and wealth. An excellent school system, a state-supported high school or gymnasium, a normal school of importance, and even a university contribute to the education of its citizens and attract people who have children to educate. Like other important cities, Manaus contains several wide boulevards, a number of important public and private buildings, and many beautiful residences and public and private *palacios.* A transportation system, electric lights, good water, and an adequate sewer system add to the attractiveness of the city.

Population. It is estimated that there are only some 500,000 people in all the state of Amazonas. Manaus and the six other larger centers of the state have 175,000, leaving for the villages and open country and the cities under 10,000 only 325,000. In an area of about 600,000 square miles, it is clearly evident that vast regions are entirely unpopulated.

The state of Pará fronts on the Atlantic Ocean and thus possesses a greater attractiveness for settlement. Yet this state of about 471,000 square miles has approximately 1,000,000 inhabitants. Of these, 235,500 live in the capital city of Belém; 300,000 more reside in the eight principal towns of the state. This leaves only about a half-million people scattered through the interior and in the other twenty smaller towns and villages. The remainder of the great interior region is populated to an even smaller degree than these two Brazilian states.

No one knows with any degree of certainty just how many Indians are scattered throughout the interior of the continent. Estimates for the lower valleys have varied from 200,000 to 10,000,000. Perhaps 500,000 would be as fair a guess as any. Whatever the correct estimate, it is certain that, considering the enormous area, Indians are very scarce. When the nature of the Amazonian region is considered, the reason for this paucity of population will become evident.

TRANSPORTATION

The interior railroad. In the interior there is no pressing need for railways or even for automobile or wagon roads, except within a radius of a few miles of the principal centers of population. During the early days of the region's rubber industry, when prices were high and everyone was overoptimistic, a railway was constructed in the Amazon region. It was built to give the produce of northern Bolivian lowlands an outlet to the Amazon navigation below the Madeira rapids. After verging on a war over boundaries several times, Brazil and Bolivia entered a treaty whereby Bolivia ceded to Brazil her claim on the area known as the Territory of Acre, located at the western edge of the state of Amazonas. In exchange for title to this large area, Brazil bound itself to construct a railway around the rapids of the Madeira River, one of the tributaries of the Amazon. The length of the railway is 219 miles, extending between Guajará-Mirim on the Rio Mamoré and Pôrto Velho on the Rio Madeira. After much difficulty and the loss of many hundreds of workmen through accidents and disease, the project was completed under the direction of engineers from the United States.

The railway opened an outlet for the rubber and other forest products of the northern Bolivian lowlands. They could now be transported by way of the Mamoré River, one of the tributaries of the Madeira, to the upper rapids. There they would be transferred to the railway and carried around the nineteen rapids and falls on the river. Below the rapids they would again be transferred to a river steamer and shipped down to Manaus. The railway was well constructed, but it has proved a financial failure. A revived interest in the rubber industry in the Amazon region may restore some of the early importance of the railroad. The greatest result of its construction was the establishment of an American hospital that has saved many lives in the region. A second valuable result lay in the settling of a border dispute of long standing between Brazil and Bolivia, which thereby insured peace and friendly relations.

Waterways and trails. Waterways provide the chief means of transportation. Along their courses, here and there, the population is concentrated. There are, however, pack trails in certain parts of the great wilderness. Along the waterways are frequent ranches, sometimes ranch-villages complete in themselves. In many places there is no swamp at all, or matted forest, but natural levees and high rolling ground with rather open forests; and occasional savannas, which invite the grazing of cattle; or, in the higher parts, plantations of exportable stuffs. Where the land near the water is swampy, these ranches or villages are located back from the river, sometimes a league or two,[4] and a well-built trail extends from the wharf back to the settlement. Many small rubber, fruit, and cacao plantations are thus found, scattered along the banks of the principal rivers, and there are frequent cattle ranches. At one time coffee was grown along the Amazon, the Madeira River, and in the interior of Peru. At the present time a great many of the plantations are unworked or have been abandoned. Those that have survived are frequently indifferently maintained. Coffee from the highlands is so superior to the Amazon Lowland product that the latter brings a very low price. A recent increase in the price of rubber may reëstablish the gathering of rubber. Cacao is subject to blights and pests. Cattle products cannot be shipped far, because of the cost, and local demands for

[4] In Spanish South America the league is usually five kilometers, or about three miles. In Brazil it is six kilometers. Distances, however, are rarely measured with anything approaching accuracy. When a native says, "It is ten leagues from here to there," he is even less accurate than a North American who "guesses" how far it is across Lake Erie.

animal products are easily met. The energy of the inhabitants of the region is never high.

Back toward the headwaters of the rivers, where the land is higher and drier, trails extend for hundreds of miles. A traveller will sometimes cover 20 leagues without observing a sign of human habitation. Suddenly he will come upon the simple homes of a small village; then he may cover another 10 leagues before sighting another house. These forest trails are the only means of passage, so anyone going through has to follow them. The traveller rides his own mule or horse and is accompanied by another mule or two to carry his food and baggage. The custom prevails, of course, for several individuals to organize a travel train to reduce the risks of the way. Then there are the longer trails back over the Andes, or in some other direction, toward the larger centers. Hundreds of miles long, they wind up and down the steep mountain sides. They cross deep crevasses over shaky suspension bridges of rope and poles that are none too safe. They stretch from the river town or village at the foot of the mountains to the larger centers on the high plateau. It is apparent that overland travel through the region is very slow, and laborious. Travel by water is likewise tedious. The time from Rio de Janeiro to Manaus is 22 days by ocean and river steamer. Eight or 10 miles an hour on a river steamer is rapid. A chartered airplane is the only means of rapid travel, but very few dwellers in the region can afford that. To most of them life is calm and unruffled. Why should they hurry from one place to another? The "tourist urge" has not yet reached Amazonas!

AGRICULTURAL AND FOREST PRODUCTS

Plantations. The larger plantations of the great central region are really small towns in themselves. The overlord owns and rules hundreds of square miles of land. He usually is a "benevolent despot," but he always rules, unless he lives in the capital and has overseers to direct his lands. He may own a thousand or two head of cattle that range over the pasturage of his lands under the care of his own herdsmen. He may have a few or a thousand acres of plantation. His are the shops, the store, the mill, the houses, the land—the entire village. His own home is not palatial, but it is large and roomy compared with the humble huts of his workmen.

Tropical rain forest. The difficulties besetting agriculture in many parts of the Amazon area are enormous. Springing from the ground are giant creepers often as much as a foot in diameter, with woody stems as tough as the hardest ironwood. They run up the trunks of giant trees, drop from the branches in loops and festoons, and tie the forest together into one solid mass of growing vegetation. Spanish moss drops in sheets from the thickets, and parasitic plants find ready hosts among the trees.

Scarcely any grass grows in this kind of forest. The ground is damp and bare, and the thickly matted vegetation overhead shuts out the light of the sun, leaving the man on the ground in semi-obscurity. Only where a creeper has choked a tree to death can the sun break through, and then the man on the ground stands amid dead branches and looks upward to the sky as from the pit of a crater, the walls of which are densely green. In half a dozen years the pit is again filled. This forest is terribly monotonous. Day after day the traveller on a river steamer passes beside the same dense walls of vegetation. The vegetation is particularly dense along the drainage pattern.

Clearing for agriculture. The clearing of tropical vegetation for agriculture is a matter of great difficulty. In the first place, the wood will not burn readily. Most of it is hardwood; all is living and wet and green; forest fires are almost unknown. The ground must be cleared with axe and saw and with mattock and root-pulling machines. A lumber crew equipped with the aids of modern machinery can clear it. A native crew without modern machinery can also clear the ground, but it is a long and toilsome process. Moreover, the jungle grows back rapidly when it is not kept under control by constant vigilance and work. Cut-over land is ready for recutting twenty years after. The difficulty of keeping agricultural land cleared is thus evident.

Pioneering in the Amazon region in the way our forefathers did in the forests of North America is physically impossible. The lone farmer cannot go in and clear an acre or two and plant his garden. The region undoubtedly will, at some future date, be more densely settled with farmers. But it will be settled by organized communities of men, adequately financed, and equipped with every modern aid to health, sanitation, and effective workmanship. Away from the Amazon itself there are frequent rises of the land into broad mounds or foothills. This ground is better drained; vegetation is neither quite so thick nor so persistent; and there are occasional grassy savannas extending for a few acres—sometimes a few hundred acres—that are excellent for grazing. In these places trees are often found in groves as in parks, not too close together, with wide-spreading branches underlaid with excellent grass. These places would normally be first selected for settlement.

The first work will be done by a logging crew, to be followed by another crew to clear the ground and eliminate stumps and root systems. The value of the lumber taken out will perhaps pay for this part of the work. These crews will be followed by a construction gang that will build the town, lay out streets, and construct homes and shops, a school, and a church. The farming families will be ready to move in the moment the land is cleared, to plant it with whatever is desired. The land will have to be cleared just as it is needed for occupation. The growth of vegetation is too rapid for preliminary clearing to be of great avail. For such colonization extensive financing, guided by a management that will eliminate waste and insure effective work, is absolutely necessary. And the settling families must be prepared for a long, hard pull.

Agriculture is not impossible, therefore, but it is difficult. Clearing the forest is simply the first hurdle to be passed. The cost of implements is very high, for they must be purchased under conditions of high import duties, and with a currency that has sadly depreciated in purchasing power. Yet the soil, when properly fertilized, is rich; water abounds—is almost too abundant at times; the warmth is conducive to the rapid growth of vegetation, whether cultivated or jungle; and there is but slight chance of a failure of crop.

Another barrier in the path of agriculture is the enervating effect of the climate upon man. The Wisconsin or Pennsylvania farmer is stored with energy from a bracing climate that inspires him to work. The same man after two seasons in the Amazon region would lose much of his energy and find himself physically incapable of enduring a hard season's labor. The benefit of winter temperature is an important factor of the intermediate latitudes that is wanting in the tropics.

Soil conditions. The mature soils or laterites of the Amazon region do not retain productivity for more than two or three years after they have been brought under cultivation, unless by means of the application of fertilizers. This condition is accentuated by rapid decomposition of organic matter and the leaching effect of a heavy rainfall, which prevents the accumulation of plant nutrients in the soil. The immature alluvial soils possess far greater fertility than the laterite.

Cooperative agriculture. An experiment in cooperative agriculture was under way before the start of World War II. The state government of Amazonas in 1927 invited Japanese settlers to come to that state. The agreement, made with Japanese civilian capitalists and not with the Japanese government, was very liberal. The company was to receive 1,000,000 hectares of well-drained land. This amounted to 2,470,000 acres, or about 3,860 square miles. On this land the company agreed to colonize families, carefully selected to guarantee that only the choicest agricultural families would be invited to come. Within fifty years 10,000 family groups were to be colonized on the land. Although the colonies were primarily agricultural, their settlements were to include necessary factories, mills, and shops. Their education was to be in terms of Brazilian language and customs, with the idea that they would become Brazilian citizens and their descendants would become amalgamated in the Brazilian culture and race. Competent medical service was assured, and all taxes were remitted for a period of ten years.

In other words, every safeguard was established to start these colonies in the direction of permanent happiness and self-sufficiency. It is only through such means as these—adequate finance and every scientific safeguard—that the natural resources of the Amazon region may be utilized.

REGIONAL DEVELOPMENT AND OPPORTUNITIES

Natural products. Various types of opportunities are open in the Amazon region for those who have capital to invest and have initiative and resource in management. Several natural products of the region are described here.

Castanha do Pará. Nut-raising has proved profitable with certain species. The Brazil nut, the three-cornered nut that sells so extensively in the United States, is called the *castanha do Pará.* The tree bears well only when very old—somewhere about 40 to 50 years of age—and continues to yield for a half century or longer. Capital would hardly be interested in such a delayed product unless it were the capital of a well-established and diversified plantation designed to continue for many generations and looking toward the future. The trees grow wild throughout much of the region, in groves of as many as a hundred together. The pods, containing fifteen to thirty nuts each, fall in December. Although the annual crop gathered varies from 20,000 to 40,000 tons, only a small portion of the available total is ever harvested. In the past half the crop was shipped to England, the other half to the United States. The nut is not only good to eat, but it produces a fine oil that is said to be far superior to coconut oil.

Andiroba. The andiroba, or crabwood, tree produces a nut containing a fine quality of oil used widely for illumination throughout the interior. It can be refined into a lubricating oil of good quality, and it is thus widely used in local areas.

Vegetable ivory. Another important product of the Amazon region is vegetable ivory, produced from the kernel of the tagua palm nut. It is extensively used in the manufacture of buttons, umbrella handles, and toilet articles.

Babassú. The babassú is one of the largest and most useful palms in Brazil, yielding great quantities of nuts. The nuts are oval shaped, three inches long and one inch in diameter, and one cluster can contain as many as 400 nuts. The ripening period extends from July to November. This valuable tree grows in the states of Pará and Amazonas. (It also grows in the states of Piauí, Maranhão, Mato Grosso, Minas Gerais, and Goiás, states south of the Amazon region.)

The oil extracted from the babassú nuts is utilized in the manufacture of fine toilet soaps and perfumery. It makes an excellent vegetable butter, may be substituted for olive oil, and may be refined into a high-grade lubricant or used as fuel oil. The kernels yield about 60 per cent of oil and today are used principally in the manufacture of soap and margarine. The cake is used for livestock feed.

Lumber. In the Amazon region are found vast quantities of splendid hardwoods. Large quantities of timber located close to the rivers have already been taken off for shipment, especially to European markets. The great forests contain no groves of any particular kind of tree, as do the pine forests and oak stands in our country. Instead, there is an almost endless variety of trees of literally hundreds of species.

Despite the prevalence of excellent woods, large quantities of pine have been imported yearly from the United States and Russia.

For many years rubber was the staple product of the region—until East Indian plantations began producing more than the world needed, and the bottom dropped out of the world market. It is altogether possible that the greatest natural resource of the Amazon region in the future will be timber. A number of serious problems will have to be solved, however, before extraction can be made profitable:

(1) These woods are largely unknown in world markets, and their excellent properties are not keenly appreciated. A user knows what he is getting when he purchases fir or oak or pine. Education is needed to create a market for these unknown tropical woods.

(2) The fact that the forests are widely diversified, with not many trees of a particular kind immediately available, creates another problem. There will be difficulty in filling large orders for a particular kind of lumber, and to dispose of many small lots of different kinds is not a simple business problem.

(3) There are logging problems. Topping and clearing and felling in the midst of a dense jungle of matted vines are vastly more complicated than the same processes in an open forest.

(4) Transportation costs are high. Heavy timber that will not float must either be taken out on barges or floated out on rafts constructed of lighter wood. Unless the logging is done on accessible waterways, it is difficult to bring the logs through the dense forest to the stream. Then, too, transportation down the many miles of river and by ocean to the consumer's market is a long voyage, correspondingly expensive.

(5) One of the great problems is that of labor. Native help in the tropics is notoriously inferior to American help in the forests of this country. And yet American labor could hardly be exported to the Amazon region, and almost certainly would not be long efficient in the constant tropical heat. The best that seems possible is the selection of American foremen whose outstanding determination permits them to work effectively and get the best service possible from native help. And this quality in a foreman is almost a gift from the gods! The foreman,

too, would have to spend frequent winters in the invigorating frost of temperate climates.

If lumbering interests could be closely associated with colonization projects, so that the ground could be entirely cleared and then replanted to agricultural uses—either pasturage or field crops, rubber, fruits or nuts, or groves of a single species of timber woods—it would be an economy. Hitherto such correlation has never been practiced. These lands are generally considered either too moist or too hot for healthful residence. It is probable that they could be neither if proper precautions were taken.

These questions about lumber have been raised because they are similar to the problems a North American capitalist would have to meet were he to invest in any Amazon region project. There are good investments to be made, with real profits, but the risks are great—in lumber as well as in every other field—and therefore no one is really justified in engaging in the venture unless he can afford to lose the sum he is willing to risk. Every year enterprises financed by limited foreign capital become bankrupt. Only very large resources in capital and in management can guarantee successful outcomes.

Rubber—Natural. Rubber-gathering was for many years the great source of income to dwellers in the region. Until 50 years ago, 90 per cent of the world's rubber came from the Amazon Valley. In 1949 less than 2 per cent originated there. The remainder was produced principally on plantations in the Orient.

Rubber trees grow in many parts of the Amazon region, in territory belonging to Brazil, Venezuela, Colombia, Peru, Ecuador, and Bolivia. There are several species. The *Hevea brasiliensis* is the most sought after, for it produces large quantities of the best-grade rubber. The plantations, in general, are producing this variety. East Indian plantations were practically all grown from seed of this variety exported surreptitiously from Brazil.

The trees grow to a height of 30 or 40 feet and begin to produce when they are 6 to 10 years old. The rate of production gradually increases as the trees become more mature. Out in the rubber territory somewhere, usually along a stream, a gatherer and his family will build a little hut. It is merely a pavilion set several feet off the ground above high water and made accessible by means of a short ladder. Walls around three sides keep out the prevailing winds. A thatched roof sheds most of the rain. The only furniture is a hammock or two, a chest or two, a few reed mats, and some earthenware pottery. Cooking is done over a homemade dirt fireplace. In some places gathering occurs only in seasons of low water; in others only when high water permits penetration of the dense vegetation by canoes. Many gatherers work during both seasons.

One rubber gatherer will tend from 100 to 200 trees. If they are close together, say on one square mile of ground, he may tap as many as 200.

If they are scattered though the jungle and separated over two square miles or more of ground, 100 is all he can reach. He carefully plans his route so that with the minimum of travel he may reach every tree. His constant walking beats a well-worn path. At the close of a day of gathering he will coagulate the latex by smoking it over a slow fire. When he has a canoe-load of crude rubber, he will paddle it down to the merchant, or *patrão,* who has staked him, and sell it. The merchant, in turn, ships his stock periodically down to Manaus or Belém, where it is sold in the open market.

The efficiency of the plantation method becomes evident when it is noted that 100 trees may be planted to the acre, 60,000 or more to the square mile, and a single attendant may care for from 500 to 600 trees.

When rubber sold at 20 cents a pound, or 50 cents or a dollar, the extraction industry boomed. Everybody in the region was happy and prosperous. Cities like Manaus spent huge sums for municipal improvements and created vast bonded debts. When the collapse came, it left the inhabitants bewildered.

In 1927 the Companhia Ford Industrial do Brasil received from the state government of Pará a concession upon which to create a *rubber plantation.* The plantation and its environs, known as *Fordlandia,* is located some 700 miles from Belém—592 miles via the Amazon River to Santarém and 110 miles up the Tapajós River. It is sometimes called Boa Vista, which was the name of a small village on the site before it was taken over by the Ford Company. Fordlandia proper measures approximately 2,500,000 acres, 75 miles along the Tapajós River and 50 miles inland. By 1934 approximately 8,400 acres had been cleared and 8,300 acres planted with 1,390,000 trees. At present the number of acres on which maintenance is continued has been greatly reduced for many reasons. The hilly terrain of the cultivated areas is found unfavorable for rubber trees; the sauva ants and other insects cut off the leaves of the rubber trees and, if not controlled, eventually kill the trees; the South American leaf disease is prevalent, a fungus attacking the new foliage during the rainy season and causing the leaves to wilt and droop; the transportation facilities are inadequate, since only the smaller river boats can navigate up the Tapajós River to Fordlandia during the dry season; the labor situation is unsatisfactory; and many other obstacles reveal the complexity of the problem. In an attempt to overcome some of these obstacles, a new site known as Belterra was acquired downstream, only 30 miles from Santarém. The new concession was a trade of 703,750 acres from the rear of Fordlandia for a like amount of land at Belterra. In 1940, the new tract showed a development of some 12,000 acres with more than 2,690,000 trees, of which 2,000,000 had been budded with high-yielding varieties, whereas Fordlandia at this time had been reduced to not much more than an experimental plantation. The problems confronting Fordlandia have not been completely eliminated or controlled at Belterra, particularly plant diseases and insects. Moreover, the scarcity and unsatisfactory character of the labor supply are serious handicaps at Belterra.

A few years ago, for reasons more economic than physical, the Ford rubber project in Brazil was turned over to the Brazilian government. It is generally conceded that the adventure was not a success. In all probability, however, Brazil will continue to produce natural rubber, both wild and cultivated, on a small scale. Of course the chief source of natural rubber is southeastern Asia.

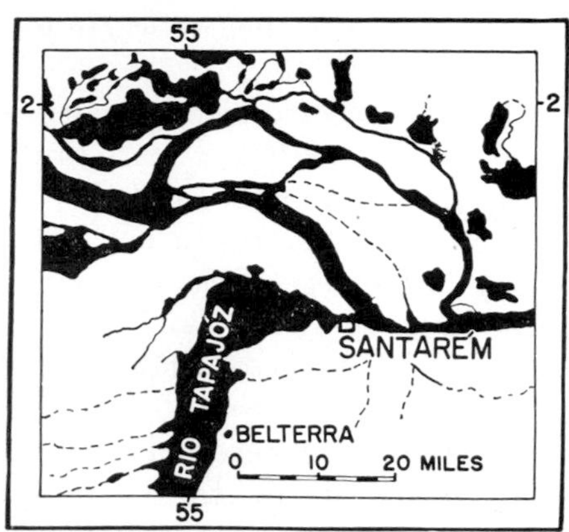

Fig. 56. Rubber plantation center.

With reference to the United States, the major consuming area of rubber, it is interesting to note that in 1945 the nation's total imports of natural rubber amounted to about 145,000 tons as compared with 750,000 tons in 1948, while the production of synthetic rubber in the United States was approximately as follows: 1945—820,000 tons, and in 1948—490,000 tons.

Cattle industry. More than 300,000 cattle roam the state of Amazonas; perhaps twice that number are in the state of Pará. On the island of Marajó, opposite Belém at the mouth of the river, there are more than 200 cattle ranches, with an estimated cattle total of more than 200,000. These lands could raise a vastly larger number of cattle, but not without difficulty. The attitude of the producers is simply this: Why should we attempt to raise more cattle than we can sell? When there is a market for larger quantities of meat, then they will, of course, be produced.

Mineral resources. Manganese ore is reported to exist in large quantities in the Territory of Amapá. Surveys have not been completed but experts estimate that there may be as many as 50 million tons of high grade ore in the territory. If the ore is developed, it can be shipped from Macapá, the seaport capital of the territory, to the United States Atlantic ports much more quickly than the ore from Minas Gerais, Central-East Brazil.

Another mineral resource associated with the Amazon region is petroleum. Reconnaissance surveys indicate the presence of oil-bearing geological formations in this area.

INDIAN LIFE

Native inhabitants. The inhabitants of the Amazon interior are chiefly of Indian blood. In many of the forest recesses foreigners have never penetrated, and Indian blood has never been mingled with any European or African strain. In other places there is a slight intermixture, and these folk form the rubber gatherers, with their more settled forest life. Those who are more equally mixed with European stocks are found in the villages or cities, or on the plantations. In places like Belém, Manaus, Iquitos, Santarém, Itacoatiara, and a few of the other larger centers, the Portuguese population is considerable. In the two capital cities especially, the dominance of the European strain is evident. There are, certainly, many families that pride themselves on their unmixed European ancestry. The great majority of these families, unless they are of recent immigration, are engaged in commercial, industrial, or governmental pursuits. They tend to concentrate in the larger cultural centers.

There are many types of Indians. Some are gentle and inoffensive; others are bloodthirsty man-killers. In general, they are peaceable and kindhearted, usually indolent until they have to work. Travellers among them are generally well received and often helped, seldom injured. There are some, however, whose savagery is practiced on chance strangers: the ill-starred Fawcett expedition into the central interior of Brazil will be long remembered.

Along the main stream of the Amazon River and its principal tributaries are Indians who use poisoned arrows that they shoot through blowpipes with deadly accuracy. The poison is *wourali* or *curare,* both fatal. While these weapons are employed principally in hunting birds and other game, there have been instances when they were turned against strangers. South of the Amazon territory, in the higher lands, the Indians do not poison their weapons. Sometimes arrows with three or four barbs are employed, and these are deadly because they are so difficult to withdraw from a wound. Frequently, Indians use clubs, occasionally lances.

Indian families are not highly prolific. Children are not very numerous among them. From two to five children are the rule, and the death rate is very high. In all likelihood the Indian population is about stationary. The homes are square or rectangular huts; roofs, usually thatched, are not very high; and walls, of reeds or boughs, enclose one room, which is occupied by the entire family.

Indian food consists largely of meat, either game or domesticated. Most tribes raise pigs and chickens, have a few cattle, and gather an abundance of wild fruits and nuts. Wild rice and bananas are favorite foods. Manioc root and sometimes a few vegetables are cultivated. On the higher ground, settled Indians have yams, pumpkins, beans, corn, and leafy vegetables, but in lower regions these are usually lacking.

When they go hunting, Indians frequently travel in groups, killing large quantities of game at one time. Trapping is common among them.

Major General Marianno Candido da Silva Rondon, a full-blooded Indian, was chief of the Brazilian government's Indian service. He laid the telegraph lines that now unite all principal cities of the interior with Rio de Janeiro. He explored the vast areas of the interior, drew maps, studied the Indian populations in their native habitat, and has been the principal source of inspiration in advancing their civilization.

Indian civilization. Some Indians have become highly civilized. Especially is this true among those found in Paraguay and Bolivia, and in the lower interior of Peru, where the Jesuit missionaries carried on extensive experiments in civilization centuries ago. They befriended the Indians, gathered them into villages, and instructed them in the Christian religion. They built churches, developed agriculture, established industries, clothed the Indians' bodies and improved their minds, and made a real beginning in civilizing these natives. The king of Spain, for several reasons that do not concern us here, finally expelled the Jesuits and left the Indians without the stimulus of friendly European guidance. These Indians have drifted back into their own primitive barbarian culture, but have never quite lost the home life or the institutions brought them by the Jesuits two centuries or more ago. Their lives are simple: they dwell in mud houses; they raise small gardens; they have their chickens and pigs and cattle; they clothe themselves. Generally they attend church, and once in a while an itinerant missionary comes along to minister officially to their spiritual needs.

The Indians of the Amazon Plain and of the lower plateaus differ in many respects from the Indians of the upper plateaus of Bolivia and Peru. It was on the upper highlands that the massive civilizations of the Incas developed, not among the valley Indians. And on the highlands today the indigenous populations are more intelligent, more industrious, more highly civilized—and the highlands are twenty times more thickly populated. Yet anthropologists have observed that, despite their Incan culture, the Indians of Peru are in general not so highly intelligent as were many of the North American tribes; neither are they so adventurous.

WILD LIFE [5]

Insect danger. To the traveller in the interior, insect life is interesting, but more often annoying. Several different types of bloodsuckers pursue him or his animals. Mosquitoes are universally present throughout the lowlands, yet one may travel a thousand miles up-river, keeping in midstream, and have no real contact with them. It is on the land or

[5] The wild life of the Amazon Plain is not peculiar to that region. Similar forms are found in many other places, particularly in the wet tropical regions.

near the river banks that they become a torment. In some places mosquitoes are of nonpoisonous varieties. In other places the anopheles is common, and, as a consequence, malaria and a number of other malignant fevers, undoubtedly due to insect or parasitic activity, are prevalent. Yellow fever, which in earlier years was a common pestilence, has now been conquered, and rarely is a case reported anywhere in the region.

A tiny fly, no larger than a small gnat, is a pest in some parts of the great interior. It is called *ihenni,* and its bite is like fire. It leaves a red spot half the size of a pinhead where the blood has been drawn to the surface. The bitten places itch and sting persistently and provoke scratching or rubbing; and this form of relief the sufferer knows will only augment the pain. In places these little tormentors literally swarm; they permit the harassed traveller no sleep at night and attack him with equal ferocity by day.

There are ticks of many varieties and sizes ranging from the invisible cousin of the North American chigger to a huge fellow that swells to the size of one's little fingernail. They seem to hang from the bushes in many parts of the open country and drop on any animal or human being that passes below and shakes the bush. The thoughtful traveller through the brush will examine his clothing carefully and bathe himself with care every night. Sometimes scores of these bloodthirsty tormentors are found on his body.

Ticks are one of the banes of cattle-growers, for they sap the strength of animals and prevent their full development. Another cattle pest is a fly that burrows under the hide in order to lay its eggs, which develop into grubs that must be cut out with a knife. In order to protect cattle, growers have imported various kinds of breeds that are resistant to these ticks. The Indian zebu is apparently the most successful, and it is being mated with imported American and European stock.

There are spiders of all kinds and sorts, from microscopic ones to giant tarantulas with a spread of four or even eight inches and a body the size of a mouse. The tarantula has eight legs covered with long, heavy, black, spiny hair and is a repulsive creature. The little scorpion, however, is worse, if anything, than the poisonous spider.

Night-flying beetles are of many varieties. These beetles fly in to the cities from the wooded hills, attracted by the bright arc lights of the streets. They fly around, then come finally to earth, never to fly again.

A beetle which causes untold damage is a huge brown roach, often three inches in length, that flies by night. Their strong mandibles will tear anything. These beetles are among the worst pests of the tropics. They are said to eat half their own weight in a single night, the preferred food being sweetened or starchy foods. They will even eat the starchy fibers from which bookbinding cloth is made and leave only a few shreds of cotton where they have eaten.

Another insect that causes great damage is a wood-eating termite. It is often erroneously called the "white ant." This insect will bore its way into any soft wood, and, once inside, will proceed to devour the wood. It will literally eat away timbers, posts, or planks, and leave nothing but a honeycomb of the resinous portions and a palpitating dust. The depredations of these termites have caused the government of Brazil to classify its building woods in two groups: those that are subject to attack, and those that are not. Every builder of a house or of furniture is emphatic in declaring to prospective customers that the wood used is *madeira da lei.* This is the legal name for wood impervious to attack by the termites.

Termites shun daylight and appear only at night, when they swarm. In the dusk of the evening, at swarming time, one will appear on the surface of a piece of wood, coming out of a hole the size of a pinhead, and fly toward the window. A moment later another appears, and they continue to follow at the rate of one or two a second for sometimes 30 minutes, when the hatching is apparently over. They fly for an hour or two, then lose their wings, drop, and scurry off to some crack in a piece of wood, where they disappear. They are attracted by artificial light. A lighted house will often be invaded by a swarm. Thousands pour in at the open window and whirl about the light. If a large pan of water is placed close up under the light, they will fall in and drown. Otherwise they will drop to the floor and disappear into cracks. These termites have soft white bodies about half an inch in length and have hard, cutting mandibles. Their wings are about one-half inch long.

When they want to get from one timber to another in a house, they will build a covered runway of clay, a quarter of an inch high and a half inch wide. One such runway was started at the base of a plaster wall 10 feet high. Within a week's time it had traversed the entire distance up the wall, with never the appearance of a single insect. The tunnel was constructed from within, and plastic clay was evidently brought from the ground below.

Ants of many different varieties build hummocks in the open fields. Sometimes the hills, as close together as they can be constructed, entirely cover a field. Often they stand 15 feet high and 10 feet or more in diameter at the base. They are honeycombed with passages and nests and must be the homes of tens of thousands of the insects—giant ant-hills.

Many other insects could be mentioned and described, but these will suffice. In a land where the life cycle is not interrupted by freezing weather, they become a greater nuisance to man than they might in a more temperate climate. Some of them—the anopheles mosquito, which carries malignant malaria, and the *bicho de Chagas,* whose bite produces a type of insanity—are positive menaces to health. Some others, such as the roach-beetles and ticks, may be carriers of disease. Most of them are simply annoyers—and there are hosts of others that do not even annoy.

Reptile, animal, and bird life. Snakes are prevalent all through the tropical interior, but not in such great numbers as are pictured in popular belief. They range from small vipers to boa constrictors of 10 or 12 feet, and up to the giant anaconda, 30 feet long. Unless they are cornered and attacked or stepped upon, most snakes will move quietly away from man.

Many natives die each year from snakebites. Barefoot, or wearing open wooden sandals that afford no real protection, the natives may easily be struck—and snakes are devastatingly omnipresent in some damp regions. In order to meet the situation, the Brazilian government has developed a snake farm, the Instituto Butantan, in the city of São Paulo. The state of Minas has another at Belo Horizonte, and there are a dozen others over the continent. People throughout the interior collect poisonous reptiles and send them in. Serums are prepared and distributed back through the interior, where they are the means of saving many lives.

Bird life flourishes throughout the region. Geese, ducks, gulls, and wild fowl of all kinds breed by hundreds of millions in the marshes of the upper Amazon tributaries, whence they distribute to the far north and south at the proper turn of the seasons. Parrots of many kinds, from the small green bird no larger than a sparrow up to the huge red macaw, abound in the forests. The real life of the Amazon jungle is in the tops of the trees, where an independent world exists in the steady brightness of the tropical sun. In the treetops will be found a rich and colorful life. Flowers abound as well as birds, parrots, small monkeys, insects, and gorgeous butterflies by the thousands. In the forest during the day there is a deep stillness. Toward evening, life begins to awaken to activity; birds, insects, monkeys, and jungle cats become alert and noisy and continue to be so until midnight, when they cease again until early morning.

Egrets are common in many places. Contrary to common opinion, the mother bird does not have to be killed while the young depend upon her for food in order to obtain the best feathers. The finest feathers are ready to be taken while the young are still helpless, but they continue fine until long after the little ones have grown and are feeding for themselves. Hunters in the interior are usually not irresponsible wandering fellows who seize their game wherever it can be found. They are settled men who have their own hunting grounds. When there are egret nests, they look after them carefully and take the female birds only after the young have grown to independence.

Bats, which most natives consider a night "bird," abound in some places but not everywhere. There are several varieties; most of them live on fruits, or upon insects that they are extremely adept at catching on the wing. Vampire bats are common in places, but they are not nearly so dangerous as has sometimes been supposed. The vampire itself is not large, and its stomach is exceedingly small. Even when a number of them attack an animal, as occasionally occurs, they can only weaken it. The danger is not from the few drops of blood the vampire sucks, but from the fact that it opens up a bleeding wound. Sometimes this wound continues to bleed for hours after the bat itself has retired.

Although the Amazon jungle contains far fewer animals than the African jungle, two common types are worthy of particular mention. The first is the wild pig, and the other is the cat family. The wild pig is called a *paca.* Herds of these pacas run in the jungles. They are absolutely fearless and vicious by nature. They run in droves of a dozen or more and attack swiftly and fearlessly.

The paca is an active, long-legged native wild hog, in appearance somewhat like the Arkansas razorback, although not so large. It is a very clean animal and never wallows in the mud. It is generally vegetarian, but when it slays an animal, it will eat the flesh. It never eats food that is even slightly tainted. Indians hunt the paca, usually in groups, armed with guns or poisoned arrows and spears.

There are several varieties of wild cats. The smallest are no larger than the North American tabby. Another type, gray and white spotted, is about two feet long. The jaguarondi, a third type, is about three feet long. The puma has a tawny body sometimes four feet long and resembles very closely the Colorado maneless mountain lion. The jaguar is a huge leopard, yellow with black spots, and weighs sometimes 300 pounds. The skin often measures five and a half feet from the nose to the root of the tail, or eight feet including the tail.

The jaguar is really a tiger. Brazilians call it the *tigre onça.* Most of them are shy of humans, and, unless hungry, will slink off into the forest as a traveller passes. Rarely does a jaguar become a killer and learn to attack human beings. Both jaguars and pumas swim readily and apparently have no fear of water. Frequently their lairs are concealed on islands in the rivers, and they swim to shore for hunting and feeding. Usually jaguars are found only in family groups—male, female, and cubs. Once in a while they breed so rapidly that a place becomes infested with them, but that is unusual.

The monkeys of the Amazon forest require little attention here. They are always small—smaller, many of them, than a rat. The largest never exceeds 40 pounds in weight. They live their uneventful lives in the tops of high trees, seldom come to the ground, and subsist on fruits, eggs, and young birds.

The insects, birds, and animals described are not entirely peculiar to the Amazon region. Jaguars are found as far south as 30° S. latitude, and within a day or two's range of the coast. They live along the fringes of civilization as well as in the fastnesses of the interior. Tarantulas, scorpions, and the huge roach-beetles are ubiquitous, as are the termites and ants and mosquitoes. In the wooded hills and valleys that form the background of Rio de Janeiro itself may be found small monkeys and lizards, large and small. One small gray lizard that grows to a length of six inches frequents most of the residences of the cities. It is nonpoisonous, and its food is insects—mosquitoes, gnats, flies. A lizard two or more feet long that may be found even down in the cities themselves is called the *lagarta.* It is large, thick-bodied, and highly edible, with meat tasting somewhat like chicken.

All Brazilian waters teem with life. Alligators measuring sometimes 10 feet in length are not uncommon, particularly on the Island Marajo. These river reptiles lie sunning themselves on every tropical river bank and especially favor sandy islands in the rivers. They are tough, exceedingly tenacious of life, and will attack any wounded thing in the water. The report that they will attack healthy animals or swimmers and upset rowboats or canoes is subject to conjecture. The skin on the underside of the great saurian makes an excellent and distinctive type of leather. Many thousands are taken from the water annually.

Fish life. The most dangerous fish in South American waters is the flesh-eating *piranha.* It is found from the far north to the far south of the interior waterways. It is blunt-jawed, with exceedingly sharp teeth, and seldom weighs more than a pound. No one swims in infested streams because of the danger of attack. The smell of blood draws these fish promptly, and they rend apart whatever wounded thing they find. They run in schools, hundreds of them together. Cattle that have to ford streams are particularly liable to attack because of the fleshy smell that is washed off in the water.

The rivers abound with edible fish whose names are utterly unknown to North Americans. The *dourado,* a fresh-water salmon three feet long, is the favorite. It is eaten and enjoyed in great numbers. Since the people of the great interior basin, in common with the rest of South America, are mostly Roman Catholic, huge quantities of fish are needed to supply the demand on Fridays and other fast days. The rivers yield nearly all that are necessary, and only along the coast are salted and dried fish imported.

SUMMARY

Vast distances and great expanses of both water and forests constantly press in upon the inhabitants of the valley and conspire to make their existence take on aspects of calmness and repose. Few people from the north have established permanent homes there, and they have been compelled to employ greater care in many respects than would be necessary in a temperate environment. Much is in store for the adventurer, the explorer, and the student of geography in the great Amazon region. It is safe to say that not more than one-third of its interior has actually been explored, and only a small portion has been surveyed.

CHAPTER VII

BRAZIL: FOREIGN COMMERCE AND SUMMARY

Foreign trade. Brazil, like most of the other Latin American countries, has always been greatly dependent on its foreign commerce. Sugar, gold, rubber, and coffee are the products that have competed for predominance in the history of Brazilian trade, each one having been in turn the controlling element. Although Brazil's production has become more diversified, coffee still constitutes about 40 per cent of all foreign shipments as compared to one-half or two-thirds in the past. Raw cotton and cotton piece goods rank next to coffee in exports. Industrial development in Brazil is growing, but the production of machinery, vehicles, fuels, and chemicals is far below the nation's demand. If facilities for the mining and the transportation of iron and manganese ores improve, and markets in the United States call for foreign ores, Brazil may become an important source of metallic minerals. Undoubtedly for many years to come foodstuffs and raw materials will predominate among Brazil's exports, and, on the import list, the leading items will be manufactures. Unless Brazil is able to obtain petroleum and better coal and to develop more adequate facilities for transporting the coal to the industrial region, fuels will continue to be important imports. Wheat and some other foodstuffs are also substantially high on the import list, despite the fact that Brazil is primarily an agricultural nation. The trend toward greater government control of its foreign trade, in the form of restrictions and exchange measures, may have considerable effect on the future composition and volume of Brazil's imports and exports.

Brazil's leading export markets are the United States, Argentina, and the United Kingdom. Other important customers include Belgium, Luxembourg, Italy, France, the Netherlands, Sweden, Switzerland, and Canada. In Latin America, Brazil's markets are Argentina, Uruguay, Chile, Peru, Venezuela, Colombia, and Mexico.

The United States is Brazil's chief source of imports; other important sources are the United Kingdom, Argentina, Belgium, Luxembourg, France, Sweden, Switzerland, and Italy. Latin American sources are, primarily, Venezuela, Chile, Peru, Argentina, and Paraguay.

BRAZIL: EXPORTS
1948

Leading Commodities	Percentage of Total Value	Leading Commodities	Percentage of Total Value
Coffee	42	Sugar	3
Raw Cotton	16	Cotton Textiles	2
Cacao	5	Canned and Chilled Meat	2
Pine Wood	4	Castor Seeds	2
Hides and Skins	4	Carnaúba Wax	2
Rice	3	Tobacco	1

BRAZIL: IMPORTS
1948

Leading Commodities	Percentage of Total Value
Machinery, apparatus, and hardware	23
Automotive vehicles	11
Petroleum products	10
Edible foods and food products (except wheat and wheat flour)	7
Wheat flour	6
Textiles and textile manufacture	6
Wheat	5
Chemical and pharmaceutical products	5
Iron and steel mill manufactures	5
Coal	2

BRAZIL: FOREIGN TRADE

	Total Value	Percentage of Total					
Exports	(*000 Dollars*)	United States	Canada	Latin America	United Kingdom	Continental Europe	All Others
1938	295,558	34.3	0.3	6.3	8.8	43.4	6.9
1947	1,145,806	38.8	1.4	14.2	7.8	28.8	9.0
1949	1,090,300	50.0	...	...	...	...	...
Imports							
1938	295,389	24.2	1.3	13.9	10.4	43.6	6.6
1947	1,216,948	61.3	1.9	8.2	6.8	15.8	5.9
1949	1,117,100	34.0	...	...	...	...	...

Brazil's two major customhouses, each registering about 40 per cent of the nation's total imports, are located in Rio de Janeiro and Santos. Other importing centers are: Recife, Pôrto Alegre, Salvador, Rio Grande, Fortaleza, Livramento, Belém, Uruguaiana, Pelotas, Maceió, and Manaus. Ports leading in exports are, first, Santos, from which 60 per cent of the total value of foreign shipments are made, and, second, Rio de Janeiro (10 per cent). Other exporting centers are: Salvador, Fortaleza, Rio Grande, Vitória, Livramento, Recife, Belém, Paranaguá, Pôrto Alegre, Manaus, Ilhéus, Natal, and Maceió.

THE FUTURE OF BRAZIL

A new policy. More and more Brazilian men of affairs are coming to question the desirability of importing foreign capital to exploit the natural resources of the nation if such capital plans to remove its profits from Brazil. This feeling is becoming prevalent, not only in Brazil, but in many other South American countries. Brazil is finding it increasingly difficult to meet interest payments on these debts. Brazilian statesmen and bankers feel that a considerable part of its difficulties lies in these debts, and they hesitate to incur more. Foreign capital for developmental purposes would be welcomed *if only the owners of that capital resided in the country or would consider making it their home, or if the profits were reinvested consistently in the country.* Most foreign investors refuse to do this. The nation is coming to question whether "Capital Investments" that send their profits abroad are really, after all, profitable.

Again, Brazilian thinkers are questioning more and more the wisdom of overindustrializing their country. "The abundant life that machinery and scientific technique make possible" has never yet been achieved by any industrialized nation in which there is not a balance in the economy between the products of industry and those of agriculture. Brazil is seeking not only to improve its agricultural resources but also to increase production of the manufactured goods it needs, but there is little likelihood that Brazil will become an industrial nation. Serious thought is being given, therefore, to the question of whether an advanced agricultural economy may not be, after all, the most beneficial to the Brazilian people.

Still further, Brazil seriously questions the ultimate value of trusting to the exploitation of mineral resources by foreign capital to satisfy the needs of the people. Brazil's leading men feel that it is of far greater importance to improve the quality of her people through an elevation of culture. Accordingly, they are seeking *to use Brazil's own resources to improve the conditions under which people live and the system of communications and transportation, and to educate the population.*

Potentialities. Brazil has a remarkable opportunity to develop a rich and energetic culture. In the northern part of the country, along the coastal lowlands, where the Negro portions of the population dwell and where climate predisposes to a more leisurely life, it seems inevitable that the development of resources and of a complex culture will lag. To the south, in the lands of Rio Grande do Sul, Paraná, and Santa Catarina, a civilization more and more European in its outlook on life may appear, growing increasingly rich as it develops forest resources of timber and maté, field resources of grain, and prairie resources of cattle and sheep. Nearly half of Brazil's population is concentrated on the great central uplands, and this portion of the population shows promise of becoming the determining factor in the nation's future.

SELECTED REFERENCES

Abreu, S. Froes: "The Mineral Wealth of Brazil," *Geographical Review,* Vol. XXXVI, No. 2 (1946), pp. 222–246.

Azevedo, Fernando de: *Brazilian Culture.* An Introduction to the Study of Culture in Brazil. Translated by William R. Crawford. The Macmillan Co., 1950.

Bishop, Dwight R.: "Brazilian Agricultural Policy," *Foreign Agriculture,* Part I, Vol. XIII, No. 4 (1949), pp. 86–89.

Bishop, Dwight R.: "Brazilian Agricultural Policy," *Foreign Agriculture,* Part II, Vol. XIII, No. 5 (1949), pp. 116–118.

Bomhard, Miriam L.: "Brazil's Oil-Yielding Palms," *Agriculture in the Americas,* Vol. VI, No. 1 (1946), pp. 6–9.

Bowman, I.: "Geographical Aspects of the New Madeira-Mamoré Railroad," *Bulletin of the American Geographical Society,* Vol. XLV (1913), pp. 275–281.

Bowman, I.: "The World's Great Rivers—The Amazon," *Journal of Geography,* Vol. IX (1910), pp. 36–38.

Chase, Agnes: "Grasses of Brazil and Venezuela," *Agriculture in the Americas,* Vol. IV, No. 7 (1944), pp. 123–126.

Coiner, Mary S.: "The Coffee-Harvest Timetable in Latin America," *Foreign Agriculture,* Vol. XII, No. 5, pp. 96–97.

Crist, Raymond E.: "Cultural Crosscurrents in the Valley of the Rio Sao Francisco," *Geographical Review,* Vol. 34, No. 4 (1944), pp. 587–612.

Deffontaines, P.: "The Origin and Growth of the Brazilian Network of Towns," *Geographical Review,* Vol. XXVIII (1938), pp. 379–399.

Foster, Mulford B., and Racine S.: *Brazil: Orchid of the Tropics,* Cattell Press, Lancaster, 1946.

Freise, F. W.: "The Drought Region of Northeastern Brazil," *Geographical Review,* Vol. XXVIII (1938), pp. 363–378.

Hainsworth, R. G.: "The Amazon River Basin," *Agriculture in the Americas,* Vol. IV, No. 10 (1944), pp. 199–200.

Hanson, E.: "Social Regression in the Orinoco and Amazon Basins," *Geographical Review,* Vol. XXIII (1933), pp. 578–598.

Hill, Lawrence F.: *Brazil,* University of California Press, Berkeley, 1947.

Hunnicutt, B. H.: *Brazil, World Frontier,* D. Van Nostrand Co., Inc., New York, 1949.

James, H. G.: *Brazil After a Century of Independence,* The Macmillan Company, New York, 1925.

James, P. E.: "Notes on a Journey up the Valley of the Rio Doce, Brazil," *Journal of Geography,* Vol. XXXII (1933), pp. 98–107.

James, P. E.: "Rio de Janeiro and São Paulo," *Geographical Review,* Vol. XXIII (1933), pp. 271–298.

James, P. E.: "The Changing Patterns of Population in São Paulo State, Brazil," *Geographical Review,* Vol. XXVIII (1938), pp. 353–362.

James, P. E.: "The Coffee Lands of Southeastern Brazil," *Geographical Review,* Vol. XXII (1932), pp. 225–244.

James, P. E.: "The Expanding Settlements in Southern Brazil," *Geographical Review,* Vol. XXX (1940), pp. 601–626.

James, P. E.: "The Surface Configuration of Southeastern Brazil," *Annals of the Association of American Geographers,* Vol. XXIII (1933), pp. 165–193.

Jefferson, M.: "An American Colony in Brazil," *Geographical Review,* Vol. XVIII (1928), pp. 226–231.

Jefferson, M.: "New Rainfall Maps of Brazil," *Geographical Review,* Vol. XIV (1924), pp. 127–135.

Kelsey, V.: *Seven Keys to Brazil,* Funk & Wagnalls Company, New York, 1940.

Killip, E. P., and Smith, A. C.: "A Botanical Trip to Eastern Peru and Amazonian Brazil," *Bulletin of the Pan American Union,* Vol. LXIV (1930), pp. 997–1009.

Maness, Hubert: "Brazil's Sugar Industry," *Agriculture in the Americas,* Vol. V, No. 12 (1945), pp. 223–226.

Marbut, C. F., and Manifold, C. B.: "The Soils of the Amazon Basin in Relation to Agricultural Possibilities," *Geographical Review,* Vol. XVI (1926), pp. 414–442.

Marbut, C. F., and Manifold, C. B.: "The Topography of the Amazon Valley," *Geographical Review,* Vol. XV (1925), pp. 617–642.

Marchant, A. D., "Diamantina: First Diamond Center of Brazil," *Bulletin of the Pan American Union,* Vol. LXVII (1933), pp. 87–100.

Muniz, J. C.: "What It Costs to Grow Coffee in São Paulo," *Bulletin of the Pan American Union,* Vol. LXIII (1929), pp. 1231–1240.

Nash, R.: *The Conquest of Brazil,* Harcourt, Brace & Company, Inc., New York, 1926.

Roosevelt, T.: "A Journey in Central Brazil," *Geographical Journal,* Vol. 45 (1915), pp. 97–110.

Schurz, W. L.: "The Distribution of Population in the Amazon Valley," *Geographical Review,* Vol. XV (1925), pp. 206–225.

Setzer, José: "New formula for precipitation effectiveness: climatic elements of São Paulo and neighboring regions," *Geographical Review,* Vol. 36, No. 2 (1946), pages 247–263.

Smith, T. Lynn. *Brazil, People and Institutions,* Louisiana State University Press, Baton Rouge, Louisiana, 1946.

Sternberg, Hilgard O'Reilly: "The Distribution of Water Power Resources in Brazil with reference to the Participation Ratio Concept," Annals of the Association of American Geographers, Vol. 38, No. 2, (1948), pp. 133–144.

Waibel, Leo: "Vegetation and Land Use in the Planalto Central of Brazil," *Geographical Review,* Vol. 38, No. 4 (1948), pp. 529–554.

Walker, R. G.: "Brazil: Political and Economic Evolution," *World Affairs,* W. S., Vol. 3, No. 3 (1949), pp. 300–309.

Willems, Emílio: "Racial Attitudes in Brazil," *The American Journal of Sociology,* Vol. 54, No. 5 (1949), pp. 402–408.

Wylie, Kathryn H.: "Coffee–A Popular World Beverage," *Foreign Agriculture,* Vol. XII, No. 11 (1948), pp. 246–249.

CHAPTER VIII

ARGENTINA: PEOPLE AND URBAN CENTERS

Early settlements. Four hundred years have elapsed since Pedro de Mendoza founded a settlement on the banks of the Río de la Plata. He sought to provide a base for entry to the western lands as well as an outpost to prevent the encroachment of other nations upon territory claimed by Spain. His primitive settlement, consisting of a fort, a church, and some crude huts, was given the title Nuestra Señora María de Buen Aire, in honor of the patron saint of the mercantile fraternity of Seville. Owing in part to the hostility of the aborigines, and in part to the adventurous spirit of the newcomers, the enterprise was soon abandoned. A new site was chosen, 1,000 miles upstream from the coast, the present location of Asunción, the capital city of Paraguay.

In 1580, some 40 years after the abandonment of Mendoza's settlement on the Río de la Plata, Buenos Aires was resettled by Don Juan de Garay. Garay was a man with keen foresight. He realized that the future wealth of these frontier lands was not in gold and silver but in the utilization of their rich pastoral and agricultural resources. His aim was to build a city that would be the gateway of the new world, open to the great markets to the east and to the vast and fertile hinterland to the west. He drew plans for a city of more than 4,000,000 inhabitants—although his party consisted of only 66 persons! His initial plan called for a city of 250 squares. The sides of each square were 140 yards, and each square was divided into four blocks, 70 by 70 yards each. The squares were to be separated by streets eleven yards wide. A phenomenal vision on the part of Garay! Today Greater Buenos Aires, a metropolis of over 3 million inhabitants, and still growing rapidly, is truly the great emporium of the south. Garay has been referred to as a man with prophetic vision. He was not so much a prophet as a good geographer, who realized the importance of the geographic position and natural resources of the lands that now are known as Argentina.

Further evidence of the strategic location of Buenos Aires is revealed in the early trade routes and development of the republic. Peru was seeking a direct outlet to the Atlantic. Its only means of communication with Europe was via the Isthmus of Panama. Chile desired a suitable overland route to Peru via Argentina. The journey by way of the seacoast was difficult because of the Atacama Desert and the Andes Mountains. Many adventurers destined for Peru, where fabulous wealth was said to exist, entered the new land at Buenos Aires. Therefore the founding of Buenos Aires was justified. Mendoza and its northern neighbor, San Juan, the oldest Argentine cities, were founded in 1561 and 1562, respectively. Tucumán, the garden spot of Argentina, was settled by Spaniards coming down from the Bolivian highlands. Tucumán was on the route from the White City, Lima, to Buenos Aires.

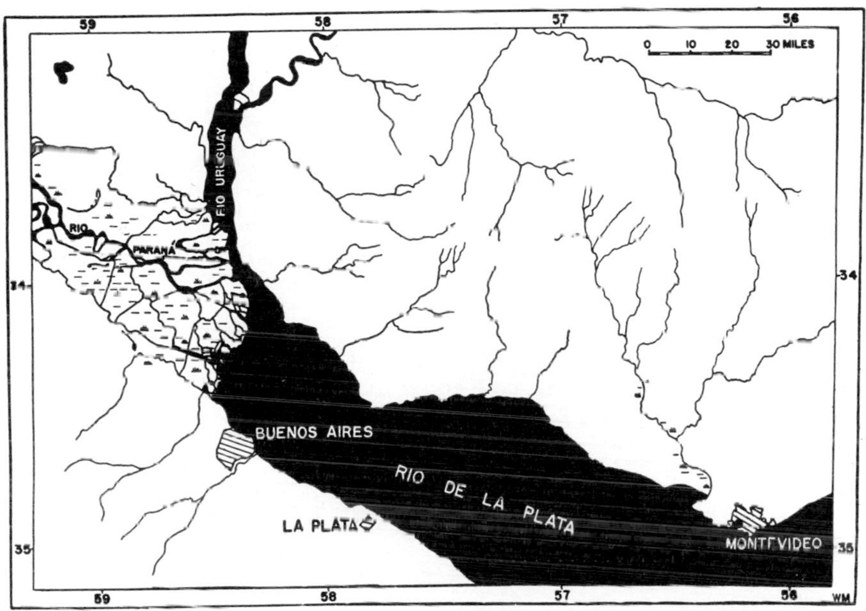

Fig. 57. Hydrographic pattern of the Río de la Plata region.

Every student of Latin American history is familiar with the Spanish monopoly of trade. Spain demanded that her colonists deal only with the mother country, and that commerce be handled through specific ports. During these early colonial days all cargo to and from Buenos Aires moved via Peru and the Isthmus of Panama, a tremendously costly overland journey. Free trade between the La Plata city and ports of Spain or elsewhere was not established until 1778, "the date of emancipation from subservience to Lima."

After this date, interior Peru, Paraguay, and the other inland provinces dispatched their cargoes direct to Buenos Aires for reshipment to Cadiz, Barcelona, and other Spanish ports. An exchange of contraband commodities soon began between Spanish America and Great Britain via

Buenos Aires. Business with the interior provinces grew rapidly. Mendoza and San Juan sent annually to the central market great quantities of wine, a practice that has continued to this day. Tucumán dispatched tanned hides and leather goods. Paraguay shipped maté, tobacco, and timber. Buenos Aires itself exported hides, wool, salted meat, animal fats, feathers, and furs.

Population composition. During the first three centuries of European occupancy, the development of the Río de la Plata lands was imperceptible. The country was confronted with internal strife, foreign invasions, hostile aborigines, and a lack of immigrants. The latter factor, the need for pioneers, was the most significant cause for the slow progress of colonial Argentina. Prior to independence Spain enforced a restricted immigration code and allowed only those to enter who had been granted official permission. It has been reported that during the 40 years from 1770 to 1810, only 700 foreigners entered Buenos Aires. Even after the period of independence, 50 years or more elapsed before immigration became a significant factor in the economic life of Argentina.

In 1857 the wave of European emigration to Buenos Aires and its rich hinterland began. Varying at high and low levels, the movement continued until the First World War with an average yearly number of more than 90,000. During the 10 years immediately preceding this conflict, some 300,000 immigrants annually entered Argentina. In recent years only a few immigrants have come to Argentina, a situation more or less prevalent throughout South America.

POPULATION

	Argentina	*United States*
1810	405,000	7,239,881
1869	1,877,000	
1895	3,955,000	
1900	5,000,000	75,994,575
1914	7,900,000	
1920	8,500,000	105,710,620
1930	11,000,000	122,775,046
1935	12,000,000	
1947	16,109,000	
1950	18,000,000	150,697,361

The difference between arrivals and departures of immigrants according to nationality from 1857 to 1939 is recorded in Chapter I. In referring to this information again, we are reminded that many newcomers did not remain permanently in Argentina but returned to their native land. For example, more than 50 per cent of the total number of Italian immigrants returned to Italy or migrated to Brazil or Uruguay. However, the statistics show that nearly three and one-half million immigrants remained in Argentina from 1857 to 1939. The nationality of the immigrants was as follows: 42 per cent Italian, 33 per cent Spanish, 8 per cent Russian and Polish, 4 per cent German and Austro-Hungarian, and others 13 per cent, including Armenians, Lebanese, Turks, French, British, Portuguese, Uruguayans, and Brazilians.

Reasons for emigration from Argentina are numerous. Disappointments, homesickness, lack of success, and seasonal work are the general causes for departure. Few immigrants find their expectations fulfilled in the new land. The competition is keen; the opportunities are few; the life of an immigrant in Argentina in general is one of hardship and sadness, particularly during the first year. Someone said that there are two classes of people in Argentina, the proud Argentinians and the sad immigrants. In a few instances immigrants acquire sufficient wealth to return to their home country and to live happily there.

The seasonal migration of laborers between Europe and Argentina has been a topic of considerable discussion. Statistics show that the movement corresponds closely to the harvest seasons. Since the seasons in southern Europe and Argentina are reversed, laborers can spend one harvest season in Europe and the next in Argentina. Although this relationship exists, it is quite likely that the migration *does not always include the same individuals.* Their wages would not permit the expense of passage. In all probability those who return to Europe have spent some time in Argentina and plan to arrive in Europe at the harvest season, and time of departure from Europe is governed to some extent by the the close of the European harvest and the opening of the harvest season on the Pampa.

A considerable amount of relocation takes place, especially after the first year in residence. The tendency is for many immigrants to move to the cities shortly after arrival. In fact, the entire republic is becoming highly urbanized. In 1870 about 75 per cent of the total population was classed as rural. Today it is more than 50 per cent urban. Similar changes have, of course, taken place in our own country. In 1890 the rural population of the United States—that is, the people living in the country and communities of less than 2,500—constituted 65 per cent of our total population. Reports of the 1940 census show that 56.5 per cent of our people are urban. In 1950 the population of the United States totalling 150,697,361 was classed as 63.7 per cent urban and 36.3 per cent rural.[1]

The distribution of immigrants within Argentina according to nationalities and occupations is interesting. Italians seem to favor an agricultural pursuit, particularly truck gardening, grape growing, and diversified farming. They also play an important part as skilled mechanics in city

[1] In 1950, the definition of an urban area differed from that employed in 1940. The 1950 urban area is based, primarily, on density of 2,000 per square mile.

occupations. Spaniards seem to favor urban activities. The majority of them remain in Buenos Aires or settle in other large cities. A great many English, Scotch, and Welsh immigrants have settled in Patagonia, where sheep raising is their major occupation. Other nationalities are widely distributed, but for the most part they select residence in cities.

In the course of the past 80 years or more all of the different nationalities have been fused or merged into what is the present "Argentine." Of course, there are Argentinians of pure Italian, Spanish, or some other European stock; Danes in Tandil and Tres Arroyos; Germans in Misiones; and elsewhere others of pure racial stock. The African Negro is practically nonexistent in Argentina. Early in the nineteenth century, some 30,000 Negroes had reached Argentina. It is stated that most of them died from tuberculosis and that the remainder have been absorbed into the population complex. The abolition of slavery by the revolutionary powers stopped at an early date the importation of Negroes as slaves. In northern and western Argentina inhabitants of mixed-blood Indian and Spanish predominated during the early days of independence. However, now there is little evidence of Indian racial heritage.

Someone rightly referred to Argentina as "Europe Overseas." José Maria Cantilo, Foreign Minister of Argentina, in 1938 stated:

> We feel ourselves closely associated with Europe by the immigration we have received from her, which has contributed so much to our greatness, by European capital, which has developed our agricultural and livestock industries, our railroads and other industries. But even more than that there still lives in our spirit the memory of the men who discovered and populated our land, as well as the cultural tradition they bequeathed us.
>
> From Spain we received our blood and our religion. From France and Great Britain as well as the United States we received the doctrinal direction of our democratic institutions. If to the mother country we owe the bases of our literature, French culture has contributed largely in the formation of our intellectual life while Italy and Germany have contributed to important aspects of our evolution. European influence predominates in the higher education of our universities just as European methods are used in our schools.

Industrialization. Argentina has made rapid strides in its manufactures in the past three decades. Outstanding development has occurred in the production of foods, textiles, building materials, paper, tires and other rubber products, shoes and leather goods, and cosmetics. In order of importance based on value, the first five manufactures are textiles and related industries, meat packing, machinery and vehicles, metal goods, and flour milling. Aside from purely local industries, whether backed by local or foreign capital, there are a number of branch factories and assembly plants of world-known industrial concerns.

Small shops and public markets are plentiful in this southern republic as in other South American countries. Also, one finds the street peddler or huckster much more prevalent in Argentina than in the United States. It would be safe to say that these occupations offer more than 75 per cent of Argentina's city employment. This is true of all South American nations.

At present, manufacturing in Argentina is confined largely to the utilization of local raw materials and the production of goods for local consumption. During the past decade the country made outstanding industrial progress and has great possibilities for future expansion.

Courtesy Pan American Union.

Fig. 58. Buenos Aires: Plaza del Congreso, with the capitol in the background.

Contrary to general opinion, the lack of available coal and iron has not dampened the industrial spirit, although it has hampered the development of some of the heavier industries.

To encourage industrialization the Government has extended protection to local industry by applying import restrictions and exchange permits. Also the Government is aiding industrial development by granting tax reductions for profits reinvested in industry and by offering credit facilities for industrial enterprises through the official Bank of Industrial Credit.

Buenos Aires, emporium of the south. Buenos Aires is the chief urban center of Argentina. It is a modern city, and one of the ten largest in the world. The latest census figures or estimates of these cities are as follows:

POPULATION OF THE TEN LARGEST CITIES OF THE WORLD (Latest Estimates available in 1950)

London	8,700,000
New York	7,835,000
Shanghai	6,000,000
Tokyo	5,417,000
Berlin	4,332,000
Moscow	4,137,000
Chicago	3,607,000
Osaka	3,253,000
Leningrad	3,191,000
Buenos Aires	3,114,000

Less than 80 years ago Buenos Aires was nothing more than a large town. Few streets were paved; the sidewalks or paths were much higher than the road; streetcars were drawn by horses. There were no palatial edifices such as the present Casa Rosada, the official residence of the president and headquarters of several government departments. The water supply was inadequate, and there was no department of police. Slaughterhouses were within a mile and a half of the Plaza Mayo. Today the city is a grand metropolis with the cosmopolitan character of New York and the national atmosphere of Washington. Nearly one-sixth of the total population of the nation lives in Buenos Aires. That the growth of the city has been steady is shown in its population statistics:

1800	30,000
1810 (Independence year)	60,000
1885	365,000
1895	665,000
1905	900,000
1922	1,700,000
1930	2,130,000
1947—Estimate	3,114,000

The natural setting of Buenos Aires is without beauty. The city rests upon an uninspiring flat plain, some of its land reclaimed from the sea. Nevertheless, the city is attractive and inviting because of its rectangular street plan, its parks, plazas, and interesting architecture. Artistic public edifices and typical London and New York shops line the principal streets. Rarely are buildings more than six or seven stories high, while two- and three-story buildings predominate. Many streets are narrow, some of the principal ones being only 35 feet wide, but there are a few broad avenues, of which the Avenida de Mayo is the most imposing. Old buildings with the architectural charm of the past stand in line with structures of modern design. Beautiful parkways and shabby slums—conditions that are found in every city—are found within the limits of Buenos Aires. All in all, however, the city is clean, practical, and progressive.

Vital statistics of Buenos Aires show that the metropolis is a wholesome habitat and compares favorably in health with New York, Chicago, and other large North American cities. Malaria and yellow fever are comparatively infrequent; few deaths from malaria are recorded, and in recent years none whatever from yellow fever.

Sports of many kinds are enjoyed by the Argentinians. Association

Courtesy Pan American Union.

Fig. 59. This apartment house is one of the highest buildings in Buenos Aires. Two- and three-story buildings predominate.

football, or soccer, is the leading national game. It occupies the same position that baseball holds in the United States. Rowing, yachting, swimming, golf, tennis, running, and fishing are all popular sports. Many pages of the leading papers are occupied with sports news daily. Another popular activity is horse racing. Thousands of admirers witness some of the finest race horses in the world on the tracks of Buenos Aires.

Other urban centers. On the Paraná River, some 200 miles from Buenos Aires, stands Rosario, second only to the federal capital in population (464,700) and commercial importance. Rosario possesses every characteristic of a modern city and has become one of the most active ports and railway centers of Argentina.

Somewhat north of Rosario are the busy urban centers of Santa Fé (168,000) and Paraná (76,000). Other important commercial centers are: La Plata (217,700), located about 35 miles from its companion city, Buenos Aires, on the La Plata estuary; Bahía Blanca (93,000), the most important wheat port of the southern region of the Pampa; and Tucumán (152,500), the most important city of the northwest.

Mendoza (105,300) is the chief urban center of the far western region. It is the capital of the province of the same name and is located 650 miles from Buenos Aires—about 20 hours by train, or three to four hours by air. It is in the foothills of the great Cordillera of the Andes, 2,477 feet above sea level, and within sight of the snow-covered peaks of the mountains. The city has admirable plazas and promenades, and it is known among the residents as the "Garden of the Andes." Within its environs wine, grapes, and fruits are produced in abundance, and a grape-packing and cold-storage plant has been established. Earthquakes occur at rare intervals, doing material damage. Rainfall is slight, and temperatures are equable.

POPULATION OF PRINCIPAL URBAN CENTERS OF ARGENTINA

Buenos Aires (Greater)	3,114,000
Rosario	464,700
Córdoba	351,500
La Plata	217,700
Santa Fé	168,000
Tucumán	152,500
Mendoza	105,300
Bahía Blanca	93,000

One of the most fascinating cities is Córdoba, situated at the western margin of the Pampa and at the foot of the Córdoba Mountains at an elevation of 1,440 feet. Much of the early architectural design has been preserved in this city, and in general the place has retained the appearance of an early Spanish town. It is the capital of Córdoba Province and is located about 432 miles from Buenos Aires. The district is renowned for its beauty and the city for its buildings. It has a university, founded in 1613. There is no more interesting center for the tourist and holiday-maker. Picturesque in itself, the town is near sierras, lakes, and waterfalls of exceptional beauty and is easily accessible. The train journey from Buenos Aires is about 14 hours via the Central Argentine Railway.

CHAPTER IX

ARGENTINA: NATIONAL ECONOMY

AGRICULTURAL RESOURCES

International position. Argentina's vast and varied agricultural resources, located for the most part in regions of favorable climatic conditions and utilized only partly by an energetic people, constitute the foundation of national wealth and international importance. For many years Argentina has been one of the world's chief exporters of wheat, meat, wool, hides, and tanning extract and has grown more corn and flaxseed for foreign markets than any other nation. As a producer of farm products for foreign markets, Argentina ranks supreme.

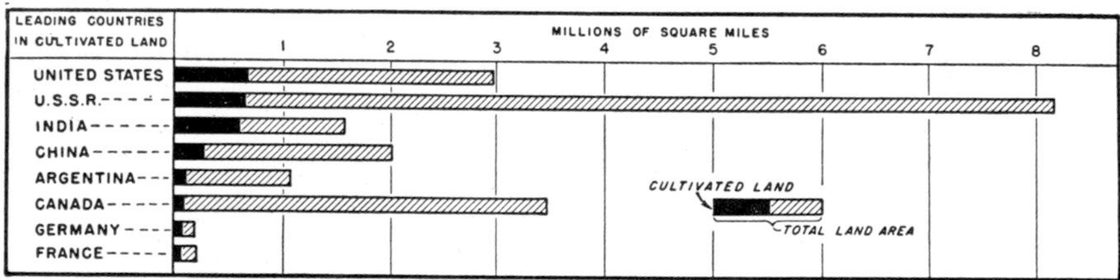

Fig. 60. Total Land Area and Cultivated Area. U. S. Department of Agriculture Estimate, 1948.

Extent of agricultural resources. The significance of the crop and pastoral economy of Argentina rests not merely in its present production of foods and raw materials. Its future potentiality is even more significant. Within its borders, covering some 1,079,965 square miles, an area equal to about one-third of the United States, are immense tracts of undeveloped land. Probably not more than 10 per cent of the arable land is under cultivation. It has been estimated that 65 per cent of her lands can be utilized for crops and pastures. The great variety of physical and climatic conditions offers an opportunity for crop diversification. In the temperate central area, the Pampa, are rich wheat and cattle lands; in the cooler southern region, Patagonia, are great sheep pasturages; in the western lands, the Andean region, are irrigated fields of grapes, fruits, and sugar cane; and in the subtropical north, the Chaco and Mesopotamia, are cotton plantations and varied forest resources. Each one of these regions awaits a more intensive form of land utilization. Collectively they could probably support a population of 50 million. Today the inhabitants of Argentina number about 18 million.

THE PAMPA

Heart of Argentina. The Argentine Pampa, commonly called *La Pampa* to distinguish it from less important pampas of South America, lies mainly between 30° and 40° S. latitude. The region is roughly comparable in latitude to that between Jacksonville and Philadelphia in the United States. It extends westward from the sea for a distance of about 400 miles. Within this relatively featureless plain of some 250,000 square miles are found the nation's leading cattle lands and the chief wheat, corn, and flax fields. It is the most densely populated and richest region of Argentina. Politically it comprises, in whole or in part, the provinces of Buenos Aires, Córdoba, Santa Fé, and Entre Ríos, and the Pampa territory.

For those not familiar with the political divisions of Argentina, it may be stated that the republic is divided into fourteen provinces, ten national territories, and a federal district. Buenos Aires is the largest province; Santa Cruz, in the southern portion of the country, is the largest national territory.

Climatic conditions. January is the warmest month, the mean temperature being 75° to 80°, and July the coolest, from 45° to 65°. In winter few places have extremely low temperatures. Snow rarely falls except in the far south. In the vicinity of Buenos Aires palms grow in all their majestic splendor, and vegetables may be seen in cultivation practically throughout the year. Plowing and seeding may be done during midwinter. The eastern portion, a region of fine cattle, generally has ample rainfall, 40 inches or more. Summer and autumn are the rainiest seasons, although the winter also has rain. In the central area the dry season is longer than in the east, usually including the five winter months. The annual rainfall is 20 to 30 inches. This is the principal wheat region of Argentina. The western margin of the Pampa is semiarid. Only drought-resisting plants are able to survive there. The rate of evaporation is high, and most of the rain falls during the warmer months of the year. At times prolonged periods of drought occur in the summer and cause heavy crop losses, but as a rule the seasonal distribution of rainfall insures satisfactory harvest conditions. The *pampero,* a cool southerly or westerly wind that blows over the Pampa with great violence, often accompanied by clouds of dust, is a peculiar characteristic of the climate of Argentina. In the heat of summer it invigorates the populated areas and seldom causes any serious destruction of property.

ARGENTINA: TEMPERATURE AND RAINFALL OF SELECTED STATIONS

Station	Buenos Aires*	Rosario†	Posadas*	Santa Cruz*	Bahía Blanca*	Córdoba*	Tucumá ‡	Salta*	San Juan‡	Mendoza*	Puerto Madryn‡
Elevation (*Feet*)	83	98.4	383	35	82	1,394	1,466	3,878	2,178	2,477	46.0
Average Temperature (°*F*)											
Period of Record	1931–1940	1901–1920	1931–1940	1931–1940	1931–1940	1931–1940	40 yrs.	1931–1940	39 yrs.	1931–1940	8 yrs.
January	74.5	76.6		57.2	71.8	76.1	77.6	70.7	77.8	74.3	68.8
February	73.0	75.2		56.5	71.6	73.8	76.4	68.9	76.4	72.1	69.4
March	69.3	71.2		53.2	66.7	70.1	72.8	67.5	71.6	66.7	64.0
April	61.2	64.9		47.8	59.2	62.2	66.8	61.3	63.0	57.2	58.6
May	56.8	58.3		39.7	53.1	56.3	60.5	56.7	54.4	50.5	51.2
June	52.3	52.0		33.8	47.8	52.3	55.5	53.1	48.5	45.1	44.9
July	51.3	51.8		34.7	47.1	51.4	55.3	52.2	48.6	45.1	44.5
August	52.3	53.6		37.8	48.6	54.7	57.2	54.5	52.0	49.1	47.0
September	55.6	58.6		43.1	51.4	58.1	64.8	60.1	58.8	54.3	50.8
October	61.1	63.5		49.3	57.0	63.7	69.7	65.8	65.2	60.8	55.0
November	65.8	68.9		52.9	64.2	68.9	73.0	69.1	70.7	66.9	59.8
December	71.1	73.9		55.8	68.9	73.4	75.3	71.4	75.9	72.5	66.3
Annual	62.0	64.0		46.8	59.0	63.4	67.1	62.6	63.5	59.6	56.7
Range	23.2	24.8		23.4	24.7	24.7	22.3	19.2	29.3	29.2	24.9
Average Rainfall (*Inches*)											
Period of Record	1931–1940	1901–1920	1931–1940	1931–1940	1931–1940	1931–1940	1901–1920	1931–1940	1901–1920	1931–1940	1901–1920
January	3.1	3.0	4.0	0.7	1.7	3.5	6.4	6.9	0.8	0.9	0.5
February	2.8	3.0	5.3	0.8	1.5	3.1	6.9	5.5	0.7	0.7	0.6
March	5.5	3.4	5.4	0.7	3.6	4.0	5.6	3.2	0.4	0.6	0.5
April	3.5	4.4	7.1	1.1	0.9	2.2	3.1	0.8	0.1	0.4	0.6
May	2.6	1.7	6.5	1.1	1.5	0.6	1.2	0.2	0.0	0.3	0.7
June	2.8	1.2	4.9	1.0	0.8	0.2	0.6	0.1	0.0	0.1	0.6
July	2.8	1.4	4.2	0.8	0.9	0.2	0.3	0.0	0.3	0.2	0.5
August	2.5	1.3	3.7	0.8	0.7	0.4	0.5	0.1	0.1	0.3	0.3
September	3.3	2.2	4.3	0.3	1.2	1.7	0.6	0.2	0.1	0.5	0.4
October	3.7	3.7	7.1	0.2	2.9	2.7	2.4	1.0	0.2	0.6	0.6
November	3.2	4.3	5.9	0.8	2.1	3.1	4.1	1.6	0.2	0.6	0.3
December	4.3	3.9	5.4	1.1	1.8	4.8	6.1	5.2	0.4	0.8	0.4
Annual	40.1	33.5	63.8	9.4	19.6	26.5	37.8	24.8	3.5	6.0	5.9

* H. Helm Clayton: "World Weather Records," *Smithsonian Miscellaneous Collections,* Vol. 79 (1927), Vol. 90 (1934), and Vol. 105 (1947).

† K. Knoch: "Klimakunde von Südamerika," *Handbuch der Klimatologie,* Band II, Teil G, Berlin, 1930.

‡ W. W. Reed: "Climatological Data for Southern South America," *Monthly Weather Review,* Supplement No. 32, 1929.

The weather in Argentina, like that in the United States, is related to eastward-moving cyclones and anticyclones, or a series of cold and warm fronts. When a depression or cyclone of the V-shaped type is passing eastward, the air masses moving from the north in front of the depression are warm and rainy; but, as the depression moves forward, the wind-shift line, or squall-line, marks an abrupt change to cooler westerly or southerly winds or air masses, thus bringing about a sudden change in temperature. These southerly or westerly winds constitute the pampero. They are most frequent in the summer.

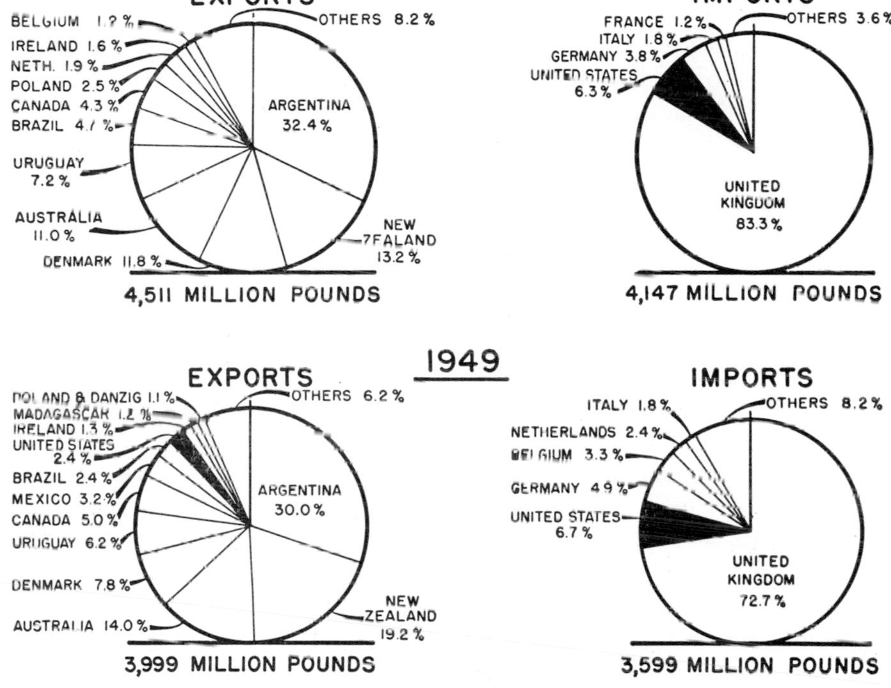

United States Department of Agriculture.

Fig. 61.

Pastoral activities. From the earliest colonial days the Pampa has been the scene of pastoral activities. Records show that the early population of Argentina was a people of the ranch, where the rustic life of the herder molded their characters and simple habits and made them true laborers. The Argentinians were never conquerors or warriors in the military sense, but liberators. Evidences abound of the success and rewards realized by their intelligent utilization of the land.

During the colonial period Spain urged the development of the livestock industry. The mother country insisted that all the governors should supervise the welfare of the industry and emphasized a humane treatment of the natives "that they might assist in the development of a grazing industry." From the early political center, Lima, colonizing enterprises brought cattle into Chile. Expeditions from Chile brought them into Argentina. Other cattle arrived from Spain directly and from Brazil. Favored by an abundance of rich grass and a mild climate, the cattle multiplied in vast numbers and rapidly spread over much of the Pampa. For a long time only hides were taken, hunters leaving the flesh to the birds and dogs. A reckless slaughter prevailed for centuries to provide hides for Spanish merchants and contraband trade and for clothing, armor, and boots.

Since pastoral activities required little learning or capital, a considerable number of settlers were attracted. Furthermore, they were offered free land, a life in the open, and a guarantee of food. In this pioneering environment originated the rural population and from it came that illustrious Argentine cowboy, the *Gaucho.* The Gaucho lived a nomadic life, pursuing cattle and branding them with his mark to lay claim to their hides. Later the Gaucho's activities became more centralized. He selected suitable corrals where he could herd his cattle for safekeeping. Finally, by 1900, his cattle were confined in permanent enclosures protected by American barbed wire. But his background is a life in the saddle, in the open, faced with all kinds of adversities and fortified with a degree of endurance and bravery that has made him a valuable soldier and a staunch supporter of rural life. Today the Gaucho, like the American cowboy, has almost disappeared from the grasslands. Since the fields have been fenced, his service is no longer needed.

During the latter part of the eighteenth century, and until about 1880, the demand for cattle products consisted of salted and dried meat and hides. These found a ready market in South America and in Europe. Prior to 1900 fresh beef was used only for local consumption. A few hundred thousand cattle were shipped alive each year to Europe. This method proved to be uneconomical and involved a large loss through death and accident on board. It was so unsanitary that European buyers in many cases prohibited the entry of live Argentine cattle into their countries. Later the processes of freezing and chilling meat were developed. This introduced a new era in the economic history of Argentina.

Over 4 million head of cattle and more than 6 million sheep and lambs are now slaughtered annually in Argentina. Most of the cold-storage meat is shipped to Great Britain. Argentina has over 41,000,000 cattle, including 2,800,000 dairy cows, exceeded in number only by India, the United States, U. S. S. R., and Brazil. Its sheep total more than 54,000,000, ranking third in world numbers, and surpassed only by Australia and the Soviet Union.

Between 1915 and 1924, a considerable quantity of frozen and chilled meats and their by-products entered the United States. In 1924–1925 the hoof and mouth disease spread rapidly in the United States and was controlled only with great difficulty. To take utmost precautions against this cattle scourge, our government in 1925 prohibited the further importation of cold-storage beef from Argentina.

Although it has been definitely established that there is danger of spreading the hoof and mouth disease by cold-storage meat, Argentina apparently feels that the refusal to import chilled and frozen meat from Argentina is an act of discrimination on the part of the United States. Reference is made to Great Britain with whom Argentina has an agreement to supply annually 200,000 tons of frozen meat.[1] It should be pointed out, however, that Great Britain has no other source than Argentina as a major supplier of meat. Great Britain's cattle industry is not comparable to that of the United States. Furthermore it should be emphasized that the United States does buy about two-thirds of Argentina's exports of canned meat, a form in which the hoof and mouth disease is not carried.

With increasing demand from foreign lands and constant improvement in the packing and shipping of animal products, Argentina has come to place greater emphasis on the quality of the meat than was the case during the days of salted and dried beef. Purebred stocks have been imported from the United States and from Europe; fields have been enclosed; alfalfa has been grown to fatten cattle; and in general the entire livestock industry has been placed on a more scientific and practical basis. The results of these efforts are shown in the growing records of pure-bred herds, in the exportation of high-quality beef, and in the improved character of many of the ranches.

Although the Pampa is quite uniform throughout its area, with a fertile well-drained soil, there are differences in climate, which are reflected in the types of cattle. In the central province of Buenos Aires the Shorthorn is the predominant purebred stock. In the hotter and more humid north, where cattle are subjected to sudden changes in temperature and to attacks of the cattle-tick, the rugged Hereford survives best. In the cooler climate of the southern region the Aberdeen Angus is the preferred breed. Previous to the improvement of the stock, the Criollo or rangy native Spanish cattle grazed these fields. Today it has been estimated that 95 per cent of the cattle in the Pampa are improved, since careful selection and breeding are universally the rule.

Crop production. The immigrants, particularly those of the last fifty

[1] Not less than 200,000 tons.

years, have fostered the cultivation of the rich Pampa soil. Unlike the Creoles (original Argentines of Spanish blood), the later southern European immigrants have favored crop production rather than pastoral activities.[2] Frequently wealthy landlords leased a part of their holdings to immigrants with the understanding that they were to till the soil for the products and, at the expiration of the lease, to leave some land planted with alfalfa.

From the earliest colonial days to the present, the Creoles have placed little emphasis on agriculture. Credit for the extensive cultivation of wheat, corn, flax, and other crops rightly belongs to the Italian immigrants. They have proved not only successful farmers but good Argentinian citizens. The result of their labor and that of others has increased the value of crops until these agricultural products now exceed livestock output in importance.

LAND IN USE

	Acres	*Per Cent of Total*
Pasture	284,542,000	41.2
Forested	221,607,000	32.0
Lakes, salt marshes, and other unproductive regions	107,283,000	15.5
Under cultivation	74,130,000	10.7
Road and railway lands	2,694,000	0.4
Cities and towns	1,236,000	0.2
	691,492,000	100.0

WHEAT PRODUCTION
(1,000 bushels)

	Average 1940–44	*1949*	*1950*
Argentina	234,585	210,000	
United States *	925,384	1,146,463	996,000
World	5,735,000	6,270,000	

* Kansas average 1937–46—167,718,000 bushels.

[2] The word "Creole" has more than one accepted definition. The following meanings are given in Webster's *New International Dictionary*.

". . . **1.** Orig., as used esp. in Spanish America and the southern French colonies, a person of European descent but born and bred in the colony.

"**2.** Hence: **a.** A person of French or Spanish descent born and raised in a colonial or remote region, esp. an intertropical region, the environment and culture of which have entailed a characteristic adaptation of the national type. **b.** In the United States, a white person descended from the French or Spanish settlers of Louisiana and the Gulf States, and preserving their characteristic speech and culture. . . .

" 'The title [*Creole*] did not first belong to the descendants of Spanish, but of French, settlers. But such a meaning implied a certain excellence of origin, and so came early to include any native of French or Spanish descent by either parent whose nonalliance with the slave race entitled him to social rank. Later the term was adopted by, not conceded to, the natives of mixed blood, and is still so used among themselves. *G. W. Cable.*

"**3.** A negro born in America;—more properly, *creole negro.*"

For a more complete definition and other meanings, see: *Webster's New International Dictionary*, Second Edition, copyright, 1934, 1939, by G. & C. Merriam Company, Springfield, Massachusetts.

CORN PRODUCTION
(1000 bushels)

	Average 1940–44	*1949*	*1950*
Argentina	259,124	118,000	
United States †	2,846,337	3,530,000	
World	5,180,000	5,990,000	

† Iowa Average 1937–46–525,879,000 bushels.

Wheat, corn, and flaxseed or flaxseed products are Argentina's leading agricultural exports. For local cattle feed, vast acreages of alfalfa are grown. The northern section of the Pampa is the heart of the corn and flax production; west and south of the corn zone the bulk of the alfalfa

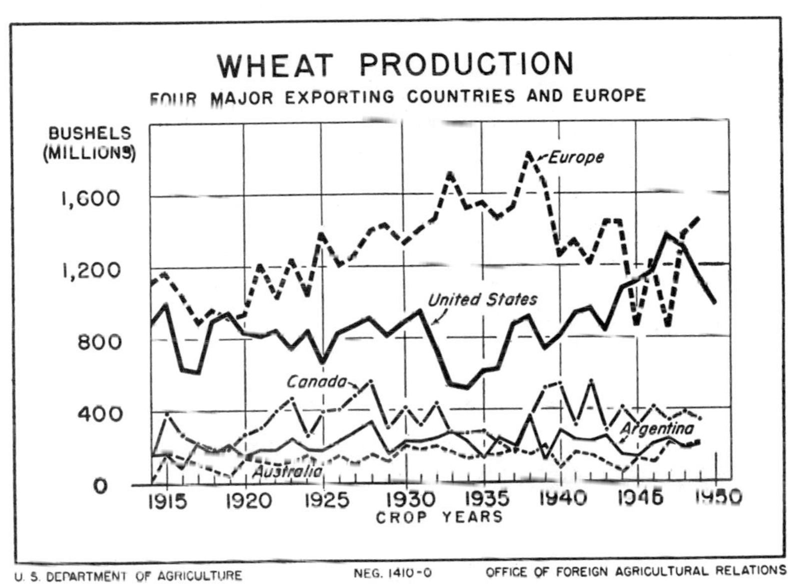

Fig. 62.

crop is produced; and the wheat acreage forms a crescent on the western side of the alfalfa area. Rainfall in the wheat zone is too light for corn and flax. The livestock area is concentrated in the eastern portion of the Pampa, beginning at the very suburbs of Buenos Aires, and extends north and south, including Mesopotamia and much of the province of Buenos Aires and adjacent lands.

One of the distinctive features of the agricultural pattern of Argentina is the extent to which crop and livestock farming are separated and carried on as independent and highly specialized types of agriculture. This specialization is reflected in the terms *estancia* and *chacra,* referring, respectively, to a livestock farm and a grain farm. Most of the estancias consist of from 6,000 to 12,000 acres, and there are 50 families with holdings in excess of 75,000 acres, each in the province of Buenos Aires. The livestock farmer, generally a landowner, does not care to grow crops. When an estancia owner wishes to cultivate a portion of the estancia, tenant farmers are called in for that purpose. Furthermore, the lack of capital and conditions of tenancy tend to restrict tenant farmers to grain

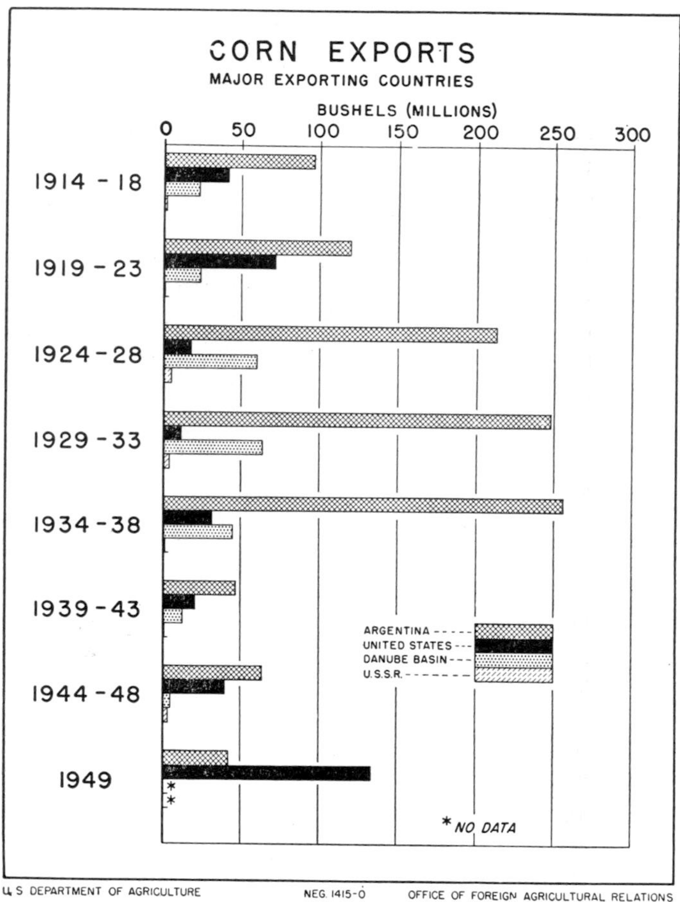

Fig. 63.

production. This unfortunate division of farming is changing, and the tendency is more toward the addition of grain farming on estancias than the addition of livestock on the crop farms.

Agricultural progress. Despite the wealth of its pastoral and crop lands, Argentina has progressed rather slowly in the development of these resources. For the past 30 years, the number of acres of land cultivated and the number of cattle, sheep, and horses maintained in

Argentina have remained about the same. Improvement, however, has been registered in the methods of cultivation and in the quality of the livestock.

An unbalanced landholding system has resulted in a lack of available land for immigrants who desire small acreage. This has affected the general agricultural system. It has been estimated that only 5 per cent of the total population of Argentina, or 900,000 persons, are landowners. Much of the land is held by a few large owners, *estancieros,* whose

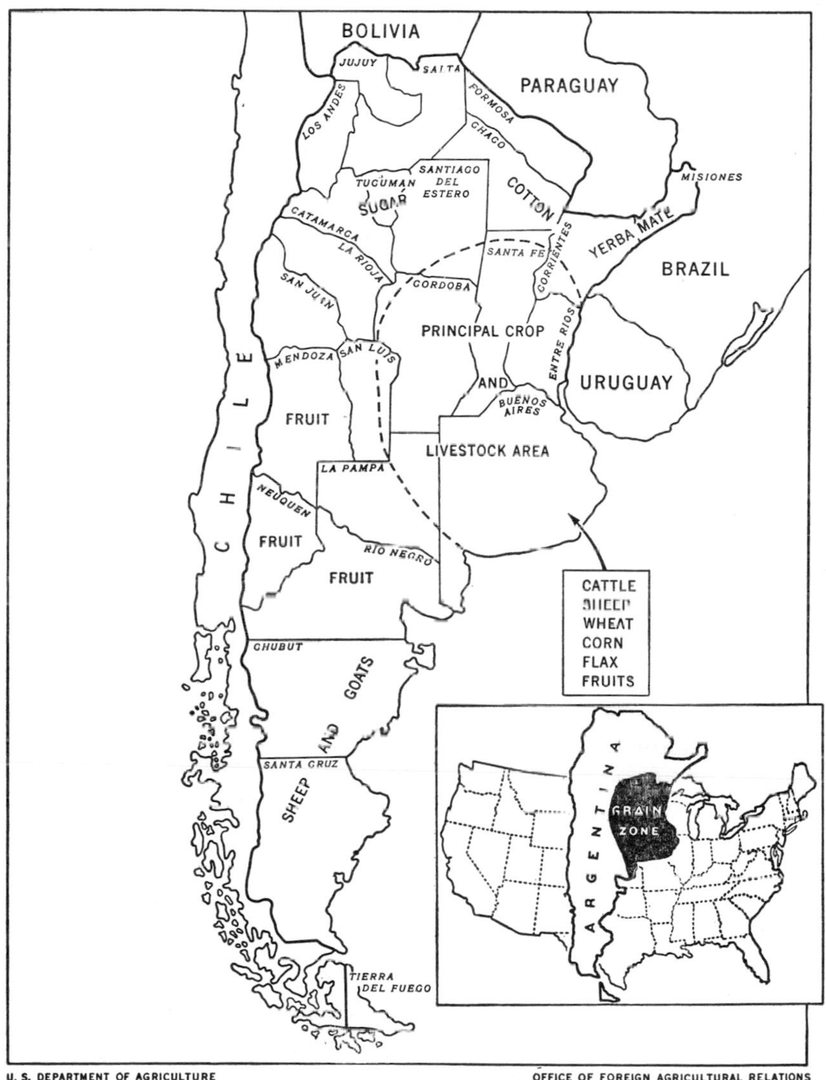

Fig. 64. The principal agricultural region of Argentina.

ranches sometimes extend 10 square miles or more. A farm of a few hundred acres in Argentina seems more like a garden plot than a farm. A change in this antiquated rural land code would greatly reduce the present importation of hundreds of thousands of dollars' worth of foodstuffs annually and place under cultivation large areas of undeveloped fertile land.

For the most part the owners of large estates are unwilling to sell a small area. They usually agree to make a sale only of 500 acres or more. Thus the agricultural immigrant of the home-loving type finds that Argentina has little to offer in the form of readily accessible land, unless several immigrants of like mind purchase a tract and subdivide it among themselves.

Large tracts of virgin country belonging to the government and to railway companies are gladly offered to the newcomer, but much of this land is without adequate transportation facilities or is far distant from present commercial or market centers. High taxes and an unsurmountable tariff are other limiting factors. The small landowner in rural areas appears to be subjected to a disproportionately high tax as compared with the owners of large tracts of land. Purchase of imported machinery is practically impossible for the laboring tenant or small landowner because of the high tariff. Coöperative selling has not proved beneficial to the small landowner because he is generally surrounded by large estates and is forced to accept the price for his commodities offered to the large landholders, who depend more on quantity than quality. Furthermore, he is likely to practice diversified farming, and his production is not great. However, in recent years there is evidence of an increase in the number of ranches or landholdings.

Another factor that has retarded the agricultural development of the Pampa until recently is the lack of good roads. Ten years ago most roads were simply graded earth—dusty in winter and muddy in summer. Now concrete roads join the capital with the provinces of Santa Fé, Córdoba, and Buenos Aires, and many thousands of miles of dirt road have been improved. The general absence of stone over the Pampa has made hard-road construction expensive. Despite the many obstacles in the path of its agricultural progress, the Pampa is, nevertheless, "one of the world's greatest farms."

PATAGONIA

Regional characteristics. South of the Pampa and east of the Andes lies Patagonia. The word Patagonia, which means "big feet," was applied by the early explorers to the aborigines. It no longer appears, however, in official Argentine reports and maps. This region is now referred to as the *Gobernaciónes*, or territories of Río Negro, Neuquén,

Chubut, and Santa Cruz. It comprises one-third of the total area of Argentina, and much of the land has not been surveyed.

Climatic characteristics. Patagonia is dry, barren, cold, and isolated; but it is also scenic and fascinating. Since it lies in the rain shadow of the Andes, its average annual rainfall is less than 10 inches. In the north the rain falls primarily during the winter, while in the south the light precipitation is fairly evenly distributed over the year. The low western portion is virtually desert in character and supports on the uplands only a sparse growth of shrubs and grasses. In the valleys the vegetation is more abundant and more nutritious. On the higher western lands the greater rainfall and slower evaporation permit the development of pines, cypress, and firs—a striking contrast to the barren landscape of the plateau on the east.

Snow falls every winter in the territories of Santa Cruz, Chubut, Río Negro, and Neuquén. It rarely reaches the province of Buenos Aires.

A number of rivers flow across Patagonia. In order from north to south they are the Ríos Colorado, Negro, Chubut, Deseado, Chico, Santa Cruz, Coyle, and Gallegos. The flow of the southern rivers is the more regular. In the north the moisture is not sufficient to maintain a regular discharge; in the south the heavier precipitation, the lower temperature, and the glacial lakes support perennial streams.

Industries. The sheep industry is the major agricultural activity of Patagonia. In the transverse valleys of the north, in western Río Negro, a few goats, probably not more than 300,000, are raised.

With the exception of limited areas, as found in the valleys of the Negro and Colorado Rivers, the entire Patagonia region is unsuited for cattle raising. The climate is dry, and very little pasturage is available on the rocky soils. Sufficient forage could be grown for cattle, but the variation in temperatures between summer and winter, especially in the southern portion, prohibits any extensive development. Moreover, it would be necessary to provide shelter for the livestock.

In the Río Negro Territory, and to a less extent in the Chubut region, irrigation has converted thousands of sterile acres into fertile and productive land where various kinds of fruits, cereals, and alfalfa grow luxuriantly. Similar projects could be successfully introduced into other parts of Patagonia.

Two of Argentina's four petroleum-producing fields, her largest domestic supply, are located in Patagonia. They are the Comodoro Rivadavia, near the sea in the territory of Chubut, and the Plaza Huincul, in the territory of Neuquén, in the upper valley of the Río Negro. The other two producing areas are the Mendoza, in the province of Mendoza, and the Salta, in the province of Salta. The Comodoro Rivadavia field is the largest producer, supplying about 70 per cent of the annual petroleum production of Argentina. All petroleum operations are completely or partly under the control of the government.

In southwestern Patagonia and in the Andes between Argentina and Chile is the most picturesque region of South America. This is the famous Southern Lake Region, the playground for Argentine and Chilean tourists. Here are glacial lakes of sparkling sapphire, such as Lago Nahuel Huapí, Lago Buenos Aires, Lago Viedma, and Lago Argentina, in the midst of evergreen forests, overshadowed by mountain peaks with eternal snows. Rushing, ice-cold streams, probably the source of future hydroelectric power, feed the seaward-flowing rivers. The dense forests

Courtesy L. Hites.

Fig. 65. Southern Patagonia, Argentina.

constitute an important reserve of soft wood for the progressive nations of Argentina and Chile.

Settlements. The principal settlements of Patagonia, including Neuquén, Viedma, Rawson, Comodoro Rivadavia, Santa Cruz, and Gallegos, are all located near the Atlantic Coast except Neuquén. Welsh-Scotch, English, and, more recently, Italian settlers compose the greater proportion of the inhabitants. Although sparsely populated, Patagonia has three railways extending from coastal cities toward the western border. Several steamship lines facilitate travel along the coast.

Tierra del Fuego. At the southern extremity of South America lies the island of Tierra del Fuego (Land of Fire), whose political status is divided between Chile and Argentina. Its eastern portion represents an extension of the plateau of Patagonia, while its western and southern highlands are related to the Andes. Although the land is farther south than Patagonia, the climate is milder than that of the immediate mainland. It supports an active sheep industry.

The name Tierra del Fuego may have originated in a native custom. The Indians signalled each other by means of fire. They used torches when hunting birds at night. Either of these customs might have been the source of the expression Tierra del Fuego. There are no active volcanoes that could have served as a basis for the name. Since it is a land of dense fogs of frequent occurrence, it may be that the smoke-like appearance of the fog suggested the name.

THE MONTE

Regional characteristics. West of the Pampa, Argentina consists principally of arid plains and mountains, a region quite similar to the dry west of the United States. Isolated mountains rise here and there above the flat, sandy, and scantily populated plains. This area is known as the Monte. The picturesque Sierras de Córdoba, having somewhat the character of our Colorado Highlands in the United States, illustrate the nature of the inviting mountains in this region. On the lowlands the summer temperatures are high but diminish in the rising ground of the highlands. In the uplands there are many fertile valleys watered by mountain streams. Some of these streams extend beyond the piedmont areas. Extensive systems of canals that supply the water needed to irrigate nearly a million acres of land have been constructed. Dams have been built to provide a uniform amount of water for crops and for human consumption. In the Córdoba hills is the Dique San Roque, the largest in the republic, having a water capacity of 200,000,000 cubic meters. On the lowlands the irrigated districts, or oases, are the chief centers of human activity. Here vast areas are utilized for the production of grapes, various fruits, alfalfa, and sugar.

Viticulture. The cultivation of wine grapes is confined largely to the province of Mendoza and its adjoining neighbor, San Juan. In these two provinces some 240,000 acres are devoted to the production of wine grapes, and 10,000 acres additional to table and raisin grapes, representing about 75 per cent of the vineyard acreage of Argentina. Besides San Juan and Mendoza, important vineyards are found in the irrigated regions of Salta, Catamarca, La Rioja, and Río Negro.

Viticulture and the production of wine are among the leading industries in Argentina. Argentina ranks fifth among the wine-producing nations of the world, its average annual output being 130 to 160 million gallons.

NORTHWESTERN ARGENTINA

Sugar the most important crop. In the northwestern part of Argentina, including the provinces of Tucumán, Jujuy, and Salta, sugar is the most important crop. Approximately 75 per cent of the republic's production of sugar is grown in Tucumán, largely under irrigation. It is interesting to note that the refining of cane sugar is one of the leading industries of Argentina, and that production about equals consumption.

"Garden spot" of Argentina. The province of Tucumán is repeatedly referred to as the "garden spot" of Argentina. It is the smallest province of the republic, but one of the most fertile. The entire northern and western portion is mountainous, while the southeastern area is flat and very rich. On the west the massive Anconquija Mountain rises to an elevation of some 17,000 feet. On its slopes the climate is temperate in summer and cold in winter. The valleys and plains are hot and humid in summer and mild in winter. Tropical vegetation abounds on the lower

Courtesy L. Hites.

Fig. 66. Northwestern Argentina, province of Salta. A street scene in a typical mountain town.

mountain slopes. In the valleys and plains are excellent pastures and agricultural lands. The fields support 350,000 cattle, while thousands of acres are devoted to sugar, rice, tobacco, corn, and alfalfa. Orange and lemon orchards flourish, and various other fruits and vegetables are grown. Rainfall is frequent, and numerous mountain torrents and streams bring ample water to the lowlands.

Pastoral activities. Western Argentina, including the Monte and the northwest, is also an important pastoral region. In number of cattle this area ranks second to the Pampa. Unimproved Criollo or native stock still predominate, while 95 per cent of the cattle in the Pampa are improved. For the most part, the area is far too barren and rocky and subject to long periods of dry weather which prohibit the development of the cattle industry on a large scale. In general, goats and sheep are better suited for this region and are found here in great numbers. There is a zone with sufficient rainfall that extends north and south and includes most of the province of San Luis and a part of Santiago del Estero where the raising of pure-bred stock is successful.

NORTHEASTERN ARGENTINA

Regional divisions. Northeastern Argentina consists of the national territories of Chaco, Formosa, and Misiones, and the province of Corrientes. The eastern portion of this region is, in general, humid, subtropical, and predominantly flat, while the western half varies from what is virtually desert and bush country of low relief to forest-covered mountainous terrain.

The lands of northern Argentina lying immediately west of the Paraná River, consisting of the territories of Chaco and Formosa, are a part of the Gran Chaco. The Chaco includes, in addition to these parts of Argentina, the bordering lands of Paraguay and part of Bolivia. In the fork of the Paraná and Uruguay Rivers, including the territory of Misiones and the provinces of Corrientes and Entre Rios, lies the fertile Argentine Mesopotamia.

Gran Chaco. The Gran Chaco, meaning hunting ground, is bordered on the north by the Chiquitos Plateau, on the east by the Brazilian Highland, on the west by the piedmont ranges of the Andes, and in the south it merges with the Pampa. Like the Pampa, it is a part of the Paraná-Paraguay Plain, representing an Atlantic embayment filled with debris from the adjacent highlands. This is the only region of the world in which quebracho is found in sufficient quantities to warrant commercial exportation. The development of this industry has been the chief reason for the colonization of the area. There are several types of quebracho—meaning "Break Axe"—but the important types are *quebracho blanco* and *quebracho colorado*. The latter, red quebracho, contains the highest percentage of tannin. The trees are widely scattered, thus adding to the difficulty of transporting the logs to the tannin factories or commercial centers. Quebracho logs, or *rollizos,* are also extensively employed for other purposes, such as railway ties, fence posts, construction timber, cabinet work, and interior decoration. They are among the most durable and heaviest woods known and will take an excellent polish. It has been estimated that the present consumption is about 300,000 metric tons per year, and that existing resources amount to some 150,000,000 metric tons. On this basis the supply should be assured for many years even if not replanted. About 40 years is required to grow the timber to a commercial state.

Besides producing quebracho, these northern lands are the centers of the cotton cultivation in Argentina. More than 90 per cent of Argentina's home-grown cotton is produced here. Reports state that the cost of cotton produced in Argentina is about one-third less than in our own country, and that the yield per acre is greater and the length of fiber is superior.

Mesopotamia. The northeastern extension of Argentina, known locally as Mesopotamia, a fertile region lying between the Uruguay and the Paraná Rivers, has many interesting features. The territory of Misiones produces annually 10,000 tons of yerba maté, which represents one-tenth of the amount consumed in Argentina. Paraguay and Brazil supply Argentina annually with another 90,000 tons. Daily more than 15 million persons in South America drink this tea.

The lack of natural advantages of favorable climate, topography, and soils has decidedly retarded the pastoral development of these northern frontiers of Argentina. The greater part of the area has a hot and humid climate. This renders present breeds of livestock, particularly cattle, susceptible to disease. There are many cattle in these lands, but the industry is still primitive. Development, however, both in agriculture and livestock, is rapidly making its way northward along the Paraná.

One of the most fascinating features of Misiones is the famous Iguassú Falls, located in the northwestern corner of the territory, where Argentina borders on Paraguay and Brazil. They are on the Iguassú River, just above its junction with the Paraná. The falls are 13,123 feet wide and 200 feet high. Niagara Falls is but 5,249 feet wide and 150 to 164 feet high. The potential hydroelectric power of Iguassú is stupendous, a factor that may eventually remove some of the present fuel difficulties of Argentina. At present the falls are not easily accessible, and it is possible that their scenic beauty will prevent their exploitation.

MINERAL RESOURCES

Within recent times Argentina's mineral industry has greatly expanded; new mineral deposits have been discovered; abandoned mines have been reopened; and new concentration plants have been built. Their development is due to favorable prices, an increasing domestic demand, and a reduction in foreign imports of mineral products. Now common salt is produced in sufficient quantities from salt beds in several provinces to meet the nation's needs. The production of gypsum, a material required in the country's growing cement industry, has increased. Other important nonmetallics showing an increase in production are borates, quartz, mica, graphite, feldspar, and the stones and earths, such as sand, clay, limestone, granite, marble, and fuller's earth. The metallic mineral increase is even greater. Tungsten, zinc, lead, tin, and silver have been doubled in production in less than five years. With respect to petroleum, Argentina's production, some 20,000,000 barrels a year, meets more than 60 per cent of its oil requirement. While it is impossible to predict the future of Argentina's mineral industry, nevertheless the recent development has given the nation greater confidence and the enthusiasm to continue to expand, with at least the possibilities of meeting more and more the national demands.

The nation's most basic problem with reference to mineral resources is the lack of good coal and a still inadequate supply of petroleum. Argentina is seriously concerned with its dependence on foreign suppliers of fuel. Plans call for further exploration and drilling and for the erection of new refineries. Progress is being made on the construction of a pipe line to bring gas from the oil and gas fields of Patagonia to Buenos Aires. A small amount of lignite has been shipped from southern Patagonia but the success of the project is uncertain. The attempt to free Argentina from its dependence upon imported fuel through the development of hydroelectric power is still primarily in the planning stage.

The Government under its Five-Year-Plan has numerous hydroelectric projects in its future plan. For the most part the sites for possible hydroelectric plants are in distant localities, chiefly in the foot hills of the Andes. At present 80 per cent of the nation's total electric-power production is generated in the Province of Buenos Aires. In 1949, 3 per cent of the total power output was hydroelectric, 14 per cent was produced in Diesel-operated plants, and 83 per cent was generated by steam turbines.

CHAPTER X

ARGENTINA: TRANSPORTATION AND TRADE

TRANSPORTATION

Railways. A number of conditions in Argentina have favored the construction and the extension of railways. Much of the land is broad and flat and slightly undulating, a condition that does not exist in any other country of South America. Mountains and broad rivers are lacking. The coast is accessible nearly everywhere. The presence of the great La Plata indentation and the invigorating climate have stimulated railway development. The republic not only ranks first among the Latin American nations in railway mileage (27,000 miles) but also compares favorably with the great nations of the world in ratio of mileage to area.

Argentina, however, is not entirely free from obstacles in the path of railway development. In many places, particularly on the Pampa, there is a disconcerting lack of roadbed material. Stone, gravel, and other ballast are shipped into the consuming areas at great expense. Lumber for railway ties and bridges is obtained from extreme northern parts of the republic, from the Andean districts, or from overseas. Some lumber for the railways now comes from the Pampa itself, but not nearly enough. The whole region was originally unwooded, but much forestation has been accomplished during the past 50 years. The Pampa now furnishes a supply of acacia posts and some softwood.

The fuel bill is an important item of operating expense on Argentine railways. The source of supply is far distant, and the cost is therefore high. Argentina has coal deposits along the slopes of the Andes, but it has not yet been found practical to develop them on a commercial basis. They lie at a great distance from centers of population, and their value is doubtful. Consequently Argentina must import her coal, practically all of it from the United States and Great Britain. In recent years the use of oil for fuel in locomotives has rapidly increased. A large proportion of the 20,000,000 barrels of oil produced in Argentina is used for railway fuel.

The first railway in Argentina was ready for operation in 1857. The line extended for a distance of 6 miles from Buenos Aires to Flores, a suburb. The equipment used in the construction of this first railroad is said to have consisted of material that had been destined for use in the Crimean War. It was broad gauge, or 5 feet 6 inches. Because of this trivial initial incident the broad gauge came into general use in subsequent railway construction. It has been extended until 15,000 miles of broad-gauge railway out of a total mileage of 27,000 now exist in the country. The broad-gauge systems cover the center and south of the republic, reaching also as far north as Tucumán. Other gauges are in use, however, particularly the standard—56½ inches—and one-meter gauges.

Courtesy International Telephone and Telegraph Corporation.

Fig. 67. The famous Statue of "Christ of the Andes." Erected in commemoration of the peaceful and friendly establishment of the international boundary between Chile and Argentina. In the foreground is the trans-Andean telephone cable. It crosses the divide in front of the statue at an elevation of more than 13,000 feet above sea level—the highest international telephone line in the world.

Standard-gauge lines lie chiefly in the region between the Uruguay and Paraná Rivers and have direct access to Buenos Aires. The one-meter railways are found in the northwest of the country and also have access to Buenos Aires as well as to the Pampa, and to Bolivia. Since lines of all three gauges have access to the chief ports and commercial centers, only a little transshipment of freight is necessary, and the inconvenience of three different gauges is reduced to a minimum.

No other country in the Western Hemisphere except the United States is so adequately served by railways as Argentina. Lines of the central network extend to all parts of the Pampa and to the far north and west of the country. A north-south line between Bahía Blanca and Rosario joins the western area of the system. There are railway connections between Argentina and her five neighbors: the trans-Andean route "from coast to coast" when in operation, via Mendoza, Argentina, and Los Andes, Chile; the new trans-Andean lie between Salta and Antofagasta, Chile; the Bolivian route, via Tucumán, Argentina, and Uyuni, Bolivia; the Paraguay route between Buenos Aires and Asunción, Paraguay, via Posadas, Argentina, and Encarnación, Paraguay; the Brazilian route via Uruguaiana, Brazil; and the Uruguay connections, of which there are four along the border.

Completion of the railway joining the Argentinian city of Salta and the Chilean seaport of Antofagasta constitutes one of the significant transportation developments in South America, as it offers northwestern Argentina direct outlet to the Pacific. Another important advance in railway transportation was made by the purchase of the former British-owned railways by the Government of Argentina. This acquisition is an evidence of the trend in Argentina toward complete centralized government control of rail transportation.

The southern lands of Argentina are served by four railways radiating from the coast to serve agricultural and sheep-raising districts and petroleum fields. They are the San Antonio Railway, the Central Chubut Railway, the Comodoro Rivadavia Railway, and the Puerto Deseado Railway. All of these lines are located in a region that is mainly semiarid in character. Sheep raising is the principal industry, except in the vicinity of Comodoro Rivadavia, where the production and transportation of petroleum are the chief activity. Irrigation projects and experimental farms are making possible increases in various agricultural products.

Highways. Until recently highways in Argentina were built primarily as feeders to railroads. For the most part they were natural earth roads, passable only in dry weather. Today conditions have been greatly improved, but wet weather still gives trouble.

A few years ago the National Highway Law was drafted along lines very similar to the United States Federal Highway Law. It recognizes that highways are an aid to national progress. Since the establishment of this point of view, records show that Argentina has made considerable strides in highway construction. There are some 250,000 miles of road, and while most of this mileage consists of dirt roads, there are also many miles of excellent all-weather roads such as the highway between Buenos

Aires and Mar del Plata and Córdoba via Rosario. Roads also project to outlying districts, namely Mendoza, and from there over the Andes into Chile; to Bahía Blanca and then down the coast to Puerto Gallegos, far south in Patagonia, near the Straits of Magellan; and northwest from Buenos Aires to Salta, Tucumán, and Jujuy.

Lack of conveniently located road-building materials constitutes one of Argentina's chief problems. Deposits of sand, gravel, and rock suitable for road construction are found only at great distances from the more populous areas. The cost of transportation is high. Large amounts of

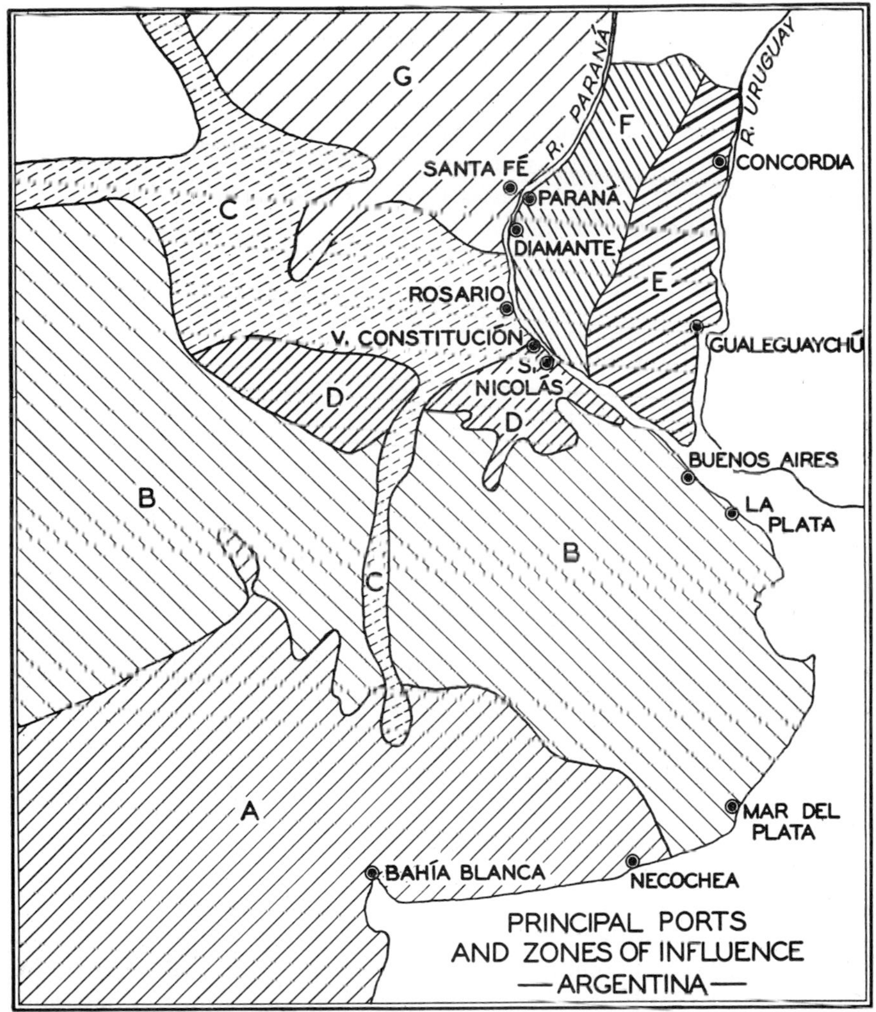

Fig. 68. A generalized pattern of trade regions and ports. Note the relation between transportation facilities and trade regions.

material are imported, mostly from Uruguay. Such materials as asphalt and cement are produced in Buenos Aires.

Shipping facilities. The harbors of Argentina have been improved to meet the growing needs of the nation's shipping. The chief ports are Buenos Aires, Rosario, Bahía Blanca, La Plata, Santa Fé, and San Nicolás.

Buenos Aires, located on the La Plata, is by far the most important exporting and importing center. Two dredged channels lead from the main channel to Buenos Aires. Frequent dredging is necessary to keep these channels open for ocean ships. The total water front of the port is about five and a quarter miles, and the total length of wharves and quays is more than 11 miles. Puerto Nuevo (the new section of the port) has quite modern accommodations for ships and the handling of cargo. The Riachuelo, or original port, is the older section. It is tortuous, and some of its quays have rotted away. The river needs straightening and dredging, and the quays need reconstructing. Puerto Madero (the enclosed-dock section) is too constricted for the operation of the large ocean vessels.

About 40 miles southeast from Buenos Aires, near the entrance from the sea, stands the important shipping center of La Plata. This port is one of the leading packing centers of South America. Here are located the Argentine branches of such American houses as Armour and Company and Swift and Company. Great quantities of grain and meat products are exported to European cities from La Plata. The harbor is readily accessible to large ocean ships.

Rosario is located on the Paraná River, some 200 miles upstream from Buenos Aires. It is the second most important port from the standpoint of trade, being surpassed only by Buenos Aires. It is the nation's chief grain port. Eight railways enter the city from different directions, although most of these roads come from the westward-lying grain fields; this partly explains why Rosario is the chief wheat port of northern Argentina. Ocean-going vessels have no difficulty in reaching Rosario, but above this port the Paraná is not deep enough for ships drawing more than 20 feet of water. A few vessels from the United States enter the port, but most of the seagoing commerce is handled by British, Dutch, Norwegian, and other foreign operators. In addition to the ocean trade, there are many small vessels that come to Rosario from upstream towns such as Suárez, Asunción, Santa Fé, and other river ports.

Bahía Blanca, located at the southern margin of the Pampa, on the Atlantic coast, is 534 miles from Buenos Aires. This is one of the most important wheat centers of Argentina. The Buenos Aires Great Southern, a broad-gauge railway, enters the city. One branch of this great railway extends from Bahía Blanca 500 miles westward to the Neuquén oil fields at the foot of the Andes.

The port of Bahía Blanca consists of five sub-ports: Puerto Belgrano, Puerto Ingeniero White, Puerto Galvan, Puerto Militar, and Puerto Cuatrero. Wheat shipments are made largely from Puerto Ingeniero White and Puerto Galvan. These sub-ports are modern and are equipped with all the latest facilities for loading and discharging ocean vessels. Puerto Ingeniero White is the port of the city proper.

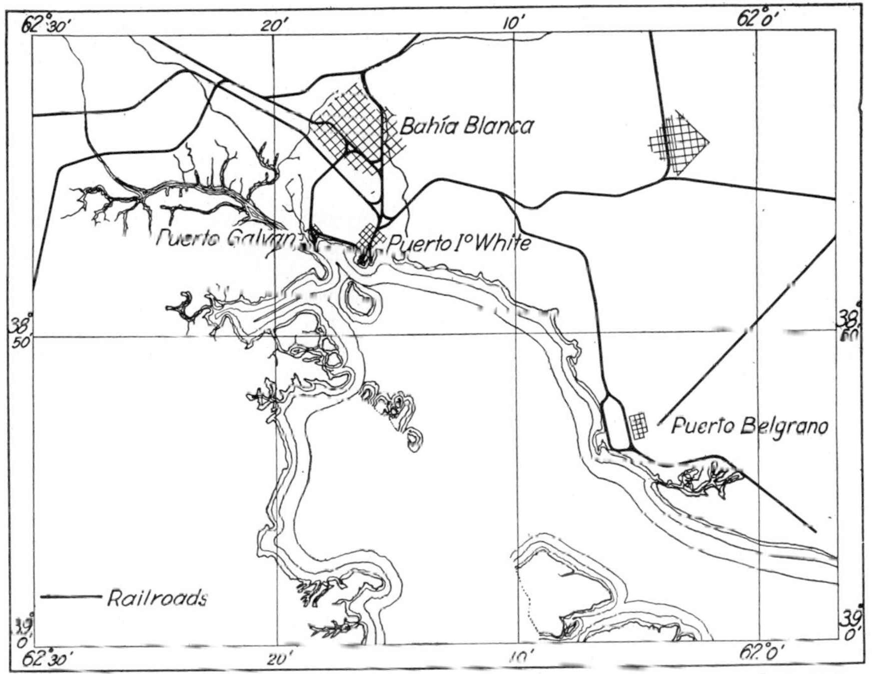

Fig. 69. Bahía Blanca, Argentina.

FOREIGN TRADE

Records of Argentine exports indicate the predominance of agricultural and pastoral products in export trade. Wheat, corn, and linseed are the principal agricultural exports; chilled beef, wool, and hides lead among the livestock exports; and quebracho extract is the chief forest export.

United Kingdom, consuming wheat, corn, and meat products, is Argentina's principal customer—as might be expected of a country that produces only a small part of its foodstuffs—and demands the reciprocal purchase of fuel and manufactured goods. The United States, not a big buyer as compared to the United Kingdom, is Argentina's best market for linseed, hides, and quebracho, and is itself an exporter of wheat and meat. American imports of preserved meat from Argentina have increased. These consist of canned or prepared meat, because the quarantine regulations prohibit the entry of fresh meat. Other countries buying goods in large quantities from Argentina are France, Italy, Belgium, and the Netherlands.

ARGENTINA: EXPORTS OF PRINCIPAL COMMODITIES *

Commodity	*Unit of Quantity*	*Quantity 1947*	*1948*	*Value in Thousands of Dollars* † *1947*	*1948*
Total Exports				1,639,359	1,718,020
				Percentage of Total Value	
Grains and Products ...	Metric Tons ‡	6,193,000	6,132,000	38.5	48.0
Meat	"	687,000	508,000	13.9	11.9
Hides	"	147,000	175,000	6.5	7.6
Wool	"	172,000	182,000	5.9	7.5

* Source: Office of International Trade, U. S. Department of Commerce. Washington, D. C. 1950.

† Values computed on the official buying rate. Exchange value of the peso is $0.2978 in U. S. currency (Jan. 1950). At par one paper peso equalled $0.4245 U. S. gold at former gold parity of the dollar. There are various selling rates ranging from $0.2680 to $0.0860 in U. S. currency. The sign for the paper currency—"moneda nacional"—is m $ n.

‡ One metric ton equals 2,204.62 lbs. avoirdupois.

AGRICULTURAL EXPORTS
(Metric Tons)

	1948	*1949*
Wheat	2,148,623	1,836,836
Corn	2,520,771	1,081,434
Oats	81,554	191,894
Barley	665,882	198,309
Rye	186,858	196,091

The United States ranks first in the Argentinian markets with respect to foodstuffs, tobacco and tobacco products, silk and rayon manufactures, petroleum and allied products, lumber and wood manufactures, machinery (including electrical implements), automobiles, rubber tires, paper, and leather manufactures. Among the chief commodities supplied by the United Kingdom are coal, railway equipment, wearing apparel, tin and copper manufactures, and miscellaneous household goods.

In 1948, the United Kingdom absorbed 35 per cent of Argentina's total exports, based on value, while the United States took nearly 10 per cent, and Continental Europe largely the balance. In the same year the United States supplied 38 per cent of Argentina's imports and the United Kingdom, 15 per cent.

Buenos Aires is the leading port of entry, handling about 85 per cent of the nation's imports. Other ports, within the first ten, are Campana, Rosario, Bahía Blanca, Villa Constitución, La Plata, Santa Fé, Posadas, General Uriburu and Ibicuy. Among Argentina's 50 exporting centers, the first ten are, in order of importance based on value, Buenos Aires (40 per cent), Rosario (18 per cent), La Plata (8 per cent), Santa Fé, Bahía Blanca, General Uriburu, San Nicolás, Necochea (Quequén), Diamante, and San Lorenzo.

ARGENTINA: FOREIGN TRADE

	Total Value	*Percentage of Total*					
Exports	*(000 Dollars)*	United States	Canada	Latin America	United Kingdom	Continental Europe	All Others
1938	409,212	8.5	0.5	11.1	32.8	44.6	2.5
1947	1,639,359	9.9	0.6	12.2	30.0	39.7	7.5
Imports							
1938	428,186	17.4	1.3	11.4	20.1	39.5	10.3
1947	1,307,708	45.3	2.4	13.6	8.3	23.6	6.8

Major problems. Land tenure is one of the major problems confronting Argentina. More than 17,000,000 acres of the farm land—nearly 30 per cent of the total—are in estates of 25,000 acres or over. As a result, laborers, both immigrant and native, find it difficult if not impossible to acquire small holdings at prices within their financial range.

Inadequate transportation facilities constitute another major problem—one that is closely associated with the peon labor situation. Argentina needs a more complete network of highways to link farm and city and to unite the country more solidly. Small farmers and homesteaders need support to free them from dependence on the railway companies. Better means of transportation would stimulate ruralization and tend to reduce existing urban problems in the highly congested city of Buenos Aires. An inadequate domestic output of petroleum and the lack of available coal constitute major national limitations.

SELECTED REFERENCES

Bunge, A. E.: "Seventy Years of Argentine Immigration," *Bulletin of the Pan American Union,* Vol. 62 (1928), pp. 1026–1034.

Church, J. E. and others: "In Argentina Tierra Del Fuego," *Geographical Review,* Vol. XXXVIII, No. 3 (1948), pp. 392–413.

Davis, Floyd E.: "Wool and Its International Importance," *Foreign Agriculture,* Vol. XII, No. 9 (1948), pp. 187–191.

De Martonne, Emm: "The Andes of the North-West Argentine," *Geographical Journal,* Vol. 84 (1934), pp. 1–16.

Egoroff, P. P.: *Argentina's Agricultural Exports During World War II,* Stanford University Press, Palo Alto, 1945.

Jefferson, M.: *Peopling the Argentine Pampa* (Research Series, No. 16), American Geographical Society, New York, 1926.

Koy, L. L.: "The Andean Lakes of Argentina," *Bulletin of the Pan American Union,* Vol. LXII (1928), pp. 365–374.

Platt, R. S.: "Perovano: Items in the Argentine Pattern of Terrene Occupancy,"

Annals of the Association of American Geographers, Vol. 21 (1931), pp. 215–237.

Reid, W. A.: *In Yerba Maté Forests of South America* (Commodities and Commerce Series, No. 4), Pan American Union, Washington, D. C., 1934.

Reilly, J. J. S.: "Buenos Aires, The Heart of Argentina," *Bulletin of the Pan American Union,* Vol. LXV (1931), pp. 221–231.

Rudolph, W. E.: "Southern Patagonia as Portrayed in Recent Literature," *Geographical Review,* Vol. XXIV (1934), pp. 251–271.

Schmieder, Oscar: "The Historic Geography of Tucumán," *University of California Publications in Geography,* Vol. II, No. 12, Berkeley, Cal., 1928, pp. 359–386.

Schmieder, Oscar: "The Pampa—A Natural or Culturally Induced Grassland?" *University of California Publications in Geography,* Vol. 11, No. 8, Berkeley, Cal., 1927, pp. 255–270.

Semple, A. T.: "Grasslands of Argentina," *Agriculture in the Americas,* Vol. V, No. 4 (1945), pp. 70–72.

Shaw, Earl B.: "Geographical Aspects of United States Argentine Relations," *Journal of Geography,* Vol. 46, No. 4 (1947), pp. 136–146.

Taylor, Carl C.: *Rural Life in Argentina,* Louisiana State University Press, Baton Rouge, 1948.

Tower, W. S.: "The Pampa of Argentina," *Geographical Review,* Vol. V (1918), pp. 293–315.

White, Langdon C.: "The Argentina Meat Question," *Geographical Review,* Vol. XXXV, No. 4 (1945), pp. 634–646.

Wylie, Kathryn H.: "Food Possibilities in Latin America," *Agriculture in the Americas,* Vol. VI, No. 9 (1946), pp. 135–138.

CHAPTER XI

URUGUAY: A LAND OF UNIFORMITY

Physical conditions. Uruguay is a country of few contrasts. The character of its land, climate, vegetation, people, and human activities is homogeneous. It is a small republic of some 72,153 square miles, one-sixteenth the size of its neighbor, Argentina, or about the area of Ohio and Indiana combined. The population of Uruguay is 2,295,000, or one-eighth that of Argentina. Almost 90 per cent of the surface consists of an undulating upland traversed by numerous streams draining into the Uruguay River, the Río de la Plata, or Lake Mirim. The eastern and southern borders are covered by a thin veneer of coastal sediments, while in the northwest the surface of the old crystalline upland passes beneath a lava plateau. In the north and west is a rolling area of moderate ruggedness. Most of the land is arable and well adapted for grazing and agricultural enterprises. The country is quite compact, almost circular in shape. Lying within the intermediate latitudes and just south of the thirtieth parallel, it has a delightful climate with warm summers and mild winters. The months of December, January, and February are about as warm as the summers of Virginia, while the winters are not so cold as Virginia winters. There are no extremes of high or low temperatures. The monthly and areal distribution of rainfall is fairly uniform throughout the country.

Rural activities. The raising and marketing of cattle and sheep constitute the major industries. Approximately 90 per cent of the land available for pasturage and agriculture is devoted to grazing, while only 7 per cent is employed in tilled agriculture. Unlike Argentina, Uruguay does not possess a deep rich soil. Until recently, comparatively little attention has been given to the cultivation of crops. Furthermore, Uruguay does not have vast areas of virgin land as its southern neighbor does. Most of the land of Uruguay is already utilized, largely for pastoral purposes.

Excellent natural forage, favorable climate, and the people's love for pastoral activities have placed Uruguay among the leading livestock nations of the world. Uruguay possesses the largest proportion of livestock to human population of any country in the Western Hemisphere.

There are eight million cattle and 22 million sheep, and a human population of 2,295,000. Compare this with the United States. Our population is about 150,000,000, and we have 78 million cattle and 34 million sheep according to the 1950 census.

HARVESTS IN CROP YEAR 1947–48

Product	*Area Sown Hectares (2.47 Acres)*	*Production Metric Tons (1.102 Short Tons) Estimate*
Wheat	526,045	456,909
Flaxseed	222,806	97,950
Corn	206,080	152,985
Sunflower Seed	79,375	44,556
Oats	64,918	37,950
Barley	20,896	13,059
Peanuts	17,766	12,131
Rice	13,372	43,715
Bird Seed	2,479	775

Uruguay has shown a marked interest in bettering the quality of its animals by importing stock from abroad. This interest has been developed largely under the influence of American meat-packing companies that have established stockyards and packing houses in the republic. Uruguayans, however, have given little attention to the shelter and feeding of livestock. The great majority of the ranchers allow their herds simply the natural forage secured by grazing on the land. They do not provide the cultivated succulent alfalfa that is so extensively used in Argentina, and the animals are seldom given shelter. In Uruguay there is a marked absence of elaborate estates similar to those found in Argentina. Cattle are raised almost entirely for beef. The dairy industry is beginning to develop. Such interest as has been shown in dairy cattle of late has been initiated largely by German and Swiss settlers.

The trend, however, is from extensive cattle ranching toward intensive agriculture and dairying. During the past few years it has been more profitable to grow plants, particularly wheat and flaxseed, than to utilize the land only for pasturage. Crop agriculture has been encouraged, also, through Government loans and subsidies. Furthermore, in recent years, owing to the high price of wool, it has been found more profitable to raise sheep than cattle.

People. One of the most distinctive characteristics of Uruguay is its racial homogeneity. More than 90 per cent of its inhabitants are classed as white, predominantly of Spanish descent, while some 10 per cent are Indians, mestizos, and Negroes. In the course of a century and a half the population of Uruguay has increased from 30,000 to more than 2 million. Previous to 1900 most immigrants came from Spain. In recent years a considerable number have arrived from Italy. At present, the rate of increase of Uruguay's population is about 25,000 per year.

URUGUAY: TEMPERATURE AND RAINFALL OF SELECTED STATIONS

	Station	Monte-video *	Mercedes †	Livramento ‡	Santa Vitória do Palmar (Brazil) ‡
	Elevation (*Feet*)	96	128.0	689.0	16.0
Average Temperature (°F.)	*Period of Record*	1921–30	10 yrs.	7 yrs.	7 yrs.
	January	72.9	75.4	74.6	72.4
	February	73.2	74.5	72.6	72.7
	March	70.1	72.0	68.6	68.2
	April	62.8	63.0	66.4	66.4
	May	55.8	55.4	60.1	59.8
	June	50.7	50.0	53.8	52.6
	July	50.4	50.7	55.7	52.8
	August	52.1	53.6	54.9	53.3
	September	55.0	56.8	59.1	56.5
	October	58.1	61.9	63.0	59.1
	November	65.7	68.5	67.2	64.6
	December	70.3	71.8	72.0	68.9
	Annual	61.4	62.8	64.0	62.3
	Range	22.8	25.4	20.8	19.8
Average Rainfall (*Inches*)	*Period of Record*	1921–30	15 yrs.	7 yrs.	7 yrs.
	January	2.6	3.5	4.5	3.8
	February	3.4	2.0	4.1	4.5
	March	3.9	2.9	6.2	5.3
	April	4.2	4.0	4.3	3.6
	May	3.5	2.4	5.6	5.8
	June	5.0	2.4	3.3	2.4
	July	2.4	2.2	4.6	4.5
	August	4.3	2.6	3.8	4.2
	September	3.4	2.3	5.0	5.5
	October	2.4	3.9	3.8	3.5
	November	3.2	2.4	3.7	3.3
	December	4.1	3.5	3.9	3.4
	Annual	42.4	34.3	52.9	49.9

* H. Helm Clayton: World Weather Records. Smithsonian Miscellaneous Collections. Vol. 90—1934.

† K. Knoch: "Klimakunde von Südamerika," *Handbuch der Klimatologie*, Band II, Teil G, Berlin, 1930.

‡ W. W. Reed: "Climatological Data for Southern South America," *Monthly Weather Review*, Supplement No. 32, 1929.

Urban centers. Montevideo, the capital city, stands on gently rising ground on the east side of a large bay. The port occupies a rocky peninsula a mile and a quarter long, east and west, and a half mile wide. Large ocean ships have access to the port, which has railway communication with all important sections of the republic. Daily steamship service is maintained with Buenos Aires, located 125 miles west. Montevideo is considered a transit port and is equipped with excellent facilities for dispatch. There are some 24,500 feet of quay space and ample depth for ocean vessels, good warehouses, rail connections to the interior, and water facilities for river transfer to Asunción and elsewhere on the

Courtesy Pan American Union.

Fig. 70. Avenida 18 de Julio (date of Uruguay's first constitution), Montevideo.

interior waterways. The port of Montevideo is under government control and is said to be the most efficiently managed port on the east coast of South America.

About 708,200 people, nearly one-third of the total population of the nation, live in Montevideo, the "City of Roses," which is the nation's political and social center. The capital city is modern, progressive, and attractive. Impressive buildings line its broad streets. The city boasts a new 20-million dollar legislative palace. A large office- and apartment-building, recently completed, is one of the highest edifices in South America. Shade trees, numerous plazas, and a profusion of beautiful flowers make this city one of the most charming in South America.

All other centers of population in the republic are virtually small villages in comparison. For the most part they are river ports of less than 50,000 inhabitants; Paysandú and Salto are among the largest.

POPULATION OF PRINCIPAL URBAN CENTERS OF URUGUAY

Montevideo	708,200
Paysandú	50,000
Salto	48,000
Mercédes	33,000
Rocha	28,500
Colonia	10,000

Leading manufactures. Meat-packing houses, called *frigoríficos*, constitute the chief industrial enterprises. Plants owned by Americans, British, and Uruguayans handle 2,500,000 animals annually. *Saladeros*, meat-drying and salting establishments, producing chiefly the jerked beef called *xarque* in Brazil, are among the best-known establishments of the kind in South America. Their products reach nearly all parts of the world. Formerly the saladeros handled all meat exports in the form of jerked beef, but now only some 4,000 animals yearly are used for the making of jerked beef. Montevideo is the center of the meat-packing industry.

In terms of exports, the relative importance of the types of meat products in 1948 was as follows:

Frozen Beef	36,253	metric	tons
Frozen Mutton	3,387	"	"
Canned Meat	16,755	"	"
Dehydrated Meat	5	"	"
Jerked Beef	2,448	"	"

Due to the high price paid for wool, the number of sheep slaughtered in 1948 was below average for previous years. The wool clip, in Uruguay, amounted to more than 68,000 metric tons—greasy wool—in the 1948–49 season, and about 60 per cent of the production was exported to the United States.

The extractive industries in Uruguay are limited largely to the production of construction materials, including sand, stone, gravel, and marble. Semi-precious stones are mined in rather substantial quantities, amounting to more than 70 metric tons annually. The production of glass is increasing, although the specialized glass products of superior quality must still be imported. Beverages and some food products, particularly canned fruits and vegetables, are produced in sufficient quantities to meet local consumption demands. The textile industry includes some 100 mills with 70,000 spindles in the manufacture of woolen yarns, and 40,000 in cotton; 1,250 looms are engaged in the production of woolen fabrics and 1,100 in cotton and rayon. Other manufactures include the paper and paper product industry, printing and publishing, leather and rubber products, and drugs and chemicals.

Transportation. The Río de la Plata, or River Plate, was so named because the earliest Spaniards to enter the estuary believed that along its upper shores would be found great quantities of silver. No such deposits exist. Nor does the stream look like silver. It is a vast, sluggish, muddy inland sea, somewhat funnel-like in shape, through which several great rivers reach the ocean. Studded with emerald-green islands in its upper reaches, it is a "sea" of contrasts—but not of silver!

Into the Río de la Plata flow two great rivers, the Uruguay, 1,000 miles long, and the Paraná, 2,000 miles long. The Paraná also carries the water of the great Paraguay River, 1,500 miles long. These rivers and their tributaries drain the southern half of Bolivia, practically all of Paraguay, the southwestern parts of Brazil, the northern third of Argentina, and the western half of Uruguay, an area roughly 1,600,000 square miles. These rivers have been internationalized, and through them vessels of all five bordering nations may freely navigate.

The Uruguay River is a significant channel of transportation in the western portion of the Republic of Uruguay. It is navigable for vessels of 12 feet draft as far as Concordia, Argentina, and Salto, Uruguay, 240 miles above Buenos Aires. These two ports are joined by ferry service, and from each point railways project to the respective national capitals. Vessels of light draft, less than 12 feet, may navigate beyond Salto to penetrate Brazilian territory.

Uruguay has more than 1,800 miles of railways of standard "American" gauge track, radiating from Montevideo to all parts of the country, and 23,000 miles of highway (5,000 paved).

Like Argentina, the population of Uruguay is concentrated near the coast where means of transportation are adequate, while the scattered interior rural settlements are in need of good roads and rail connections. In 1948 the British-owned railways in Uruguay were purchased by the Uruguayan Government. A similar action was recently exercised in Argentina and other countries in Latin America. Uruguay is served by a number of local and international air lines.

Foreign Trade. The United States continues to be the largest participant in Uruguay's foreign trade. In percentage of Uruguay's total trade, however, the United States showed a decline in 1948 as compared with 1947. Our exports dropped from 43 to 34 per cent, while the United Kingdom, Belgium, India, Canada, Sweden, and France increased their share of exports to Uruguay. In terms of imports the opposite took place; the United States bought more from Uruguay in 1948 than in 1947.

The leading import items in 1947 were raw materials, 28.9 per cent of total imports; dry goods and general merchandise, 9.8 per cent; automotive vehicles, 9.2 per cent; foodstuffs, 8.1 per cent; construction materials, 6.9 per cent; combustibles and lubricants, 6.3 per cent; and live animals, 2.4 per cent.

EXPORTS IN PRINCIPAL COMMODITIES

Items	*1947 Percentage of Total Value*
Wool	43.8
Industrialized Farm Products	17.4
Meat	15.7
Hides and Hair	12.7
Natural Farm Products	4.7
Cloth Products	2.4
Extractive Industries	1.0
Miscellaneous	2.3

The European Recovery Administration has stimulated Uruguay's export trade. A total of $5,000,000 of E.C.A. funds were allotted for purchase of Uruguay's commodities for shipment to Europe. All Uruguayan exports are subject to export permits, a condition that Uruguay will, undoubtedly, continue so long as her foreign trade shows an import balance. There is also control of imports by means of import limits and foreign exchange permits.

URUGUAY: FOREIGN TRADE

	Total Value	*Percentage of Total*					
Exports	*(000 Dollars)*	United States	Canada	Latin America	United Kingdom	Continental Europe	All Others
1938	61,660	4.0	0.3	14.1	26.2	51.8	3.7
1947	162,503	28.6	0.1	7.7	12.3	45.2	6.1
Imports							
1938	61,567	11.7	0.3	19.2	20.4	36.0	12.4
1947	215,108	[illegible]	1.8	31.1	8.3	15.7	4.8

Approximately 95 per cent of Uruguay's imports arrive at Montevideo. Other ports of entry include Rivera, Nueva Palmira, Fray Bentos, Paysandú, Salto, Colonia, Puerto del Sauce, and Carmelo. The leading export centers are Montevideo (80 per cent), Fray Bentos (6 per cent), Rivera, Mercedes, Carmelo, Dolores, Colonia, Puerto del Sauce, Rosario, and some 20 others.

Summary. Homogeneity, in culture and landscape, fully characterizes the progressive Republic of Uruguay. The rural life is mainly one of pastoral activities. Only 7 per cent of the land is cultivated. There is, however, a marked trend toward an increase in crop land. Coal, petroleum, and other essential minerals have not been found in Uruguay, and the supply of forest resources and water power is decidedly limited.

Like many other Latin American countries, the capital of Uruguay is the major political, economic, and social center. And Montevideo is one of the finest cities of Latin America.

SELECTED REFERENCES

De Sherbinin, Betty: *The River Plate Republics.* Coward-McCann, Inc., New York, 1947.

Hudson, W. H.: *The Purple Land,* Dutton, New York, 1927. (Reprinted in several editions.)

Lemert, B. F.: "Uruguay and the Uruguayans," *Journal of Geography,* Vol. XXXIII (1934), pp. 289–303.

Marden, Luis: "The Purple Land of Uruguay," *National Geographic Magazine,* Vol. 94, July–Dec., 1948, pp. 623–654.

"Mining and Manufacturing Industries in Uruguay," *United States Tariff Commission Report, American Republics Series,* Vol. 55, Nos. 1–2, Washington, D. C., 1949.

CHAPTER XII

PARAGUAY: AN INLAND REPUBLIC

A land of many misfortunes. To the northwest of Uruguay on the Paraguay River, entirely surrounded by Argentina, Bolivia, and Brazil, lies the little-known republic of Paraguay, a land of misfortune. From the time that Juan de Ayola and his followers, a remnant of Mendoza's colony, established the settlement of Asunción in 1537, until this day, Paraguay has been a party to international disputes. At the time of independence in 1811 (May 14—Day of Independence—is a national holiday) Paraguay was apparently ready to become a progressive nation. Its territory was large, covered thickly with plantations and cattle ranges. In the middle of the past century a "strong man," Carlos Antonio López, became the first constitutional president. At his death, Paraguay was rich, populous, and progressive—one of the most progressive nations on the continent at the time. His son was a headstrong, foolish tyrant who dreamed of becoming a South American Napoleon.

When Francisco Solano López, the son of the able dictator, attempted to create his empire in the heart of South America with Paraguay as the center, he brought upon his country war with Brazil, Argentina, and Uruguay, a triple alliance. His army was strong and he was an able general, but the other nations overwhelmed him with men. As a result of this bitter and devastating conflict, which lasted five years, from 1864 to 1870, Paraguay was almost annihilated. It was compelled to cede 56,000 square miles of territory to its adversaries. Nearly the entire male population was destroyed, and many of the women and children died of pestilence or starvation. From a prosperous nation of a million inhabitants, Paraguay was reduced to a ragged and hungry few hundred thousand—all because of a foolish tyrant.

It is idle to speculate on what "might have been." But Paraguay has all the natural resources necessary to an important nation, and it once had the men. The entire history of interior South America "might have been" different. It is curious to note, however, that adolescent Paraguayan youth of the present idolize the picturesque López—just as the "big shot" of gangdom is worshipped by some American youth.

Even now Paraguay shows evidence of its destructive past. Eighty years is a short time in which to overcome such a disaster. The nation has had to reconstruct its population and its national economy from the ground up. A marked improvement in its affairs was evident during the ten years preceding 1930, and Paraguay appeared to be on the road to recovery. The per capita purchasing power was increased; national revenue was enlarged; the government established credit abroad; a new port was built; pastoral enterprises were revived with the establishment of packing houses; foreign trade was increased; the general living conditions of its people were improved. The total population was about a million. But again Paraguay entered the field of military conflict in a dispute with Bolivia.

People and area. Unlike Uruguay's inhabitants, who are primarily pure white, the people of Paraguay are descendants of early Spanish settlers and Guarani Indians. Even today, both Spanish and the Guarani tongues are spoken in Paraguay. The Guarani as a pure race is almost extinct; some 8,000 are reported to live in western Paraguay, the Chaco region. Until a few years ago, however, Paraguay increased its foreign-born population at the rate of about a thousand a year. These included Germans, Spaniards, Italians, Austrians, Russians, and French. Some 2,000 Mennonites—the real "children of the earth"—many coming from Canada, have established a settlement 100 miles north of Asunción.

There are comparatively few Negroes in Paraguay. In general, Negroes were brought to the coastal settlements and very rarely sent to the interior. Since Paraguay is an inland country, it was not subjected to the ingression of African slaves as were the coastal lands of Brazil, the Caribbean region, and the United States. Furthermore, slaves were in demand in those regions where agricultural activities required cheap and abundant labor. Wherever crops such as sugar, cotton, and tobacco were staple commodities of a colonial settlement, these areas tended to become centers of a colored population. Paraguay was largely a cattle-raising and forest country, one in which Negroes were not needed. Even today few Negroes in the Western Hemisphere are engaged in the livestock and forest industries. When Paraguay began the cultivation of sugar, cotton, and tobacco under the first López, the importation of Negro slaves had long ceased.

According to official estimates in 1948, the area of Paraguay is 157,000 square miles and the population is 1,165,000. Most of the inhabitants live along the Paraguay and Paraná rivers and the area served by the railroad from the Capital City Asunción to Encarnación. The latter terminal is located on the Paraná river across from Posadas, Argentina. About 16 per cent of the nation's total population lives within the capital city or within a radius of approximately 20 miles of it. Seventy per cent of the Paraguayans are engaged in agricultural or pastoral activities.

POPULATION OF PRINCIPAL URBAN CENTERS OF PARAGUAY

Asunción	150,000
Villarrica	50,000
Concepción	55,000
Encarnación	20,000

Regional pattern. Paraguay is divided into two regions by the broad Paraguay river. To the west is the Chaco, known also as El Chaco Boreal, with an area of 95,300 square miles, and east of the Paraguay river is the Eastern Region, an area of 61,700 square miles. The Chaco region is a low, undulating plain, with a maximum elevation of some 750 feet above sea level, interrupted by great swamps and sluggish rivers. Its surface cover is grasslands, woodlands, and a conspicuous fan-leaf palm, called *carandai.* In the northern portion of the Chaco are forested areas, extending inland from the Paraguay river, from which the country obtains the well known quebracho extract.

The annual precipitation of the Chaco has been estimated at 54 inches. Drought and floods are not uncommon. In the south the average summer temperature is about 72°F., and in the north about 75°F. However, the temperature in summer often rises above 100°F., while in winter it falls at times below freezing. The hot north winds that blow frequently during the summer are probably the most distressing feature of the climate.

El Chaco Boreal in politics. In the heart of South America, a thousand miles from either the Pacific or Atlantic, is El Chaco Boreal, a "disputed territory." For many years it was claimed by Bolivia on the west border and by Paraguay on the east. This sparsely populated region, about twice the size of Uruguay, possesses natural resources, including abundant water, rich soils, virgin stands of the valuable quebracho wood, excellent grasslands, and petroleum. It has the shape of an isosceles triangle, its apex at Asunción, the capital of Paraguay, and its sides running along the Paraguay and Pilcomayo rivers. The Paraguay River divides it from eastern Paraguay, and the Pilcomayo from the republic of Argentina.

For at least a half century El Chaco Boreal, so called in order to distinguish it from the Chaco (Austral) lands of Argentina, has been disputed territory. That it should be claimed by Bolivia and Paraguay, two countries with much in common, is the natural expectation. Both republics share the fate of having no direct access to the sea. Moreover, each has experienced the loss of great portions of its territory as the result of wars with its neighbors.

Bolivia became especially interested in the Chaco after her defeat in the war with Chile (1879–1883), when she lost her Pacific coastline. Since the Paraguay River in eastern Chaco is accessible to fairly large vessels to Bahía Negra and beyond, Bolivia wished to secure a port there and thus have an outlet to the Atlantic. Paraguay was intent upon claiming the territory because it would nearly double her national area. Both countries anticipated that the future development of the region would bring lucrative returns.

PARAGUAY: TEMPERATURE AND RAINFALL OF SELECTED STATIONS

	Station	Asunción *	Villarica *	Corrientes (Argentina)†
	Elevation (*Feet*)	207	433	177.0
Average Temperature (°*F.*)	*Period of Record*	1933–47		39 yrs.
	January	84.9		81.6
	February	83.3		81.2
	March	80.6		78.9
	April	74.1		71.6
	May	70.9		65.6
	June	66.9		61.6
	July	65.7		62.0
	August	69.4		62.8
	September	72.3		67.4
	October	76.6		71.2
	November	79.3		76.0
	December	83.5		80.0
	Annual	75.6		71.7
	Range	19.2		20.0
Average Rainfall (*Inches*)	*Period of Record*	1933–47	1931–40	1901–1920
	January	4.3	4.6	4.2
	February	4.4	5.4	4.3
	March	6.3	5.4	6.0
	April	4.8	8.5	5.6
	May	4.0	7.0	4.0
	June	3.2	4.6	1.8
	July	2.3	4.3	2.1
	August	1.5	2.1	1.6
	September	2.6	4.3	2.7
	October	4.4	5.1	5.0
	November	5.3	5.4	5.2
	December	4.3	6.1	5.9
	Annual	47.4	62.8	48.4

* Paraguay, Dirección General de Estadística, *Memoria,* 1934–1947.

† W. W. Reed: "Climatological Data for Southern South America," *Monthly Weather Review,* Supplement No. 32, 1929.

Another phase of the controversy, one that has added to the accumulation of national bitterness on the part of both Paraguay and Bolivia, is foreign investments. A certain amount of foreign capital invested in tannin-producing and -extract establishments, stock-breeding *estancias*, and petroleum enterprises is at least partially responsible for the present conflict. It appears that the oil possibilities of the Chaco are the chief concern of those working in Bolivia, while in Paraguay the champions of the tannin-extract industry are aroused over the situation.

Although, during the past 75 years, numerous attempts were made by both Bolivia and Paraguay to establish their claims, actual hostilities did not begin until about 1932. They lasted three years. After complete exhaustion by both parties, peace negotiations were set in motion, and in 1938 a treaty of peace was signed in Buenos Aires. Paraguay succeeded in securing most of the disputed area.

Transportation. Paraguay lacks adequate highway facilities. There are about 400 miles of gravel- and 75 miles of macadam-surfaced all-weather roads. It is estimated that there are an additional 4,000 miles of unimproved nonsurfaced roads. One highway extends southeasterly from Asunción for approximately 100 miles to San Ignacio, and plans call for its projection to Encarnación. Another main route joins the Capital City and Villarrica, a distance of 115 miles. In the rural areas the oxcart is the chief means of transportation, while in the cities motor vehicles are much in evidence.

The British-owned Central Railway, a standard gauge running from Asunción to Encarnación, a distance of 274 miles, is the major line in Paraguay. It connects with Argentina's North Eastern Railway by means of a train ferry to Posadas, Argentina. There is through passenger service between Buenos Aires and Asunción. A number of small gauge railroads are operated in the area of quebracho logging along the upper Paraguay River.

Air routes are confined, largely, to two international lines, one Argentine and the other a Brazilian Company, and a domestic line, a Government enterprise under the direction of the Paraguayan Air Force. At present no United States air line operates into Paraguay.

Paraguay is favored with a good river system, the Paraná-Paraguay. It is an international waterway, serving not only Paraguay but also Argentina and Brazil. The Paraná provides transportation for such important cities as Rosario, Sante Fé, and Corrientes, all in Argentina. Vessels of 20-feet draft can navigate as far as Rosario. Above Rosario, vessels of 7-feet draft can move with safety at all times of the year to Asunción. During the period from April to December when there is usually high water, the maximum draft for vessels operating between Rosario and Asunción is 12 feet. Corumbá, a Brazilian city on the

Paraguay River and 1,800 miles from the Atlantic, has regular boat service to Asunción. In favorable seasons vessels of less than 5-feet draft can reach the town of Cuiabá, capital of the State of Mato Grosso, Brazil. The Alto Paraná, generally, is open to navigation by boats of 6-feet draft from Corrientes, Argentina, to Encarnación, Paraguay. Smaller vessels may navigate as far as Porto Mandes, Brazil. Approximately 400,000 metric tons of cargo move over the Paraguay and Paraná rivers annually.

To consider the future development of the La Plata river system, representatives from Argentina, Uruguay, Paraguay, Bolivia, and Brazil have met in conference. These nations, wholly or in part, lie in the Plata drainage basin, an area nearly half that of the United States. The Plata River system is extensively used to carry exports abroad and to the neighboring nations. Owing to customs barriers, freight rates, and currency exchange, the trade among the Plata countries has been greatly restricted. If these obstacles were lowered, Bolivian petroleum and Paraguayan lumber, tobacco, and quebracho extract would move in greater amounts to the southern markets. In return, Uruguay, Brazil, and Argentina could ship grain, meats, textiles, and other products to the land-locked countries. To further this possibility, Argentina, Uruguay, and Brazil have agreed to grant trade concessions to Bolivia and Paraguay.

Resources and Production. The chief resources of Paraguay are agricultural, forest, and pastoral. The leading cash crops are cotton (57,000 bales in 1947); tobacco, another important export crop; and yerba maté, likewise largely exported. Paraguay produces about 10 per cent of the world's supply of yerba maté, also known as Paraguayan tea. Enough sugar is produced for local consumption. Citrus fruits and bananas are shipped to nearby countries in limited quantities because of transportation and handling problems. The livestock industry is another significant activity. It provides meat for local consumption as well as canned meat and hides for exportation. The main food products in the Paraguayan diet are beef, manioc, corn, beans, and onions.

The forest resources of Paraguay are relatively extensive, considering the size of the country and the fact that more than half of the forests have been exploited. Both soft and hard woods prevail. More than 20 per cent of the total world production of quebracho tanning extract is supplied by Paraguay.

According to available records, Paraguay is lacking in mineral resources. However, there has been little field work in search of minerals.

Paraguay has the distinction of leading the world in the production of petitgrain oil, an agent used as a base for some perfumes. The oil is obtained by distillation from the leaves of a species of bitter orange tree.

Other manufacturing in Paraguay consists of small-scale production of beverages, matches, wool and cotton textiles, shoes, leather goods, soap, edible oils, and tobacco products.

Foreign Trade. Paraguay's exports consist almost entirely of agricultural, pastoral, and forest products. Imports are chiefly consumer goods. Argentina is the principal source, followed by the United States, Brazil, and the United Kingdom. Her markets, in order of export values, are Argentina, the United Kingdom, Uruguay, the United States, and Brazil.

The leading exports are cotton, corned beef, slaughterhouse products, cattle hides, quebracho extract, essence of petitgrain, lumber and logs, tobacco, yerba maté, coconut oil, and castor oil. Imports include foodstuffs, textiles, transportation equipment and accessories, ferrous metals and machinery.

The United States imports from Paraguay consist, primarily, of quebacho extract, essence of petitgrain, wild animal skins, canned corned beef, and salted cattle skins and other slaughterhouse by-products. Exports from the United States to Paraguay include metals and metal manufactures, machinery, automotive vehicles and parts, lubricating oil and greases, and pharmaceutical preparations.

PARAGUAY: FOREIGN TRADE

	Total Value	*Percentage of Total*				
Exports	*(000 Dollars)*	United States	Latin America	United Kingdom	Continental Europe	All Others
1938	6,966	12.2	22.8	13.0	23.8	28.2
1947	21,261	2.2	86.6	9.7	0.7	0.8
Imports						
1938	7,584	9.6	42.2	9.6	22.6	16.0
1947	22,033	29.4	52.6	6.0	9.1	2.9

The future. Paraguay may again become an important agricultural nation. Its resources in excellent land are great. Only 1 per cent of the country's total area is cultivated, while approximately 50 per cent is arable land. The government is doing much to encourage native production and to improve marketing methods. Paraguay hopes to meet its own needs through local production of such foodstuffs as butter, potatoes, fresh vegetables, and fruits, now in part imported from Argentina.

Lack of adequate transportation facilities, long distances to markets, high freight rates, the absence of a seaport, a sparse population, a hot summer climate, a low standard of living, and international difficulties are the chief obstacles in the path of Paraguay's development.

SELECTED REFERENCES

Compton, G. C.: "Highway to the Sea," *Americas,* Vol. 1, November, 1949, pp. 16–19.

De Wilde, J. C.: "South American Conflicts," *Foreign Policy Reports,* Vol. IX, No. 6 (1933).

Geneva Research Center: "The Chaco Dispute," *Geneva Special Studies,* Vol. V, No. 2 (1934).

Grubb, W. B.: "The Paraguayan Chaco and Its Possible Future," *Geographical Journal,* Vol. LIV (1919), pp. 157–178.

Johnson, E. C.: "Paraguay Improves Its Agriculture," *Agriculture in the Americas,* Vol. IV, No. 4 (1944), pp. 63–65.

Kerr, G. A.: "The Quebracho Forests of South America," Bulletin of the Pan American Union, Vol. LIV (1922), pp. 9–34.

"Mennonites in Paraguay," *Bulletin of the Pan-American Union.* Vol. 82 (1948), pp. 593–594.

Piers, E. A.: "Latin America, 1948," *Bulletin of Hispanic Studies,* Vol. 26, No. 101 (1949), pp. 3–25.

Ynsfran, P. M.: "Paraguay: Its Discovery and Settlement; Its Two Languages; Its Products and Customs," *Bulletin of the Pan American Union,* Vol. LXV (1931), pp. 1217–1229.

CHAPTER XIII

BOLIVIA: AN INLAND REPUBLIC

Physical features and their geographic significance. Bolivia is an inland nation without a seacoast or seaport of her own. Although located entirely within the low latitudes, the climate, like that of all other Andean countries, is determined more by altitude than by their location near the equator. From many a mountainside one can look down into a succession of temperature zones, each with its associated form of agriculture and native vegetation. At the highest point is the *puna brava*, often covered with ice or snow. Just below is the *puna*, where barley, potatoes, and quinoa grow at altitudes of 11,000 to 12,500 feet. Below that, from 8,000 to 11,000 feet, extends the cabecera de valle, or upper valleys, the region of wheat, rye, barley and oats. Then comes the *valle* zone, from 4,000 to 8,000 feet, with corn and many temperate-zone fruits, followed by coffee, cotton, and sugar cane interspersed with groves of oranges, bananas, and coconuts. And below extends the matted green of the tropical rain forests or savanna grasslands. In fact, a few years ago it was no uncommon experience to see llamas laden with ice from Mt. Illimani standing in the La Paz markets side by side with mules bearing hampers of oranges from the subtropical valleys below the city.

The area of Bolivia has been estimated at 416,000 square miles and its population at 3,788,000. About 40 per cent of the population is composed of Indians, chiefly of the Aymará and Quechua tribes.

About 60 per cent of Bolivia's territory lies in the lowlands of the Amazon and the Paraguay-Paraná River systems. The remaining 40 per cent is high tableland and mountain ranges, constituting the widest part of the Andean region. Four topographical regions predominate—the Cordillera, the Altiplano, the Yungas, and the eastern lowlands.

Cordillera. Two principal mountain ranges extend from northwest to southeast through this territory. On the west, the main Cordillera de los Andes, here known as the Cordillera Occidental, serves as the boundary between Bolivia and its neighbors, Chile and Peru. This range is largely volcanic, and volcanic debris thickly overlies the sedimentary Jurassic and Cretaceous rocks that form this part of the Andes. Passes over this range from the coast are exceedingly high, 12,000 feet or more.

A hundred miles to the east the Cordillera Real rears its frame, extending southward from northern Peru and joining the Cordillera Central. A lower Cordillera lies eastward, the Cordillera Oriental. Several noble peaks are found in the Cordillera Real, the majestic Illimani (21,179 ft.) near La Paz, and Ancohuma (21,484 ft.) and Illampú (21,276 ft.) north of that city. The formations, and those to the east, are formed primarily of Paleozoic rocks, with granitic intrusions.

Deploying from the Cordillera Real, the Cordilleras Central and Oriental extend eastward for 200 miles. In this section of Bolivia

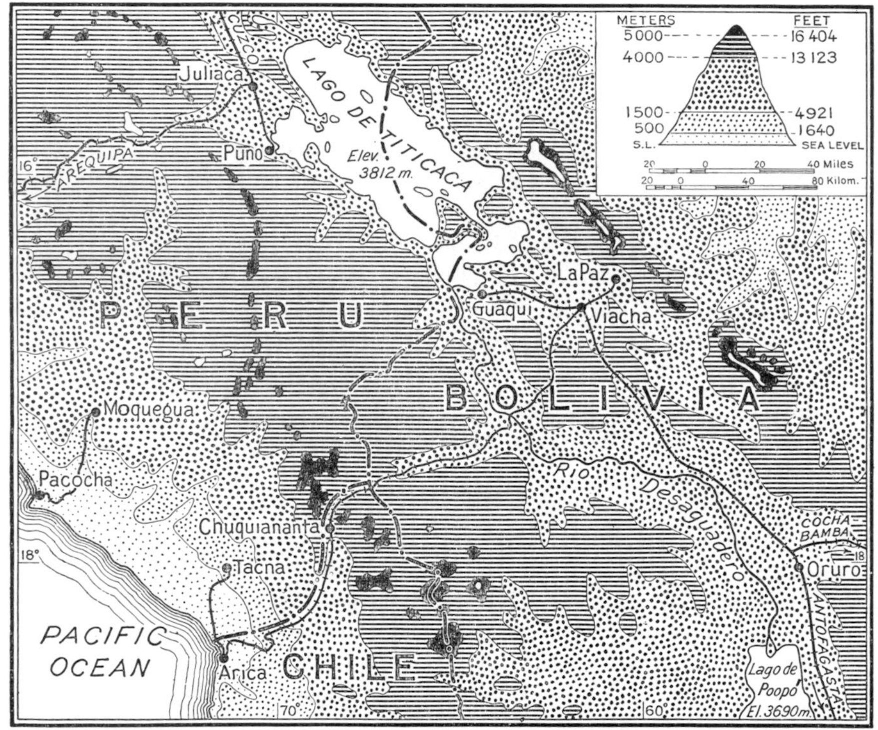

F. A. Carlson. Adapted from map of Hispanic America—American Geographical Society, New York.

Fig. 71. The Altiplano region. The Altiplano is a high and dry interior plateau extending from southern Peru to central Bolivia.

mountain ridges and sierras extend in bewildering confusion, with numerous well-watered valleys between them drained to the northeastward by the headstreams of the Río Mamoré and Río Beni. This area, of perhaps 100,000 square miles, including the Cordillera Real and the ranges to the east, is the great mineral-producing region of Bolivia. Here tin, gold, and silver especially are found. Here population is concentrated. Copper is found in both the eastern and western ranges.

Altiplano. Between the Cordilleras Occidental and Real lies the high tableland known as the Altiplano, 500 miles long and 40 to 60 miles wide. This plateau is covered with fresh-water deposits and volcanic debris penetrated by ridges of red sandstone or Paleozoic, fossil-bearing rocks. Its average altitude is about 12,000 feet, a little higher in the north than in the south. It is an area of interior drainage, the waters from the snows of the Cordillera Real moving to Lake Titicaca, and from that point south, until they finally evaporate in salty desert pans or pass underground.

The altitude of this plateau is too high, and it is too poorly watered in most places, for profitable agriculture. Yet it is here that the Inca civilization developed its massive structures, around Lake Titicaca; and this region, despite its inhospitable character, is still the home of many Indians. They raise potatoes, barley, and a small grain known as quinoa, which is frequently used while still green. Their llamas graze on the almost bare hillsides.

Where erosion has cut depressions in the plateau, as at La Paz, the altitude is lower and moisture is more plentiful. Consequently, vegetation flourishes and cities have developed. Most of the significant population centers of Bolivia are found in valleys such as these.

Yungas. The region, extending eastward from Cordillera Real, is known as the Yungas or Las Yungas.[1] This is the leading agricultural and cattle-raising region in Bolivia. The altitude varies from 8,000 to 4,000 feet or less and the climate is subtropical. A large percentage of the area is heavily forested. As yet most of the region is undeveloped and awaits more adequate transportation facilities.

Lowlands. The eastern land area of Bolivia lying below the Yungas is composed of plains, swamps, jungle, and forest. This is an area of heavy rainfall and sluggish waterways. Consequently, drainage is slow, and much of the land is swampy. In the northern portion of these lowlands, rainfall occurs throughout the year. To the south there is a well-defined wet and dry season. Much land is under water during the rainy season. There is some higher ground, however, with good drainage, where agriculture and stock raising are possible.

The forests of the lowland are rich in rubber trees and tropical hardwoods. In times past, before the era of rubber plantations, the wild product was a significant item in Bolivia's export column.

This part of Bolivia is very thinly populated, most of the inhabitants, except in a few small river towns, being forest-dwelling Indians of whom little is known.

---

[1] The term *Yungas* has not been clearly defined by geographers. Some apply the term to the eastern slopes of the Bolivian Andes, while others employ the term to refer to the narrow subtropical valleys in the Andes east of the Cordillera Real, recorded on maps as Las Yungas.

BOLIVIA: TEMPERATURE AND RAINFALL OF SELECTED STATIONS

	Station	Sucre *	Cochabamba *	La Paz †	La Quiaca * (Argentina)
	Elevation (*Feet*)	9,350	8,448	12,002	11,358
Average Temperature (°*F.*)	*Period of Record*	1915–1923	3 yrs.	1931–40	1901–1920
	January	54.7	65.3	50.5	54.5
	February	54.7	65.8	50.7	54.3
	March	56.5	63.1	50.7	53.4
	April	55.0	62.4	49.6	51.4
	May	52.5	60.1	47.7	42.8
	June	50.0	57.2	45.5	37.4
	July	49.5	59.5	45.1	37.4
	August	52.7	61.3	46.4	42.1
	September	55.6	63.9	48.7	48.0
	October	55.9	67.5	51.4	51.4
	November	58.1	68.0	53.1	54.0
	December	57.2	66.2	52.1	54.7
	Annual	54.3	63.1	49.3	48.4
	Range	8.6	10.8	8.0	17.3
Average Rainfall (*Inches*)	*Period of Record*	1883–1919	1882–1885	1931–40	1901–1920
	January	6.2	4.1	5.3	3.2
	February	5.0	3.8	3.6	2.6
	March	3.7	2.4	2.4	2.0
	April	1.8	0.4	0.9	0.3
	May	0.3	0.4	0.5	0.0
	June	0.1	0.3	0.1	0.0
	July	0.2	0.2	0.2	0.0
	August	0.2	0.2	0.5	0.0
	September	0.8	0.7	1.1	0.0
	October	1.4	0.6	1.1	0.2
	November	2.4	1.3	1.6	1.1
	December	2.4	3.9	3.8	2.1
	Annual	26.2	18.2	21.1	11.3

* Source: K. Knoch, "Kilmakunde von Südamerika," *Handbuch der Klimatologie,* Band II, Teil G, Berlin, 1930.

† H. Helm Clayton: "World Weather Records," *Smithsonian Miscellaneous Collections,* Vol. 105 (1947).

Lake Titicaca. Lake Titicaca, located in the Altiplano region, which belongs partly to Bolivia and partly to Peru, deserves particular mention. It is the highest large lake, without an outlet to the sea, in the world.

Several streams enter it, but only one stream leaves it, the Desaguadero, which empties into Lake Poopó, 180 miles to the south and east. This drainage keeps the water in Titicaca low in mineral salts. Lake Poopó has no surface outlet except in times of high water, when it overflows into a neighboring salt swamp. Lake Titicaca's greatest length is 138 miles and its greatest breadth 69 miles, nearly half as large as Lake Ontario. It lies at an altitude of 12,500 feet above the sea, in a semiarid terrain. Numerous bays, inlets, and peninsulas vary the shore line. Several islands, including those of the Sun and the Moon, of Inca fame, rise above the surface.

Around this lake, Inca tradition is rich, and vast ruins dating both from Inca days and from peoples of pre-Inca times are to be seen. Giant fortresses, palaces, and temples are constructed of stone, which is not found anywhere near at hand. The blocks weigh often 20 tons or more. These structures are located at several points near the lake. The Island of the Sun and the Island of the Moon were particularly sacred places.

Lake Titicaca is important now, not merely because of its intriguing history and its scenic beauty, but because it is a route of passage between Bolivia and Peru. Puno is the Peruvian port at the northern end of the lake, and Guaqui is the Bolivian port at the other end. Puno is the inland terminal of the Southern Peru Railway, the other terminal being the port of Mollendo, on the coast. One important branch of this railway leads to Cuzco, 200 miles northwest of the lake. From Guaqui at the Bolivian side a railway extends to La Paz. From this point Bolivian lines reach southward to all the principal points on the plateau. Farther south they join with the Argentine lines leading to Buenos Aires, and with the Chilean lines leading to the port cities of Arica and Antofagasta.

Improvement in service on Lake Titicaca is part of a plan being developed by both Bolivia and Peru to provide accommodations and service that will attract tourists. Splendid new hotels have been constructed in Cuzco and Mollendo; railway time schedules have been improved; better cars have been put into service; automobile roads have been constructed around Cuzco; and steamship service on the lake itself has been augmented—and now all is in readiness for the advertising to bring the tourist throngs! Bolivia has not been slow to do its part. The federal government has joined with the cities, the hotels, the businessmen, the steamship companies, the railways, and the chambers of commerce in a movement to improve accommodations and to bring the attractions of Bolivia to the attention of both European and American tourists. The Bolivian government has created a Department for the Promotion of Touring. Chile, Argentina, and Brazil have created similar offices.

Population and culture. A government estimate of population shows an average of about 8 persons to the square mile. What this means can be seen by a comparison. Bolivia as a whole is about as thickly populated as Utah, whereas its area of some 400,000 square miles is about 5 times that of Utah, or 10 times the area of Ohio. Her population, however, is only one-half that of the North American commonwealth of Ohio.

Of Bolivia's total population, it is estimated that 500,000 are whites, principally of Spanish descent. A million and a half are Indians, and the remaining 1,500,000 or more are mixed.

There are three principal racial stocks among the Indians of Bolivia: (1) the Aymará and Quechua of the upper plateaus, who formed a highly civilized unit of the Inca empire, and who have become the miners and farmers of present-day Bolivia; (2) the Chiquitos and Mojos Indians of eastern Bolivia, among whom the Jesuits established their famous missions in the seventeenth century, converting them to Christianity and introducing them to the arts of farming and stock raising and simple handicrafts; and (3) the Chiriguanos, a Guarani tribe that moved westward from Brazil long ago and settled on the plateaus and lowlands of southeastern Bolivia. Besides these, there are unknown Indian groups in the jungle who have entered into little or no relationships with the whites.

Urban Centers. Bolivia has no cities that rank in population with Rio de Janeiro or Buenos Aires, or even with Lima or Santiago. In scenic beauty and general interest, however, several of her cities are distinctive.

Principal among them is La Paz,[2] a city of 319,600, situated 60 miles southeast of Lake Titicaca. The only level place in the city is the Plaza de Armas. Around this the government buildings are grouped. Because of its strategic location, it became the most important center of population on the plateau. The main portion of the city lies in a deep, broad canyon with a small stream winding through its center—a stream that becomes a torrent in times of heavy rain. The famous El Alto golf course, which belongs to the city, is located on the upper edge of the canyon at an altitude of more than 13,000 feet. The business section lies a thousand feet down in the canyon. The residential portion of the city lies still farther down, at an elevation of 11,000 feet above the sea. Electric trains and streetcars safely negotiate the hills. Despite the difficulties presented by steep grades in a rarefied atmosphere, automobiles (mostly taxicabs) are numerous.

POPULATION OF PRINCIPAL URBAN CENTERS OF BOLIVIA

La Paz	319,600
Cochabamba	76,500
Oruro	48,000
Potosí	45,000
Sucre	32,000

[2] La Paz—Peace—is named after the Peace of Ayacucha.

The difference in climate at the various levels is surprising. On the unprotected golf course cold winds may howl while the weather is balmy in the city just below. In the residential section and lower down in the valley, palm trees and tropical fruits flourish and frost is unknown.

La Paz is the unofficial capital of Bolivia. All governmental functions except the sessions of the supreme court are held there. In this city are found the government palace and the home of the president, the military and aviation schools and the national university, and the buildings of the various governmental departments. La Paz is also the business and financial center of Bolivia and the terminus of several main lines of its railway system. One line passes northwest to Lake Titicaca, where it connects with the line from Mollendo and Cuzco. Another leads southwest to Arica. One serves the south, with extensions leading to Potosí, Cochabamba, Antofagasta, and Buenos Aires. A short line of 32 miles leads down directly from La Paz into the rich agricultural lands of the valley immediately below the city.

The second city of importance is Cochabamba, 150 miles southeast of La Paz as the crow flies—but two days distant by train—with a population of 76,500. At an altitude of 8,500 feet, surrounded by mountains, it is the center of a rich mining and agricultural section. Its days are warm and its nights cool. Consequently, such temperate-zone forms of vegetation as wheat and corn, as well as some subtropical plants, thrive in the valley.

Sucre [3] is officially the capital of Bolivia, although for all practical purposes La Paz serves in that capacity. Sucre, however, is recognized as the cultural center of the nation. A city of 32,000 people, located 50 miles northeast of Potosí, at an altitude of 9,350 feet, and the home of many wealthy residents, it is a delightful place seldom visited by tourists.

Potosí and Oruro are two mining centers located at high altitudes. They are about the same size, each with a population of some 45,000. The first is situated at the base of the famous Potosí Mountain, which is still rich in silver but is now exploited principally for tin. There are said to be at least 2,000 shafts penetrating its sides. The second city is a center for tin and copper. Both places are situated at high altitudes; Potosí at 14,300 feet and Oruro at 12,000.

Santa Cruz, the most easterly community of current importance in Bolivia, is a city in a class by itself. At one time the heart of a thriving

---

[3] Sucre has been the legal capital of Bolivia ever since the foundation of the republic. The city was named after General Sucre, who helped in drawing up the constitution of the nation. The supreme court of Bolivia still sits in the city; but La Paz, because of its accessibility—the fact that it was in the west influenced it to take an active part in the construction of railways, which began about 1904—has been the actual capital. The diplomatic corps resides in La Paz, and perhaps it will continue to be the actual seat of government, especially since a new capital building was recently erected there.

rubber trade, it prospered just as other Amazon region cities did during the rubber boom. Quinine was also much sought in the region, and for many years had an excellent cash market. But rubber is practically out of the picture; quinine is a relatively small item; and the city languishes. Santa Cruz is an ancient city located at the eastern edge of the Cordillera Oriental. It is surrounded on three sides by dense vegetation. From it radiate many trails through the jungle fastnesses. Nearby, petroleum is produced. At the height of its glory, during the rubber boom of 1910–1912, the city had 40,000 inhabitants. Now it has fewer than 30,000. It is the center of an exceptionally rich agricultural region where cattle thrive and coffee and sugar grow luxuriantly.

But Santa Cruz has a future. It is already an important aviation center. When transportation facilities are adequate and the products of her forests and fields find an outside market, the city will undoubtedly regain prestige as one of the important centers of Bolivia.

Agriculture. The permanent riches of Bolivia are both mineral and agricultural, and this fact in part determines the distribution of population. At least 80 per cent of the population is on the upland. Ten of this 80 per cent, perhaps, are shepherds or miners on the upper plateau; the remainder, concentrated in fertile valleys just below the plateau floor, are engaged in agriculture. About 10 or 15 per cent inhabit the fertile Yungas, and not more than 5 per cent, if that many, live in the lower plains and along the rivers. In the Amazon lowlands the population is infinitesimal.

In the Yungas, at altitudes of 4,000 to 8,000 feet, agricultural wealth lies available to those who will cultivate it. It is here that the important fruit, grain, and cattle regions of Bolivia are at present located. Such products as sugar, cotton, coffee, and other staples are grown, as well as quantities of tropical fruits of all varieties. Agricultural possibilities are vast and rich. Their development has been slow, and it has been dictated by immediate demand rather than by an aggressive export economy.

For instance, coffee of superior grade is grown on the slopes of the eastern Andes. A sufficient amount is produced to meet local demands, and a small amount is exported. Argentina and Chile import their coffee. Why not from Bolivia? Cacao groves were planted in the Beni district by the Jesuit missionaries, and a product is available, equal in richness and flavor to the cacao of Ecuador. It could be shipped by water to the Atlantic; transportation rates would be high, but careful planning would make the venture economically feasible." Principal agricultural exports are coca leaves, dried fruits, animal products (hides, cattle, wool), cinchona bark, coffee, and rubber.

All the domesticated animals of Europe have prospered in Bolivia—cattle and horses, sheep and goats, swine and poultry. The llama and alpaca alone are native.

The llamas almost supply a living for some of the plateau Indians. They are the pack animals most commonly used in the mountains. Mules are excellent at altitudes up to 11,000 or 12,000 feet. Above that they have a very high death rate. Llamas are excellent beasts of burden at any high altitude. They are the source of the Indian's meat, clothing, and leather, and even of his fuel. The llama produces a coarse wool from which natives make their garments. The alpaca produces excellent silky wool that is used for finer clothing or is exported. Herdsmen are increasing the size of their flocks, which graze on the coarse grasses and shrubs of the high plateau. To the Indian, the llama is a friendly creature, but for strangers it reveals a strong dislike, often kicking or biting or spraying him with mucus blown from its nose.

The wide diversity of climatic levels permits all agricultural products to be grown within an area of a few miles. Several important plants are native to the region—potatoes, sweet potatoes, manioc, Indian corn, quinoa (a very small grain cereal that will mature at higher altitudes than any other hardy grain), squashes, pumpkins, peanuts, guava, pawpaw, bananas, cashew, and avocados. Many other plants were introduced by Europeans, such as barley, wheat, oats, rye, beans, orange and lemon trees, grapes, figs, and dates. Among native forest products are vanilla and sarsaparilla, once of soda-fountain fame; and ipecac and quinine, of medical repute. Bolivian cinchona, from the bark of which quinine is derived, is obtained from the forests, and the trees are now being planted in groves—as vanilla has been planted in Mexico and rubber in Brazil. Coca, from the leaves of which cocaine is extracted, has been cultivated in the Yungas area by Indians for untold centuries.

One of the principal problems of the government is to encourage settlers to move from the plateau to the fertile land below, and to engage in agriculture. They have always been highland Indians, and they hesitate to change their mode of living. The Indians live on a very simple plane of civilization and are virtually illiterate. The government seems keenly alive to the need for education and social advance for the Indian population. The Bolivian Indian is the workman, the farmer, the miner, the stock grower—but he is primarily an upland man.

Despite Bolivia's rich agricultural potentialities, the industry is of secondary importance in its economy. Bolivia continues to import substantial quantities of foodstuffs, particularly, meat, lard, and wheat from Argentina. The principal local crops for home consumption are wheat, corn, rice, and potatoes. In recent years Bolivia has increased its production of wheat and meat. The Ministry of Agriculture reports a growing interest in agriculture in the Department of Santa Cruz on the part of cooperatives, especially that of Guarayos, a project involving 5,000 people. The Government hopes that within three years it will be able to produce enough rice to supply the entire nation, in addition to important quantities of peanuts, palm oil, sugar cane, and cotton. Bolivia's principal agricultural exports are rubber, coca, quinine sulfate, Brazil nuts, and wild animal skins.

BOLIVIA: EXPORTS OF PRINCIPAL COMMODITIES

Commodity	*Percentage of Total Value* 1947	1948
Tin ore	70	69
Antimony ore	5	4
Lead ore	3	6
Tin slag	4	6
Silver ore	4	1
Tungsten ore	3	2
Copper ore	2	2

Courtesy Pan American Union.

Fig. 72. A potato market at Oruro, Bolivia.

Mineral resources. Bolivia is known to us as the land of tin. It is the only tin-producing country in North or South America. Tin, however, simply happens to be the metal to which major attention is now given. Other metals exist in much greater quantities than tin. Silver, zinc, copper, lead, antimony, and wolfram, as well as gold, all exist in at least commercial quantities, but they are not readily accessible and are not extensively exploited—although all of them find their way into the export column. Tin is by far the most important just now. The relative significance of the other metals is shown in the table on Bolivian exports (pages 214, 217).

The government has estimated that during the sixteenth and seventeenth centuries more than two billion dollars in gold was extracted from Bolivian mines. During the eighteenth century one ancient mine near La Paz yielded more than $125,000,000 in gold. From the Tipuani field, more than 150,000 ounces of fine gold were taken within a period of six years during the past century. A single acre from this alluvial deposit in 1931 produced $100,000 from 40,000 cubic yards of sand, or an average of $2.50 a yard. The gold fields of Bolivia are of two types: veins in the cordilleras and the plateau, and the alluvial deposits in the river valleys of the eastern slopes of the Andes.

Enormous quantities of silver have been taken from the mines of Potosí and Oruro. During the present century, for various reasons, many mines have remained unworked, and the total output of silver and gold is small. Potosí, Bolivia's greatest silver deposit, now yields tin as well as silver.

Tin leads in the mineral production of Bolivia, largely because of the business initiative of the late Bolivian capitalist, Don Simón I. Patiño. In 1952, about 25 per cent of the Bolivian tin industry was owned by United States investors.

The principal uses of tin are for plating, in making cans, in solders, and in anti-friction alloys that are used in bearings and bushings of many kinds. In the past 25 years the world demand for tin has doubled. This increase is due largely to the growth of the automobile industry and to the increased use of tin-plated containers for food in the United States. For given purposes no satisfactory substitute for tin has yet been discovered or produced.

Until recently Bolivia's tin concentrates were shipped to England for refining. After refining, large quantities were sent to the United States. During the First World War some Bolivian ore was smelted in the United States. With the Second World War, again plans called for the operation of smelters of Bolivian ore in the United States.[4]

Bolivian tin is mined from lodes in granitic rock at altitudes above 12,000 feet. The principal lodes are near the towns of Llallagua and

[4] In 1942, a $12,000,000 tin smelter plant financed by the Reconstruction Finance Corporation was erected at Texas City, Texas. The Longhorn smelter, known as the Tin Processing Corporation, produced about 45 per cent of the world's tin during World War II and in recent years about 20 per cent. The plant is designed to use low grade Bolivian ore with annual output of about 35,000 tons of tin.

A tin reclaiming plant, the Vulcan Detinning Company, is in operation at Sewaren, New Jersey, with a yearly production of about 3,000 tons.

Uncia, in the department of Potosí. A 90-mile privately owned railway joins the mines with the principal railway line. The concentrates shipped out for extraction average 55 per cent pure tin, in contrast with 70 per cent or more from the ores of Malayan and East Indian origin. The eastern ores are produced from open cuts by dredging. Owing both to Bolivia's method of extraction and the lower percentage of tin in the concentrates, its production cost is higher than that of its competitors. In consequence, low prices strike it particularly hard.

As mentioned above, Bolivia is rich in other minerals besides tin. It possesses copper fields that may possibly rival those of Chile and Peru. They are either inaccessible to transportation, belong to corporations that are not yet ready to develop them, or they have not attracted the attention of capital necessary to open them to production. Along the Arica-La Paz railway, for instance, lies the important copper zone of Corocoro, operating at only a fraction of its full capacity. When world demands increase, it will undoubtedly be opened to intensive production.

The nitrate and copper fields of the Atacama Desert were formerly held by Bolivia. Until 1879 Bolivia possessed the broad territory of Antofagasta, bordering the Pacific Ocean. In that year it was taken by force by Chile. The possession of these minerals enabled Chile to become a great nation. If Bolivia had retained and exploited them, it might possibly have been today a greater nation than it is. Bolivia still feels keenly that it has been unjustly deprived of its Pacific ports and nitrate fields. Its statesmen are continually insisting that those territories must some day be returned.

Large silver resources still remain within the rock formations of Potosí Mountain, and half a million dollars' worth is extracted each year. Along the western Andes, rich silver deposits are known to exist. The opinion prevails that Bolivia might well in the future turn its attention to silver and gold for a time and place less reliance upon her tin export.

Mineral fields that have been exploited are found either in the high tablelands or in the ranges of the Andes. Below the mountains, however, in the lower eastern lands, there are apparently commercial deposits of petroleum. Geological indications point strongly to the existence of large potential petroleum deposits in this area, and the government is optimistic that in the near future petroleum will be discovered in such quantities and at such proximity to transportation facilities as to make a real contribution to its national finances. The government has taken over complete control of its oil resources.

Yacimientos Petroliferos Fiscales Bolivianos (YPFB) is the Bolivian official petroleum monopoly. Its attention is centered not only on an increase in oil production but also on refineries and adequate facilities for transporting the crude oil and petroleum products. Plans call for the completion of a pipeline from the southeastern oil fields to Sucre and

Cochabamba and for the development of refineries. Bolivia expects to supply all her needs for motor fuel from local production in the near future, and to be 85 per cent self-sufficient in all petroleum products when the refineries are completed. Production in recent years amounted to about 350,000 barrels annually.

The accompanying table shows the relative importance of Bolivia's mineral resources, not including petroleum, as measured in terms of exports.

ESTIMATES OF VOLUME OF EXPORTS OF MINERALS *

	1947	*1948*
Tin	33,200 †	36,000
Lead	11,311	23,500
Zinc	14,612	21,000
Copper	6,242	6,500
Silver	193	240
Antimony	10,856	12,100
Wolfram	1,000	1,250

* Metallic content of ores.
† Metric tons. One metric ton equals 2,204.62 pounds.

Extent of industrial development. Bolivia manufactures very little for its own use and nothing for export. The great mass of the rural people are simple Indians who require but little to keep them comfortable. Most of that little they make for themselves. Clothing is produced from native wool, often home-woven and -fashioned. Fuel on the highlands is seldom used for heating, and that required for cooking is either charcoal or animal dung. The harness required for mules or llamas is made either by the drivers themselves or in little wayside shops. Food is of the simplest nature. Even the houses are made almost entirely from materials immediately at hand—stones, wood, and grass. Only in the cities is there any pretense of using manufactured articles. These, again, are usually simple and made in small shops. Imports have always been low. It was not long ago that the first refrigerating plant, designed to supply fresh chilled meats, was constructed in La Paz.

Railways. The railway system of Bolivia was planned and constructed as a series of separate units. They really form, however, a closely integrated system. All lines reach a common central point. New lines now under construction are additions to the present system. Most of the railways are government-owned and -operated, although private mining enterprises have been responsible for not a small part of the pioneer construction. The principal development occurred within the past 20 years. The gauge of all Bolivian railways is one meter.

Although there are only 1,700 miles of railway in a country nearly a sixth the size of the United States, they join the principal cities and the principal mining centers of the nation and provide four routes to the ocean. Through service has been provided on the principal lines, with day coaches for first-class passengers as comfortable as those in the United States or Europe and Pullman cars with private compartments. Railway transportation extends from the nation's population centers to the southern border where connections can be made with the railway system of Argentina at La Quiaca. The distance from La Paz to Buenos Aires is about 1,580 miles, requiring less than three days of travel. Three routes are open to the Pacific coast: the La Paz-Lake Titicaca-Mollendo route, the La Paz-Arica route, and the La Paz-Antofagasta route. The Peruvian Corporation owns the Southern Peruvian Railways and the steamers on Lake Titicaca. It now provides 35-hour service between Mollendo, on the coast, and La Paz, including the daylight trip across the lake, a total distance of 526 miles. The Chilean government owns and operates the line from the copper and tin port of Antofagasta up to Uyuni, where it joins the Bolivian lines. Arica is 283 miles from La Paz, and 20 hours is required to make the trip over the Andes. This railway was also constructed by the Chilean government. That traffic on these railways is light is indicated by the fact that through trains run only once or twice a week.

In competition with the popular Mollendo to La Paz route, the Chilean government has been hard at work improving Arica and advertising the advantages and the wonders of the railway from that port to La Paz. Bathing beaches and other attractions are designed to delight visitors from passing steamers. Arica is located in an oasis, created by the Azapa River, on the coast. In striking contrast to the desert that reaches in from all sides, it is surrounded by rich vegetation and enjoys a temperate climate the year 'round. The railway leaving Arica makes a steep ascent and provides gorgeous mountain scenery. The steepest section of the road, the track here rises 2,250 meters (7,380 feet) in a distance of only 26 miles. This enormous rise requires a rack and pinion track and locomotives of great power. The crest of the range, the high point on the line, is 14,000 feet above sea level. This railway now uses coal for fuel, but plans to electrify it throughout have been completed.

At present the railroad to Antofagasta is extensively used for the export of minerals, since it taps a great mineral-producing territory. The Mollendo route is preferred for passenger and tourist travel because it includes a visit to Lake Titicaca. The Arica route is much the shorter line of the three and is becoming increasingly popular as a commercial exit for the La Paz district.

Plans call for more adequate transportation facilities by rail and highway between the Altiplano region and the eastern lowlands. Cochabamba is connected with the highlands by rail, and it is proposed to project this line to Santa Cruz, and then eastward to join a completed railway that extends westward from Puerto Suárez. This development would offer an all-rail route to Corumbá, Brazil, and the Atlantic seaboard.

Motor roads. In line with its road program and its desire to attract tourist automobile traffic, the government is setting up metal guide signs on all principal highways. These point the way to all cities, towns, and points of interest.

The government has of late taken an interesting stand on highway and railway construction, strongly favoring the development of highways. One route of the Pan-American Highway will, when completed, cross Bolivia on the way to Brazil and Argentina. If the highway system of Bolivia is well developed, it will interlock admirably into the Pan-American system. This should prove of enormous value to Bolivia.

Courtesy Frank E. Williams.

Fig. 73. Llamas, excellent beasts of burden at high altitudes.

The nation, through its recent experience in the construction of railways, has discovered that the enormous difference in the cost of the two types of transportation is in favor of motor roads. It has discovered that automobile traffic is almost as advantageous, when considered in all its phases, as rail traffic. There is greater flexibility because it is not limited to rails. It is not controlled by timetables, is much less expensive to construct, and has an insignificant overhead for maintenance. Further, the government has been brought to see that motor transportation is an urgent requirement. Where large volume is not demanded by a dense population, it is highly effective. In line with this belief there was organized in 1931 the Bolivian Automobile Club. The sponsors of the club undoubtedly had at hand the constitutions and working plans of progressive clubs in the United States as well as suggestions from the International Automobile Association, for the club is organized along standard lines.

Difficulties in constructing motor roads are great, of course, but less serious than those in the construction of railways. The plateau is cut by numerous valleys and canyons. Mountain ranges are as impassable as are mountain ranges anywhere, but in Bolivia they are much higher and have severe grades. Consequently, owing to the altitude and the grades, motor transportation presents peculiar problems. In portions of the lower-lying Yungas and plains, tropical vegetation is lush and waterways are frequent. This makes highway construction unusually expensive. Nevertheless, the government, convinced that national unity and progress may not be so well secured in any other manner, is making constant progress.

The most important transportation project recently reported by Bolivia is the extension eastward to Santa Cruz of the existing highway between the Altiplano region and Cochabamba. The road is under construction,

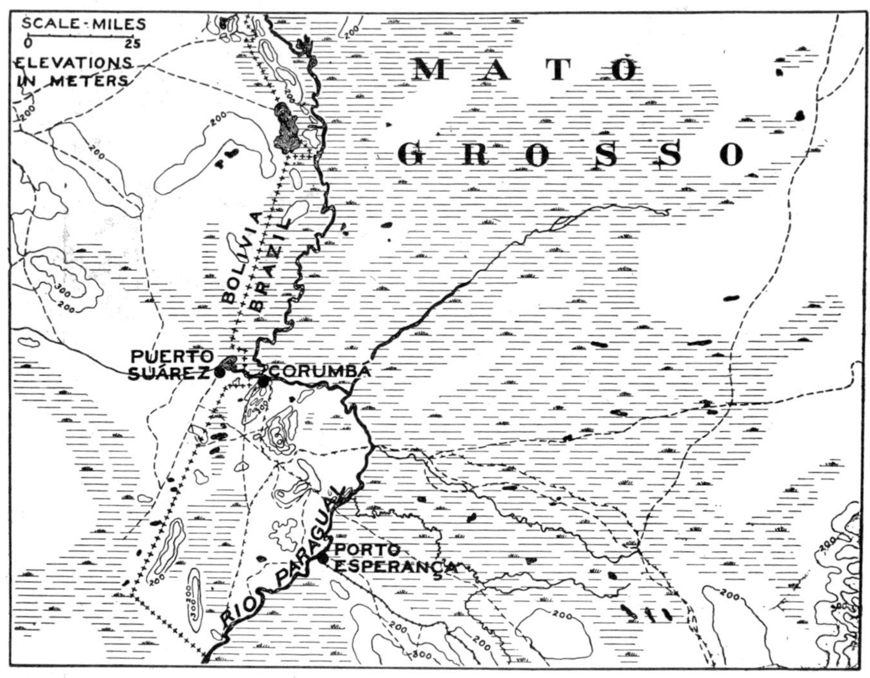

F. A. Carlson.

Fig. 74. Interior Lowland. A railway joins Pôrto Esperança and São Paulo, Brazil, a distance of 1,026 miles. Airplane service connects Puerto Suárez with the cities of the Bolivian plateau.

but prolonged interruptions have been caused by lack of funds. The Public Roads Administration estimated that the highway would cost $26,000,000.

Airplane routes. A significant movement has been inaugurated to join the principal population centers of Bolivia by airplane routes. Three such routes now lead to foreign parts: one from La Paz down to Arica on the Pacific Coast, where it meets the international airmail; a second down the eastern side of the Cordillera and Central Real to Buenos Aires; and a third eastward across jungles and savannas to Puerto Suárez, near the terminus of the Brazilian railway that extends to the Atlantic Coast. The plane to Puerto Suárez regularly traverses the 16 extra miles to visit Corumbá.

The airline from Buenos Aires extends northward to Santa Cruz. From this point radial lines reach all the principal cities—to the west, La Paz, Cochabamba, Oruro, and Sucre; to the east, Puerto Suárez; and to the far north, Trinidad, Santa Ana, Riberalta, and Villa Bella. Projected lines, when placed in service, will double the number of centers reached. The Lloyd Aereo Boliviano (LAB) and the Panagra were the most active companies operating in Bolivia in 1950. Braniff and Pan American also operate across Bolivia.

Rivers. A part of the eastern border of Bolivia is the Paraguay River, which separates that country from Brazil. Puerto Suárez, the Bolivian free port on the Paraguay River, is located about 16 miles north of Corumbá. Corumbá may soon become the inland terminal of Brazil's longest interior railway. This port is at the head of about 7-foot water and has regular steamship service both up and down the river. Since the five-power treaty (Argentina, Brazil, Uruguay, Paraguay, Bolivia) has made the La Plata and its principal tributaries an international waterway, Bolivia does have access to the Atlantic Ocean in her own right.

The northern one-third of Bolivia's territory is included in the Departments of Beni and Pando, a lowland region producing rubber, cattle, and cacao. Exit from this region is by water, via the Beni and Mamoré Rivers and their numerous tributaries. In earlier days there was a costly portage around a series of rapids and falls on the Mamoré. As a result of a territorial adjustment with Brazil, in which Bolivia ceded the rich rubber-producing territory of Acre, Brazil constructed the famous Madeira-Mamoré Railway around these falls to provide free exit for Bolivian products. This line is still in operation, although, since the collapse of the rubber boom, the volume of traffic is small.

Foreign trade. Tin exports, an important block in the foundation of Bolivia, comprised over 72 per cent, in value, of the nation's exports in 1939, 77 per cent in 1940, and about 70 per cent in 1948. The United States and the United Kingdom are the principal markets for Bolivian products. Generally speaking, the United States receives approximately

60 per cent of exports and the United Kingdom about 35 per cent. Argentina, Peru, and Brazil purchase most of the remainder.

Imports by principal customhouses are as follows: La Paz, 42 per cent of total; Oruro, 15 per cent; Uyuni and Villazón. Among the leading customhouses in terms of exports are Uyuni, 60 per cent of total; Oruro, 25 per cent; La Paz, Villazón, and Villa Bella.

BOLIVIA: FOREIGN TRADE

	Total Value	*Percentage of Total*				
Exports	*(000 Dollars)*	United States	Latin America	United Kingdom	Continental Europe	All Others
1938	34,784	4.6	4.0	62.5	28.6	0.3
1947	81,429	60.6	3.2	35.4	0.9	
Imports						
1938	24,959	26.4	28.4	7.2	29.8	8.2
1947	59,556	49.4	41.3	3.8	4.8	0.6

Summary. Bolivia's development has been and probably will continue for many years to be greatly retarded by: (1) the unfavorable environment in which most of her people live; (2) an Indian and mestizo population with relatively low standards of living; (3) the control of the best land, wealth, culture, and politics in the hands of a few—less than 15 per cent of the total population; and (4) unstable political conditions. Bolivia will continue for some time to mine and export minerals, but it is equally certain that the mineral industry will eventually decline. It is also quite probable that Bolivia will in time contribute substantially to the world's supply of petroleum. Other new mineral resources may be discovered, but all in all the trend will be downward.

The future of the country, however, lies not in the high plateau of present human occupancy, but in the eastern lowlands, a region of potentially rich agricultural resources and, probably, petroleum. Before this area can be developed there must be political stability—a prerequisite to economic security. Until such conditions develop, Bolivia will continue as it has for the past four centuries, exporting minerals and trying to eke out an existence in the more unfavorable portion of its land.

SELECTED REFERENCES

Alberts, Hugo W.: "Quinoa—Ancient Food Crop in South America," *Agriculture in the Americas,* Vol. VII, No. 12 (1947), pp. 150–152.

Alberts, Hugo W.: "The Bolivia-Paraguay Boundary Dispute," *Geographical Review,* Vol. XIX (1929), pp. 151–153.

Bowman, I.: "The Distribution of Population in Bolivia," *Bulletin of the Geographical Society of Philadelphia,* Vol. VII (1909), pp. 74–93.

Bowman, I.: "Trade Routes in the Economic Geography of Bolivia," *Bulletin of the American Geographical Society,* Vol. XLII (1910), pp. 22–37, 90–104, 180–192.

Higbee, E. C.: "Agriculture across the Andes," *Agriculture in the Americas,* Vol. IV, No. 1 (1944), pp. 3–7.

Keller, Frank L.: "Finca Ingavi–A Medieval Survival on the Bolivian Altiplano," *Economic Geography,* Vol. 26 (1950), pp. 37–50.

Leonard, O. E.: "La Paz, Bolivia: Its Population and Growth," *American Sociological Review,* Vol. 13 (1948), pp. 448–454.

Leonard, O. E.: "Locality Group Structure in Bolivia," *Rural Sociology,* Vol. 14 (1949), pp. 250–260.

Mather, K. F.: "Along the Andean Front in Southeastern Bolivia," *Geographical Review,* Vol. XII (1922), pp. 358–374.

Milstead, H. P.; "Bolivia as a Source of Tin," *Economic Geography,* Vol. III (1927), pp. 354–360.

Monge, Carlos: *Acclimatization in the Andes,* Johns Hopkins Press, Baltimore, 1948.

Ogilvie, A. G.: "Geography of the Central Andes," a handbook to accompany the La Paz sheet of Map of Hispanic America, *Publication No. 1,* American Geographical Society, New York, 1922.

Romecin, E.: "Agricultural Adaptation in Bolivia," *Geographical Review,* Vol. XIX (1929), pp. 248–255.

Rudolph, W. E.: "Bolivia's Water Power Resources," *Geographical Review,* Vol. XXX (1940), pp. 41–63.

Rudolph, W. E.: "The Lakes of Potosí," *Geographical Review,* Vol. XXVI (1936), pp. 529–551.

Spinden, H. J.: "The Population of Ancient America," *Geographical Review,* Vol. XVIII (1928), pp. 641–660.

Troll, K.: "An Expedition to the Central Andes," *Geographical Review,* Vol. XIX (1929), pp. 234–247.

Weeks, David: "Bolivia's Agricultural Frontier," *Geographical Review,* Vol. 36, No. 4 (1946), pp. 546–567.

CHAPTER XIV

CHILE: A COUNTRY OF DIVERSIFIED AND PROGRESSIVE INTERESTS

Geographical structure. Chile is a land of extreme regional contrasts. In the north, a rainless, treeless, forbidding desert, thinly scattered with fruitful, tropical, and subtropical oases, contains a population given over almost entirely to mining. These oases may be enlarged through irrigation. Extensive reclamation projects have been outlined by the government, and some have been carried through. In the farthest south the mists and fogs envelop the cold and forbidding Tierra del Fuego, where a scant population devotes itself mainly to sheep raising and lumbering.

Between these two extremes of desert north and rainy south lies central Chile, a land of high fertility and gorgeous beauty. The part of middle Chile around Santiago, the capital, enjoys a light rainfall, a mediterranean climate, and sustains the larger part of the population. The air is nearly always clear and bracing—the yearly rainfall is only 14 inches. Sunshine is brilliant and stimulating. This is a rich agricultural district; fruits—olives, oranges, grapes, apples, peaches, and pears—are abundant. Almond, walnut, and poplar trees line the roads. Irrigation plus climate makes this possible. It is here that Chilean culture is at its best. The southern region, extending southward from Puerto Montt for more than 1,000 miles to Tierra del Fuego, has a marine climate with heavy rainfall and is thickly forested. While rich in potential forest wealth, it does not offer an agreeable climate in which to live. The cold Peruvian Current, sweeping up from the far south Pacific, chills the onshore winds. The annual rainfall ranges from 90 to more than 140 inches.

Behind each of these regions—north, central, and south Chile—extend the high ridges of the Andes, running like a backbone through the entire nation, separating it from Argentina and Bolivia. The frontiers of Chile extend to the top of this system on the east.

Throughout the Andes of Chile, as through all the west-coast countries, volcanic cones are numerous, and some of them are active. Their snow-covered peaks rise above the central valley, the nation's most bountiful region. In middle Chile a low coastal range separates the narrow expanse of the central valley from the sea.

Because the southern Andes are continually drenched by cold rains or snows coming from the Pacific Ocean, the upper mountains are the sites of many glaciers. Glacial erosion and deposition have created lake basins that are filled with water from the rain and melting ice and snow.

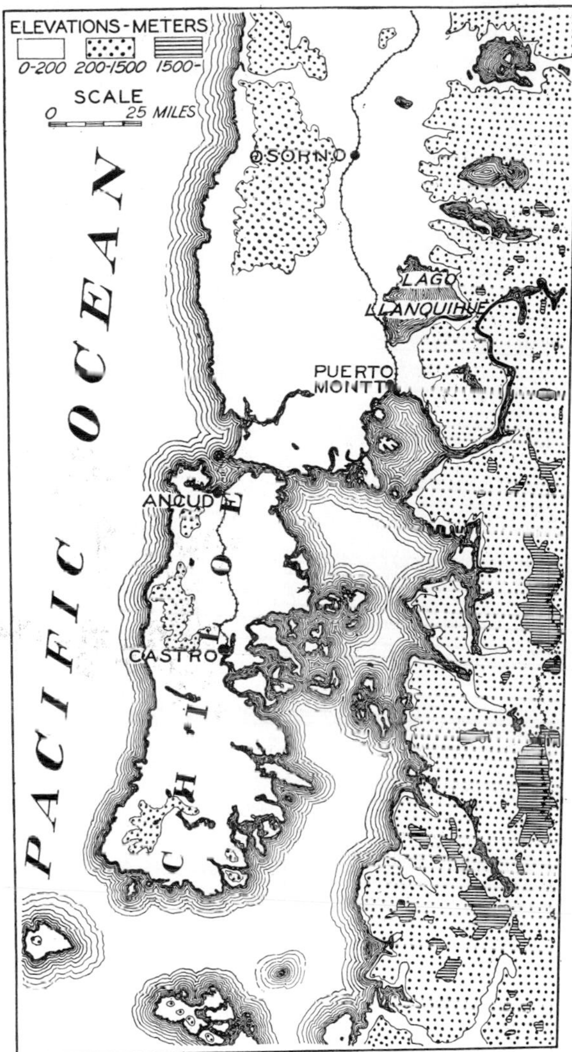

F. A. Carlson.

Fig. 75. The Chilean Alps. The magnificent lake region of south central Chile.

In the lake region of the south central, not far from Puerto Montt, Chile boasts of alpine scenery of a quality and wonder sufficiently magnificent to please the most exacting Swiss taste. Already numerous lake resorts and hotels have been opened, manned usually by Chileans of German descent. An itinerary over a chain of these lakes has been laid out for the tourist and summer trade. The government has advertised its attractions abroad, and an increasing number of visitors are finding their way each year to this region of beauty. A ten-day trip has been outlined by the government's tourist bureau; it begins and ends at Santiago, and covers selected beauty spots.

Off the coast, some 30 hours by steamer from Valparaíso, lie the Juan Fernández Islands. Among these is Robinson Crusoe's island. Here Alexander Selkirk, who inspired the famous Crusoe story, is said to have spent four lonely years before he was finally rescued.

Courtesy Pan American Union.

Fig. 76. Ensenada, Chile: The Osorno volcanic mountain and Lake Llanquihue.

Of Chile's total area of 286,396 square miles, 40,000 are under cultivation. And another 60,000, consisting of the heavily forested slopes of the southern Andes, are, in part, potentially suitable for agriculture. Of the total population of 5,538,000, more than three-fourths is concentrated in the central valley. The remainder of Chile's territory, two-thirds of the total area, is poor and infertile. For the amount of agriculturally useful land, the country is now well populated—an average about 130 people supported by each square mile of farmland. While it is estimated that 90 per cent of Uruguay and 65 per cent of Argentina are productive, not more than 15 per cent of Chile's surface may be utilized for profitable agriculture. Another 15 to 20 per cent is in timberlands.

Nevertheless, Chile has so successfully exploited her copper and nitrates in the past quarter of a century, and has developed the agri-

CHILE: TEMPERATURE AND RAINFALL OF SELECTED STATIONS

	Station	Punta Arenas *	Valdivia †	Puerto Montt †	Valparaíso *	Concepción *	Santiago ‡	Coquimbo †	Antofagasta †	Iquique †	Tacna †
	Elevation (*Feet*)	92	19.7	32.8	135	300	706	88.6	308.4	29.5	1837.3
Average Temperature (°F.)	*Period of Record*	37 years	1911–1921	1911–1921	24 years	8 years	1931–1940	1911–1924	1911–1913 1919–1924	1911–1924	1919–1924
	January	52.0	61.9	59.5	64.0	66.0	69.1	64.0	69.6	69.8	70.3
	February	51.0	60.4	58.1	64.0	65.0	67.5	63.7	69.4	69.6	71.4
	March	48.0	57.9	55.9	62.0	62.0	63.3	62.1	67.3	67.6	69.4
	April	44.0	53.1	52.3	60.0	57.0	57.0	58.8	63.3	65.1	65.7
	May	39.0	49.6	49.6	57.0	53.0	51.4	56.8	61.0	63.1	61.2
	June	36.0	45.5	45.9	54.0	51.0	47.3	54.3	57.6	61.3	57.2
	July	35.0	45.7	45.9	54.0	49.0	46.0	53.6	57.2	60.1	55.4
	August	37.0	46.4	46.0	54.0	50.0	48.7	54.0	58.1	60.3	56.3
	September	40.0	48.0	47.3	56.0	53.0	52.3	55.0	59.7	61.2	57.9
	October	44.0	52.0	51.1	58.0	56.0	57.2	57.0	61.3	63.0	60.8
	November	47.0	55.0	53.6	60.0	60.0	62.1	59.4	64.0	65.7	63.3
	December	50.0	59.0	57.0	63.0	63.0	67.1	61.7	67.5	68.2	67.3
	Annual	44.0	52.0	51.8	59.0	57.0	57.4	58.3	63.0	63.1	63.0
	Range		16.4	13.6				10.4	12.4	9.7	16.0
Average Rainfall (*Inches*)	*Period of Record*	20 years	1852–1925	1862–1915	31 years	45 years	1931–1940	1900–1925	1910–1921	1886–1925	1919–1924
	January	1.2	2.4	4.6	0.0	0.7	0.2	0.00	0.00	0.00	0.28
	February	1.2	3.0	4.4	0.0	0.8	0.2	0.00	0.00	0.00	0.00
	March	1.0	5.6	5.9	0.4	2.4	0.1	0.04	0.00	0.00	0.00
	April	2.1	9.4	7.4	0.5	0.8	0.2	0.04	0.00	0.00	0.08
	May	2.2	15.2	10.6	4.4	7.8	2.9	1.10	0.02	0.00	0.00
	June	2.0	17.0	10.0	5.7	9.8	3.1	1.50	0.04	0.00	0.00
	July	1.8	16.1	10.8	3.9	9.8	2.5	1.06	0.04	0.04	0.16
	August	1.9	13.2	9.3	2.7	7.3	1.8	0.51	0.00	0.00	0.20
	September	1.6	8.7	6.3	1.3	4.0	0.9	0.16	0.00	0.00	0.24
	October	1.0	5.2	5.5	0.5	2.8	0.7	0.04	0.04	0.00	0.12
	November	1.8	5.0	5.5	0.2	1.8	0.2	0.04	0.02	0.00	0.04
	December	1.3	4.1	5.1	0.2	1.0	0.3	0.00	0.00	0.00	0.04
	Annual	19.2	105.4	86.1	19.8	51.0	13.1	4.49	0.16	0.04	1.18

* U. S. Weather Bureau, *Technical Paper No. 8,* U. S. Department of Commerce, Washington, D. C.

† K. Knoch: "Klimakunde von Südamerika," *Handbuch der Klimatologie,* Band II, Teil G, Berlin, 1930.

‡ H. Helm Clayton, "World Weather Records," *Smithsonian Miscellaneous Collections,* Vol. 105, 1947.

cultural possibilities of her central valley so profitably that it has made itself the leading nation on the western coast. Chile's people as a whole are better educated, more highly industrialized, and healthier than the people of any other South American nation, with the possible exception of Argentina and Uruguay.

Population and culture. The Chilean people are not all white; neither are they Indian. They are a distinct, somewhat homogeneous race, with Spanish and Indian ancestry in varying degrees behind most of the present population. Around Santiago, Spanish blood strongly predominates, and throughout the central valley the white race is decidedly preponderant. The present race has been strengthened through the addition of numerous British, French, German, and Italian immigrants. Government estimates indicate that as many as 180,000 of the inhabitants in the Frontera, or Indian forest, in the south-central region are pure Araucanian Indians. There are few Negroes in Chile.

The Araucanian Indians, who held middle Chile before the Spanish came, had successfully resisted all efforts of the Incas to include them in the great empire. They had developed ideas of independence that marked them off from the other races to the north and east. In their mountain or forest fastnesses south of the Río Bió-Bió, they had developed a culture all their own. It was a hardy fighting culture, with independence and isolation as cardinal aims. When the Spanish came from the north, after the relatively easy conquest of Peru, the Chilean Indians fiercely resisted their advance. Two results followed, one *racial*, the other *cultural*.

The racial result was forced fusion. With the almost inexhaustible resources of the manpower of Spain to draw upon, the Spanish military kept up a constant warfare against the Indians. The soldiers who conquered Chile were hardy men from northern Spain. Although vast numbers of Spaniards were slain, equally vast numbers of Araucanian fighting men were slain. Their women became the possession of the Spanish soldiery. There were almost no Spanish women, and consequently the birth rate of children with Spanish fathers and Indian mothers was high. Spain acclaimed the increase in mestizos.[1] Colonial administrators urged constantly the importance of the largest possible infusion of Spanish blood, culture, and religion in the New World. This was a long time ago, and the fusion is now complete. In the native population of middle Chile there is a far greater homogeneity, with a far larger proportion of Spanish blood, than among any other people on the west coast. The wars continued throughout the entire period of colonization, down to the time of the republic. Indians were not completely subjugated until the middle of the nineteenth century.

The cultural result was equally remarkable. In Peru and Colombia the relatively early conquest of the Indians left the Spanish free to develop a rich colonial civilization in peace. Consequently, an elaborate culture

[1] The Araucanians were not the only Indian groups living in middle Chile. Descendants of other groups still live in the area.

developed very early in these nations. Art, architecture, education, and religion accompanied political and economic advance. In Chile, by contrast, an early crystallization of culture was impossible. Military necessities largely swallowed up the cultural. Attention was continually focused upon Indian wars. When the struggles for independence were ended in the early nineteenth century, the northern nations had a culture that was already crystallized. The Chilean people, still in the midst of a vitally military atmosphere, were not so set. Chile, therefore, vigorous and independent, had the rare privilege of constructing her own civilization without much drag from the past. To almost the same extent this privilege was enjoyed by Argentina.

The land-tenure system of colonial days had brought the possession of agricultural land into the hands of a few families. Not more than 50 great family groups held the land. The remainder of the people were their tenants or lieutenants. These 50 great families have furnished the governmental, educational, and economic leadership of the nation. When revolutions occurred during the past century, it meant that one group of these great families, who were the "outs," was seeking to wrest governmental control from other great families, who were "ins." A number of the most distinguished families bear English or Irish names, reminiscent of leadership in the war for Independence—O'Higgins, O'Brien, Cochrane, Walker, Tupper, MacKenna, Edwards.

The composition of the Chilean people, however, made it inevitable that with this type of social structure a working-class consciousness would sooner or later arise. Within the past thirty years this has been the case. Labor organizations have arisen; class consciousness has developed; and an educated proletariat has gradually come into power. The political upheavals of the early part of this century have been to a considerable extent fomented by these folk. The revolution that resulted in 1931 in a change of presidents and of governmental policies was engineered by students in the national university at Santiago, most of whom are from middle-class homes.

Until the first quarter of this century there was practically no Chilean middle class. The development of this group is one of the results of the new program of industrialization that has been operating since 1920.

This same middle-class agitation for better political, economic, and social conditions and the attempt to improve the social conditions of the laboring classes has made Chile outstanding among South American republics. There are compulsory retirement insurance for all office employees, indemnities for dismissed workers, unemployment relief, and provision for the payments of medical costs. Whether the nation can permanently maintain this social legislation in force, and can free it from certain apparently inevitable political abuses, is a question that only the future can answer.

One of the significant movements in Chile, as in most South American nations in recent years, is the construction of low-priced but clean and sanitary homes for workmen. Just as significant, perhaps, is the plan to establish public hospitals throughout the land—one to about every 25,000 people. Most of these have now been constructed.

Large landholdings by the leading families have prevented colonization by immigrants in middle Chile.[2] No land is available for settlement, except at prices too high for immigrants to pay. Consequently, the government has had to set aside agricultural land toward the south for immigrant settlement, or to purchase land from large estates. Under this enlightened policy, considerable numbers of Germans, French, Swiss, Italians, and Spaniards have established homes. Some English and Irish have come to join them. The tendency, however, is for these immigrants to abandon agriculture sooner or later and find their way into the larger cities. Their mechanical skills have caused them to be preferred over the native Chileans as technical workers.

Between 1904 and 1934, some 65,000 immigrants arrived, 40,000 of whom were Germans. They were steady and home loving people. They soon became owners of land and rose to the position of independent small farmers—the backbone of any society. Many became mechanics in the cities. The present trend toward industrial development is guided largely by Chileans of German descent.

A few years ago the government advertised, probably not accurately, that Chile could assimilate 60,000 European immigrants a year, and that its potential agricultural resources would support a population of 15,000,000. In 1928 a fund of 100,000,000 pesos was set aside for the purchase of land, the construction of roads, and the establishment of settlers upon the land. The effect of increased white immigration would be beneficial to Chile—it needs the new blood to stimulate progress in the race—but it is doubtful whether it can attract and hold Europeans in the large numbers it desires.

The central valley, an agricultural region. At the time of independence, 1818, and indeed up to 1850, middle Chile stood isolated and alone. The mineral value of the northern deserts was unrealized; the Indian *Frontera* effectually prevented contact with the south by land; and south Chile was largely unknown and uninhabited by white men, except on the Island of Chiloé. The Frontera is the beginning of the forested area of the central valley. It is about 300 miles south of Santiago, limited on the north by the Bío-Bío River.

With its magnificent climate, very similar to that of California, its high agricultural possibilities, and its rugged and homogeneous population,

---

[2] Reports show that 60 per cent of the cultivated land in central Chile is owned by a thousand land-owning families.

central Chile is the heart of the new nation. From it has developed the nation of today.

Central Chile lies between mountain ranges. Beginning north of Santiago and extending south to Puerto Montt, the maritime Andes chain is paralleled by a low coastal mountain range, with a fertile valley separating them. On the east lies the main cordillera of the Andes, rising to 20,000 feet in places, falling swiftly into the valley below. On the west the low coastal range averages about 1,000 feet in height.

The valley is from 20 to 40 miles wide and some 900 miles long. The rainfall in the eastern Andean Mountains is heavy but periodic. In winter the mountain peaks are heavily coated with snow. The melting snow forms streams, which cross the valley and provide excellent moisture for crops. The rainfall in the valley, in contrast with that in the mountains, is very light toward the northern end and very heavy toward the southern end. The rain falls mostly during the winter months, while the summer months are dry. At Santiago the precipitation is only 14 inches a year. In the north, therefore, agriculture is carried on largely under irrigation, in a dry atmosphere, while in the south the atmosphere is much more humid, and natural precipitation cares for all needs. The northern end of the valley is subtropical; it has a Mediterranean climate—a light rainfall occurring during the low-sun period, or so-called winter. The south is more temperate; it has a modified marine climate—moderate rainfall throughout the year—and is heavily forested.

For climatic reasons, the southern part of the great central Chilean valley is given over largely to farming and dairying and to the raising of such staples as wheat and potatoes. Surrounded on all sides by heavy forests, it is here that lumber industries have developed. Several excellent cabinet woods are found, as well as pines and a species of timber closely resembling oak. European poplar was introduced many years ago and is now plentiful. Some fine cabinet woods are exported. In the middle and north, buildings are constructed generally of brick, seldom of wood. In the south, more wood is used in building. An association of lumber dealers has recently been formed, one of whose purposes is to coöperate with the government in the scientific reforestation of areas not needed for agriculture. In reforestation the less desirable woods are, of course, being eliminated. This association is also seeking, in coöperation with the government, to encourage the use of Chilean lumber and thus reduce imports. Significant results have already been achieved in both fields of operation.

The northern part of middle Chile produces vast amounts of subtropical fruits, honey, and grapes. There are more than 35,000 vineyards in Chile. It is estimated that more than 40,000,000 gallons of wine are made annually, most of which is consumed in Chile. The wine growers have organized into an association, one purpose of which is to encourage export. Vast amounts of grapes are used fresh and as raisins. The same fruits, vegetables, and cereals that are grown in the United States produce abundantly throughout this central valley. While domestic demand is high, and this portion of the country must supply a major portion of the food needed for the far north and far south as well as for the inhabitants of the valley, some effort is being made to grow a surplus for export.

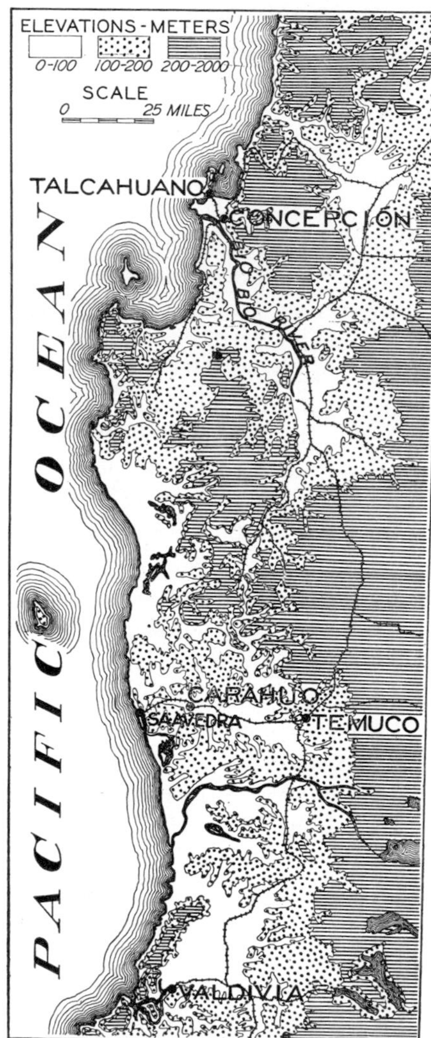

F. A. Carlson.

Fig. 77. South-central Chile, a region rich in agricultural, forest, and mining resources.

Attempts have been made to ship fresh fruits. During the gold rush to California, around 1850, Chile shipped large quantities of vegetables and flour to California. Some of her citizens came as miners. However, as soon as the rush was over, most of them returned home. As the demand for foodstuffs was increasingly supplied by home-grown crops, shipments from Chile ceased. During recent years, however, small shipments of at least two fruits, Chilean grapes and peaches, have arrived in the United States during December, January, and February.

Ports and inland cities. About halfway between the Atlantic and the Pacific Oceans, on the Strait of Magellan, stands the city of Punta Arenas, often referred to as Magallanes. About 33,000 people live in this busy city, the most southerly outpost of Chilean territory. Except for the small Argentine settlement of Ushuaia, at the very southern point of Tierra del Fuego, this is the most southern city of importance in the world. The environs of Punta Arenas are one of the great sheep-raising districts of the world. The most active season is January, February, and March, the summer months. During the early part of this period, some 2,500,000 sheep are sheared and the wool baled and transported to Punta Arenas for shipment. Twelve thousand tons are exported to foreign markets; the remainder is used in Chile. During the latter part of January the freezer-abattoirs begin to operate, and they continue until April in the killing and freezing of more than 1,000,000 sheep and lambs. From 16,000 to 20,000 tons of fresh meat are exported each year.

Punta Arenas also serves as a coaling station. The Loreto mines are located within five miles of the port and are connected with it by a narrow-gauge railway. No extensive deposits of petroleum have yet been tapped. However, near Punta Arenas three successful oil wells and two gas wells have been drilled. Steamers make frequent sailings up the eastern coast to Buenos Aires, a distance of 1,300 miles, and also up the western coast to Valparaíso, a distance of 1,400 miles. A Chilean company maintains a regular service of new passenger steamers between Valparaíso and Rio de Janeiro, thus linking Argentina, Uruguay, Brazil, and Chile, and increasing commerce and cultural contacts among them.

In order to encourage the development of a Chilean merchant marine, the government has given a monopoly of coastwise transportation to vessels of national registry. This means that foreign vessels may not carry passengers or goods from one Chilean port to another, except en route to or from the home port.

The western coast of South America, from Valparaíso to northern Peru, is comparatively straight and unbroken. There are few indentations that serve as naturally good harbors. North of Peru there are a number of sheltered havens for ships, with the bay of Guayaquil as the largest and best. From Valparaíso to the extreme southern tip of South America the coastline is irregular and possesses numerous excellent harbors. The cold

Peruvian Current from the south Pacific Ocean sweeps along the western coast and cools the land. This is in distinct contrast to the warm equatorial current that flows southward along the Brazilian coast.

At a distance of 1,200 miles north from Punta Arenas, or 200 miles south of Valparaíso, is the bay of Concepción, one of the finest harbors on

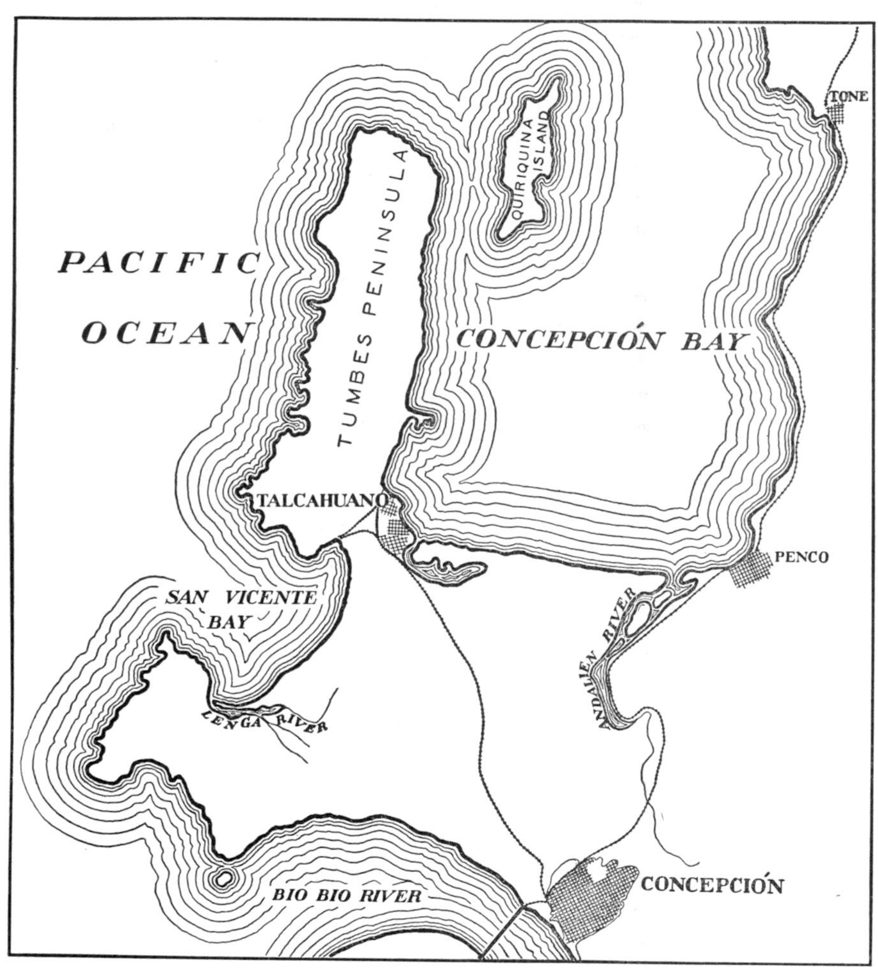

F. A. Carlson.

Fig. 78. The physical setting of Concepción, the metropolis of south-central Chile.

the coast of Chile. On the shores of this spacious and sheltered haven stand several ports, including Talcahuano, Toné, and Penco. Talcahuano is the largest and serves the city of Concepción, the metropolis of south central Chile, which is located some nine miles inland. The two cities are joined by a railway and an excellent motor road. A hinterland rich in agricultural resources and mineral deposits, well watered, and inhabited by industrious Chileans, many of German descent, has favored the development of this region.

POPULATION OF PRINCIPAL URBAN CENTERS OF CHILE

Santiago	1,088,000
Valparaíso	245,000
Concepción	100,000
Temuco	84,700
Antofagasta	80,000
Viña del Mar	70,000
Talca	56,700
Iquique	56,600
Valdivia	49,400
Talcahuano	41,500
Punta Arenas	33,000
Arica	16,600

Valparaíso is the major port on the western coast of South America. The harbor is semicircular in form, a vast expanse of sheltered water protected in all directions except the north. During the winter season occasional northern winds cause a heavy rolling sea. Ships sometimes experience considerable difficulty in holding their moorings. Large vessels that are anchored in the bay often go out to sea during approaching storms to avoid being washed ashore. In this harbor the largest ships can load and discharge at piers. There is railway communication with all parts of Chile, and lines run to Argentina and Bolivia. The city of Valparaíso is built on the slopes of the hills that surround the bay and give the entire port the form of a great amphitheater. Only the business section lies along the shore, on reclaimed ground. The city was almost entirely destroyed by an earthquake in 1906, but was subsequently rebuilt on a bigger scale.

Southeast of Valparaíso, at an elevation of some 1,700 feet above sea level in the central valley of Chile, stands Santiago, the nation's capital. This city justly prides itself on being the center of Chilean culture, industry, and trade. Although a cosmopolitan city, Santiago has nevertheless remained more distinctly Spanish in sentiment and custom than the cities of eastern South America. It is a beautiful city, modern and progressive, with many parks, paved streets, excellent transportation facilities, a good drainage system, and pure water.

About 130 miles north of Valparaíso is the port of Cruz Grande, mentioned here because it is the port from which the Bethlehem Steel Corporation ships iron ore to its plant at Sparrows Point, Baltimore. The ore is obtained from the Tofo mines, located nearby. It is handled entirely by machinery. It is first broken up by blasting, then placed on cars by large steam shovels. After being crushed, it is carried by electric trains down to the coast. The ore trains as they run downgrade to the sea generate the electricity that pulls the empty cars up the hill again. At the coast, the ore, after being weighed automatically, is dumped into large bins. The ore ships, owned or chartered by the company, dock alongside these bins. When the freighter comes alongside, the bins are opened, and the ship is loaded in a very short time. Tofo is a town of about 2,000 inhabitants, of whom 90 per cent are Chileans.

Courtesy Pan American Union.

Fig. 79. Panoramic view of Valparaíso, Chile.

The port of Caldera warrants attention for two reasons. First, the railway built by the well-known William Wheelwright from Caldera to Copiapó, a distance of about 50 miles, is said to be one of the oldest railways in South America. Second, Caldera is the site of an important smelting works. Piers are available for landing and embarking passengers. There is also a railway pier from which copper, manganese, and other minerals, some concentrates and others in ore, can be loaded directly into ships moored alongside.

Antofagasta is identified as the Pacific terminal of the Antofagasta-Bolivia railway and the Antofagasta-Argentina railway. Previous to the War of the Pacific, this port was Bolivia's outlet to the sea. Antofagasta is supported by two other ports, Caleta Coloso on the south and Mejillones on the north. These ports are all connected by railways. At Antofagasta, cargo is handled in lighters. Passengers come ashore in launches or rowboats. Large ocean ships cannot dock, but anchor in the open harbor. Bolivia uses this port as one of her shipping points for copper bars, tin concentrates, and silver ore. A huge smelter partly refines much of the silver and obviates the need for shipping raw ore. Mejillones, Caleta Coloso, and Antofagasta are outlets for the products of the world's largest copper mines, located at Chuquicamata.

Iquique, a famous nitrate port, is located 800 miles north of Valparaíso. A railway connects Iquique with the nitrate plants in the interior and joins the longitudinal railway at Pozo Almonte. The roadstead at Iquique is unprotected. There are several piers in front of the town and a few on the north side of Iquique Island, but the water's depth will not permit ocean-going vessels of any size to approach them. Cargo is handled in lighters. Iquique is a waterless and virtually rainless town. Its water supply is piped 75 miles across the desert from springs at the foot of the Andes.

Arica, the most northern of the important ports of Chile, is best known for its railway connections with the Bolivian Plateau and with the Peruvian city of Tacna. This is the shortest route to La Paz. Arica has been destroyed a number of times by earthquakes, which visit the entire western coast of South America with some frequency. A disastrous quake occurred in 1868. It was followed by a tidal wave that caused the death of nearly all the inhabitants of Arica. Two United States ships, the *Santee* and the *Wateree*, were dashed ashore at Arica. During the war of 1879 the hull of the *Wateree* was used as a hospital, and later was used as a lazaretto during a plague.

Transportation. The railway pattern of Chile is indicative of the country's physical, political, and commercial characteristics. There are now more than 4,600 miles of line in operation, of which three-fifths are operated by the Chilean State Railways.

The longitudinal railway, extending some 2,000 miles from Puerto Montt in the south to Pisagua in the far north, emphasizes the elongated nature of the country. Past political difficulties with Spain, Bolivia, and Peru are in part responsible for the extensive railway development of the north. During the war in which Spain was the aggressor against the four west-coast countries (Ecuador, Peru, Chile, Bolivia), Chile discovered to her dismay that she could not transport troops to defend threatened points. She vowed never again to be caught so unprepared. From that occasion her longitudinal railway was conceived and rapidly evolved. The nitrate resources of the Atacama Desert, as well as the minerals of Bolivia, are also factors contributing to Chile's interest. She needs railway facilities in the northern part of her lands to transport products, as well as for defense.

The difference in climate between the north and south is another geographic factor of importance in the discussion of Chilean railways. The agriculturally productive central valley of Chile must provide food and material for shelter and clothing for the inhabitants of the mining towns and communities of the north.

Many feeders and branch lines unite the longitudinal railway with the port cities. There are numerous individual port lines—that is, railways connecting mineral areas with the coast. On this western side of the continent, railways do not branch out from a single port like the ribs of a fan, as they do from so many ports on the east coast.

Chile has railway connection with Argentina and Bolivia. Perhaps the most magnificently scenic railway in the world is the Trans-Andean, a part of the route from Valparaíso to Buenos Aires, a distance of 868 miles. The railway depends for its existence upon freight between Argentina and Chile. Both these nations have stifled imports by tariff walls, seemingly the only way to reduce imports and balance national budgets. Consequently, freight for the Trans-Andean Railway has been greatly reduced.

F. A. Carlson.

Fig. 80. Life, snow, and barren slopes in the high Chilean Andes. A railway laborer's hut and son.

Daily airliners between Santiago and Buenos Aires have taken some of the through passenger service and increased the financial difficulties of the Trans-Andean Railway. Daily plane service has also been in operation for several years between La Paz, in Bolivia, and Pacific Coast ports, competing with railway passenger service over the Andes.

Chile is improving and extending its domestic air transportation service and its international operations in Argentina and Peru. All lines crossing Chile's territory must arrange for traffic stops, and most of these made must be at Santiago. Chile is known for its rigorous international air-transport policy, and maintains a Civil Aeronautics Board patterned after that of the United States.

A railway that crosses the border of Peru, joining the much-discussed towns, Tacna and Arica, was constructed as a result of the final settlement of the long-standing territorial dispute between Chile and Peru. A line from Arica over the Andes to La Paz, 283 miles long, is the shortest and best route to Bolivia from the Pacific Coast. From Antofagasta one Trans-Andean railway climbs the sierra to central Bolivia, then proceeds north to La Paz, a total distance of 722 miles; another line extends to Salta, Argentina.

The railway between Antofagasta and Salta, opened in 1948, warrants particular attention. It may serve as a means of crossing the Andes at times when the historical Trans-Andean route, farther south, is blocked by snow. It joins the desert land of Chile, with its mineral resources, with agricultural and forest regions of Argentina. The extent to which traffic may move over this route, however, still remains problematical. In the first year of operation the volume of cargo carried was far below expectations.

From an engineering standpoint, the construction of the Antofagasta-Salta railway is noteworthy. The length of the route is about 555 miles. It extends from sea level to approximately 14,000 feet at Socompa, on the Chilean-Argentine border. There are 12 tunnels, 13 viaducts, and 32 bridges, some of which are more than 600 feet in length. The line is single track of 3 feet 3⅜ inches gauge. Some of the crossties are of quebracho wood.

In the vicinity of Valparaíso and Santiago is found the most intensive pattern of railway development in all Chile.

In all, it can be said that Chile is well served with railways, and that these railways have meant much in the creation of a spirit of national unity.

Coal, oil, and electricity are used as power. The line from Valparaíso to Santiago is electrified. The northern railways use both coal and oil.

Numerous roads suitable for automobiles have also been constructed. The government has under way an extensive plan for the building and improvement of roads to give access to railway systems and consuming centers. Motor roads in Chile, however, as in all other portions of South America, are confined largely to the urban centers and their immediate vicinity. Development promises to be rapid, however, because future progress in Chile as well as in all of South America will require improved highways for motor transport service.

Mineral resources. Chile is known in North America chiefly as a producer of nitrates and copper. In the northern deserts are enormous deposits of natural nitrates and salts. The land along much of this desert section drops off sharply into the sea. Behind these coastal cliffs lie the deserts, stretching in barren waves back to the Andes. In these deserts, in a field some 500 miles long, lie the nitrate and copper deposits, most of them within 35 miles of the coast—the closest 15, the farthest 90 miles.

Beginning in the middle of the past century, nitrates were exploited by citizens of Chile, Peru, and Bolivia. The territory at that time belonged to Bolivia and was uncontested. The Chileans, however, were the more active in their exploitation of the industry. Because of conflicts between these nationals and the governments, in which each government took the side of its own citizens, the War of the Pacific finally came (1879–1883). The defeat of Peru and Bolivia in that sharp but decisive conflict resulted in a rearrangement of large portions of the coast. Chile drove Bolivia from the Pacific, absorbing its entire province of Antofagasta, including the seaport by that name. It also insisted on taking Peruvian territory up to and including the province of Arica. This war gave Chile complete possession of the entire nitrate deposits.

Bolivia has never ceased to protest the loss of its seaboard, and still insists that it must be restored. Peru continued vehemently to protest the loss of Tacna and Arica, and the matter was finally settled in 1930 by giving Tacna definitely to Peru and Arica definitely to Chile. A liberal indemnity of $6,000,000 and the construction of a railway at Chile's expense from the port of Arica to the interior Peruvian city of Tacna eased the settlement.

The nitrate industry has experienced many vicissitudes. Beginnings in 1850 were small, but from that time until 1913 there was a constant increase in the amount produced. After a sharp decline, the demands of the First World War caused production to leap to almost 3,000,000 tons in 1916. Following that war there was a sharp decline as compared to the world's total production. The drop, of course, is due to the increased production of synthetic nitrogen in other parts of the world. The annual output of Chilean nitrate is approximately 1,500,000 metric tons.

COPPER: PRODUCTION IN METRIC TONS *

Country	*1937*	*1946*	*1948*
Chile	413,010	358,848	414,289
Peru	36,649	24,592	18,068
Bolivia	3,699†	6,127	6,616
Ecuador		2,699	482
United States	763,844	552,234	757,326
Canada	240,416	166,892	217,614
U. S. S. R.‡	94,250	150,000	180,000
Belgian Congo ‡	150,588	143,885	155,481
N. Rhodesia	249,835	191,546	226,472
World Total	2,329,598	1,846,000	2,321,000

* Source: Bureau of Mines, Department of the Interior, Washington, D. C.
† Copper content of exports.
‡ U. S. S. R. and Belgian Congo—smelter content.

Under an agreement with world producers of synthetic and by-product nitrates, the Chilean industry is fighting desperately to continue to hold its own. Lower world prices and heavy export charges have compelled its industrialists to improve methods of extraction. At the present time Chile is probably producing less than one-fifth of the world's total supply, and the likelihood is that it will produce constantly less of the total. Since a considerable part of the governmental income and almost half the funds needed to balance foreign exchange have been derived

Courtesy Pan American Union.

Fig. 81. Copper mining in Chile. The Braden Copper Company.

from this source, the necessity for a great change in national affairs is obvious.

Farther inland in the same deserts with the nitrates lie extensive copper deposits. These are among the most important deposits in the world. Open-face mines, with consequent ease of production, and enormous reserves, guarantee the future of this industry if world demand for copper remains high. Chile's average annual production of copper under normal conditions is about 400,000 tons of high-grade copper. The two present fields, at Chuquicamata and Potrerillos, could probably greatly increase their output if necessary. In middle Chile, at El Teniente, about 70 miles southeast of Santiago, enormous deposits also exist. Many smaller mines are in operation. Their production is limited. It is not impossible that other vast resources in copper may yet be uncovered. Until 1875 Chile was the world's chief source of copper, and still ranks first in the world as exporter of copper. In total production, however, today Chile is surpassed by the United States, the world's largest producer. In 1948 Chile produced about 415,000 short tons of copper, and in the same year the United States imported Chilean copper amounting to about 300,000 tons.

Gold and silver have been mined in hundreds of places throughout the Andes, but rich concentrations have not been found in Chile. The majority of the Chilean gold mines are alluvial washings, located in the northern half of the nation's territory. Chile possesses ore deposits of lead and zinc, aluminum, manganese and tungsten, and other minerals. Chile and California produce most of the world's supply of borax.

Iron is present in several districts, principally in the two northern provinces of Atacama and Coquimbo. One of the largest iron ore deposits, known as the Tofo mines, is located near Coquimbo. Chile's annual output of iron ore is more than 1,500,000 tons. The Tofo production is shipped, as previously mentioned, from the artificially created harbor at Cruz Grande and it is smelted at Sparrows Point, Maryland. The iron mountain at Tofo contains reserves estimated at 200,000,000 tons. Output is governed largely by availability of shipping space, and not by productive capacity.

Chile is the leading South American country in the production of coal. Its principal coal resources are in the south from the vicinity of Talca to the Strait of Magellan. Over two million metric tons are mined annually; this production is sufficient for the entire national consumption. A high tariff wall has shut out most of the foreign competition. Chilean coal, however, does not make good coke, and therefore is supplemented by foreign coking coal or coke for the manufacture of iron and steel.

Mention has already been made of Chile's limited domestic production of petroleum. An intensive search for oil is in progress, but in the meantime Chile depends upon imports from Peru, Argentina, Venezuela, and the United States.

Industrialization. Self-sufficiency is Chile's major industrial objective. Its factories are producing most of the simpler manufactures needed by its people, and they have some products to export. Chile is now undertaking more complex manufactures. Work is progressing on a steel plant, located in the region of Concepción, a growing industrial center. In 1948, Chile for the first time produced storage batteries, automobile radiator hose, and garden hose. A spun rayon plant came into operation near San Antonio. A new fish-freezing plant began operations in Iquique, and three woolen mills in the Concepción area started production. A new cotton mill has been added to the textile industry in Santiago and one in Valparaíso. In addition to these new developments, Chile's manufacturing output increased in plants producing soap, glass, paper, silk piece goods, matches, gas, coke and tar and their products, beverages, woolen piece goods, chemicals, refined sugar, and processed foods.

The United States purchased 58 per cent of Chile's exports in 1940, as compared with 31 per cent in 1939, 16 per cent in 1938, and about 45 per cent in 1947. The United States furnished 48 per cent of Chile's imports in 1940, compared with 31 per cent in 1939, 28 per cent in 1938, and about 44 per cent in 1947.

For the past two decades or more, the two leading exports have been copper and nitrate, amounting to about 60 per cent, in value, of the total exports in 1948. In 1930 nitrate held first place in Chile's exports, but since that date the most important commodity in the nation's foreign trade has been copper. Other important products in the export trade are beans, wool, malt, iodine, fibers, wines, lentils, and fresh and frozen meat.

CHILE: FOREIGN TRADE

	Total Value (000 Dollars)	*Percentage of Total*					
Exports		United States	Canada	Latin America	United Kingdom	Continental Europe	All Others
1938	141,010	15.7		4.6	21.8	31.4	26.6
1947	280,043	44.5		16.5	10.6	24.3	4.2
Imports							
1938	103,035	27.8	0.3	13.8	10.1	40.7	7.2
1947	269,965	43.7	1.2	34.4	5.2	10.2	5.4

CHILE: EXPORTS OF PRINCIPAL COMMODITIES

Commodity	*Quantity in Metric Tons* 1947	1948	*Percentage of Total Value of All Exports* 1947	1948
Copper ingots	366,903	414,603	55.0	59.6
Nitrate	1,666,356	1,697,164	12.4	16.2
Iodine compounds	1,179	639	1.0	0.4
Iron ore	1,746,998	2,625,068	0.6	1.7
Wool	5,965	7,490	1.6	2.1
Malt	23,408	20,875	1.5	1.3
Beans	33,557	36,086	2.4	2.2
Lentils	8,647	23,905	0.5	1.1
Henequen fiber	4,684	1,514	0.8	0.2
Forage barley	2,483	36,882	...	1.2

Source: Office of International Trade, United States Department of Commerce, Washington, D. C., 1950.

Chile's leading export centers, in order of value of exports, are: Antofagasta, San Antonio, Tocopilla, Chañaral, Valparaíso, Iquique, Coquimbo, Talcahuano, Valdivia, Caldera, Taltal, and Puerto Montt. In order of value of imports, the leading ports are Valparaíso, Talcahuano, Antofagasta, Tocopilla, Punta Arenas, San Antonio, Valdivia, Chañaral, Coquimbo, Iquique, Penco, and Los Andes.

The future of Chile. The mineral industry has been the foundation of Chile's development. It has provided it with good railways and equipment, port facilities, modern cities, and employment for its citizens. But the time has come when Chile will not be able to rest so heavily as in the past on the returns from its mineral resources. Chile can no longer depend upon the revenue derived from an export tax on nitrates to care for a large part of the governmental expenses. There are no other minerals to bear the burden in place of nitrates, although to a small extent Chile can expect returns from an export tax on copper and iron ores.

The future of Chile depends on a more evenly balanced economy based on raw materials and industries—agriculture, mining, and manufactures. Chile must utilize more completely the agricultural lands of its central valley and the grazing possibilities of its southern provinces. This does not mean large-scale expansion, because Chile's productive crop- and grazing-lands are decidedly limited. The potential agricultural land, however, is sufficient in area, if properly utilized, to improve materially the nation's economy. The main objective is to improve the standards of living of the low-income group—comprising about 80 per cent of Chile's total population.

SELECTED REFERENCES

Bowman, I.: "Desert Trails of Atacama," *Special Publication No. 5,* American Geographical Society, New York, 1924.

Briegleb, P. A. and Haig, I. T.: "The Forest Resources of Chile," *Agriculture in the Americas,* Vol. IV, No. 12 (1944), p. 223.

Ellsworth, P. T.: *Chile: An Economy in Transition,* The Macmillan Company, New York, 1945.

Guest, Paul L.: "Chile's Pattern of Agricultural Production and Trade," *Foreign Agriculture,* Vol. 10, No. 3 (1946), pp. 106–114.

Hanson, Earl P.: *Chile, Land of Progress,* Reynal & Hitchcock, New York, 1941.

Hanson, Earl P.: "Out-of-the-World Villages of Atacama," *Geographical Review,* Vol. XVI (1926), pp. 365–377.

Hitchcock, Charles B.: "Empresa Borsari—Italian Settlement in Tierra Del Fuego." *Geographical Review,* Vol. 39, No. 4 (1949), pp. 640–648.

Jefferson, M.: "The Rainfall of Chile," *Research Series, No. 7,* American Geographical Society, New York, 1921.

Light, Richard and Mary: "Atacama Revisited—Desert Trails, Seen from the Air," *Geographical Review,* Vol. XXXVI, No. 4, pp. 525–545.

McBride, George McCutchen: *Chile: Land and Society,* American Geographical Society, New York, 1936.

Rich, John L.: "The Nitrate District of Tarapacá, Chile: An Aerial Traverse," *Geographical Review*, Vol. XXXI (1941), pp. 1–22.

Rudolph, W. E.: "The New Territorial Divisions of Chile, with Special Reference to Chiloé," *Geographical Review*, Vol. XIX (1929), pp. 61–77.

Rudolph, W. E.: "The River Loa of Northern Chile," *Geographical Review*, Vol. XVII (1927), pp. 553–585.

Sedgwick, Ruth: Frontier Stories of Southern Chile, *Bulletin of the Pan American Union*, Vol. 82, No. 1 (1948), pp. 1–9.

Sedgwick, Ruth: "Chile's Economic Problems," *The World Today*, Vol. 5, No. 1 (1949), pp. 39–46.

"Settlement of the Tacna-Arica Boundary Dispute," *Geographical Review*, Vol. XIX (1929), pp. 501–503.

Skottsberg, C.: "The Islands of Juan Fernandez," *Geographical Review*, Vol. V (1918), pp. 362–383.

Tercero, J.: "Chile Revamps the Nitrate Industry," *Bulletin of the Pan American Union*, Vol. LXVIII (1934), pp. 334–342.

Williams, F. E.: "Crossing the Andes at 41° South," *Bulletin of the Geographical Society of Philadelphia*, Vol. XXXII (1934), pp. 1–9.

Wilson, J. P.: "Chile's Land of Magellan," *Agriculture in the Americas*, Vol. V, No. 1 (1945), pp. 8–9.

CHAPTER XV

PERU: A LAND OF ANCIENT AND MODERN CULTURE

Ancient culture. When Francisco Pizarro reached Peru in 1532, he found a remarkable people, the Incas. These native Indians had established social and political institutions and had developed a well-ordered form of agriculture. On the highlands of southern Peru they had erected a civic unit, the capital of the Inca empire, now known as Cuzco. Many of the remains of this early civilization—walls, buildings, citadels, and irrigation systems—are still intact.

Peru has continued, with some interruptions, to maintain an important place in the affairs of South America and the world at large. Its mountains are the source of valuable minerals. On the coastal lowlands are extensive regions of cotton and sugar. Modern cities and comparatively good transportation facilities exist within its borders.

Regional characteristics. Peru is divided into four well-defined regions: (1) the coastal desert, (2) the Andean ranges and associated plateaus, (3) the montaña, or foothills and valleys east of the mountains, and (4) the Amazon Plain. The physical and cultural composition of these four regions are widely different.

The coastal area. Along Peru's entire shore line, from the Gulf of Guayaquil on the north to a spot near the port of Arica on the south, lies a narrow coastal lowland from 10 to 40 miles wide. On one side a steep escarpment drops off sharply into the Pacific Ocean. The other side merges into the foothills of the maritime cordillera of the Andes.

Nearly all of this area is rainless during the entire year. The southern half is benefited by a heavy fog, accompanied frequently by a light drizzling rain during the months from June to September. The far northern section receives an occasional shower during these same months, but the prevailing winds bring no moisture. These winds come from two sources. First, a breeze accompanies the Peruvian Current from the far south. Coming from a colder to a warmer temperature, this wind absorbs moisture and does not give it up. Second, the trade winds blow across the Atlantic from east to west and reach the coast of Brazil on the far side of South America. They are heavily laden with moisture, and as they rise over the slopes of the Andes precipitation occurs in the form of rain or snow. When they descend the western slopes of the Peruvian ranges, these winds are dry because of adiabatic heating. They have no moisture of their own to deposit, and tend to absorb what little exists in the parched soil.

Most of the rain and snow deposited against the slopes of the mountains finds its way into the Amazon region. In many places, however, streams break through the western range and descend to the Pacific Ocean; they water the desert as they cross and produce fertile oases. About half of these streams rise either in permanent highland lakes or are fed by perennial waters from the snow-clad higher peaks. They have, therefore, a permanent flow. The other half rise in the western range, where the summits do not extend above the snow line. These streams are full, therefore, in the rainy season, but are dry during the major portion of the year. Wells dug in their beds give some supply of water.

Where the streams from the mountains cut across the desert, there are oases of splendidly fertile land—made possible by irrigation—and profitable plantations support thriving villages and cities. The total area of the coastal desert, not including the foothills and mountain slopes behind, comprises altogether some 50,000 square miles, not more than a tenth of Peru's total area. Perhaps one-tenth of the desert is under cultivation, but altogether not more than 5,000 square miles.

The coastline of 1,400 miles is cut by 50 or more streams, an average of approximately one in 25 miles. The greatest single extent of desert is 70 miles. The streams are, therefore, fairly well distributed.

From the earliest Inca days these small rivers have been used to irrigate the coastal desert through which they flow. This practice is still followed, and more and more land is being constantly reclaimed. For the most part the irrigation system is simple. Water follows dirt-bound canals that radiate from the upper levels of the streams, supplies first the needs of the higher fields, and gradually seeks lower levels. It has been claimed many times that, if more impounding dams were constructed, a considerable additional area of fertile land could be reclaimed. Much of the desert, however, is unfit for production, even if irrigated. It is composed of sand and gravel, from the surface of which much of the finer sand has been blown. A barren waste of coarse gravel is left. The fine sand travels along the desert in crescent-shaped dunes, called *medanos*, frequently with crests that are 10 to 12 feet high.

In this coastal region is produced most of the sugar and cotton that form so large a part of Peru's exports. The climate is tempered by the cool waters of the Pacific and is generally mild. More than a million people, a seventh of the nation's total population, live in this narrow irrigated strip or in fertile oases formed by streams higher upon the mountain sides. Near the mouth of each major river is a town or small city settlement, the port of shipment for the agricultural products of the irrigated valley above. Lima, the capital of Peru, and the villages and farms within a radius of 50 miles, have a combined population of more than half a million people.

Mineral deposits of various kinds are found in the desert and in the adjacent foothills. The most important mineral resource at present is petroleum, which is found far below the sands of the far northern desert. Talara, one of the points of shipment for petroleum and its refined products, is the westernmost city of South America. It is almost directly south of Cleveland, Ohio.

Courtesy Frank E. Williams.

Fig. 82. Petroleum field in northern Peru. Petroleum is one of Peru's leading natural resources. An active refinery is located at Talara.

Earthquakes occur frequently along the Peruvian coast, particularly throughout the southern half. The Cordillera Maritima contains numerous volcanic cones, concentrated in Ecuador and in the southern half of Peru, but distributed along the entire maritime chain. Some of these Peruvian volcanoes are active, but most of them are not. They are undoubtedly associated with the frequent earthquakes, some of great intensity, that have visited the region. In 1746 the port of Callao was destroyed by an earthquake and attendant tidal wave, with enormous loss of life. In 1868 and again in 1877 earthquakes destroyed Arequipa, an important city located halfway up the Andes, 90 miles from the sea; and the accompanying tidal wave overwhelmed the Chilean ports of Iquique and Arica. Earth vibrations are of frequent occurrence, and some of the city buildings have been constructed to resist them.

Off the coast of Peru lie 50 or more islands. One of the largest is the island of San Lorenzo, four and a half miles long. It is located just off the coast and partly forms the bay of Callao, Peru's principal port. Along the coast the headlands are often abrupt. The waters teem with fish, upon which feed innumerable birds. The islands and headlands have been enriched through many centuries by the droppings of these

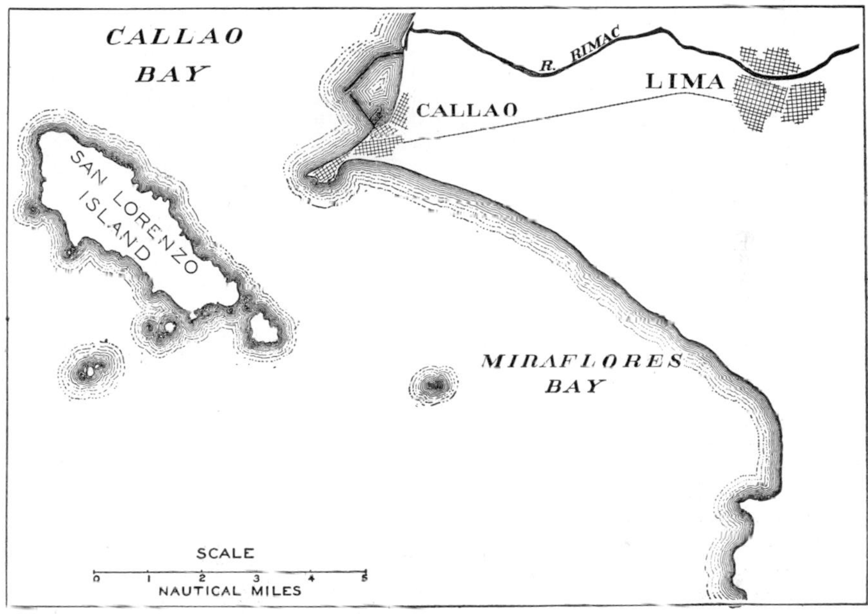

Fig. 83. The island of San Lorenzo and the Bay of Callao. Callao is Peru's principal port.

birds. The guano has been preserved, and it has retained its precious ammonia and other mineral salts because of the absence of rain. The most famous of the guano deposits are on the three Chincha islands, although guano occurs on practically all of these barren islands and headlands along the coast. For many years the product was exported, but now the greater part is consumed locally to enrich the fields of Peruvian and Chilean agriculturists. Exploitation of the guano deposits is now under strict governmental regulation.

The Andean system. Between the western desert and the eastern plains rise the towering ranges of the Andes. A rugged, chilly plateau averaging 12,000 feet in elevation, cut by numerous valleys, lies between

PERU: TEMPERATURE AND RAINFALL OF SELECTED STATIONS

	Station	Arequipa*	Mollendo†	Callao*	Lima‡	Cuzco†	Trujillo*	Iquitos*
	Elevation (*Feet*)	8041.3	80.	S. L.	420	10,728	196.9	347.8
Average Temperature (°*F.*)	*Period of Record*	1888–1920	10 yrs.	1900–1903	1931–1940	1931–1943	1896–1915 4 yrs.	1 yr.
	January	57.0	70.2	68.9	71.2	54.7	77.2	77.5
	February	57.0	70.7	70.2	72.9	54.7	77.0	78.3
	March	56.3	69.6	70.9	72.3	54.7	74.3	76.3
	April	57.4	67.3	69.8	68.9	54.1	72.0	77.0
	May	56.8	65.3	66.9	64.2	51.6	68.0	75.6
	June	55.8	61.7	65.5	61.2	50.4	63.0	74.3
	July	55.6	59.5	63.0	59.9	49.3	64.0	74.1
	August	56.8	59.4	62.4	59.5	51.3	64.2	76.3
	September	57.9	59.9	62.4	60.3	53.8	63.7	76.3
	October	56.5	62.1	64.2	62.1	55.6	67.5	77.2
	November	57.0	65.8	65.1	64.6	56.1	68.7	78.4
	December	57.4	68.4	68.5	67.6	55.4	72.0	77.9
	Annual	56.8	64.4	66.6	65.4	53.5	69.3	76.6
	Range	2.3	11.3	8.5	13.3	6.8	14.2	4.3
Average Rainfall (*Inches*)	*Period of Record*	1888–1924	10 yrs.	3 yrs.	1931–1940		2-4 yrs.	1 yr. 7 mo.
	January	1.18	0.04	0.00	0.05	5.4	0.16	10.0
	February	1.81	0.07	0.04	0.02	4.1	0.47	10.6
	March	0.59	0.00	0.00	0.02	3.2	0.28	12.0
	April	0.16	0.03	0.00	0.02	1.1	0.04	6.6
	May	0.04	0.07	0.04	0.13	0.3	0.00	9.8
	June	0.00	0.05	0.04	0.21	0.2	0.04	7.3
	July	0.04	0.04	0.47	0.31	0.1	0.08	6.5
	August	0.00	0.18	0.20	0.33	0.2	0.00	4.5
	September	0.00	0.19	0.08	0.31	1.4	0.00	8.8
	October	0.04	0.10	0.12	0.10	1.6	0.00	7.1
	November	0.04	0.06	0.00	0.07	2.2	0.08	8.5
	December	0.35	0.02	0.00	0.04	3.7	0.04	11.3
	Annual	4.17	0.85	0.98	1.61	23.5	1.18	103.3

* K. Knoch: "Klimakunde von Südamerika," *Handbuch der Klimatologie,* Band II, Teil G, Berlin, 1930.

† Perú, Ministerio de Aeronáutica Departamento de Meteorología, *Boletín, Anual Meteorológico,* 1935–1943.

‡ H. Helm Clayton: "World Weather Records," *Smithsonian Miscellaneous Collections,* Vol. 105, 1947.

the two high cordilleras of the Andes. A third range passes through the plateau from north to south.

Great areas of this plateau, known as the *puna,* are so inhospitable that they are neglected and uninhabited except by occasional miners or shepherds.[1] Wide swamps, areas of shifting sand, a wilderness of barren rock, as well as thousands of miles of unscalable mountain heights, repel habitation.

The highland population of Peru, like that of Bolivia, is concentrated in valleys or on mountain slopes that drop below the floor of the barren plateau and afford opportunity for streams to find their way to lower rivers. The fertility of these valleys, some of them steep and carefully

Courtesy Vanadium Corporation of America.

Fig. 84. Vanadium mine, Minas Ragra, Peru. Elevation 15,800 feet above sea level. Peru has the largest vanadium mine in the world, supplying about 80 per cent of the world's output.

terraced, is in striking contrast with the almost desert *puna* by which they are surrounded.

The lower valleys are tropical in verdure, the upper ones produce temperate-zone vegetation; and on the higher plateaus, up to 14,000 feet altitude, the hardy cereals are found.

Three great ranges of mountains traverse Peru from northwest to southeast and come together in two places to form a tangled mountain complex. In the far southeast, the Cordilleras de Caravaya, Vilcanota, and Vilcabamba, great mountain masses with many ramifying branches, unite to form the northern boundary of the Titicaca Basin. To the northwest, other cordilleras complete the eastern flank of the Andes.

The far eastern ranges rise abruptly from the Amazon Basin in places,

[1] *Puna* is a general term applied to the dry-cold highlands extending from Ecuador to central Chile. In Bolivia the region is known as Altiplano.

and form the boundary of the basin. These ranges, composed largely of Paleozoic rocks, attain altitudes of 18,000 feet. The western ranges, separated mostly by a rather narrow plateau, are Mesozoic, overlaid by volcanic ashes and lava. In places, notably in the valley of the Oroya River above Lima, carbonaceous rocks, containing seams of coal, occur. The western ranges are a bit higher than the eastern, the highest peaks reaching 20,000 feet. Volcanic eruptions occur with such frequency and regularity that the people are always on the alert for them. Lava and volcanic ashes produce a very fertile soil, and at the foot of some of the volcanoes is found the finest agricultural land of Peru. Because of the volcanic activity, this region abounds in thermal springs, many highly mineralized.

In the mountains forming the western chains are found numerous alpine lakes, the sources of streams that flow mostly to the Pacific Coast. These are the breeding grounds for the myriads of ducks and other wild fowl of the region. In Lake Lauricocha, just north of Cerro de Pasco, less than a hundred miles from the Pacific Ocean, the Marañón River rises. The Marañón is one of the principal headstreams of the Amazon. It flows 350 miles northwest from Lake Lauricocha, between mountain ranges, before it descends eastward to enter the Amazon Basin. The torrential nature of the Marañón, like that of other sierra streams, is shown in its drop from an altitude of 12,000 feet to 575 feet in the course of 350 miles.

The second river of importance is the Huallaga, which also originates just north of Cerro de Pasco. It flows between the central and the eastern ranges, is augmented by numerous tributaries, and in the lower plain connects with the Marañón.

The third great river system of the Peruvian Andes is that of the Ucayali. Its many tributaries and headstreams drain most of the region between Cerro de Pasco and Vilcanota. Flowing north, south, east, and west, these streams finally merge and break through the eastern sierra at about 9° S. latitude. From this point the Ucayali moves sluggishly through the lowland until it joins the Marañón.

In general, highland rivers rush as torrents through deep gorges and canyons that are practically inaccessible to man. In numerous places, however, these canyons broaden into wide and fertile valleys at altitudes of 4,000 to 10,000 feet. These fertile subtropical and temperate valleys are the population centers of highland Peru, and in them nestle the principal communities.

The ancient people of Peru, Incas and pre-Incas, terraced the steep sides of many narrow valleys with great care and cultivated them to support a population much larger than this region boasts today. Most of these terraced fields are now abandoned, and many are almost inaccessible.

The Montaña. To the eastward of the Andes are places where the mountains rise abruptly from the lowlands. Often in a distance of 15 or 20 miles a descent of two miles occurs, from a plateau of 15,000 feet to upland valleys at 5,000 feet, or from mountain ridges at 6,000 feet to flat lowlands at 500 feet above sea level. Rugged hills, almost impassable escarpments, plunging cascades, and great water-worn crevasses are the rule in these areas. On the higher levels, plant life is limited to shrubs, small flowering plants, and mosses. Halfway down the bare sides of the escarpments extensive areas of candelabra cacti may appear; these are indications that the barren soil is alkaline. Forests flourish in more favored valleys. In Peru these lands, transitional between the high

Courtesy Ynés Mexía and Pan American Union.

Fig. 85. Mango tree in Montaña region, Peru.

Andes and Amazon lowlands, are known as the *montaña;* in Bolivia they are called the *yungas.*

Many spurs from the Andes extend eastward and thrust their way into the jungle. They are covered with forests; their slopes are well drained, they are well supplied with water; their soil in many places is rich; and they make excellent agricultural land.

The climate of this region is intermediate between the humid oppressiveness of the lower forest and the bitter cold of the plateau. As yet population is sparse in the montaña, although there are many excellent plantations of coffee, sugar, cacao, and fruits, as well as of cotton and coca.

The Amazon Plain of Peru. Below the montaña lie the heavily forested lowlands. Rainfall is heavy; vegetation is lush; population is scant; drainage is poor because land surface is nearly flat; and altitudes are seldom greater than 400 feet above the sea. This territory is threaded with broad waterways that are navigable for hundreds of miles by small craft. Much of it has never been explored. It is inhabited by scattered Indians. Except for a few river ports and the production of small amounts of rubber, Brazil nuts, ivory nuts, and timber, the region has but little commercial value today. The only city of importance at present is Iquitos. It is situated at the head of ocean navigation, and consequently it is the point of transshipment.

Peru's total area of something over 500,000 square miles includes, approximately, 50,000 miles of coastal desert, 200,000 miles of mountain and plateau, 30,000 miles of montaña, and perhaps 220,000 miles of Amazon lowland forests.

Population. The population of Peru has never been accurately ascertained. It is estimated to number between seven and eight million persons, nearly all of Indian or Spanish blood. (The official estimate is 7,860,000.) On the highlands and in the smaller towns the Indian predominates, while in the principal cities, especially toward the coast, Spanish types are more frequent. On the coastal desert small numbers of Chinese and Japanese have settled. These Orientals came in when inexpensive labor was needed on the plantations. Treated harshly at first, they have made their way to economic independence, and they are becoming increasingly influential. They have practically a monopoly on the small meat and grocery businesses and on the restaurants. Intermarriage between them and Peruvians is common. In northern Peru there are some 50,000 Negroes. It would be a safe estimate, however, that at least 80 per cent of the population is either entirely Indian or so largely Indian as to be considered such.

The Indians come from two distinct racial families, the Aymará and the Quechua. The first are the larger, the more stolid, the more resistant to Spanish domination of the land. The Quechua were the Incas. They came into power about the year 1200 and continued until the Spanish conquest. When Pizarro came in 1532, he found it a relatively simple matter to overthrow their empire and establish in its stead a viceroyalty of Spain.

The Peruvian Indians submitted to the Spanish conquest without great resistance, and their placid response to the authority of the whites has continued to this day. Fusion of Spanish and Indians was never widespread, and this fact accounts for the high percentage of pure Indian stock.

The Spanish dominate politically, economically, and culturally, and the aristocracy is largely white. Inheriting the choicest lands and the richest mines from their ancestors, the *conquistadores*, these folk have kept their advantage through the centuries. Their descendants of pure Spanish blood led in the movements for independence. They seized political power a century or more ago and have retained it ever since.

The white, or creole, children have enjoyed whatever advantages of education there were, while the offspring of Indian parents have remained uneducated. Normally, therefore, the Spanish became the merchants, the captains of industry, the religious and educational leaders, the officers of army and navy. And so it continues today. Most of the Indians are simply peons who serve the white or mixed-blood owners of the land. They give three days a week service as rental for the miserable huts they occupy. It is the exceptional family of pure Indian blood that has risen to wealth or position in the nation, although a few have accomplished it. *The welfare of the Indian should be Peru's major challenge.*

The Peruvian government is making extensive efforts to open the foothills of the eastern Andes, the montaña, to agricultural development, and has attempted to encourage natives—particularly Indians—and foreigners to consider the possibilities of the region. The land is well watered and rich; the climate is equable; and the future is assured if initial difficulties can be overcome.

Cities. Peru contains a number of interesting cities. The capital, Lima, lies in a coastal oasis eight miles from the Pacific, at an altitude of about 400 feet. It is located in the Rimac Valley, and behind it towers the hill of San Cristóbal. Established by the conqueror Pizarro some 400 years ago, it early became the seat of Spanish political authority in the New World. Into it poured the wealth of the continent, and here centered the culture, the art, the education, and the commercial interests of Spanish South America. Pizarro selected the site for his capital, not only for its beauty and fertility, but also because it lies just above a most excellent harbor.

The heart of the city is the Plaza de Armas (many cities of western South America have their Plazas de Armas), about which are grouped the most important public buildings. From this plaza streetcar lines radiate to all sections of the city. The University of San Marcos, located in this city, is one of the oldest institutions of its kind in North or South America, having been established in 1551. It now includes schools of theology, law, and medicine, the traditional courses with which it began, and also schools of philosophy, literature, and political science. This university recently organized a summer course for students from the United States and Europe who might wish to spend a culturally profitable vacation there.

Lima is the commercial as well as the political capital of the nation. Located only eight miles from Callao, a thriving seaport, it is practically the "upper city," with Callao the "lower city." Most importing houses have headquarters in Lima and warehouses in the port. The principal foreign banks have their branches there, and, of course, foreign legations and consulates are centered in Lima. A railroad and a beautiful automobile road connect the capital directly with the port. On the coast near Lima are several attractive seaside towns and bathing resorts, the residences of the more prosperous families. The city is thoroughly modern and European. A preponderant portion of the population of Lima and its suburbs is of Spanish descent.

Courtesy A. Guillen. Supplied by C. Langdon White.

Fig. 86. Peru: Street scene in Otuzco.

POPULATION OF PRINCIPAL URBAN CENTERS OF PERU

Lima	533,600
Callao	84,400
Arequipa	60,000
Cuzco	45,000
Trujillo	41,600
Iquitos	40,000
Mollendo	15,000

In sharp contrast with Lima is the capital of ancient Inca culture, Cuzco, which has hardly been touched by modernizing European influences. It is about 11,000 feet above sea level, 200 miles inland, and is the northern commercial terminus of the Southern Railway of Peru. Its population is about 45,000, principally Indians. In the period of its glory, Cuzco had a quarter of a million inhabitants. It is situated in the center of a thickly populated valley that is well watered and fertile. The more prominent Incan ruins are to be found around this city—although such ruins are scattered throughout the land, from the ancient pre-Incan cities of the northern coastal desert to the magnificent temples, cities, and fortresses around southern Lake Titicaca.

Cuzco was rebuilt by the Spaniards in colonial times, and many Spanish buildings are constructed upon foundations of Incan origin. In and around the city are the remains of many outstanding specimens of Incan architecture. Here were palaces of the rulers, the fortress of Sacesahuaman (the mightiest ancient fortress in existence), a bridge built by the Incas over the Rio Guatenay, and the Temple of the Sun, upon the site of which has been constructed the convent of San Francisco.

Around Lake Titicaca, however, the most massive of the pre-Incan ruins are discovered. Many huge megalithic structures appear, with stones weighing 20 tons or more. There are many ancient tombs here. On the Island of the Moon, in the lake, are remains of several temples.

Arequipa, so often referred to as the political and the military, as well as the commercial, center of southern Peru, is located on the railway leading from Mollendo to the interior. Consequently, Arequipa has rail connections with the city of Cuzco and the Lake Titicaca region.

Peru has two principal ports and a number of smaller ones. Mollendo, a small oasis port to the south, has earned its importance as a railway terminal rather than as a haven for ships. Mollendo serves the southern portion of Peru and also serves as the port of entry for the Cuzco region, Lake Titicaca, and northern Bolivia. Since there are no through longitudinal railways in Peru, coast travel and transport are handled in ships.

Callao is the principal port of Peru and serves as the port of entry for Lima, the capital. Callao has one of the few fine harbors on the Pacific Coast of South America. A modern $6,000,000 pier, completed in 1931 by a North American construction company, provides docking facilities for ocean-going vessels. Railway connections, extending north and south from the port, serve a rich agricultural district and continue on through Lima to the interior. San Lorenzo, a large island, lies at the entrance to the bay of Callao and protects the harbor from direct ocean storms.

On the northern extremity of the Peruvian coast stands the small desert town of Talara, the chief petroleum port of the republic. Oil is piped from the fields to Talara, where it is refined and shipped.

Along the coast, each stream from the mountains forms an oasis in the desert; such oases are usually intensively cultivated. Small settlements have developed in each oasis. These towns are the seats of local culture. Frequently they are connected to small ports by railroads.

Iquitos, a town of about 40,000 permanent inhabitants and a floating population of 2,000, is the only city of importance found in the upper Amazon Basin. It is situated in territory formerly in dispute between Ecuador and Peru, but now definitely conceded to the latter. Iquitos is important because it is at the head of navigation for ocean-going steamers on the Amazon.

Transportation. Several railway lines radiate from small port towns at the mouths of streams and extend inland for short distances. They serve local irrigated districts where sugar and cotton are the principal crops. Only two main lines have been constructed, the Central Railway and the Southern Railway.

The Central Railway originates in Lima and its port, Callao. One branch extends north and south along the coast for a hundred miles or more. It connects Lima with a number of small but important towns, and serves a rich agricultural district. The principal line extends inland from Lima. With an enormous outlay of capital and the overcoming of exceedingly difficult engineering problems, the line was extended. At Oroya, a prosperous city in the sierra, it divides—one branch extending south to Huancavelica, the other extending north to serve the Cerro de Pasco copper mines. This northern branch was constructed by the mining company as a private venture. The southern branch may some day extend as far as Cuzco, to link that important center and the Lake Titicaca region with the capital.

Lofty plateaus, deep longitudinal valleys, steep divides, few transverse valleys, precipitous coastal slopes, rocky deserts, and few harbor indentations characterize much of Peru. This type of terrain makes very difficult the construction of railway lines. Difficulties of construction in the Andes are illustrated in the efforts of the Central Railway to climb the sierra. This is one of the most remarkable railways in the world, not only because of the altitude attained at its highest point, 15,865 feet above sea level, but as a feat of engineering unequalled in railway construction. There are 65 tunnels, 67 bridges, and 16 switchbacks at points where the steepness of the mountain slope permits no other way of ascent. Racks or cog-rails have not been used. Some trains have engines attached at both front and rear, in order to save time on switchbacks. The largest of the 67 bridges on this line, spanning the Verrugas ravine at a height of nearly 300 feet, is 575 feet in length. The central span of this bridge, 235 feet in length, rests on two vertical towers, each 175 feet in height. The largest of the 65 tunnels is the Galera, 3,857 feet long. On a branch line from Ticlio to the mines at Morococha, an altitude of 15,865 feet is reached. This is the highest point of any standard-gauge railway in the world. The highest altitude attained by a railway in the United States is on the Pike's Peak Line, which reaches to 14,109 feet above sea level. In Switzerland the Jungfrau railway reaches an altitude of 11,340 feet, the highest in Europe.

The Southern Railway of Peru enters from the coast at Mollendo. It ascends a difficult sierra until it reaches Arequipa, the most important city in southern Peru. This city of 60,000 people is known as the "wool market of Peru." It also happens to be a military station in which many revolutions have originated. From Arequipa the line passes on until it reaches the junction town of Juliaca. A branch turns northward at Juliaca to Cuzco and Macchu Picchu, while the main line turns south a

Courtesy Grace Line.

Fig. 87. Cuzco street scene, Peru. Cuzco was once the capital of the Inca empire.

short distance to Puno, the Peruvian port on Lake Titicaca. The traveller may cross this lake by steamer and on the Bolivian side take a train to La Paz; from there he can entrain for Buenos Aires or places in Chile.

Like other South American nations, Peru has sought to develop airlines. The great distances and the difficulties of constructing either railways or highways have encouraged this development. At the present time planes, en route from New York to Buenos Aires, serve all the west-coast cities of importance and cross the Andes behind Santiago in Chile. An airline connects the inland port of Iquitos with two principal cities on the plateau, Moyobamba and La Merced. Peruvian domestic air transport has expanded considerably. The principal domestic airlines, the Cia. de

Aviación Faucett and the Aviación Nacional del Sur (Andes), have greatly increased their operations. The Pan American, Panagra, and Braniff are the active United States airways serving Peru internationally.

Eastern Peru has river transportation on some of the main branches of the Amazon system. In this broad wilderness the rivers are the roads. Iquitos, the most important city in the upper Amazon region, is some 2,000 miles from the mouth of the great river and about 1,200 miles from

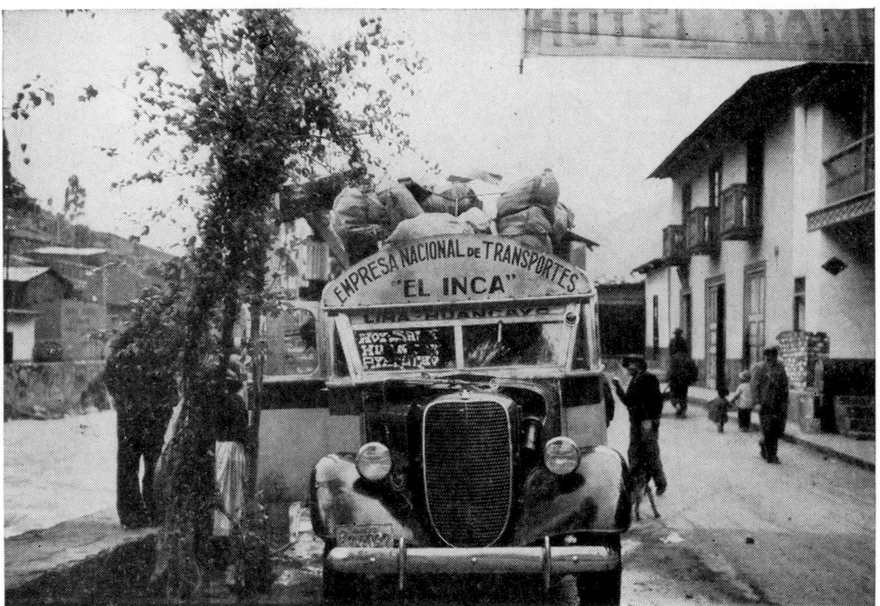

Courtesy Pan American Union.

Fig. 88. An all-important means of transportation in any land. Matucana, Peru.

Lima. An overland journey from Lima to Iquitos formerly included railroad from Lima to Oroya, motor from Oroya to La Merced, and muleback down the sierra to Puerto Jessup, in addition to a canoe or launch trip the remainder of the way—a journey requiring three weeks at the minimum. The same journey may now be taken in three or four days by using the plane service from La Merced down to Iquitos.

For several years the Peruvian government has had in mind the necessity of constructing highways adequate for motor vehicles. Slowly, these highways are being constructed. In the coastal regions one may travel in the vicinity of any of the principal cities without trouble, and a highway now extends the entire length of the country.

In the Andes the nature of the terrain makes it difficult to construct either railways or highways. Roads, however, have been completed between the dry coastal land and the humid tropical montaña country.

The Central Highway ascends the mountainous terrain to Oroya and from there extends to La Merced. Another road extends from Lima via Cerro de Pasco and Huánuco to Tingo María in the Huallago valley. From here a road has been completed to Pucallpa, located in the Ucayali lowlands. A new highway is under construction from Quince Mil toward Puerto Maldonado in the southeastern Peruvian Montaña region.

Mineral resources. Peru is thought of by North Americans primarily as a mineral-producing nation. In point of value, copper from Cerro de Pasco Mines in the high Andes and petroleum from the far northern coastal region are the principal mineral resources based on value. The

Courtesy Cerro de Pasco Copper Corporation.

Fig. 89. Copper mines—Morococha, Peru. Copper is closely associated with silver and lead production in Peru. Chile, Mexico, Peru, Cuba, and Bolivia are the principal copper-producing countries of Latin America.

annual output of copper is more than 20,000 metric tons and petroleum production averages yearly between twelve and fourteen million barrels. Most of the copper is shipped to the United States, and about one-half of the petroleum remains in Peru for domestic consumption. It is used in the operation of various industries, including some of the railways, and provides fuel for the constantly increasing number of automobiles.

Besides copper and petroleum, Peru produces quantities of silver. Much of it is mined as a by-product of copper, since the copper now being exploited contains a large silver residue. Gold, lead, zinc, vanadium, and other metals are produced in smaller quantities. Peru possesses the richest known deposits of vanadium in the world. Vanadium is basic to many steel alloys. It increases tensile strength, does not shatter, and withstands high temperatures.

It should be said, too, that perhaps the richest sources of mineral wealth in Peru have not been tapped. Petroleum may exist in the eastern slopes and lowlands of the Andes as well as in undeveloped regions of the Talara desert. Copper deposits are known to exist that may, when developed, rival those of Cerro de Pasco. They wait for extensive outlays of capital in the construction of railways and equipment before they can be exploited. In the department of Ica, the Marcona iron deposits are estimated to contain 200,000,000 tons of 56 per cent ore. This deposit is owned by the government.

Courtesy Servicio Aerofotográfico Nacional de Perú. Supplied by C. Langdon White.

Fig. 90. Peru: Pueblo di Viru. Agriculture in the desert coastal lands.

Although coal deposits have been reported in Peru, their inaccessible location has prevented exploitation. The Cerro de Pasco Copper Corporation mines small quantities of coal for use in connection with its smelting. There is no domestic coal available for the general market. The United States, Australia, and Chile export coal to Peru. The central Railway uses oil from the Talara fields, while the Southern Railway uses both oil and coal. There is a tendency to dispense with coal entirely and use only oil on the railways.

Agricultural resources. The real riches of Peru, like those of the other Andean nations, are not mineral. They are agricultural. Where irrigated, the coastal desert produces abundantly of tropical and subtropical vegetation. Fruits of all sorts—grapes, oranges, bananas, peaches, and pears—as well as many fruits not commonly known to North Americans, abound and are consumed locally or shipped to the cities. Vegetables were cultivated by the Incas and their predecessors. Potatoes, sweet potatoes, squashes, beans, and several leafy vegetables had been developed to a degree of high excellence long before the Spaniards came. These and many vegetables of European origin are produced abundantly for local use. Potatoes of several varieties grow well at altitudes of 12,000 feet, and even higher. The potato that draws the immediate attention of North American visitors is a deep golden yellow. Barley is produced even up to heights of 14,000 feet. Four months are usually required for

Courtesy Runcie. Supplied by C. Langdon White.

Fig. 91. Peru: Threshing with oxen in the Peruvian Sierra. Note crops on steep slopes and soil erosion.

barley to mature. A new variety that matures in 100 days, developed in the United States, has recently been introduced. The *quinoa*, a small grain of starch-protein value, is produced at still higher altitudes. It yields a heavy crop that is extensively used when either green or ripened.

The three export crops of Peru are cotton, sugar, and coffee. Because of the desert conditions under which the cotton is produced, often with no rainfall at all, the crop is unusually clean and fine; and insect pests that thrive in moist climates are almost unknown. Peruvian cotton ranks in quality with the best cotton of the same variety in the world.

Pastoral activities are highly important from the standpoint of foreign relations. No statistics are available, but estimates suggest that there may be as many as 2,600,000 cattle, some 17,000,000 sheep, 1,500,000 alpacas, and 700,000 llamas. The llamas are the principal beasts of burden, although native Indians frequently act as pack carriers. The wool from the llamas and the alpacas, probably better classified as hair, is consumed locally and also exported.

Wheat and rice are heavy imports for home consumption. Most of the wheat comes from Argentina, and Ecuador supplements Peru's local rice production. "Barbasco" is one of Peru's singular commodities. It is known as the source of the insecticide rotenone, and most of the output is exported to the United States.

Courtesy Runcie. Supplied by C. Langdon White.

Fig. 92. Peru: Llamas grazing in their native habitat in the Sierra.

Any description of Peruvian resources would be incomplete without mention of two distinctive but very different products—guano and coca.

We have already mentioned the guano islands and headlands along the Pacific Coast. From 100,000 to 150,000 tons of guano are now extracted each year in Peruvian territory. Most of it was formerly sold abroad, but considerable quantities are now used to fertilize the cotton and sugar fields in the lower desert. The Chilean government, as well as the government of Peru, has established a strict monopoly on extraction.

Coca is an alkaloid product from which cocaine and its narcotic derivatives are produced. It is cultivated in the highland valleys of the Andes, and several million pounds are produced annually. The leaves are mixed with quinoa leaves or with hydrated lime for flavor and made into a preparation that is widely employed as a stimulant. Indeed, it is much more commonly used than alcohol for that purpose. It is said that an

Indian undertaking a long and exhausting journey can endure almost unbelievable hardships and lack of food if he uses coca to stimulate himself. Coca, however, is a narcotic and every effort should be used to abolish its production and use.

Manufacturing. Peru's manufacturing industry is not unlike that of most of the Latin American countries. It is limited largely to the production of goods for home consumption, including such food items as flour-mill products, canned milk, beverages, and canned fish. Other industries are: textiles, paints, chemicals and drugs, leather and shoes, cement, glass, paper, tires, and silver manufactures. Of course, the activities associated with the mining and petroleum industries in refining and the like constitute an important phase of manufacturing or processing.

Foreign Trade. The chief Peruvian agricultural export crops are cotton and sugar. Petroleum and its products, generally, rank as the third most important export group. Ranking fourth are lead bars, and in fifth place are copper bars.

PERU: EXPORTS OF PRINCIPAL COMMODITIES

Commodity	*Quantity in Metric Tons*		*Percentage of Total Value of All Exports*	
	1947	*1948*	*1947*	*1948*
Sugar	275,546	351,406	29.9	21.2
Raw cotton	55,906	51,538	22.3	26.3
Crude petroleum	249,981	310,284	2.3	3.8
Gasoline	300,804	358,372	5.9	9.4
Mixed bars or ingots of copper with silver and gold	17,931	12,491	7.5	4.7
Electrolytic lead bars or ingots, refined	25,971	37,996	4.5	7.7
Zinc concentrates	99,678	84,920	3.4	3.9

Source: Office of International Trade, United State Department of Commerce, Washington, D. C., 1950.

The United States and Chile are the principal markets for Peruvian products, accounting for about one-fourth and one-fifth of the combined export value, respectively; the United Kingdom, generally, shares to the extent of about 10 per cent. The bulk of Peruvian exports of metals and minerals, sheep wool, canned fish, raw hides and skins, and many minor commodities are shipped to the United States, whereas the Chileans buy Peruvian sugar, cotton, and petroleum products. Crude petroleum, cotton, and sugar are the chief exports to the United Kingdom, Colombia and Argentina.

PERU: FOREIGN TRADE

	Total Value (000 Dollars)	Percentage of Total					
		United States	Canada	Latin America	United Kingdom	Continental Europe	All Others
Exports							
1938	76,705	26.8	4.9	20.1	20.0	24.1	4.1
1947	154,253	29.3	0.1	41.7	8.6	17.2	3.1
Imports							
1938	58,328	34.3	1.9	10.7	10.1	35.7	7.3
1947	167,999	58.3	2.3	20.1	6.6	9.0	3.8

For the past decade the order of the exports based on value has remained approximately the same. The nation's leading export centers are Callao, Talara, Chicama, Mollendo, Salaverry, Pisco, Paita, and Chancay. Imports are received primarily at Callao, Talara, Mollendo, Salaverry, Lima, Pisco, Paita, Iquitos, Pimentel, and Eten.

Summary. Much of Peru is inaccessible waste land. There are no extensive regions of arable land with adequate transportation facilities. Agricultural development on the coastal lowlands requires irrigation and this necessity adds to the cost of production. However, Peru has made remarkable progress in agriculture and is able to supply the farm products necessary for its people and to have a surplus for export. Revenue from taxes on minerals has added to the federal income and will probably continue to do so. Peru, unlike Bolivia, has made a definite move toward a balanced agricultural and mining economy. But, like Bolivia, a large percentage of its people are Indians, many of whom are classed as inactive, and they contribute little if anything to the nation's welfare. Peru's problem is the betterment of its middle class, particularly, landless inhabitants of Indian heritage.

SELECTED REFERENCES

Bowman, I.: *The Andes of Southern Peru,* American Geographical Society, New York, 1916.

Gibson, Charles: "The Inca Concept of Sovereignty and the Spanish Administration in Peru," *Latin American Studies IV,* The University of Texas Institute of Latin-American Studies, The University of Texas Press, Austin, 1948.

Holstein, Otto: "Chan-Chan: Capital of the Great Chimu," *Geographical Review,* Vol. XVII (1927), pp. 36–61.

Hoy, Harry E.: "A Survey of Rubber on the Middle Marañón Peru," *Papers of the Michigan Academy of Science Arts and Letters,* Vol. 30 (1944), pp. 433–448.

Longmore, W., and Loomis, C. P.: "Health Needs and Potential Colonization Areas of Peru," *Inter-American Economic Affairs,* Vol. III, No. 1 (1949), pp. 71–93.

McBride, G. M.: "Features of the Agrarian System in Peru," *Geographical Review,* Vol. XV (1925), pp. 137–139.

Miller, O. M.: "The 1927–1928 Peruvian Expedition of the American Geographical Society," *Geographical Review,* Vol. XIX (1929), pp. 1–37.

Milstead, H. P.: "Distribution of Crops in Peru," *Economic Geography,* Vol. IV (1928), pp. 88–106.

Murphy, R. C.: "The Oceanography of the Peruvian Littoral with Reference to the Abundance and Distribution of Marine Life," *Geographical Review,* Vol. XIII (1923), pp. 64–85.

Parró, Alberto Area: "Census of Peru," *Geographical Review,* Vol. XXXII (1942), pp. 1–20.

Platt, R. S.: "Six Farms in the Central Andes," *Geographical Review,* Vol. XXII (1932), pp. 245–259.

Rowe, J. H.: "The Distribution of Indians and Indian Languages in Peru," *Geographical Review,* Vol. 37, No. 3 (1947), pp. 202–215.

Shippee, R.: "The Great Wall of Peru, and Other Aerial Photographic Studies by the Shippee-Johnson Peruvian Expedition," *Geographical Review,* Vol. XXII (1932), pp. 1–29.

Shippee, R.: "Lost Valleys of Peru: Results of the Shippee-Johnson Peruvian Expedition," *Geographical Review,* Vol. XXII (1932), pp. 562–581.

Townsend, C. H. T.: "Vertical Life Zones of Northern Peru, with Crop Correlation," *Ecology,* Vol. VII (1926), pp. 440–444.

CHAPTER XVI

THE REPUBLIC OF ECUADOR

Regional delineation. When the wars of independence came to a close in the 1820's, one of the political regions carved out of the Spanish domain was New Granada, which later became known as Greater Colombia, or Colombian Conferate. This area included all that has since become Venezuela, Colombia, Panama, and Ecuador. Boundaries with Brazil, Peru, and British Guiana were poorly defined. By 1831, for political and religious reasons that do not concern us here, and because of geographical circumstances, the greater republic had split into three, and Ecuador had begun its separate existence. Panama, of course, was a part of Colombia until 1903.

The boundaries of Ecuador, in common with those of her neighbors, were poorly defined. Now, a classic international manner of settling boundary disputes has been employed by some countries. A strong nation waits until a weak neighbor has a particularly weak administration. Then it urges upon the weaker nation's leaders—sometimes by threat of war, sometimes for undisclosed "considerations"—a solution to the boundary question. Ecuador's political leadership has seldom been strong. Consequently one slice after another of her territory has been taken from her for reasons that the stronger nations can easily justify!

At the present time Ecuador has clear title to only a fraction of her former recognized domain. There is the 500 miles of seacoast, a broad coastal area of lowland and upland, and a series of mountain ranges and plateaus, all together not over 100,000 square miles in area. This is undisputably Ecuadorean territory. Ecuador also claims, but has never exercised effective jurisdiction over, approximately another 100,000 miles or more of Amazon lowlands, down to and including the Amazon River port of Iquitos. But Peru also claims this territory, and it now appears that the Peruvian nation has permanent control of this lowland, which includes some of the most desirable timber and grazing lands of the entire Amazon region. This will have the effect of limiting the territory of Ecuador to the comparatively small area of the Andes and associated plateaus and the maritime region below—a total area of approximately twice that of New York State. A tentative agreement between Ecuador and Peru was reached in 1942. The dispute, however, is far from being completely settled.

Ecuador has had numerous boundary disputes with Colombia as well as with Peru. In 1925 diplomatic relations between the two nations were severed because of a dispute over a section of boundary. Although the question has never been publicly settled, diplomatic relations were again resumed in 1931, after more than six years of discussion.

In the Pacific Ocean, 550 miles west of the mainland, lie the Galápagos Islands, a volcanic group of 16 islands containing a total of 2,868 square miles of land. The official name is the Colón Archipelago, and the islands belong undisputably to Ecuador. The word "Colón" is the Spanish for Columbus, hence its frequent use among Latin American nations. Galápago is the Spanish word for a large sea tortoise found in great numbers in the vicinity of the archipelago. These islands served in early days as a prison colony. It is said that pirates frequented them in the days of the Spanish Main, and many an expedition has searched diligently for supposedly concealed pirate gold. At present, the principal interests in the islands are military and biological research. Probably less than 500 inhabitants live on the islands.

Maritime region. Between the mountain ranges and the Pacific Ocean extends a coastal plain, 50 to 100 miles wide, broken by numerous mountain spurs and hills, and intersected by a number of small streams. It is composed of detritus washed down from the mountains. The slopes of the marginal highlands are frequently drenched with heavy rains, and consequent erosion through the ages has brought down large deposits of volcanic sand and rock fragments that have decomposed into excellent soil. The geological structure of the bedrock of the coastal area is extremely complex; it is severely folded and metamorphosed, and extends in time from Eocene to recent formations. Most of the coastal lowlands, rising rather abruptly for 200 feet or more above the shoreline, are well drained. The southern portion of the coastal region receives little rainfall and merges with the dry coastal land of Peru, while the northern portion has generally a light to moderate precipitation.

The alluvial lowlands are the most productive part of Ecuador. Here is produced cacao, and rice, the principal agricultural exports of the nation. Coffee of excellent quality is grown on the lower slopes of the Andes. Recently many new plantations have been set out, and within a few years coffee exports should increase. Enough sugar is produced for local use, and a very small amount is exported. On the Santa Elena Peninsula petroleum is found, and at present this is the most important exportable mineral resource of the nation. Large areas of the lower river valleys are unbroken swamp and jungle, at present unproductive and largely uninhabited—even unexplored. By far the majority of the inhabitants of Ecuador live not in the Pacific lowlands, known for their richness in natural resources, but in the high inter-Andean basins.

ECUADOR: TEMPERATURE AND RAINFALL OF SELECTED STATIONS

	Station	Guayaquil *	Quito †	Ambato *
	Elevation (*Feet*)	39.4	9,248	8595.8
Average Temperature (°*F.*)	*Period of Record*	3 yrs.	1931–47	5 yrs.
	January	79.3	55.8	58.5
	February	79.3	55.8	57.9
	March	79.7	55.8	58.1
	April	80.4	55.9	58.1
	May	78.8	55.8	57.2
	June	77.4	55.6	55.8
	July	75.4	55.6	54.5
	August	76.1	55.9	54.5
	September	77.2	56.1	55.8
	October	76.6	55.6	57.7
	November	78.4	55.2	58.5
	December	80.2	55.8	58.1
	Annual	78.3	55.7	57.0
	Range	5.0	0.7	4.0
Average Rainfall (*Inches*)	*Period of Record*	3 yrs.	1935–47	15 yrs.
	January	9.7	4.0	1.8
	February	10.5	5.5	1.7
	March	7.4	5.6	2.2
	April	5.3	6.5	2.6
	May	2.1	5.8	2.1
	June	0.7	2.0	0.7
	July	0.4	0.7	0.9
	August	0.0	0.8	0.7
	September	0.1	3.2	1.0
	October	0.4	4.8	1.5
	November	0.3	3.3	1.4
	December	1.9	4.0	17.9
	Annual	38.4	46.2	1.3

* K. Knoch: "Klimakunde von Südamerika," *Handbuch der Klimatologie,* Band II, Teil G, Berlin, 1930.

† Ecuador: Servicio Meteorológico, *Boletín Meteorológico,* Nos. 1, 2, Quito. 1944, 1945. Ecuador: Dirección General de Estadística y Censos, *El Trimestre Estadístico,* 1945–1947.

Mountains and their plateau basins. Two great mountain chains cross the republic from north to south, a distance of nearly 500 miles. The eastern chain is known as the Andes of Ecuador, or the Cordillera Oriental; the western, as the Cordillera Occidental. Their peaks, 20 or more, range from 14,000 to 21,000 feet in altitude. The snow line is 15,700 feet above sea level in Ecuador, and therefore many of these peaks are crowned with snow and ice throughout the year. Perpetual snow means continually flowing streams, even during the dry season, and a consequent stabilization of agriculture. As in other sections of the Andes, most of these mountain masses rise from upland plateaus. A peak 18,000 feet above sea level may rise only 5,000 or 6,000 feet above its basic plateau. Among the most impressive scenic beauties of the region are

Courtesy Pan American Union.

Fig. 93. The Pan-American Highway in view of Chimborazo, Ecuador.

the towering peaks of Mt. Chimborazo (20,500 feet) and Mt. Cotopaxi (19,300 feet).

Many of Ecuador's peaks are volcanoes, some dormant, but many active. Ecuador has more volcanic activity than any other South American nation. Its "Avenue of Volcanoes," as Humboldt named the two ranges of cones and their intervening valley, is particularly imposing.[1] Cotopaxi and Sangay are perhaps the most permanently active cones, but Pichincha, which overshadows the capital city, Quito, is particularly noteworthy. Five violent eruptions of this volcano have occurred since the Spanish conquest of the Indians. Four times Quito was almost

[1] G. Edward Lewis has written an interesting article on the volcanoes of Ecuador. It appears in the *National Geographic Magazine,* Vol. XCVII, No. 1 (1950).

overwhelmed by lava and earthquakes. Once portions of the city were literally veneered with volcanic ash.

Numerous spurs and subsidiary ranges ramify from the central masses toward the Amazon region or toward the Pacific Ocean. Drainage from large areas of the central plateau and from the Cordillera Occidental is toward the west. Near the border of Colombia to the north, and near

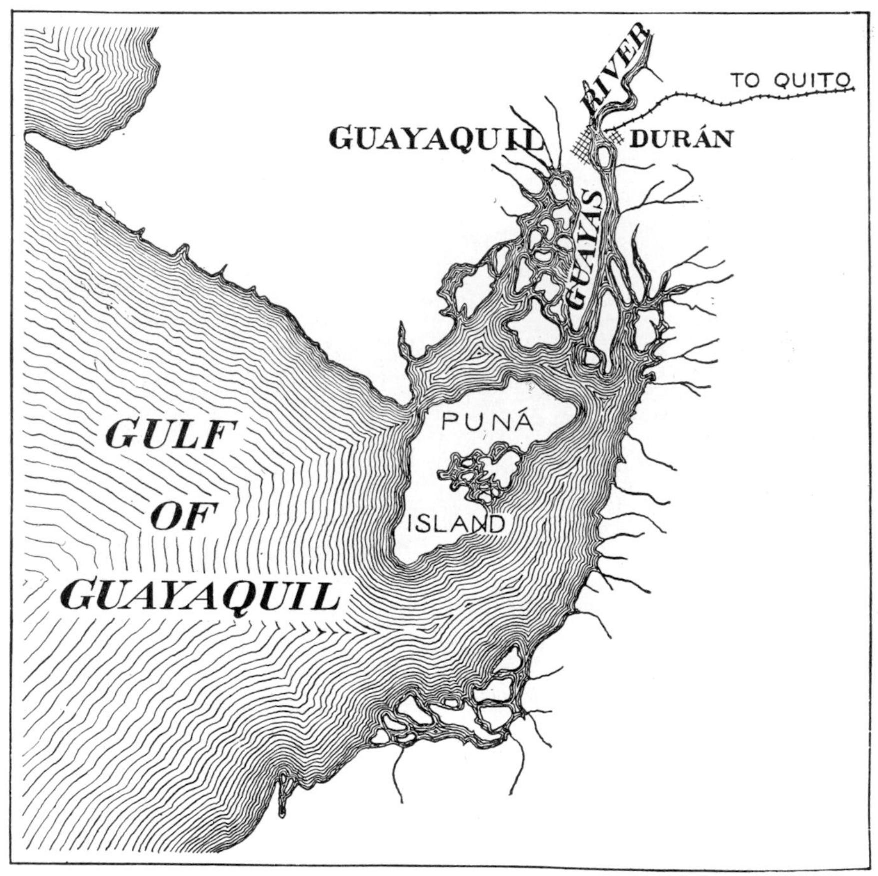

F. A. Carlson.

Fig. 94. The port of Guayaquil, Ecuador.

the boundary with Peru to the south, the two dominant ranges come together in large knots. Between the two ranges and extending for nearly 300 miles is an Alpine plateau trough from 20 to 30 miles wide and divided into four drainage basins by transverse ridges. The northern basin is the highest, over 9,000 feet in altitude, and shelters the city of Quito, capital of the nation. This region is well watered and fertile. The second basin contains the cities of Latacunga and Ambato, and the third, Riobamba. They rest at an average elevation of about 8,000 feet.

The basins are fertile and fairly well watered, but they do not possess the agricultural possibilities of their northern neighboring basin. Still farther to the south is the basin in which Cuenca, the principal population center of the south, rests. This region is poorly watered, and consequently is not agriculturally prosperous. South from Cuenca the two dominant ranges come together in an almost arid knot, a wilderness of broken ranges and peaks with occasional fertile valleys.

East of the mountains. The upper Amazon Basin extends to the foot of the mountains in Ecuador. Possession of this area is a moot question, and it is likely that final settlement of the question will give it to Peru. The region is similar to that described in the chapter on Peru—a series of descending mountain spurs separated by well-watered valleys, below

Courtesy Nels A. Bengtson.

Fig. 95. Typical home of the more wealthy people of the rural areas near Guayaquil, Ecuador.

which the heavily timbered plains and grass land of the Amazon lowlands extend to the horizon. This is fertile country, ranging in elevation from 300 to 3,000 feet, with heavy rainfall. Its many rivers are navigable during low water for 1,300 miles, and in high water for more than 2,000 miles. No population centers of great importance exist, for the inhabitants are principally uncivilized Indians.

Rivers. Ecuador has three Pacific rivers of note. The Guayas flows to the south and drains a valley more than 100 miles long. Its drainage basin includes some 14,000 square miles and embraces considerable areas of the central plateau. The mouth of the river is an estuary known as the Gulf of Guayaquil, at the upper end of which is the port city of Guayaquil. In the gulf is the island of Puná, 29 miles long and 8 to 14 miles wide, the only large island near the mainland. Headwaters of the Esmeraldas River originate just north of the headwaters of the Guayas and drain an area nearly 100 miles square, the tributaries reaching up to

Quito, on the plateau. This river discharges into the Pacific through a narrow gorge. At the mouth of this stream is the port city of Esmeraldas. The Mira River and its tributaries drain a smaller area still farther to the north—the Ibarra Basin, in which rests the city of Ibarra—and form part of the boundary between Ecuador and Colombia. Besides these three more important river basins, numerous smaller streams make their way across the plains to the Pacific. East of the Andes the Amazon, known in Ecuador as the Marañón, affords means of transportation to the Atlantic.

Population. The number of inhabitants in Ecuador has never been accurately determined. An estimate of between 3,000,000 and 3,350,000 is perhaps as close as can be made, with a strong likelihood that the former figure is more nearly correct—possibly even generous. Of the population, at least one-fourth, perhaps one-third, are of unmixed Indian blood. Ten to 15 per cent may be considered entirely Spanish. Perhaps 20,000 Negroes live in the coast lands. The remainder of the population is of mixed blood, Indian predominating. Efforts have been made to encourage the immigration of European colonists to fertile agricultural lands, but these efforts have never borne fruit. There has been very little immigration during the past century.

Slaves were freed throughout all of New Granada in 1821. This was one of the first acts of the young republic and was influenced, undoubtedly, by the fact that Negroes and Indians coöperated actively with the white settlers in the struggle for independence. The fact that Negroes are so scarce in Ecuador is not, however, due to foresight or to prejudice. It is simply another accident of history. Negroes were not brought into Ecuador in great numbers as slaves and have not cared to migrate there in considerable numbers. A contrast between Latin American culture and that of the United States should here be noted. Throughout South America, the Negro has inherited the Latin culture and has become almost completely Latinized. He is more than a century removed from slavery (except in Brazil). His blood has mingled freely with that of the Indian and Spanish population. The Negro is not, therefore, set off from the remainder of the population because of his color, but is inherently a part of the culture group. The only social discrimination practiced against the Negro is by certain cultured white groups that are proud of their unmixed Spanish ancestry and prefer not to marry outside the Spanish heritage.

Population distribution follows that of other west-coast countries. Those predominantly Spanish tend to congregate in urban centers of culture; Negroes tend to settle primarily in the warm, moist lowlands; Indians have always preferred the temperate climate of the upper valleys and highlands.

Guayaquil. The largest indentation on the coast is the Gulf of Guayaquil, into which flows the Guayas River (see map, page 272).

This river is the largest stream on the western coast of South America. During the rainy season, which along the northern coast is from December to May, this river may be navigated by small steamers for 40 miles, and canoes and smaller craft navigate its tributaries for an additional 200 miles. Numerous small towns and plantations have been established along its shores.

The city of Guayaquil is a thriving center of 216,000 inhabitants, the largest city in Ecuador and in many respects the most progressive. It serves as port city and as the cultural and commercial center for the entire region. Port facilities are not adequate, although they have been greatly improved in the past few years. Along the quay narrow wooden piers extend to floats that are the landing places for river steamers. Large ocean-going vessels must anchor in the bay and discharge by lighters. A new pier for the use of the customs authorities has recently been constructed.

Until 1918 yellow fever was practically endemic in Guayaquil, and bubonic plague was a frequent visitor. For that reason, vessels of foreign nations shunned the harbor. If they entered, they were quarantined at the next port of importance, and quarantine expenses and delays are always costly. The commerce of Ecuador, and its cultural intercourse with the outside world, lagged as a consequence. In 1918 the sanitary engineers and physicians of the Rockefeller Foundation, in coöperation with health authorities of Ecuador, undertook the sanitation of the port and its environs. They completed the task two years later. As a result, the city has been placed on the United States government's approved list of South American ports, and commerce has been greatly facilitated. Guayaquil receives 85 per cent of Ecuador's imports and transmits 65 per cent of her exports.

A cultural and educational accompaniment of the port's sanitation is of interest to students of geography. In connection with the sanitation of this one port, and in coöperation with public school authorities, the Foundation carried forward a piece of educational work that profoundly influenced the nation. Public interest in health and sanitation, both among adults and children, was stimulated, and "clean-up" became the watchword of the city and its environs. Newspapers coöperated actively in the campaign. Because they circulate throughout the entire republic, the repercussion was widely felt and led to an awareness of sanitary backwardness in many other places. The improvement has made residence in the republic possible and attractive for many citizens and tourists from the United States and Europe who shunned Ecuador before.

Other urban centers. Quito, the capital city of Ecuador, is situated in a basin on the plateau at an altitude of 9,250 feet. It is an ancient city, the northern capital of the Inca empire long before the Spanish conquest. Climate is temperate, although the city is located within 20 miles of the equator. In the environs of Quito are fertile soils, and agricultural products, both subtropical and temperate, are cultivated. The population of the city is estimated at more than 212,000.

POPULATION OF PRINCIPAL URBAN CENTERS OF ECUADOR

Quito	212,000
Guayaquil	216,000
Cuenca	54,000
Riobamba	24,000
Ambato	30,000
Loja	18,000
Latacunga	18,000
Esmeraldas	11,000

Cities of importance south of Quito in the central valley-plateaus are: Latacunga, Ambato, and Riobamba, all situated on the Guayaquil-to-Quito railway; and Cuenca, a center of culture and industry in the south, located in an oasis region 60 miles from the coast. Loja is an important city of 18,000 in the more distant south, about 75 miles from the coast. In the farther north, Ibarra, a city of 10,000 inhabitants, situated on the headwaters of the Mira River, is the only important population center. It is reached by rail and road from the capital.

Besides Guayaquil, numerous smaller port cities may be mentioned. The most important of these is Esmeraldas, in the far north, at the mouth of the Esmeraldas River. A railway and motor road from Esmeraldas into the interior have been proposed.

Transportation facilities. Facilities for transportation in Ecuador are scant, but hardly inferior, all in all, to those of Colombia and Peru. A few streams in the coastal region are navigable by small vessels. Some 2,000 miles of waterway in the Amazon region are navigable, although they are seldom used because of sparse population. Motor highways have not been built to any appreciable extent, but trails for pack animals reach every hamlet in the nation. Several short railway lines have been constructed, a total of about 700 miles, of which about 350 miles are in operation.

One significant railway operates between the capital city, Quito, and Duran, on the Guayas River opposite Guayaquil. The railway does not cross the broad estuary into Guayaquil, but originates at Duran. On leaving Duran, the line imediately turns away from the river toward the sierra. To cover the distance to Quito, 288 miles, two days of travel are required. In approximately 12 daylight hours the train climbs the sierra to Riobamba, where passengers remain overnight. A question often raised about South America's smaller railways is: "Why do they not operate at night?" The answer is simple: "Why operate trains, especially passenger trains, during the night in a region where traffic is light, nearly all local, where there are no sleeping cars or funds to buy them, where passengers have worlds of time and enjoy getting on and off trains during the long waits at stations, where a train ride is really a holiday? Besides, there is the danger of rock slides in the mountains and washed-out roadbeds." After remaining overnight at Riobamba, the train moves on the following day and in another 12 hours reaches the capital. Train movement is slow, and there are long pauses at stations.

The Guayaquil-to-Quito railway was constructed by an American firm and was completed in 1908. It is now owned and operated by the government, as are most other lines in Ecuador. Like other west-coast railways, it is an engineering feat worthy of note. Beginning at 12 feet above sea level, it reaches an altitude of 11,841 feet at Urbana, the highest point on the road. In one zone of 50 miles the ascent is 10,500 feet. The gauge is 42 inches. There is one switchback, where a rise of 300 feet occurs in a quarter of a mile; and there are 72 bridges and 3 tunnels. Besides this and additional short railways, other methods of travel in Ecuador are by water, by muleback over mountain or along jungle trails, or by plane.

Plans call for a railway from Quito to the northern port of Esmeraldas. The line, if ever constructed, will be 100 miles shorter than the road to Guayaquil and will open to transportation an excellent agricultural region. It will also open the port of Esmeraldas to development.

Mineral resources. Although Ecuador's mountain ranges have never revealed the deposits of minerals as extensive as those discovered in the territory of neighbors to the north and south, there is no reason to doubt that important resources exist. Petroleum and small amounts of gold and silver are produced yearly. The production of petroleum increased from 100,000 barrels in 1924, to more than 1,650,000 barrels in 1941, and to 2,564,000 barrels in 1950.

Agricultural resources. Agriculturally, Ecuador is potentially rich. Her widely varying altitudes produce every fruit and vegetable of the tropical and temperate climates, and this makes her almost completely self-sufficient from the standpoint of food supply. The mean annual temperature ranges from around 80° F. on the coast to one of perpetual snow on the mountain ranges. At Quito the mean annual average is 55° F.

Ecuador's most important money crops are rice and cacao. In 1924 two devastating diseases, "witches'-broom" and "monilia," attacked the cacao trees, and production of this crop has not yet fully recovered from the effects. Yet cacao remains a leading export. Rice is comparatively a new crop in Ecuador's export trade, but it is now about equal to cacao in value. Coffee ranks next to rice and cacao. Its coffee is so excellent and so well received in world markets that many new plantations are being made. The forests supply tagua nuts, also known as ivory nuts.

These are used in the manufacture of buttons and imitation ivory goods. About 75 per cent of the world's small demand for this nut is supplied by Ecuador; Colombia and Brazil supply the greater part of the remainder. A little rubber is also grown commercially. Of the grains, wheat and barley grow at altitudes up to 11,000 feet and are extensively cultivated for domestic use; quinoa is grown on the plateaus; and rice in the lowlands. Inspired by the success of Peru in the cultivation of sugar and cotton for export, Ecuador is now giving some attention to these crops.

The llama and the alpaca, so common in Peru, are seldom found in Ecuador. Domestic animals, brought to the country by Europeans in earlier days, include cattle, horses, sheep, goats, pigs, chickens, and the ever-present burden-bearing burro and mule.

Leading industries. The Panama hat is the principal manufactured article from Ecuador with which the world is familiar. These hats are made from selected straws of the *Carludovica palmata,* commonly known as the jipijapa, which is not, incidentally, a palm tree. The plant grows from six to ten feet high, is fan-shaped, and resembles the saw palmetto. The hats are made in villages on the western coastal plain, in the transition belt from desert to humid lands. Monte Cristo and Jipijapa are the chief centers. The manufacture is a handicraft at which both men and women work, but women and girls are said to make the finest hats. As long as the quality of the product remains superior, the United States market will absorb all that is produced. The genuine Panama hat, however, is now suffering from increasingly keen competition from soft-straw hats manufactured in the United States and other parts of the world.

Other industries are shoe production, flour milling, the refining of petroleum, and the production of sugar, cement, and beverages.

Ecuador, like all other Latin American countries, has experienced a change in direction of foreign trade as a result of the war. Greater inter-American commerce has developed, and to some extent the increased hemispherical business has replaced the prewar trade with continental Europe and Japan.

Ecuador's leading exports consist of rice, cacao, petroleum and products, copper (blister), copper concentrates, lead concentrates, gold-bearing ore, quinine and derivatives, handicrafts, Panama hats, tagua, kapok, hardwoods, balsa wood, coffee, and fruits. The greater portion of the cacao is shipped to the United States, Colombia, and Europe. The chief markets for the rice exports are Venezuela, Cuba, Jamaica, Panama, and the Canal Zone. Considerable shifting, however, occurs from year to year with respect to the foreign destination of its rice. The metallic mineral exports go mainly to the United States, whereas the petroleum and products move to Argentina, Uruguay, Netherlands West

Indies, Peru, and the Canal Zone. The United Kingdom is Ecuador's chief market for its foreign shipments of hardwoods. Cinchona bark, quinine, and derivatives are destined, primarily to other Latin American Republics and the United States. France and the United States were the principal buyers of tagua in 1947. Fruits, particularly bananas, are sent southward to Peru and Chile. Handicrafts, including hats, woolen blankets, and leather handbags and cigarette cases, are widely distributed among the other Western Hemisphere countries as well as Europe.

ECUADOR: FOREIGN TRADE

	Total Value (000 Dollars)	*Percentage of Total*					
Exports		United States	Canada	Latin America	United Kingdom	Continental Europe	All Others
1938	11,972	37.5		22.9	4.7	32.0	2.9
1947	45,932	42.4	0.1	35.9	1.2	8.8	11.6
Imports							
1938	10,501	34.6	0.5	6.6	7.7	41.5	9.2
1947	44,792	71.1	3.5	10.8	6.8	6.8	1.0

ECUADOR: EXPORTS OF PRINCIPAL COMMODITIES *

Commodity	*Quantity in Metric Tons*		*Percentage of Total Value of All Exports*	
	1947	*1948*	*1947*	*1948*†
Rice	62,981	68,285	31.2	38.1
Cacao	20,757	17,185	30.4	36.5
Coffee	10,394	8,434	8.2	7.7
Hats of toquilla straw (thousand)	3,116	‡	7.7	0.6
Bananas (thousand stems)	2,687	‡	3.7	6.3
Gold concentrates and dust (kilo grams)	13,469	‡	4.0	‡

* Source: Office of International Trade. United States Department of Commerce. Washington, D. C. 1950.

† Data for 1948 not comparable; statistics cover exports through port of Guayaquil only.

‡ Not available.

About 65 per cent of Ecuador's exports are shipped from its leading port, Guayaquil. Other important centers are Salinas, Manta, and Esmeraldas. The major portion of the imports are handled at Guayaquil (85 per cent), Salinas, Puerto Bolívar, and Manta.

SELECTED REFERENCES

Bengtson, N. A.: "Some Essential Features of the Geography of the Santa Elena Peninsula, Ecuador," *Annals of the Association of American Geographers,* Vol. XIV (1924), pp. 150–158.

Bennett, H. H.: "Some Geographic Aspects of Western Ecuador," *Annals of the Association of American Geographers,* Vol. XV (1925), pp. 126–147.

"Ecuadorean–Peruvian Boundary Negotiations," *Bulletin of the Pan American Union,* Vol. LXVIII (1934), p. 257.

Fletcher, Merna I.: "Balsa Industry of Ecuador," *Economic Geography,* Vol. 25, No. 1 (1949), pp. 47–54.

Little, Elbert L.: "Trees in Ecuador," *Foreign Agriculture,* Vol. XII, No. 3 (1948), pp. 54–59.

McBride, G. M.: "The Galápagos Islands," *Geographical Review,* Vol. VI (1918), pp. 229–239.

Sheppard, G.: "Notes on the Climate and Physiography of Southwestern Ecuador," *Geographical Review,* Vol. XX (1930), pp. 445–453.

Sheppard, G.: "The Rainy Season of 1932 in Southwestern Ecuador," *Geographical Review,* Vol. XXIII (1933), pp. 210–216.

CHAPTER XVII

COLOMBIA: A LAND OF CONTRASTS

General characteristics. Colombia exhibits a multiplicity of terrain and climatic conditions. Flat plains extend to the very foot of steep and rugged mountains. Lofty plateaus rise to elevations considerably over 8,000 feet above sea level. Snow-capped mountain peaks are in view of "steaming-hot" jungles. Arid tropics merge with regions of dense forests.

The border of Colombia reaches from 12° 24′ N. latitude, the most northern projection of South America, to 4° 17′ S. latitude. It is the only country of South America that has a coastline on both the Pacific and Atlantic Oceans. Within its borders, marked with violent physical contrasts, are some 439,828 square miles of territory and about 10,350,000 people.

Physical landscape. Near the border between Ecuador and Colombia the massive Andean system branches into three distinct ranges running roughly parallel north and south, with intervening valleys that descend to the Caribbean lowlands or run head on into the sea. These fingerlike ranges, known as *Cordillera Occidental, Cordillera Central,* and *Cordillera Oriental,* have intervening or adjacent valleys offering access, although difficult, to the interior. In all other Andean countries the mountain ranges tend to parallel the coast. The central range is separated from the western range by the Cauca Valley, where flows the Río Cauca, the principal affluent of the Magdalena. From north of Popayan to north of Cartago, the Cauca Valley is some 20 miles wide, while in the department of Antioquia the valley assumes the width of the Cauca River, from whose banks rise the central and western cordilleras. The Magdalena River valley lies between the central and eastern cordilleras. It is more than 30 miles wide throughout the lower half of its course. The western and central cordilleras terminate in Colombia, but the eastern cordillera lies in both Colombia and Venezuela. The northern portion of the eastern cordillera, the Sierra de Perijá, lies along the boundary between the two countries, while the other arm, Sierra de los Andes, extends into Venezuela.

North of Buenaventura, the chief Pacific port of Colombia, the western cordillera is separated from the Pacific by the Atrato Valley and the

Cordillera del Chocó. The latter is a comparatively low ridge bordering on the Pacific. It extends northward into the Isthmus of Panama.

The Cordillera Central is a highly dissected mountain range that consists primarily of eroded masses of volcanic material in the form of ranges and lofty peaks. A number of the volcanic cones are snow-capped throughout the year, and much of the region lies above 10,000 feet.

The Cordillera Oriental and associated features bear locally different names. The broad open portion, around Bogotá, an ancient erosional tableland, bears the name Sabana de Bogotá. This high plateau, interspersed with hills, is one of the densely populated regions of Colombia. It has an elevation of some 8,600 feet and is 150 miles wide and 300 miles long. Adjacent ranges attain elevations considerably over 10,000 feet. Many of their peaks project above the snow line. In this high zone, known as *páramo* in Colombia, are cirque-like depressions, probably of glacial origin. In their midst rise streams that descend to the plains below.

West of the Sierra de Perijá, in northeastern Colombia, is the Sierra Nevada, a triangular massif of granite occupying an area of 2,800 square miles. Its snow-crowned peaks rise to an elevation of 19,000 feet and overlook Santa Marta, the most extensive region of banana culture in South America.

In the northern portion of the Guajira Peninsula are a low, rolling plateau and volcanic peaks. This upland region is not a part of the Sierra de Perijá, the most northern extension of the Andean system.

Eastern Colombia, known as the "Oriente," is largely a region of river plains embracing 290,000 square miles. It is divided between the affluents of the Amazon and the Orinoco. The Colombian headstreams of the Orinoco, of which the Guaviare and the Meta are the major streams, cut through immense Llanos, marked with small groups of trees and clumps of palms. Large areas are flooded during the rainy seasons. In the south and southeast is the selva or tropical rainforest of the upper Amazon region, drained by tributaries of the Ríos, Negro, Japurá, and Icá.

Vegetation and climate. The northern lands of South America fall within the low latitudes, a location that would ordinarily suggest a hot climate. Fortunately, this condition does not universally prevail. The elevation of the mountainous regions modifies the effects of the equatorial sun and brings out many types of climates.

Interesting correlations have been made between temperature and altitude. Although the results are not absolute, nevertheless they may prove useful in making general comparisons. Four temperature zones have been distinguished—namely,

Tropical zone	0 to 4,000 feet
Subtropical zone	4,000 to 6,000 feet
Temperate zone	6,000 to 10,000 feet
Páramo zone	10,000 to 14,000 feet

At sea level the mean annual temperature is about 82°, with about 100° for the mean maximum and 65° for the minimum. At the elevation of Bogotá, 8,727 feet, the corresponding records are 58°, 75°, and 40°. Between 10,000 and 14,000 feet, in the Páramo zone, it is cold, and frosts and snow are frequent. The perpetual snow line lies at about 16,000 feet, but some peaks of only 14,000 feet have snow most of the year.

Temperature, however, is not the only factor responsible for seasonal differences. Rainfall is another significant element. A survey of the seasonal rainfall shows that there is heavy rainfall on the western coast of Colombia and a light annual precipitation on the middle Caribbean Coast. Western Colombia is subjected to rains more or less all the year round. In general, the more populated regions of these northern lands, whether low or high, have a rainy season from the beginning of May to the end of October and a dry season the remaining part of the year. In some areas, however, particularly in the regions around Medellín and Bogotá, there are two wet and two dry seasons. The wet seasons are April-May-June and October-November-December.

The floral coverings of these lands bring out the striking differences in climate. There is a degree of harmony between plants and their environment that is not found in the relation of man and animals to their habitat. The plant kingdom serves as an index to the character of the climate, topography, soils, and even human behavior. In this respect the abundant and varied flora of northern South America ranks supreme. More than 7,000 species of plants have been identified, and, when the region has been thoroughly explored, this number may be doubled.

The distribution of flora and its density are governed largely by temperature and rainfall. Thus it is observed that each climatic region has to a marked degree its own vegetation or floral character. In the high Andes, the Páramo areas, characterized by perpetual cold and light but frequent rainfall, vegetation is comprised primarily of grasses, small herbaceous plants, and dense masses of low bushes. Such northern plants as buttercups, daisies, and lupines adorn these high southern lands. In many respects they are similar in plant life to the higher regions of our Rocky Mountains, or the plains of the Arctic meadows. Except for limited grazing purposes, the Páramo has little agricultural importance.

The temperate areas are favored with a working climate. It is never very cold, and the amount of rainfall is seldom excessive. Extensive and luxuriant forests prevail where man has not cleared them away for agricultural purposes and for fuel. In the temperate regions are found blankets of dense clouds yielding frequent showers favoring the growth of ferns, mosses, trees of the laurel family, and Spanish cedars. All of the typical grains and vegetables of the United States—including wheat, barley, oats, corn, potatoes, pumpkins, yams, squashes, tomatoes, beets, and carrots—are grown in these uplands. At the lower elevations, from

COLOMBIA: TEMPERATURE AND RAINFALL OF SELECTED STATIONS

	Station	Cali *	Bucara-manga *	Bogotá †	Medellín *	Andagoya †	Barran-quilla *
	Elevation (*Feet*)		2999	8727.0	4649	249.3	
Average Temperature (°F.)	*Period of Record*	1934–1946	1924–1941	6½ yrs.	1926–41	1917–1925	1932–1946
	January	76.2	73.8	57.9	71.1	82.0	79.9
	February	76.8	74.6	58.3	70.9	81.9	79.7
	March	76.8	73.9	59.0	70.5	82.0	81.0
	April	75.7	73.5	58.8	70.3	82.4	82.9
	May	75.4	74.5	58.6	70.2	81.9	83.5
	June	75.7	73.9	58.3	70.0	81.7	83.5
	July	76.4	73.7	57.2	71.1	81.3	84.2
	August	74.5	74.1	57.2	70.5	81.3	84.0
	September	76.4	73.9	57.4	70.0	81.5	83.7
	October	74.9	73.7	57.9	68.9	81.7	82.4
	November	74.8	72.6	58.3	69.1	81.0	81.9
	December	75.4	73.0	57.9	69.3	81.0	81.9
	Annual	75.8	73.8	58.1	70.2	81.7	82.4
	Range	2.3	2.0	1.8	2.2	1.4	4.5

Average Rainfall (*Inches*) *Period of Record*		1921–1941	49 yrs.	1926–41	1914–1925	1932–1946
January	3.0	1.6	2.3	1.8	23.7	0.0
February	2.8	2.6	2.6	2.8	21.8	0.0
March	3.7	3.4	4.0	3.3	18.5	0.1
April	6.2	3.2	5.7	5.9	26.4	0.9
May	6.3	4.9	4.4	7.2	23.9	3.9
June	2.9	3.9	2.4	5.4	25.5	3.6
July	0.9	2.6	2.0	3.8	23.2	1.8
August	1.5	3.8	2.2	5.2	25.3	5.7
September	2.6	6.3	2.4	5.7	26.3	6.0
October	5.5	5.6	6.3	7.4	21.3	7.7
November	4.8	4.3	4.7	6.2	23.4	4.9
December	4.8	2.4	2.6	3.6	20.2	0.4
Annual	45.0	44.6	41.8	58.3	279.1	35.1

* Ministerio de la Economía Nacional. Departamento de Irrigación, Sección de Meteorología y Aforos. *Anuario Meteorológico,* 1934–1946. *Boletín de Agricultura,* 1930–1935. *Anuario Estadístico de Colombia,* 1935–1937.

† K. Knoch: "Klimakunde von Südamerika," *Handbuch der Klimatologie,* Band II, Teil G. Berlin, 1930.

4,000 to 6,000 feet above sea level, coffee is the commercial crop.

In the tropics, the varied distribution of species and abundance of plant life reaches a climax. On the basis of vegetation, the tropical area may be divided into four types: (1) the area of arid plants, (2) deciduous forest, (3) rainforest, and (4) grassy plains.

Along the middle Caribbean Coast the vegetation approaches desert characteristics. Leguminous species, such as acacias and mimosas, and spiny trees with wide depressed tops and twisted trunks dot the landscape. Cacti and mesquite remind one of the characteristic plants of southwestern United States and northeastern Mexico. The divi-divi, whose pods yield valuable tannin, is an important plant of both Colombia and Venezuela. Logwood, a source of valuable dyes, also grows in these arid plains. A few species of palms are found here and there. Often a characteristic chaparral or bush formation, as well as small trees and coarse shrubs, border the dry regions. The sandpaper tree is one of nature's many interesting contributions in this region. Its rough leaves are employed to polish wood and metal.

Probably half the forests of northern South America may be classified as deciduous. These predominate in those regions where moderate wet and dry seasons exist. In tropical areas, the effect of the dry season is quite similar to that of the winter in the intermediate latitudes. During this season many herbaceous plants die or shrivel up, and trees shed their leaves. Moisture is almost absolutely lacking. The rainy season is the period of growing and flowering. However, the seasonal change in the forests of the tropics is not so homogeneous as that in temperate-zone, deciduous forests. Some tropical trees retain their leaves, and many shrubs and herbs continue in flower until death. Furthermore, tropical forests are highly diversified. One does not find extensive stands of a given species, as in the pine and fir forests of the United States. Among the commercial trees of the deciduous forests are those of the sapodilla family, the source of chicle; the balata, a variety of rubber; the Brazil nut; the cusparia, the bark of which is used in preparation of Angostura bitters; the balsam; and the mahogany.

Rainforests present the most luxuriant floral development on earth. Western Colombia, drenched with rain throughout most of the year, abounds in plant life. Tall trees with creeping vines, orchids and ferns, and a tangled undergrowth of shrubbery and herbs characterize this jungle vegetation. Often trees are supported by buttresses that look like brackets. Here in the wet tropics the palm attains its most profuse development. The number of species seems almost beyond botanical classification. The bamboo is representative of this zone as well as of the lower portion of the temperate region.

The native cuts and burns the trees and carries on a crude form of agriculture on the spot for two or three years. Then he moves on to repeat the operation on a new piece of land. Contrary to general opinion, the mature soils of the wet tropics do not long remain fertile and are not well suited to permanent agriculture without the application of plant nutrients. The heavy precipitation rapidly leaches the soil and carries away the plant foods. The heavy covering of rank vegetation prevents the penetration of light to some extent, and this tends to favor the accumulation of toxic material.

The most fertile soils of Colombia are found in the great Llanos. These are savannas or grasslands interspersed with small groves of palms and, occasionally, dense thickets. They have much of the character, as far as soils are concerned, of the prairies of the United States. Unfortunately the alternate wet and dry seasons, diseases, and insects, among other adverse conditions, have retarded the development of these regions.

Fig. 96. "Cow tree" (Brosimum galactodendron), Brazil. Similar trees are found in Colombia.

Many interesting and useful vegetables and fruits are found in the tropics of Colombia. The arracacha (a plant of the celery family), the savory palm hearts, the chayote (a vine related to the cucumber but of which both vine and fruit are eaten), the mangoes, the avocados, the plantains, and the star apple are some of the food products of the tropics. Bananas, oranges, and lemons are also widely distributed in both the tropical and subtropical regions of these lands. The cow tree, *Palo de Vaca,* is an unusual tropical tree. From a cut in the trunk is obtained a liquid resembling milk that is consumed by the Indians. Some physicians have reported the liquid as poisonous, but evidently it does no harm to the natives. The tree is valuable not alone for its "milk," but also for its bark, which supplies some Indians with part of their clothing and bedding. Vegetable ivory is obtained from the tagua palm. Kapok, or silk cotton, adds to the wonders of the plant kingdom of northern South America. Kapok is used in life preservers and for stuffing pillows, and makes a much cooler mattress than cotton. These products not only are common in Colombia, but are found throughout much of tropical South America.

Numerous medicinal roots and extracts come from the forests. Few of the poorer people of the rural districts patronize a physician. They simply employ forest remedies prepared by some local herb dispenser. The deadly strychnos, or nux vomica, a poison used on arrows, is also found in these forests.

Among the commercial resins, waxes, varnishes, and vegetable oils of local origin are carnauba wax, quika resin, various types of ceroxylon, and palm nut oils.

Social involution. How many Indians inhabited Colombia before the coming of Europeans is a matter of conjecture. Valid reasons exist for the opinion that the aborigines have been greatly reduced in number during the past 400 years. At present, probably not more than 200,000 persons of unmixed Indian blood live in the republic. Only in less accessible and more barren regions where white men have not cared to penetrate have the Indians retained their racial purity and customs. Since the early days of foreign conquest the South American Indians have intermarried with the Spaniards. Far more than half of the total population of "the near north" is now of mixed blood.

It would be well to define three terms here: *mestizo* is white and Indian; *mulatto* is white and Negro; *zambo* is Negro and Indian. A variety of different native words is used to describe mixtures in which all three races participate. It is very likely that the larger part of the population is composed of people in whose veins flows the blood of at least two races.

One of the most independent Indian tribes in all of South America is the Guajira, occupying the Guajira Peninsula, which extends into the Caribbean from northern Colombia between Santa Marta and the Gulf of Venezuela. Ethnologically, it is said that these people belong to the Carib group. For centuries these Guajira Indians have successfully resisted the advance of civilization. Their strong, persistent, and warlike character has made it possible for them to retain their lands and remain free from foreign fusion. In accordance with their ancient customs, the fields are tended by women. Potatoes, corn, manioc, bananas, and plantains are their chief cultivated crops. They trade cattle, horses, hides, pearls, Brazil wood, and divi-divi for cotton cloth, hardware, arms, and many other manufactured articles. Because of the semiarid character of the Guajira Peninsula, much of the land is unfit for agriculture. Along the coast, fishing is one of the few useful commercial activities. Despite the efforts of these Indians to remain isolated, however, there is a tendency toward peaceful amalgamation. In recent years a considerable number have been coming into the communities of the Lake Maracaibo region, where they have accepted work on sugar plantations and in oil fields. Many Guajira women are employed in the homes of Maracaibo, Venezuela.

In the mountains extending south from the Guajira Peninsula are found the Ahruaco Indians, who belong to the Chibcha family. These natives are more docile and constructive than the Guajiras. They live in permanent villages of huts, have developed their agriculture to a high degree, and are improving their grazing animals. Unlike the Guajira Indians, who seem to have very little use for clothes in their tropical habitat, the Ahruacos, in their more temperate environment, wear heavy cotton clothes and mantles. Although the slopes of the mountains to 10,000 feet are well adapted to coffee culture, the Indians are not interested in the development of this industry.

The Chibchas, living in the highlands of the present state or department of Cundinamarca and adjacent areas, with Bogotá as their chief tribal center, are the most renowned of all early peoples in Colombia. Like the Incas, the Chibcha nation consisted of several tribes pursuing an agricultural and commercial life. In the field they produced maize, potatoes, cotton, tobacco, and leguminous plants; and in trade they bartered salt, copper, and textiles for skins, fruits, plumes, and cane from the tropical regions. As a whole, the Chibchas were not the craftsmen that the Incas proved to be. The Chibchas, however, excelled at spinning and weaving cotton and in the making of pottery. Their homes reflected a cold and rainy mountain climate. They were made of stone or wood, covered both inside and out with clay, and had roofs of thatched grass. If the family were wealthy, cotton hangings curtained the windows and gold plates appeared above palisaded doorways. The interior was covered with cane mats, skins, and finely woven cotton cloth. Evidences of the industrious Chibchas are still found in Colombia. In fact, most of the mountain peoples living in the present departments of Cundinamarca, Santander, and Santander del Norte are of Chibchan origin.

In the region bounding Colombia and Venezuela, west of Lake Maracaibo, live the Motilone, one of the few surviving families of savage Indians in South America. They are, probably, of Carib stock and are divided into many tribes, each remaining more or less independent. They maintain a comparatively simple culture, based partially on a nomadic existence and a primitive form of agriculture. Generally, the Motilones remain in one site or camp for a year or more until the local game and crops have been depleted; then they move to another region. During the rainy season they stay within their immediate camp region, hunting or working in the fields, but during the dry season they travel great distances from their temporary homes. The Motilone village or camp consists of one or two communal buildings of palm leaves supported by poles—with or without covered sides, depending on weather conditions—surrounded by the family huts of similar construction. Straw mats are used for sleeping; hammocks have not been found among the Motilones. Also contrary to most Indian customs, the men do most of the work, such as hunting, planting, and weaving cloth and baskets. Among other Indian groups, weaving is generally considered a feminine duty. The Motilone has a harsh and cruel disposition. His deadly weapon, the black palm bow and arrow, has been the cause of much anxiety, particularly among the employees of the oil companies.

With few exceptions, the Andine Indians are physically and intellectually superior to the aboriginal inhabitants of the lowlands. They are engaged in agricultural pursuits and minor forms of manufacturing. From the fibers of the moriche palm they make cloth. Earthenware, baskets, and beads are among their manufactures. In the highland cities they are employed in all types of enterprises. The selling of *carbón,* or charcoal, on the city streets is one of their characteristic occupations.

A century ago a number of missions were located in Colombia. These missions were suppressed through political influence, and today not the slightest evidence remains of their former existence. The converts are fewer in number, and most of them have returned to the mode of living their ancestors employed before the missions were established. It is an interesting commentary on the quality and intellectual caliber of these lowland Indians that as soon as the influence of the white man is withdrawn, they apparently revert to simpler primitive states.

In the coastal regions and in the tropical valleys the inhabitants are predominantly Negroes and mulattoes. It is estimated that within the area of Colombia there are 1,000,000 Negroes and mulattoes out of the total population of 10,350,000.

During the colonial period the Spaniards imported Negro slaves from Africa and the West Indies to assist in the exploitation of mineral and agricultural resources, and in the construction of buildings, roads, and bridges. The great wall surrounding Cartagena was built by Negro slaves. The abolition of slavery in 1821 did not check the immigration of West Indian Negroes. They have continued to migrate to the mainland.

Few colored folk in these regions are pure-bred Negroes. Mulattoes and zambos constitute more than 75 per cent of the total black population. It is difficult to identify some of the Negro element. Many mulattoes are classified as mestizos or whites. There is a tendency to say that a person is white unless he is entirely Negro—whereas in the United States we say that a person is Negro unless he is entirely white.

The adaptability of the Negro to the heat and intermittent humidity of the tropics has given him a definite place in the economic structure of these lands. He is employed on the banana plantations in the vicinity of Santa Marta and Ciénaga. West Indian Negroes work in the cacao groves and in the sugar and tobacco fields. On the docks, the colored man is a predominant figure in the handling of cargo. In all these regions, Negroes and part-Negroes make up the greater proportion of the humbler classes.

In the valleys of the Magdalena and Sinú Rivers the Negro races have largely displaced the aborigines. In general, Indians prefer independence, regardless of its economic status, and avoid employment. They seem able to care for themselves if they have freedom of air, land, and water. Negroes, on the other hand, require supervision and association and prove more successful when engaged in some form of directed employment. Thus Negroes tend to become permanent residents of a settled district. Native Indians either disappear into the dominant race or migrate to more isolated lands where they can retain their desired modes of living. The Atrato River region and valleys south, known as the Chocó region, have a total population of 80,000, of which 90 per cent is composed of Negroes and mulattoes or zambos, and of which not more than 5 per cent is white. The colored people work in the platinum- and gold-producing placer mines of the rivers. Some collect vegetable ivory nuts, chicle, rubber, and medicinal plants. Others grow corn and plantain and cut cedars, which are transported down the river. On the western coast stands Buenaventura, the chief Pacific port of Colombia. Ninety per cent of its 15,000 population is colored.

The standards of living and the purchasing power of these people in general are low. A one- or two-room house located in one of the poorer quarters of the cities, with no conveniences whatever, represents the average Negro laborer's home.

Rice forms an important item in the diet of the Negro family. It is grown throughout the inhabited tropical regions. In the temperate areas of the high interior districts the consumption is lighter, partly because the population has a smaller percentage of Negro blood. Furthermore, rice is not produced on the highlands and is therefore more expensive. The Indian and white inhabitants of the interior, particularly on the mountainous and plateau lands, prefer corn, wheat, and vegetables. Another reason for its extensive use in the lowlands is that rice is cheaper than most imported foodstuffs. This adds to its popularity among laboring classes. In general, Colombia spends more money for imported rice than for any other single foreign foodstuff, except wheat, and it produces large amounts locally. Other important foodstuffs in the lowland areas are beans, manioc, corn, and coconuts—and of course the ever-present banana and orange. Great quantities of beef are consumed in the cattle districts, particularly in Barranquilla, Cartagena, and Medellín, and the omnipresent swine and chickens further enrich the poor man's diet.

The merchants and professional men of Colombia are either of the white race or mestizos. Germans, Syrians, and Italians are among the active businessmen in the ports. Syrians appear to be particularly well adapted physically to these regions of high temperature, and have been successful in trading with the Colombians. One of the interesting sights in the interior of most South American countries is the Turkish or Syrian itinerant merchant. A pack mule or two carries his cases of clothing and trinkets, and he wanders from village to village selling and buying—gaining with every trade. In the cities, a few Englishmen and Americans hold positions in branch banks, cable offices, shipping offices, and consular and diplomatic posts. In recent years packing plants, banana plantations, and oil enterprises have attracted a number of Americans and Europeans.

The majority of Colombians, who are largely mestizos and whites, live in the upland valleys and highlands at altitudes from 4,000 to 9,000 feet above sea level. These highland environs are favored with a salubrious climate and rich mineral and agricultural resources. The occupants of this region are an energetic people. Here are found, therefore, the chief political, economic, and social centers, such as Bogotá and Medellín.

Bogotá and Medellín have the largest number of white people, largely descendants of the early Spaniards. Medellín, located in an upland valley, in the department of Antioquia, has an interesting group of inhabitants said to be descendants of Spanish Hebrews. Many of these people are light complexioned, with blue eyes and fair hair, even among the lower classes. Inhabitants with similar characteristics are found in other districts of Antioquia. They are thrifty, honest, and hard working, and have contributed substantially to the industrial and commercial development of the country.

Since almost half of the total population of Colombia consists of mestizos, it is to be expected that they are widely distributed and engaged in varied activities. Furthermore the mestizos do not constitute a homogeneous group of people. For centuries there has been an intermixture of Indian and white stock. The Indians, as pointed out above, are of several tribes, some quite intelligent and progressive, others less so. Likewise the Spaniards are of different stock, including Iberians, Celts, Teutons, Basques, Moors, and Hebrews. These different races and types, intermixed under different environmental conditions, must create resultants of differing qualities, both mentally and physically.

Health conditions. Throughout the larger cities public health conditions are being rapidly improved. This is due in part to the influence of the Pan American Union, which has promoted international gatherings of health officers for a number of years. It is due also in part to the efforts of the Rockefeller Foundation, which maintains nurses and physicians in the country, who not only work independently, but coöperate intimately with health officials. In part this growing interest is due to the excellent work of the medical schools attached to the national universities of Colombia, which have sought to stimulate public consciousness in matters of health, both personal and public.

In rural communities health conditions are still very poor. Impure water and inadequate disposal of sewage are the greatest rural handicaps. There is also a lack of refrigeration for stored foods, and, consequently, meat, which is used in large quantities, must be cooked as soon as it comes from the slaughterhouses.

Americans visiting any of the rural areas would do well to avoid the use of raw vegetables. Water, except in the larger cities that have adequate supplies controlled by boards of sanitation, should be boiled before using. Fruits, unless they are picked by the person himself, should be peeled before eating. In this way infections may usually be avoided. Foreigners are advised to refrain from eating too much meat. Since vegetables of nearly all kinds may be purchased at any season of the year, the preparation of a diet list is not a difficult matter for those who maintain homes. Excellent pensions, boarding houses which cater particularly to English and American visitors, are found in principal cities, and provide the sort of food these people desire. With few exceptions, necessary health precautions can be successfully observed without undue discomfort.

Transportation. The essential interrelation of waterways, railways, and highways is profoundly impressed upon the student of transportation of Colombia. Bogotá, Medellín, Manizales, Bucaramanga, and other important cities depend upon the linking of railways and waterways for transportation to coastal towns and ports. To a considerable extent, airway service has overcome some of the inherent difficulties of passenger and mail transportation in Colombia.

The Magdalena River, over 1,000 miles long, and its numerous tributaries, is the natural but inadequate artery of transportation through the central area of Colombia. This great river system, however, would be even less useful for commercial purposes than it is today if railways did not overcome some of its obstacles. Until 1935, the delta mouth of the Magdalena was not deep enough for ocean-going vessels. Consequently ships docked at Puerto Colombia, and cargo and passengers moved over an 18-mile railway from the seaport to Barranquilla on the Magdalena River. Numerous attempts were made to dredge the river mouth, but in 1935 nature came to man's aid in the form of a ponderous submarine slide that carried away millions of tons of silt and freed the entrance of the Magdalena River. As a result, ships of the sea now navigate to the very docks of Barranquilla. Silting in the lower Magdalena often prevents or delays transportation, however. Cartagena, another important port on the Caribbean coast of Colombia, is connected by railway with the Magdalena at Calamar. The distance from Cartagena to Barranquilla is about 80 miles.

From the Caribbean coastal region to the interior highlands of Colombia, transportation facilities are seriously inadequate and difficult.

On the Magdalena, river transportation is subject to frequent delays, particularly during the dry season, because of the shallow water. River craft, somewhat similar to the flat-bottom, stern-wheeler steamboat used on the Mississippi, ply the Magdalena between Barranquilla and La Dorada, a distance of 600 miles (this requires six days to go upstream, three downstream). From La Dorada to Bogotá are railway connections, a roundabout route of over 184 miles.

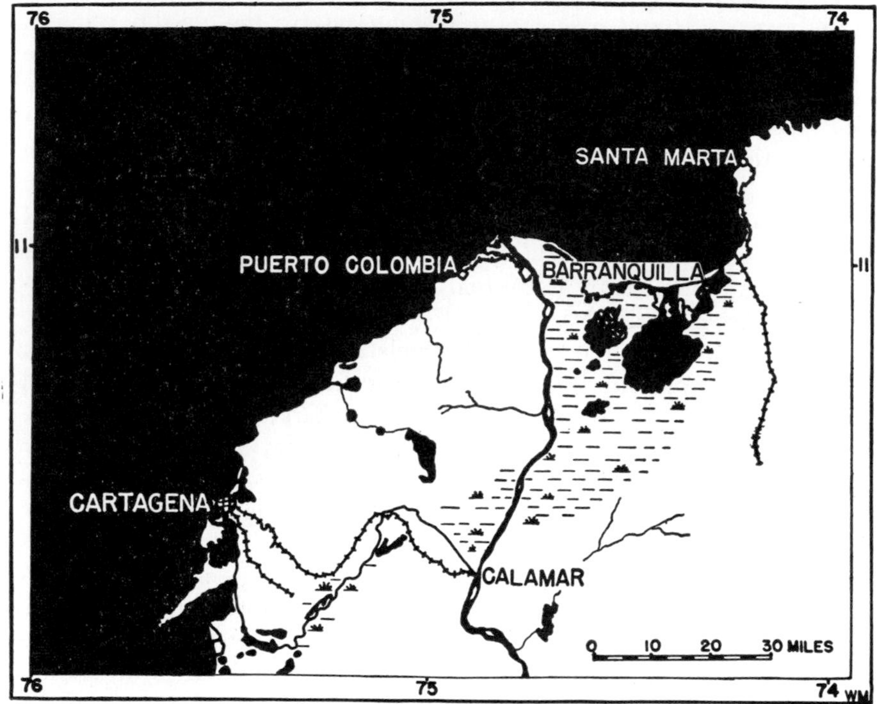

Fig. 97. Colombia's Caribbean region.

The journey by water and rail from Barranquilla to Bogotá takes ten days and by plane only two and a half hours. The first commercial airway in Latin America and the second oldest in the world was the Sociedad Colombo-Alemana de Transportes Aéreos, better known as Scadta. This company was formed in 1919 and operates between Barranquilla and Bogotá. In 1940 a new organization replaced the German-owned Scadta (see Chapter XXXIII).

Direct railway communication exists between Bogotá and Buenaventura, on the western coast of Colombia, except for a distance of about 70 miles, between Armenia and Ibagué. An excellent motor road extends between these two places.

Among other railways of commercial importance in Colombia are the

Antioquia Railway, the Santa Marta Railway, and the Cúcuta Railway. The first mentioned joins the city of Medellín, the second largest city of Colombia, to the Magdalena River at Puerto Berrío. In 1929 a tunnel between Limon and Santiago was opened on this line. Formerly, direct connection between Medellín and Berrío was broken by the Quieba Mountains between Limon and Santiago. Motor service had to be provided over the mountains. This is now unnecessary.

The Santa Marta Railway runs along the Caribbean coast as far as

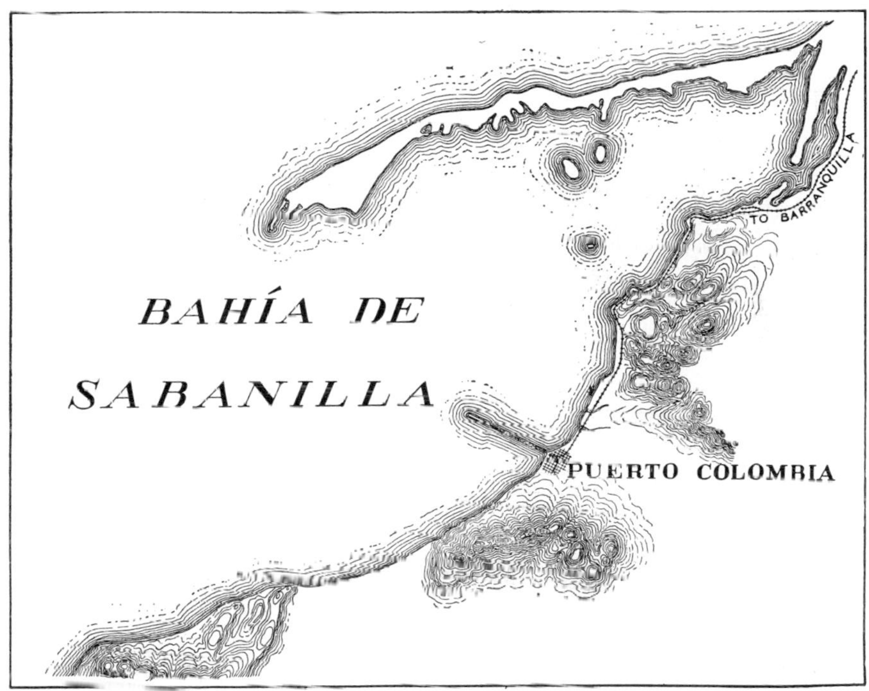

Fig. 98. Puerto Colombia.

Ciénaga; from there it takes a southeast direction, and then turns south to Fundación, a total distance of 94 kilometers—about 58.4 miles. The railway serves the banana plantation region. The Cúcuta Railway projects from Cúcuta to Puerto Villamizar, on the Zulia River, where a line extends to Encontrados, Venezuela. Water transportation exists from Encontrados to Maracaibo and other lake ports. Shipments of Colombian coffee are made over this route.

Practically all of the coal, oil, and wood used for fuel in locomotives comes from local mines and fields. Most of the coal mined in Colombia is from the Cali district, which includes the area in the Cauca River basin and that east of the Cordillera Occidental. Oil is obtained from

F. A. Carlson.

Fig. 99. Political divisions of Colombia.

the Tropical Oil Company's fields near Barranca Bermeja, in the upper Magdalena Valley, or from the fields of Santander, in eastern Colombia.

The difficulty in transportation in Colombia has been in part the result of the construction of unrelated railways in widely separated regions, whereas a greater concentration in one or two areas might have proved more valuable to the national welfare. It seems possible that competition between various parts of Colombia is responsible, at least in part, for her diversified railway pattern. Indeed, the character of the land, the position of the river systems, the location of natural resources, and other geographical factors have played a vital part in bringing about the sectional pattern of Colombian culture.

Caribbean urban centers. Colombia has never experienced a gradual frontier movement on a broad front as has the United States. There have been no great population waves such as those that opened up successive regions of our own Western frontier. The establishment of settlements occurred spontaneously throughout the entire area. Towns and cities sprang up in the very beginning in widely separated regions. Fear of attack by the corsairs sailing along the coast and unfavorable climatic conditions in the tropical lowlands led to the settlement of the upland valleys and highlands. Agricultural and mineral resources also lured settlers to the highlands and to the distant and apparently inaccessible hinterland to the south. On the coastal lands agriculture and port activities explain the presence of the littoral settlements.

Ports and their hinterland. Barranquilla is the nation's leading import center, a position made possible after the submarine slide in 1935, which opened the mouth of the Magdalena to deep-draft vessels. However, in 1948 the silting at the mouth of the river caused diversion of a number of ships from Barranquilla to Cartagena (see Fig. 97, page 294). In recent years, Barranquilla has made considerable industrial progress in the establishment of textile mills, flour mills, and factories for the production of shoes, hats, soaps, oil, and the like. Within its urban limits are tall modern buildings, as well as single-story straw-thatched houses and streamlined cars passing horse-drawn carriages. From the contrasting center of old and new move the ships of the sea to foreign lands and the planes of the air to the interior of Colombia and more distant lands of Latin America and the United States.

On an island near the coast stands Cartagena, a city of antiquity (see Fig. 97). It was not only one of the first settlements, but also one of the most celebrated places in the New World. Here Spain controlled the monopoly of commerce with South America during colonial times. In its spacious harbor, protected on all sides by fortresses, the Spanish merchant ships found refuge from pirates and buccaneers. When these sea rovers made it unsafe to ship the precious cargoes of gold and silver by the Pacific, it was transported overland from Bolivia, Peru, Ecuador, and New Granada by way of the Andes, and descended the Cauca and Magdalena Rivers to Cartagena. Fleets of galleons, as the merchant ships accompanied by war vessels were called, plied between Seville, Spain, and Porto Bello, on the Isthmus of Panama, and Cartagena, Colombia, as it is now known. A massive wall over 20 feet thick had been built to protect the venerable city of Cartagena from attacks by marauders, but without success. Such notorious buccaneers as Drake, Morgan, Pontis, and Vernon besieged and sacked it, but the walled city of the Caribbean survived and presents to this age a memorial of Spanish grandeur. White buildings with tiers of balconies and grated windows; patios of ancient homes, adorned with flowers and tropical plants; plazas shaded with palms; enticing narrow streets; towering churches; a majestic cathedral; and several monastic institutions—these characterize the cultural pattern of Cartagena.

The harbor of Cartagena is formed by the coastal configuration and by the island on which the city stands. The channel leading to the port is deep enough for large ocean vessels. Passengers and cargo are landed directly on the pier. In exports Cartagena surpasses all other Colombian ports.

Another important port of Colombia on the Caribbean is Santa Marta. Its prosperity depends largely on the banana trade. During the active season at least one ship a day loads bananas at the port. The bay is crescent-shaped and opens to the southwest. Large vessels can enter the bay and dock alongside the piers, where the latest devices for loading the fruit have been installed.

POPULATION OF PRINCIPAL URBAN CENTERS OF COLOMBIA

Bogotá	462,600
Medellín	228,300
Barranquilla	215,800
Cali	141,300
Cartagena	104,100
Manizales	113,700
Ibagué	81,900
Cúcuta	74,900
Bucaramanga	68,700
Pasto	61,700
Santa Marta	42,600
Popayan	35,300

Upland settlements. In contrast with the early tropical settlements on the coast is the plateau city of Bogotá. Far from the Caribbean waters, an airline distance of about 450 miles, at an elevation of about 8,700 feet above sea level, lies the capital of Colombia. Formerly one of the most inaccessible cities of Latin America, Bogotá is now less than nine hours from Miami, Florida, by airplane. In 1538 Gonzalo Jimenez de Quesada took possession of the present site of Bogotá in the name of the Emperor Charles V. The name is from *Bacatá,* the old Chibcha capital, where one of the most powerful Indian tribes of the Andes had its headquarters.

Being a native of Granada, in Spain, Quesada named the land that he had discovered and conquered the United Kingdom of Granada. Not until after the war of independence was the name changed to Colombia. For a long time Bogotá was the capital of the viceroyalty of New Granada. It has grown from a village of wooden huts and one church, constructed by Quesada and his followers, into an intellectual and cultural center of more than 462,000 inhabitants. The pioneers who established the city manifested a glorious disregard of transportation difficulties.

In Bogotá there is almost entire absence of the Negro element that forms a large part of the population in the coastal area. Sturdy descendants of the Chibchas are indigenous to this region. White people who have apparently maintained the purity of their Mediterranean inheritance are in evidence. There is elegance in the Spanish spoken by even the most humble persons. Bogotá is an important literary and cultural center, often called the Athens of America. On the streets appear well-dressed men and women of pure Spanish stock and ragged peons of the humbler classes. There are great contrasts between these two extremes, made all the more prominent because there is no real middle class. But all people seem to possess the qualities of being friendly, well mannered, and kindly. In general they are not overenthusiastic. Eager faces among them are not the rule—although in a quiet, friendly fashion they will meet in homes or on the street corners and discuss politics and economics and world trends, and display a well-informed and interested mind.

A great deal of attention is given to dress in this remote Andean city. The tendency is for both men and women to dress in simple, dark-colored attire. The *ruana,* the Colombian equivalent of the poncho so extensively used elsewhere in South America, is worn by aristocrats as well as by the poor. It is particularly useful for protection against the cold winds and drizzling rains of these highlands. Here the climate is temperate as compared with the excessive heat and unremitting humidity of much of the tropical lowlands. In the wet season the temperature sometimes, although rarely, drops as low as 40°. Houses are not heated, except in the case of the homes occupied by foreigners or some of the more progressive Colombians who are financially able to have furnaces in their homes.[1]

Bogotá possesses all of the fine features of a Latin American city. A public square, the Plaza Bolívar, marks the civic center of the city. On the south side of the plaza is the capitol building, an imposing edifice of

---

1 The ruana is particularly prevalent in the rural areas.

white granite, and on the east side stand the cathedral and the old Spanish viceregal palace. The cathedral, as in many Latin American cities, is the most notable structure in the capital. With the exception of the presidential palace, the national library, and a few other public buildings, the churches and monasteries attract most attention from visitors.

Residences are usually two-story houses. Their walls are always of mud bricks finished with plaster. The older buildings and many of the newer ones reveal a Moorish style of architecture, a balcony on the second floor facing the street, a large single entrance, and a courtyard (*portón* and *patio*) on which the rooms open to the rear. Often, the patios are made very beautiful with flowers and shade trees.

In general, the city is clean and has many broad streets, parks, and plazas, in addition to the Plaza Bolívar. Among the most intriguing scenes to visitors in Bogotá are the open markets, where a great variety of commodities are offered for sale, and where different types of native folk gather. These open markets are familiar sights in all South American population centers, large and small.

Another important upland city is Medellín, located in the department of Antioquia. It is the leading industrial center of the country and ranks second in population—228,300. Its adjacent lands are rich in agricultural, pastoral, and mining resources. It is one of the progressive cities of Colombia.

South of Antioquia lies the department of Caldas. Until recently this was one of the most isolated regions of the inhabited areas of Colombia because of its ruggedness. Now a railway joins its leading city, Manizales, with the Pacific port of Buenaventura. Manizales has a population of 113,700. It is located at an altitude of 7,000 feet above sea level and enjoys an equable climate. Coffee is the chief export product of the department.

From the upper valley of the Magdalena River to the border of Venezuela are two other important departments—Santander, and Santander del Norte. Both departments have important oil-producing fields. Bucaramanga is the leading municipality of Santander, with a population of 68,700. It is a center of distribution in a rich coffee-growing district. In the department of Santander del Norte, Cúcuta is the chief political and commercial center. It depends in part for access to foreign lands upon an outlet through Venezuela.

The chief distributing center of western Colombia is the city of Cali, in the department of Valle del Cauca. There is communication with Armenia, Cartago, and Manizales to the north, Popayan to the south, Buenaventura to the west, and Bogotá to the east. Railway connections exist from Cali to all of these places, except on the route from Cali to Bogotá there is a section between Armenia and Ibaqué without rail connections. Some 141,300 persons comprise the population of Cali. Coffee is the chief crop of the department, but sugar, cotton, and tobacco are of no slight importance. Coal is mined in this region, and there are reports of gold, silver, and platinum deposits. The climate varies from tropical on the Pacific lowlands to subtropical at the altitude of Cali, 3,000 feet. Buenaventura, the leading Colombian port on the Pacific Coast, serves as an entrepôt for this potentially rich hinterland.

The Oriente. More than half of the total area of Colombia, a region larger than the state of Texas, lies south and east of the Andes. This vast area of 290,000 square miles is practically unknown. Limited information, much of which is highly generalized, tells us that the land is a comparatively flat plain with its drainage east and southeast. From the foothills of the Andes to the central portion of the Oriente, the region is classified as the Llanos of Colombia, while the remainder has been described as a tropical forest region of innumerable swamps and flooded rivers during the heavy rains.

A road from Bogotá via Bella Vista to Villavicencio was completed in 1936. Over this route, a tortuous one rising from the Llanos to Bogotá, a climb of two thousand feet in eight miles, pass the region's chief export, cattle. Generally the cattle are driven from distant haciendas, and corralled at Villavicencio to regain sufficient strength before making the difficult trek to Bogotá. In the past, considerable quantities of alligator skins were shipped out of this region.

Although the Oriente is not well known physiographically or economically, it has come to our attention politically. In the far south, a wedge of Colombia includes a portion of the Amazon River. On its bank stands Leticia, a "port" consisting of a few dilapidated houses. Beyond the border is Peru, and for unstated reasons this neighboring country claimed Leticia. As a result, a quarrel was started that lasted for two years. In 1934 the League of Nations decided in favor of Colombia, restoring to this nation a right to Leticia and the Amazon River.

Agricultural industry: Coffee. Coffee is the leading commercial crop of Colombia, and in the world's total production Colombia ranks second.

Most of the coffee is grown on the slopes of the Andes at varying altitudes. The most general range seems to be between 3,000 feet and 6,500 feet above sea level. The ideal temperature range is from 65° to 75° F.

Colombian coffee matures at various seasons, the time depending upon climate. The two main crops mature in the fall or winter and in the spring. However, coffee is picked, prepared, sold, and exported during the entire year.

The most important coffee regions are found in the departments of Antioquia, Caldas, Santander, Santander del Norte, Valle del Cauca,

Magdalena, Nariño, Cauca, and the Intendencia del Chocó. In this area the larger harvest usually falls in the months of October, November, and December, and the smaller harvest during April, May, and June.

The second best district includes the departments of Cundinamarca, Tolima, Huila, Boyacá, Intendencia del Meta, and the Comisaria del Putumayo. In this district the larger harvest usually takes place during March, April, and May, and the smaller harvest during November, December, and January.

The greater part of the Colombian coffee is grown on small farms producing from 35 to 50 bags or less a year; the farm owners, with the aid of their families and hired labor, plant, cultivate, and gather the crop.

Very little coffee is sold on the farms. The more important planters usually sell their coffee in one of the 10 or 12 principal coffee-buying centers, such as Girardot, Medellín, Manizales, Bucaramanga, and Cúcuta. The smaller farmers usually sell their crop to brokers in the nearest small town, and the brokers in turn sell the coffee to the larger buyers in the more important centers.

The development of coffee plantations and farms preceded the construction of railways and roads. The terrain of the coffee districts is rugged, and few of the farms are situated near railway stations or navigable rivers. Old and new methods of transportation are therefore employed in shipping Colombian coffee from the plantations to the ports. With few exceptions, the coffee is first moved by muleback to the railways, rivers, highways, or cableways. In some sections of the country, United States-made motor trucks are used. Since the product is grown in practically every department of the republic, and since the industry consists of thousands of small private farms—with the exception of the department of Cundinamarca, where large plantations are owned by families residing in Bogotá or abroad—no single system of transportation could adequately fulfill the requirements. In recent years the tendency has been to construct railways and highways to serve as conveniently as possible the actual and potential coffee-growing areas. But, owing to the importance of mules and oxen as draft animals, and the fact that the cost of building railways and highways is high and the topography is rugged, it is believed that farm animals will continue to serve as burden bearers for many years. Obviously, the necessity of employing several means of transportation and the numerous handlings increase the landed cost of Colombian coffee in the United States and Europe.

The Magdalena River is the most important artery for the transportation of Colombian coffee to the coast. Coffee is brought to the river ports by railways, cableways, motor trucks, and mules.

The coffee crop of Colombia is about one-fourth as large as that of Brazil, but it commands a higher price in world markets. Colombia, however, leads in the production of mild, or so-called blending coffee.

Cotton. Colombia has made comparatively little progress in the production of cotton. The supply is not sufficient for the needs of the cotton mills. Nearly one-half of the raw cotton consumed is foreign-grown. Statistics also show that cotton goods constitute one of the major classes of imports. These conditions can be largely remedied if Colombia would make more efficient use of its natural cotton-growing resources.

While cotton is grown in many parts of the country, the most extensive areas of production are in the departments of Magdalena and Antioquia. However, the most suitable region for extension of cotton culture lies in the central Cauca Valley. In this region the soil bears a striking resemblance to the cotton lands of Texas, where some of our best American cotton is grown. This area also has the advantage of fairly good railway transportation to textile centers. There are also good cotton lands in Atlantico in the coastal regions, and in Antioquia, Boyacá, and Santander.

Sugar. Small sugar plantations exist in nearly every inhabited district of the tropical and subtropical regions. The largest estate is at Sincerin, about 28 miles from Cartagena, where cane is grown without irrigation on some 15,000 acres. The most suitable area for sugar production is in the Cauca Valley.

The refining of sugar has made but little progress in Colombia. At present there are probably not more than ten modern refineries. In general, unrefined sugar, or *panela,* is used. This product can be made by a very simple process, without the aid of complicated machinery. Colombia is now self-sufficient in sugar.

Tobacco. The climate and soil conditions in many regions in Colombia are notably favorable for the production of tobacco. Most of the crop is cultivated for local use. The chief producing districts are Santander and Tolima.

Bananas. The commercial cultivation of bananas is principally carried on in the hinterland of Santa Marta, extending along the lowlands between the Sierra and the lagoon south of Cíenaga. In prewar years, the banana industry furnished the nation's second largest item of food exports, but suffered a sharp decline during the war. Banana exports have increased, amounting to some 4,000,000 stems in 1948, largely due to the renewed operations of the Compania Frutera de Sevilla, Colombian affiliate of the United Fruit Company. Most of the bananas are grown on holdings ranging in size from less than an acre to 2,000 acres. The market is primarily the United States.

Other crops. The tagua, or vegetable ivory nut, used in making buttons, handles, and similar articles is the product of a palm tree grown on the lowlands of both coasts. Rubber, balatá, and chicle are found in the Magdalena and Atrato regions. Cacao, divi-divi, and agave are other products of international significance grown in Colombia.

Domestic food crops. In many cases records of subsistence food crops are not available. The production of food for local consumption is, nevertheless, big and important business. In Colombia, based on volume, corn is the leading crop. Other food crops are rice, grown in the lowlands, and wheat, barley, and potatoes in the uplands.

Livestock industry. The livestock of Colombia is classified as follows: cattle, 14,000,000; sheep, 1,000,000; goats, 2,000,000; swine, 1,500,000; horses, mules, 1,500,000.

The principal cattle regions are the Llanos of eastern Colombia, the highlands of Bogotá, the savannas of Bolívar, and the Cauca and Patía Valleys. The best results have been obtained in the highland region, where the climate is more favorable for cattle raising. In the savanna regions the dry season, which is frequently a period of prolonged drought, is decidedly unfavorable to the grazing industry. In general, the native animal is the long-horned type, of inferior quality. The meat is coarse and poor, and the milkers yield very little. Beef animals are more in demand than dairy cattle. Very little improvement has been made in the quality of the stock. Hides and skins constitute an important source of income.

The dairy industry is developing in importance. Through the importation of breeding cattle from the United States and Canada, the dairy herds have been greatly improved.

Mineral production. Petroleum is one of Colombia's leading exports, and ranks first among the minerals. The Tropical Oil Company, a subsidiary of the International Petroleum Corporation, a Standard Oil Company of New Jersey interest, holds a concession located in the Magdalena Valley in the department of Santander. The main producing fields, known as the El Centro area, are located north and south of Barrancabermeja, the site of a refinery, about 350 miles up the Magdalena River.

Transportation difficulties in Colombia are well illustrated in the case of this enterprise. Material shipped to these fields enters through the port of Barranquilla or Cartagena; by boat to Galan; by narrow-gauge (30-inch) railway from Galan to El Centro; and from El Centro to the oil fields by trucks and tractors. The difficulty of transportation arises, not only from the numerous modes of shipment and the many transshipments, but also from the intense heat and multitudinous insects. During the rainy season the flooded streams add another element of adversity.

Oil is transported to the coast without much trouble. A 10-inch pipe line, 350 miles long, with a capacity of 52,000 barrels daily or nearly 20,000,000 barrels annually, runs from Barrancabermeja to El Mamonal, 10 miles across the bay from Cartagena. At El Mamonal the company has a tankyard consisting of some fifteen 80,000-barrel tanks, sufficient storage space for about 24 days of pumping.

Another oil region that has attracted attention is in the Catatumbo area of northeastern Colombia, an extension of the Maracaibo region of Venezuela, known as the Barco field. At present, Petrolea is the only producing field, yielding from 10,000 to 12,000 barrels a day. A pipe line transports the oil to Covenas, located west of Cartagena. Both gas and oil are produced there. Other possible sources of oil are on the western coast and the coastal plain, the latter stretching across the northern portion of the country from the Santa Marta region to the Panama border.

Colombia produced in 1950 about 30,000,000 barrels of oil, surpassed in Latin America by Venezuela (500,000,000) and Mexico (70,000,000). In 1950 Latin America produced 18 per cent of the world output of petroleum.

The world's chief source of platinum is the Pacific Coast of Colombia, between the Atrato River and the border of Ecuador. The present workings, all of the placer type, are in the Chocó area. The center of greatest production is in the Condoto River area.

Colombia is further distinguished by producing the world's largest supply of emeralds. All persons in Colombia engaged in cutting or selling emeralds are required by law to register with the government. Gold, the mineral that was first to attract settlers to Colombia, is still produced in amounts ranging from 300,000 to 500,000 fine ounces, annually. The principal mines are in Antioquia, Cauca, and Caldas. Other metallic minerals, including silver, copper, zinc, and lead, are produced in small quantities. Coal and iron ore are found in many places within Colombia, but only small amounts are mined to meet the limited domestic demand. No accurate information is available concerning the iron ore reserve of Colombia.

Manufacturing. Existing industrial establishments are expanding and new ones are being established, despite the lack of machinery, some raw materials, and capital. High prices and quantitative import restrictions have motivated national production of many manufactured goods. This is particularly true in the production of such items as textiles, glassware and containers, beverages, toilet and pharmaceutical products, plastics, cement, leather goods, and tubes and tires. Outstanding progress has been made in the production of cotton and rayon goods, and the output of tubes and tires is sufficient to meet national demand.

Foreign trade. The United States supplied about three-fourths of Columbia's exports in 1940, compared with one-half in prewar days. In 1947 about 85 per cent of Colombia's total exports were destined for the United States, and about 70 per cent of its imports originated in the United States.

The leading Colombian exports are coffee, crude petroleum, and bananas. Most of the exportable coffee moves to the United States, Canada, and the Near East; crude petroleum to the United States, Canada, Curaçao, Argentina, and continental Europe; and bananas to the United States and continental Europe.

COLOMBIA: FOREIGN TRADE

	Total Value (000 Dollars)	*Percentage of Total*					
Exports		United States	Canada	Latin America	United Kingdom	Continental Europe	All Others
1938	80,774	52.7	9.8	0.9	0.5	24.1	11.9
1947	254,332	84.4	3.1	2.3	0.7	4.3	5.3
Imports							
1938	89,054	49.9	1.7	1.8	11.1	32.7	2.8
1947	363,793	72.3	2.2	9.2	4.2	10.2	1.8

COLOMBIA: EXPORTS OF PRINCIPAL COMMODITIES

Commodity	*Quantity*		*Percentage of Total Value Al All Exports*	
	1947	*1948*	*1947*	*1948*
Coffee (thousands of sacks)	5,342	5,600	76.4	78.6
Crude petroleum (thousands of barrels)	19,596	19,163	14.5	15.7
Bananas (thousands of stems)	3,339	4,716	1.8	2.2
Platinum (troy oz.)	38,715	19,019	0.6	0.4
Cattle hides (metric tons)	4,956	4,689	1.5	1.2
Leaf tobacco (metric tons)	3,893	3,019	0.6	0.6

Source: Office of International Trade, United States Department of Commerce, Washington, D. C., 1950.

Exports by customhouses, in order of value, are: Cartagena (35 per cent), Barranquilla (17 per cent), Santa Marta (8 per cent), Cúcuta, Tumaco, Ríohacha, and others. In 1937, Santa Marta was in second place, but since the decline in Colombia's banana production, Santa Marta's only export, the port has dropped to third or fourth position. Barranquilla (47 per cent) is Colombia's leading import center, followed by Buenaventura, Cartagena, Cúcuta, Tumaco, Santa Marta, and others.

Distinctive features. While mining led to the exploration and conquest of Colombia, as in many other Latin American countries, it has never employed a large percentage of the nation's people. Agriculture has long been the leading industry of the country, with coffee the chief export. Petroleum ranks next to coffee, and is the leading mineral export. In all probability the oil industry will expand and continue to contribute for some time to the nation's revenue. Colombia is also making some progress in manufacturing. There are marked improvements in highway construction, civic institutions, and health and sanitation conditions. The varied landscape, natural resources, and industries of Colombia rightly give to this nation the title "a land of contrasts."

SELECTED REFERENCES

Allen, Paul H.: "Indians of Southeastern Colombia," *Geographical Review*, Vol. XXXVII, No. 4 (1947), pp. 567–582.

Bates, Marston: "Climate and Vegetation in the Villavicencio Region of Eastern Colombia," *Geographical Review*, Vol. XXXVIII, No. 4 (1948), pp. 555–574.

Beyer, R. C.: "Transportation and the Coffee Industry in Colombia," *Inter-American Economic Affairs*, Vol. 2, No. 3 (1948), pp. 17–30.

Culbertson, Raymond E.: "Colombia Goes Ahead of Transportation and Agriculture," *Agriculture in the Americas*, Vol. VI, No. 10 (1946), pp. 155–159.

Fowler, R. I., and Salinas, Jorge E.: "Colombia's Chocolate Crop," *Agriculture in the Americas*, Vol. VII, No. 2 (1947), pp. 27–30.

Gray, L. M.: "The Magdalena River of Colombia," *Bulletin of the Pan American Union*, Vol. LXV (1931), pp. 731–743.

Hitchcock, C. B.: "Notes on a trip from Caracas to Bogotá," *Geographical Review*, Vol. XXXVII, No. 1 (1947), pp. 121–136.

Hoffman, H. T.: "Colombia in the First Postwar Year Scored Advances—Faced Problems," *Foreign Commerce Weekly*, Vol. 26, No. 9 (1947), p. 6.

James, P. E.: "The Transportation Problem of Highland Colombia," *Journal of Geography*, Vol. XXII (1923), pp. 346–354.

Kurtz, F. M.: "Colombia's Coffee Land Almost Unlimited," *Tea and Coffee Trade Journal*, Vol. LVI (1929), pp. 673–674.

Martin, F. O.: "Explorations in Colombia," *Geographical Review*, Vol. XIX (1929), pp. 621–637.

Murphy, R. C.: "The Littoral of Pacific Colombia and Ecuador," *Geographical Review*, Vol. XXIX (1939), pp. 1–33.

Murphy, R. C.: "Racial Succession in the Colombian Chocó," *Geographical Review*, Vol. XXIX (1939), pp. 461–471.

Notestein, F. B., and King, R. E.: "Sierra Nevada de Cocuy," *Geographical Review*, Vol. XXII (1932), pp. 423–430.

Romoli, Kathleen: *Colombia, Gateway to South America*, Doubleday, Doran, New York, 1941.

Seifriz, W.: "Sierra Nevada de Santa Marta: An Ascent from the North," *Geographical Review*, Vol. XXIV (1934), pp. 478–485.

Smith, A. C.: "Mountain Tops and Lowlands of Colombia," *Economic Geography*, Vol. VI (1930), pp. 398–407.

Taylor, M. M.: "Development of Petroleum Industry in Colombia," *Commerce Reports*, Vol. II (1927), pp. 706–708, Bureau of Foreign and Domestic Commerce, Washington, D. C.

Torrijos, F. L.: "Bogotá," *Bulletin of the Pan American Union*, Vol. LXV (1931), pp. 1113–1126.

CHAPTER XVIII

THE UNITED STATES OF VENEZUELA

Early settlement. Almost a hundred years before the founding of the Jamestown Colony, a permanent European settlement had been established on the northern coast of Venezuela. It is known today as Cumaná, one of the oldest cities founded by Europeans in South America. Columbus and Americus Vespucius were among the early explorers to visit these northern shores. In 1513 the Dominican Friars began the missionary work among the Indians that led to the establishment of Cumaná. By 1763 the population was some 5,000. This ancient city now claims slightly more than 30,000 inhabitants. This early occupancy of the northern coast of Venezuela can be attributed, primarily, to its location near the old sailing route between Europe and the new southern continent.

Three significant facts should be mentioned with respect to Venezuela's location. First, Venezuela is the only country of South America that lies wholly north of the equator. Its area of some 352,170 square miles extends approximately from 1° to 12° N. latitude. Second, Venezuela is situated in close proximity to the Caribbean islands. Ever since the colonial period, Negroes have entered Venezuela from these islands to the north, either as slaves—before the abolition of slavery—or as free laborers to work in the cacao plantations, the ports, or the oil fields. Today more than 8 per cent of Venezuela's total population of 4,299,600 is classified as black, 15 per cent as white, 5 per cent as Indian, and the remaining 72 per cent as mixed races, including 60 per cent mestizos and 12 per cent mulattoes. Third, only Venezuela and Brazil, of all South American nations, have a common frontier with a European possession—namely, British Guiana. Brazil also borders Dutch and French Guiana.

Regional pattern. Venezuela consists of four major geographical regions: (1) the Andean Highland and associated lowland; (2) the Maracaibo Lowland; (3) the Orinoco Plain; and (4) the Guiana Highland. The Andean Highland partly incloses the Maracaibo Basin or lowland and separates it and the coastal lands of Venezuela from the Orinoco Plain. The Guiana Highland occupies the southeastern portion

VENEZUELA, ARUBA, AND CURAÇAO: TEMPERATURE AND RAINFALL OF SELECTED STATIONS

	Station	Ciudad-Bolívar *	Caracas*	La Guaira†	Maracaibo*	El Perú†	Aruba ‡	Curaçao ‡	Mérida *
	Elevation (*Feet*)	125	2,992	S. L.	16.4	721.8		75.5	5,292
Average Temperature (°*F.*)	*Period of Record*	1934–1942 1944–1946	1934–1946	3 yrs.	1931–1936 1938–1946	1910–1921		1898–1912	1934–1941 1944–1946
	January	79.5	65.8	78.4	81.1	75.6		77.7	64.8
	February	80.4	66.4	78.4	81.1	76.3		77.7	65.7
	March	81.5	67.6	79.3	81.9	77.2		77.9	66.7
	April	82.4	70.3	80.2	83.1	79.0		79.3	67.3
	May	82.0	70.7	81.1	83.5	79.2		81.1	67.3
	June	81.0	70.0	81.7	84.4	77.7		81.3	66.7
	July	80.6	69.6	81.1	84.6	77.5		81.1	66.6
	August	81.7	69.8	82.6	85.1	78.3		81.3	67.5
	September	82.8	70.5	82.9	84.7	78.6		81.9	68.2
	October	83.0	70.0	82.6	83.1	78.3		81.7	66.7
	November	82.0	68.7	81.5	82.6	77.7		80.4	66.2
	December	80.4	67.1	78.8	82.0	76.5		78.6	65.5
	Annual	81.5	68.9	80.8	83.1	77.5		80.1	66.6
	Range	3.5	14.9	4.5	4.0	3.6		4.2	3.4
Average Rainfall (*Inches*)	*Period of Record*	1931–1946	1931–1946	1920–1925	1934–1946	1910–1922	1919–1932	1894–1912	1931–1946
	January	1.4	0.7	0.5	0.1	3.9	1.9	2.4	2.0
	February	0.5	0.3	0.2	0.0	3.2	0.5	1.3	1.9
	March	0.5	0.3	0.8	0.5	2.1	0.4	0.9	2.0
	April	1.8	1.1	0.2	0.9	3.1	0.3	0.7	6.3
	May	6.0	4.1	0.6	2.8	5.8	0.4	0.4	10.6
	June	5.5	3.3	0.9	2.0	8.0	0.3	0.7	6.6
	July	6.8	3.5	1.0	1.7	6.9	1.0	1.2	4.5
	August	7.4	4.0	1.1	2.4	7.0	0.7	1.3	6.4
	September	3.5	3.6	1.2	2.1	4.6	1.7	1.2	7.3
	October	3.4	4.8	1.6	6.3	3.4	2.5	3.5	11.4
	November	2.4	3.7	1.6	3.0	3.6	5.0	5.4	10.4
	December	1.9	1.8	1.5	0.8	4.1	3.3	3.5	3.7
	Annual	41.1	31.2	11.1	22.6	55.8	17.7	22.5	73.1

* Ministerio de Fomento, Dirección General de Estadística, *Anuario Estadístico de Venezuela,* 1938-1946.

† K. Knoch: "Klimakunde von Südamerika," *Handbuch der Klimatologie,* Band II, Teil G, Berlin, 1930.

‡ R. De C. Ward, and C. F. Brooks: "Climatology of the West Indies," *Handbuch der Klimatologie,* Band II, Teil G, Berlin, 1930.

of the republic and extends beyond the border of Venezuela into British, French, and Dutch Guiana.

Andean Highland and associated lowland. The eastern cordillera of the Andes sends one range toward the north to form the western boundary of Venezuela, and another branch extends northeastward as a great anticlinal arch called the Sierra Nevada de Mérida. In this region are found some of the highest mountain peaks in Venezuela: La Columna or Pico Bolívar (16,400 feet), Pico Humboldt (16,200 feet), and many others over 15,000 feet. East of the Maracaibo Basin the highlands form a double range known as the Serrania Costanera and the Serrania Interior, or coastal and interior ranges.

The outer or coastal range rises from the sea at an average elevation of about 4,000 feet, and east of Caracas, the capital of Venezuela, are found peaks that exceed 8,000 feet above sea level. It continues through the Paria Peninsula at a much lower elevation but is broken in the vicinity of Barcelona, where the coastal plain merges with the Orinoco Lowlands to the south. The interior range is lower than the coastal range, and in many places it is broken by transverse valleys.

North of where the Sierra Nevada de Mérida swings eastward into separate ranges lies a broken mountain area called the Falcon region.

Climatic conditions. The average annual temperature in the Andean Highland region of Venezuela is approximately 81.5° F. at 350 feet above sea level; 77.5° F. at 700 feet; 68.5° F. at 2,992 feet (Caracas); and 67° F. at 5,292 feet (Mérida). In Caracas the average annual precipitation is about 32 inches. A dry season with less than an inch a month prevails from January through March; from June through October the average is more than four inches a month; in November over three inches; and in December, April, and May between one and two inches. On the associated coastal lands the precipitation is between 11 and 20 inches. At La Guaira less than an inch of rain occurs each month from January through June, and only slightly more than an inch each month during the remainder of the year.

Vegetation. In Venezuela, as well as in Colombia and Ecuador, the altitudinal life zones in the Andes are divided into tropical, subtropical, temperate, and páramo. Each one of these zones shows striking relationships between plant life and climate.

The tropical zone, or tierra caliente, extends from sea level to an altitude of about 2,400 feet. It covers by far the largest area of Venezuela. The more important regions are the Caribbean Coastal Plain, the Maracaibo Basin, and the extensive Llanos. Many important agricultural crops are grown within the tropical region, such as sugar, cacao, coconuts, cotton, tobacco, bananas, and corn. It is also the principal cattle region of the republic. The natural vegetation of the tropics varies from the rain-forest regions of the lower Maracaibo Basin to the grasslands of the Llanos. In dry areas such as the La Guaira region are xerophytic plants including the mimosas and cacti.

The land from 2,400 to 6,000 feet above sea level is classified as the subtropical region, or tierra templada. Much of this region was originally covered by a luxuriant forest. It is one of the nation's principal agricultural regions and is particularly favorable to the production of coffee.

From 6,000 to 9,000 feet above sea level lies the temperate region, or tierra fría. It represents only a small portion of Venezuela and is restricted mostly to the three Andean states of Táchira, Mérida, and

Courtesy Nels A. Bengtson.

Fig. 100. Cactus jungle about 10 miles west of the city of Maracaibo, Venezuela.

Trujillo, south and east of Lake Maracaibo. The average annual temperature of the temperate region ranges from 46° to 54° F., and the precipitation is appreciably less than in the subtropical region. Because of the light rainfall and low temperature, the wild vegetation is sparse and scrubby. Wheat and potatoes are the principal agricultural crops. The yield is generally low because of the primitive methods of cultivation and poor seed. In the rural areas, Indians and mixed races constitute a majority of the population.

In the páramo region, which extends from 9,000 feet to about 14,000 feet above sea level, is found a comparatively small territory that includes portions of the three states just mentioned: Trujillo, Mérida, and Táchira. Agriculturally, the region is of little importance. Wheat, potatoes, a few cattle, and sheep supply bare subsistence for the local Indian population.

POPULATION OF PRINCIPAL URBAN CENTERS OF VENEZUELA

Caracas	362,800
Maracaibo	116,100
Barquisimeto	79,500
Valencia	60,600
San Cristóbal	45,100
Maracay	37,600
Puerto Cabello	33,300
Ciudad Bolívar	22,800

Regional associations. The Andean Highland embraces the nation's leading political and economic centers. In the picturesque valley of the Guaira River, on the southern slopes of the mountains, rests the capital city, Caracas, the birthplace of Simón Bolívar. West of Caracas are the progressive cities of Maracay and Valencia at distances of 77 and 121 miles, respectively, from the national capital. La Guaira and Puerto Cabello are the chief ports serving these important cities. The manufactures of leather, shoes, furniture, cigarettes, glass, chocolate, and textiles are among the major industries of Caracas and Valencia. The city of Valencia is the most important manufacturing center of the republic. Moreover, it is located in the center of an extensive agricultural region. Maracay, a new city built by the late President Gómez, is one of the nation's most modern and beautiful communities. It is one of the few cities carefully planned in advance. Maracay is also known for its paper factories, which supply much of the paper used in Venezuela.

Agriculture. The most highly developed agricultural region is the basin of Lake Valencia, which lies west of Caracas and inland from Puerto Cabello. Coffee is the principal crop of this area. It is grown in many other parts of the country and yields best at elevations between 1,600 and 6,500 feet above sea level.

The three principal coffee-producing regions are: (1) the district of Táchira, Trujillo, and Mérida, exporting through Maracaibo; (2) eastern and western sections of the coastal range and farther inland, shipping through Puerto Cabello; and (3) the central region of the coastal range, inland from La Guaira, the port of exportation. Coffee is Venezuela's most important agricultural export, and since the outbreak of World War II more than 80 per cent of the total coffee exports have been shipped to the United States.

Cacao ranks second in value of agricultural crops. The regions of cacao production are distributed throughout: (1) the coastal range from west of Puerto Cabello to Carenero and inland as far as the hills of the Llanos south of Caracas; (2) in the coastal range east of Barcelona and around Carúpano; (3) and in the Trujillo, Mérida, and Lake Maracaibo districts. The largest production occurs in the districts of Caracas and

Puerto Cabello. The major portion of the export shipments of both coffee and cacao is through Puerto Cabello.

While the production of cacao has increased over the 1938 period under the combined stimulus of high world prices and an export subsidy, the industry is in a rather depressed state. Reasons for the decline are acute scarcity and high cost of labor; absence of new plantings (85 per cent of the existing trees are estimated to be over 20 years old); spread of diseases, especially, "witch's broom, monilia, and pod rot"; and the over-all high cost of production.

Tobacco, sugar, and cotton are other important crops grown in Venezuela.

Mineral resources. In northeastern Venezuela, about 30 miles from the coast of the Gulf of Paria and near the San Juan River, lies the Bermúdez asphalt lake. This phenomenal deposit covers an area of 1,000 acres, about ten times the size of the asphalt lake of Trinidad. Although the Bermúdez asphalt is not deep, the depth averaging about three feet, nevertheless the area is so great that the amount of this valuable construction material is practically unlimited at the present rate of consumption. Guanoco is the center of the asphalt industry, and from it shipments are made to many parts of the world. Petroleum is also produced and exported from the Guanoco district.

The Maracaibo Lowland.[1] Today, the Maracaibo Lowland is probably the best known as well as the most economically-important region of Venezuela. Though it is a small portion of the nation, its importance as a petroleum-producing center gives Venezuela a high position in world affairs. The sudden rise to greatness as a petroleum producer has superimposed upon the landscape of the Maracaibo Lowland a decidedly new and foreign cultural pattern, which, associated with the old forms of occupance, gives to this region a decided quality of geographic uniqueness

The pattern of occupance of the Maracaibo Lowland is conspicuously intermittent and spotty. In this small region of about 25,000 square miles several different types of occupance are characteristic. At the narrow entrance to Lake Maracaibo is the lake-shore coconut and fishing area. Inland in the northern semiarid bush land is the grazing district. The eastern and western shores of the lake, and the eastern part of the lake are the oil-producing regions; while tropical agriculture, chiefly sugar and cacao, occupy the wet alluvial areas of the crescent-shaped southern part of the lowland.

Along the shores of the narrows at the northern end of the lake is the copra and fishing-village region. There coconut palms, drying copra, and

---

[1] Adapted from R. S. Platt: "Pattern of Occupance in the Maracaibo Basin," *Annals of the Association of American Geographers,* Vol. XXIV (1934), pp. 157–173.

fish are the conspicuous elements of the little lake-shore villages, some of which are built on piles out in the lake as a safeguard against insects and against floods in the wet season.

Inland in the northern dry bush land, small, widely scattered goat ranches are outstanding factors in the pattern of utilization. The ranch, or hatico, centers about a small ranch house, a water hole, corral, and small fenced garden. The rest of each ranch consists of a large unfenced expanse of dry forest land from which most of the bush except the herbaceous divi-divi has been removed. Since fences are not used, the limits of the grazing units are poorly defined. The ranches merely grade out into unclaimed and unused land. From these rather meager holdings, little besides bare subsistence is obtained. The skins of the goats and the pods gathered from the divi-divi, from which tannic acid is extracted, are the chief cash products. These products are taken usually to Maracaibo city, on the west shore of the narrows.

South of the narrows the occupance changes decidedly. The eastern shore and adjacent lake area, chiefly north of San Lorenzo, is the petroleum landscape, while the rest of the basin is a tropical agricultural region. In the southern portion of the lowland numerous short streams enter the structural basin and flow into the lake from the encircling uplands. Debris carried from the highlands by these streams has been deposited upon the floor of the lowland. Coarse material has been deposited near the highland rim, while fine alluvium has been widely spread over the entire lowland surface. Swamps and lagoons are conspicuous features of the terrain in the broad southwestern portion of the basin. Because of the numerous streams that are fed by the heavy seasonal rains of the southern section, the swamps and lagoons contain fresh water. Even Lake Maracaibo itself is only slightly brackish in the southern portion, owing to the influx of fresh water and the retarding of the saline sea water at the narrows.

In the southern portion of the lowland, from San Lorenzo to the Catatumbo River, numerous lakeside as well as a few river towns and villages characterize the occupance. This is the region of tropical alluvial agriculture. Sugar and cacao plantations, although widely scattered, are the dominant features. Sugar occupies the alluvial lands on the lake shore and the lower river courses, particularly in the southeastern portion, while cacao is grown on the better drained alluvial land farther upstream. Lagoons and swamps are numerous in the western and southwestern portion of the lowland, and sugar and cacao plantations are less conspicuous. Of course, the characteristic tropical subsistence crops of corn, manioc, and beans on the plantations, as well as such tree crops as breadfruit, papaya, mango, and coconuts, are a part of the spotty pattern of the wet southern portion of the lowland.

Several small railroads cross the southern and southeastern lowland

and connect the highland southeast of the basin with several lake-shore towns. By means of these railroads coffee grown in the highland is carried to the lake-shore towns, whence it is shipped by boat to Maracaibo city for export.

The sugar and cacao plantations, the forest clearings, the goat ranches, and the fishing villages built on piles in the lake are all elements of the old pattern of occupance. The new pattern of occupance, the one for which the lowland is commercially important today, is the petroleum field. Although petroleum has been discovered on both sides of the lake as well as beneath it, the outstanding petroleum-producing landscape occupies the portion of the northeastern lake shore from San Lorenzo northward to the narrows. Lagunillas is perhaps the very heart of the petroleum region. There the presence of oil-bearing sands beneath the lake and its eastern shore is the natural element upon which the new and important cultural pattern has been constructed.

With a production of over 500,000,000 barrels per year, the Maracaibo Lowland places Venezuela in third or fourth place in world petroleum production. Conspicuous in the occupance of the petroleum region are the forms and functions of oil transportation. Ships of shallow draft are used to transport the oil from the lake to deep-water ports, where it is either stored, refined, or shipped directly. Because of the shallowness of the entrance to the lake, fleets of small tank ships wait for the tide and move in or out en masse when the water is deepest. The nearest deep-water harbor to the lake is Amuay, on the Paraguaná Peninsula, where petroleum is stored or refined. Most of the oil, however, is transported to Aruba and Curaçao, where it is refined for shipment primarily to the United States or Europe.

The Dutch islands of Aruba and Curaçao are barren islands to which food as well as oil-handling equipment must be taken. Their position and ownership in relation to the Maracaibo Lowland is one of importance in the pattern of occupance of the region. Near Willemstad, on the island of Curaçao, Dutch Shell built a refinery at the time of World War I, which is said to be one of the largest in the world. In 1925 the Dutch-English and American oil company built refineries on Aruba that now surpass those of Curaçao in export value of petroleum. Crude oil is shipped to the Dutch islands from the Maracaibo basin, as well as from Venezuela's eastern fields, Trinidad and Colombia.

Thus the Maracaibo Lowland is made up of several contrasting although intermittent regions all centering on the lake, and finally upon Maracaibo city, as the focus for the whole area. From the numerous lakeside villages of the wet, tropical southern part of the basin small boats bring to the wharves of Maracaibo city the sugar, cacao, and *lignum vitæ* of the wet lowland and coffee from the adjacent highland. Goat skins and divi-divi pods from the northern basin and petroleum for storage from the oil fields move to Maracaibo city. Despite the fact that Maracaibo city is located on the shallow waters of the neck of Lake Maracaibo, it has become a leading port of Venezuela. Its function as a

PETROLEUM PRODUCTION IN THOUSANDS OF BARRELS

	1938	*1948*	*1949*	*1950*
Venezuela	187,369	490,015	482,316	542,401
Mexico	34,794	58,508	60,910	71,967
Colombia	22,450	23,792	29,722	33,640
Argentina	16,937	23,734	22,961	23,108
Trinidad	17,736	20,111	20,617	20,247
Peru	15,839	14,069	14,790	14,646
Ecuador	2,246	2,563	2,617	2,564
Bolivia	107	464		
Brazil		144		
Total Latin America			634,775	710,075
United States	1,213,254	2,016,282	1,840,307	1,972,809
World Total	1,978,340	3,425,283	3,398,455	3,780,973

Sources: United States Bureau of Mines. Department of the Interior, Washington, D. C. Figures for 1950 (preliminary) from *World Oil*, Vol. 132, No. 3, Feb. 15, 1951.

focus for the whole lowland is its outstanding significance. Thus the Maracaibo Lowland on the savanna Caribbean Coast of South America, a structural depression partially surrounded by interior highlands and containing a shallow bottleneck arm of the sea, is the natural scene upon which the several patterns of occupance have developed. The combination of these several indigenous and foreign patterns and functions constitutes the geographic uniqueness of the Maracaibo Lowland.

Orinoco Plain. Between the Venezuelan Andes and the Guiana Highland is an elongated plain, generally called the Orinoco Llanos. It is a sedimentary lowland with interstream ridges, low hills, and extensive swells and depressions, or swales. In the west it merges with the Andes through a system of well-defined terraces. Its lower portion projects seaward in the form of a delta.

Within the Llanos are great areas of grass, succulent in the rainy season from April to October and parched during the remaining six months of little or no rain. In the deeper swales, particularly along the rivers, are regions of forest cover.

Cultural features. Ciudad Bolívar, 200 miles from the ocean, on the Orinoco River, is the chief commercial center. All foreign merchandise consigned for places in this region or beyond it must pass through the city, which is the only port of this great area with a customhouse. The population is about 23,000. The cattle industry is the major activity on the surrounding plains. It has been estimated that there are 1,500,000 cattle in this vast expanse of more than 100,000 square miles. In general, inaccessibility and unfavorable climatic conditions are the most serious obstacles in the development of the cattle industry in the Llanos.

Gold from the famous E. Callao mine in the Guiana Highland near the Yuruari River, balata rubber and tonka beans from the valleys of the Orinoco and its tributaries, and beautiful egret plumes are other products for which Ciudad Bolívar serves as a collecting and distributing center.

Recently the production of petroleum in the eastern portion of the Orinoco Plain has reached a significant position. Several oil fields have been developed north of Ciudad Bolívar, and one on the extreme northwestern tip of the Orinoco Delta. Extensive wild-cat drilling has been in progress, and reports indicate that new fields will materially add to the present output.

The latest economy associated with the Orinoco region is the development of iron ore in an area south of the Ciudad Bolívar and Palua.

Guiana Highland. The southeastern portion of Venezuela is generally depicted on maps as a mountainous region called the Venezuelan Guiana Highland. Much of this region, which represents about 200,000 square miles, or 60 per cent of the total area of Venezuela, has been unexplored. From the limited information available it may be said that these highlands consist of a part of the ancient continent of northeastern South America, similar to the oldland of the Brazilian Highland. Within its borders rises the Orinoco River, which flows northward in a great arc along the southwestern flank of the Highland. To the south the Guiana Highland forms the divide between the headstreams of the Amazon River and the drainage northward to the Orinoco.

On the south, the Serra do Curupira continues as the Serra Parima. East of the Serra Parima is an arc-like escarpment, convex toward the south, known as the Serra Pacaraima. It, like the Serra do Curupira and the Serra Parima, carries a section of the boundary between Venezuela and Brazil. The Serra Pacaraima is one of the highest ranges of the Guianas. This range joins the mountain system in which Mt. Roraima stands, a great irregular mass with a summit area of some 25 square miles at an elevation of about 9,216 feet above sea level. Future information may reveal that the southern ranges, the Serra Pacaraima and the Serra Parima, are great plateaus that slope northward to the Orinoco Plain. Another mountain generally shown on maps is the Cerro Duida, standing at an elevation of 7,019 feet above sea level, near the upper Orinoco River.

Resources. The extent of natural resources in the Venezuelan Guiana Highland is unknown. An examination of the shipments to Ciudad Bolívar from the Venezuelan Guiana Highland shows a variety of products, including gold, rubber, balata, tonka beans, chicle, balsam, hardwoods, dyewoods, and many other items of lesser importance.

Transportation situation. The transportation situation in Venezuela is in striking contrast to that of Colombia. River traffic is quite independent of railway transportation. The railways of Venezuela, totalling some 597 miles, serve to the very best commercial advantage. The railways give access to the immediate coastal highlands, but there are none in the central or southern portions of the country. The coal used for fuel in locomotives is in part supplied by local mines and in part by the United States and Great Britain. The oil fields supply the necessary fuel oil.

An excellent highway extends from La Guaira to Caracas, a distance of some 25 miles. The winding and climbing road is a remarkable piece of engineering and opens a superb expanse of mountain scenery and a wonderful view of the Caribbean waters. Another highway, the Bolívar, one of greater national significance, projects from Caracas for more than 750 miles west to the Colombian border near Cúcuta over a route of breathtaking beauty and splendor. This road forms the Venezuelan sector of the Pan-American Highway. The road crosses a northern spur of the Andes at an altitude of 14,000 feet. It joins a Colombian highway, thus providing a through route between Bogotá and Caracas. Other roads project to the southwest and the east from the Andean highway.

Caracas is also connected by road with Soledad on the Orinoco immediately across the river from Ciudad Bolívar. The road, however, is only passable during the dry season from November to March. Work is in progress to make it an all-year highway.

Prior to 1908 there was not one mile of modern highway in Venezuela. At present more than 9,000 miles of road have been constructed and serve as the nation's chief means of land communication. This development can be attributed primarily to the income from oil royalties.

Road building, however, is difficult and costly in Venezuela. Many geographical obstacles are encountered. On the plains large ramparts and long drains must be built to insure proper drainage of swamps. Periodic floods add to the cost of construction and maintenance of highways. In the mountains, deep cuts must be made; numerous bridges and tunnels must be built; and a great amount of filling is needed.

The great Orinoco River and its tributaries are navigable for 1,500 miles. This system is restricted to vessels owned by Venezuelans and those ships that fly the national flag. Ciudad Bolívar is the only port of entry for this region. It serves the great hinterland of the Llanos and the Guiana Highlands. Cattle, hides, balata, tonka beans, egret plumes, and gold are exported from this city. Many products are shipped to Port of Spain, Trinidad, to await overseas transport. From the Orinoco region overland trails lead to the north. Cattle are driven to Puerto Cabello, to Barcelona, and to Guanta from the Llanos. During the rainy season, from April to October, the trails are flooded and impassable. At the time of the dry season, November to March, much of the region is parched and waterless.

Air service is rapidly being developed. It is now possible to reach all of the principal port cities and the capital, and to go up the Orinoco River to Ciudad Bolívar, as well as to the gold fields of the far interior. Four airlines, the Pan American Airways, Royal Dutch Airways, Linea Aeropostal Venezulana, and Chicago and Southern Airways provide direct service between the United States and Venezuela. Direct service also exists between Venezuela and Cuba, Colombia, Netherland West Indies, British West Indies, and all major capitals of western Europe.

Petroleum industry. Venezuela produces about 14 per cent of the world output of petroleum, ranking either second or third to the United States. In terms of petroleum exports, Venezuela surpasses all other countries—almost 98 per cent of its total production is marketed abroad. The principal oil fields are found along the eastern shore of Lake Maracaibo and in the Monagas and Anzoatequi fields in the eastern part of the country. Of the total production of 490,015,593 barrels in 1948, the western fields—Maracaibo region accounted for about 350,000,000 barrels, and the remainder, some 140,000,000 barrels, was produced in the eastern fields.

Previous to 1945 the crude oil destined for foreign lands was shipped in tankers to Aruba or Curaçao and a small amount to storage tanks on the Paraguaná Peninsula. In 1943 a law was passed by the Venezuelan Government stipulating that within five years after the end of World War II, or as soon as the availability of materials permits, 10 per cent of all oil obtained from Venezuelan concessions be refined on the mainland. In compliance with this law, oil companies have under operation and construction refineries at the deep-water port of Amuay and at Punta Cardon on the Paraguaná Peninsula.[2] Other evidence of the oil industry is found in the completion of a number of pipe lines.

Venezuela's economic life is dependent upon the oil industry. Oil has brought United States dollars to the nation to finance imports and meet the needs of other industries. The direct revenues—including royalties, income taxes, and foreign exchange differential—derived from the petroleum companies account for, approximately, 32 per cent of the Government's total revenue.

Iron ore resources. In the future, the development of the nation's iron ore resources may add materially to Venezuela's economy. A number of iron deposits have been identified south of the Orinoco River in the northern margins of the Guiana Highlands. The Bethlehem Steel Corporation has placed under operation an iron ore region near El Pao, located approximately 30 miles southward from San Felix. Loading docks have been constructed at Palua near San Felix at the confluence of the Orinoco and Caroni rivers. By late 1951, Bethlehem Steel hopes to ship some 2.4 million tons annually. The El Pao is an open-pit mine with an estimated reserve of some 60 million tons. In another area, somewhat south of Ciudad Bolívar, the United States Steel Corporation has several

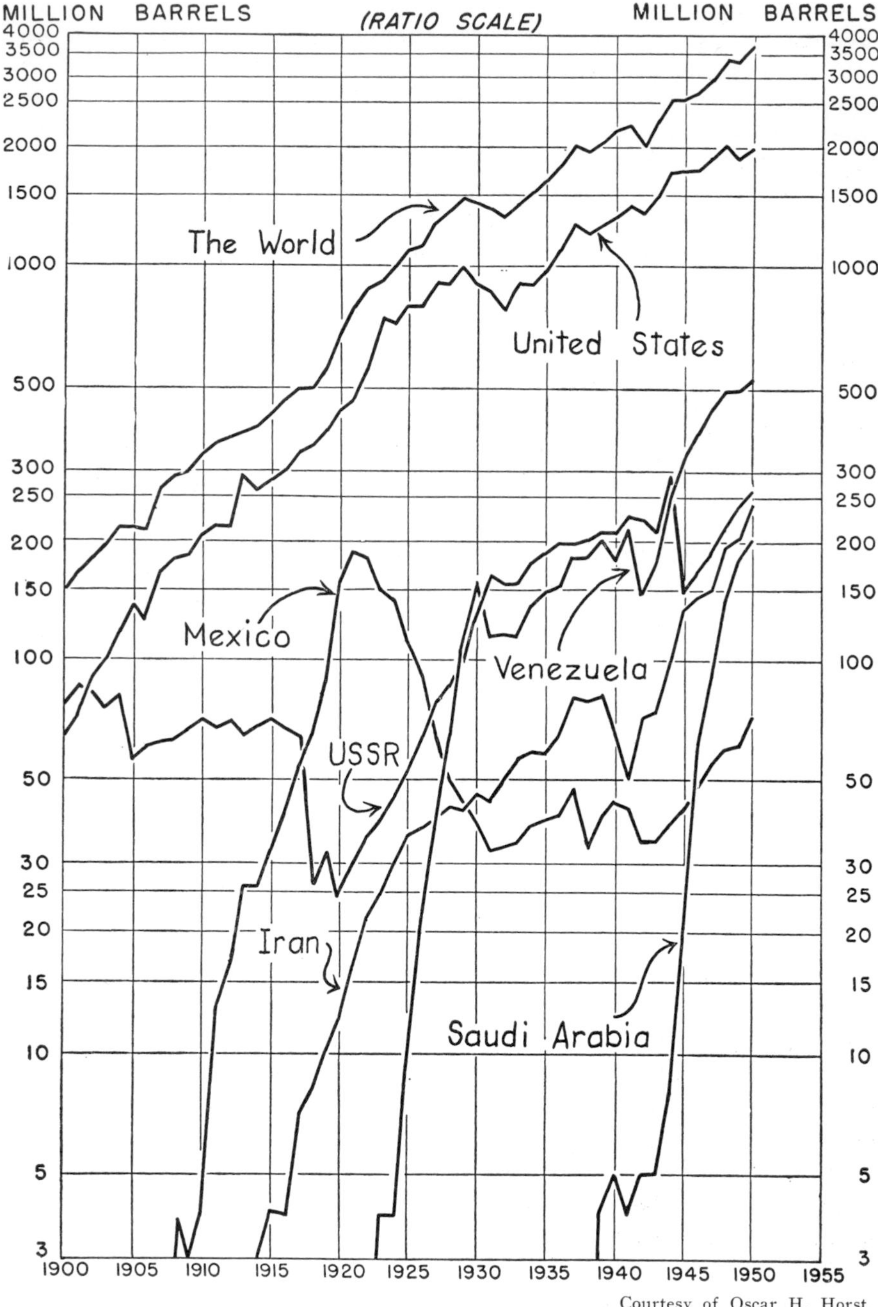

Courtesy of Oscar H. Horst.

Fig. 100a. Graph showing petroleum production.

iron ore regions under concessions. The La Parida area, now called Cerro Bolívar, has been drilled, and indications are that the iron ore reserves exceed a billion tons. Deposits of iron, other than those held by the United States Steel Corporation, are known to exist in the Cerro Bolívar region.[3]

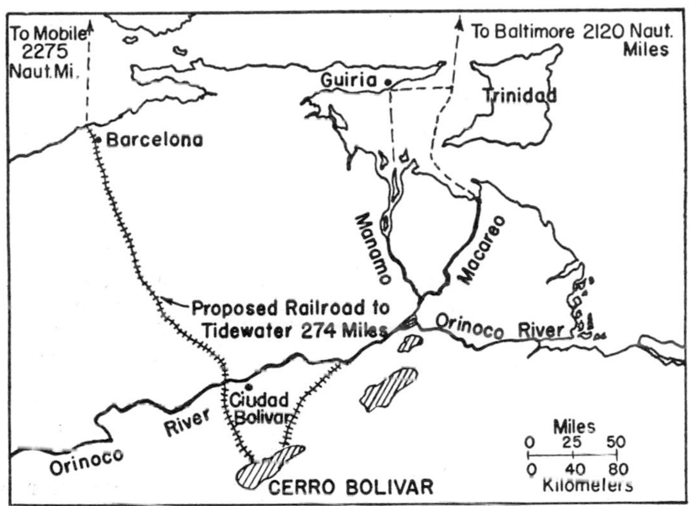

From *Engineering and Mining Journal*, August, 1950.

Fig. 100b. Sites of the ore projects in the Orinoco region.

The method of transporting the ore to tide-waters has not been determined. In all probability, Bethlehem Steel will ship the ore by rail to the Orinoco, and then by water via the Cano Manamo River and the Gulf of Paria to Puerto Hierro. From Hierro, ocean carriers will transport the ore to the United States. United States Steel may move its ore by rail for 90 miles from the mines to the confluence of the Orinoco and Caroni rivers, and from there follow the same course as that of the Bethlehem Steel Company. Another route proposed by United States Steel extends across the land from Cerro Bolívar to a tide-water terminal on the north coast near Barcelona, a distance of 274 miles.

Petroleum and petroleum products comprise about 90 per cent of Venezuela's annual exports. The remainder, 10 per cent, consists, first, of coffee and uncoined gold, followed by cacao, hides and cattle. Commodities other than petroleum are handled primarily at Puerto Cabello,

---

2 The Creole Petroleum Company, a United States Company, produces about 50 per cent of the country's total oil output.

3 The United States Steel Corporation does not operate directly any iron and steel works but it does control through stock ownership a number of ore- and steel-producing subsidiaries. The Bethlehem Steel Corporation is in a similar position

La Guaira and Ciudad Bolívar, Carúpano, Cumaná, Turiamo, and Tucacas.

VENEZUELA: EXPORTS OF PRINCIPAL COMMODITIES

Commodity	*Quantity in Metric Tons*		*Percentage of Total Value of All Exports*	
	1947	*1948*	*1947*	*1948*
Petroleum and derivatives			90.4	95.9
Coffee	30,454	35,737	2.3	2.0
Cacao	11,945	17,913	1.3	1.4

Source: Office of International Trade, United States Department of Commerce, Washington, D. C., 1950.

VENEZUELA: FOREIGN TRADE

	Total Value (000 Dollars)	*Percentage of Total*					
		United States	Canada	Latin America	United Kingdom	Continental Europe	All Others
Exports							
1938	181,440	20.5	1.4	0.9	5.0	8.0	64.2
1947	643,200	29.4	1.7	3.5	2.5	4.4	58.6
Imports							
1938	97,483	56.4		0.9	7.0	32.2	3.5
1947	541,000	73.9	3.7	13.4	5.2	3.4	0.4

The future of Venezuela. The present economy of Venezuela is somewhat similar to the earlier state of affairs in Chile. As mineral nitrate made Chile, so oil is making Venezuela. Petroleum contributes about 90 per cent of the total value of Venezuela's exports. It is the accepted security for large investments made by foreign countries in Venezuela. Development of highways, ports, and other economic and social conditions may be attributed to the income from oil resources. Freedom from foreign debt can also be chiefly attributed to the revenue from oil. A pertinent question is "How long will this source of prosperity last?"

Despite the importance of the oil industry, Venezuela, like Colombia, is essentially an agricultural country. Only 15 per cent of the population gainfully employed is engaged in the petroleum industry. Coffee and cacao are the chief agricultural exports. The extent to which the livestock industry may develop in the Llanos is unknown. Any development that takes place will be extremely slow, largely because of the inadequacy of rainfall throughout the year. Industrially, Venezuela is advancing in the manufacturing of textiles, leather goods, shoes, glass, tobacco products, and paper. Electric light and power are available in the cities and in most of the large towns. The development of its iron ore mines may add another significant source of revenue.

Venezuela should place greater emphasis on the production of domestic food products. The efficiency of agriculture lags far behind that of industry and mining.

SELECTED REFERENCES

Chardón, C. E.: "Life Zones in the Andes of Venezuela," *Bulletin of the Pan American Union,* Vol. LXVII (1933), pp. 620–633.

Crist, R. E.: "Along the Llanos-Andes Border in Zamora, Venezuela," *Geographical Review,* Vol. XXII (1932), pp. 411–422.

Crist, R. E., and Chardón, C. E.: "Changing Patterns of Land Use in the Valencia Lake Basin of Venezuela," *Geographical Review,* Vol. XXXI (1941), pp. 430–443.

Fletcher, R.: "A Hydrometeorological Analysis of Venezuelan Rainfall," *Bulletin of the American Meteorological Society,* Vol. 30, No. 1 (1950), pp. 1–9.

Hanson, E.: "Social Regression in the Orinoco and Amazon Basins," *Geographical Review,* Vol. XXIII (1933), pp. 578–598.

Hitchcock, C. B.: "The Orinoco-Ventuari Region, Venezuela," *Geographical Review,* Vol. XXXVII, No. 4 (1947), pp. 525–566.

James, P. E.: "The Possibilities of Cattle Production in Venezuela," *Bulletin of the Geographical Society of Philadelphia,* Vol. XXII (1924), pp. 45–56.

Lippert, T. W.: "Cerro Bolívar," *Journal of Metals and Mining Engineering,* February, 1950.

Miller, E. W.: "Petroleum in the Economy of Venezuela," *Economic Geography,* Vol. XVI (1940), pp. 204–210.

Powers, W. L.: "Soil Development and Land Use in Northern Venezuela," *Geographical Review,* Vol. XXXV, No. 2 (1945), pp. 273–285.

Standley, P. C.: "The Flora of Venezuela," *Bulletin of the Pan American Union,* Vol. LX (1926), pp. 978–990.

Vogt, William: *The Population of Venezuela and Its Natural Resources,* Division of Agricultural Cooperation, Pan-American Union, Washington, D. C., 1946.

Whitaker, A. P.: *The United States and South America, The Northern Republics,* Harvard University Press, Cambridge, 1948.

Whitford, H. N.: "Forest Conditions of Colombia and Venezuela," *Bulletin of the Pan American Union,* Vol. XLVI (1918), pp. 468–483.

Williams, L.: "The Caura Valley and Its Forests," *Geographical Review,* Vol. XXXI (1941), pp. 414–429.

CHAPTER XIX

THE GUIANAS: BRITISH, NETHERLANDS, AND FRENCH COLONIES

General characteristics. The Guianas lie along the northeastern coast of South America and extend for about 600 miles southeastward from the delta of the Orinoco to the Brazilian border. They stretch inland for some 300 miles from the sea to the highest ranges of the Guiana Highland. The total area of the three colonial possessions is about 172,000 square miles. They are the only remaining colonies in South America. The westernmost, largest, and most important commercially is the British colony; the next in importance and size is *Surinam*, or the Netherlands Guiana; and *la Guyane française*, the French colony, is easternmost, smallest, and least important.

Fig. 101. The Guianas.

As low-latitude colonies, these European possessions are identified with tropical and subtropical agriculture, especially sugar and coffee. In all three the same general natural conditions are present in much the same pattern. Human conditions are likewise much the same, but the occupance, the patterns of culture, have turned out differently under the domination of the respective mother nations. In all three the low, wet coastal plain is the life center; it contains all of the cities and most of the population and is the most productive region. A narrow grassland zone extends inland from the coast, while the remainder, by far the larger part of the three colonies, is essentially a tropical, forest-covered, highland country. Recently Surinam and British Guiana have become important suppliers of bauxite, a commercial source of the metal aluminum.

Physical relationships. Climate is one of the chief obstacles to the development of the Guianas. The lowlands are hot and humid. There is little variation in temperature throughout the year. At Georgetown, British Guiana, the annual range is less than 3.0° F. In the uplands of the interior the temperature is only slightly lower. Most of the land receives considerably more than 80 inches of rainfall per year. Although it rains every month, the maximum falls between December and July. The drier season occurs during the autumn months.

Owing to frequent inundations and resultant swamps, much of the coastal land supports only marshy grasses. In areas of better drainage are found trees and regions of savanna flora. However, through the control of flood waters and the introduction of adequate drainage, the coastal plain has become the chief agricultural region of the Guianas. Sugar cane and rice, both favored by a hot, muggy climate and a high soil-moisture content, are the principal crops.

The upland valleys and plateaus permit the growth of forests, one of the major natural resources of the Guianas. But, in common with the conditions of most of tropical South America, timber resources are not extensively utilized because of the lack of adequate transportation facilities. Balata is the leading forest product, and among other important resources of the forests are dyewoods, cabinet woods, and resinous products.

British Guiana. Tropical agriculture, forest products, and bauxite mining characterize the sparsely populated British colony, with its area of about 83,000 square miles. About half of the 376,000 inhabitants are engaged in sugar production, the major activity. The sugar lands are all on the low coastal plains and along the estuaries of the four principal rivers. These alluvial sugar areas, which likewise contain almost all the agriculture, are the result of an earlier occupancy of the region by the Dutch. An elaborate system of diking, empoldering, and draining similar to that used in the Netherlands has been worked out. Sea walls with floodgates keep the flood tides from covering the low coastal plain, while

THE GUIANAS: TEMPERATURE AND RAINFALL OF SELECTED STATIONS

	Station	Georgetown Br. Guiana *	Paramaribo Dutch Guiana *	Cayenne Fr. Guiana †
	Elevation (*Feet*)	22	12	19.7
Average Temperature (°*F.*)	*Period of Record*	1931–40	1931–40	1893–1914
	January	79.6	79.7	79.2
	February	79.7	80.2	79.5
	March	80.2	81.1	79.5
	April	80.9	81.1	79.9
	May	80.9	80.8	79.9
	June	80.3	80.4	79.9
	July	80.3	81.1	80.2
	August	81.1	82.4	81.7
	September	82.1	83.7	82.6
	October	82.2	83.8	82.6
	November	81.7	83.1	81.7
	December	80.5	80.6	80.2
	Annual	80.8	81.5	80.6
	Range	2.6	4.1	3.4
Average Rainfall (*Inches*)	*Period of Record*	1931–40	1931–40	51 yrs.
	January	10.0	7.9	14.1
	February	4.5	5.0	13.2
	March	5.1	7.3	15.6
	April	6.2	10.1	19.1
	May	10.8	10.6	21.5
	June	12.5	11.7	15.7
	July	10.5	9.5	6.8
	August	7.9	7.5	2.7
	September	2.6	3.1	1.2
	October	3.8	3.4	1.3
	November	14.1	3.9	4.7
	December	11.5	7.3	10.5
	Annual	89.4	87.3	126.3

* H. Helm Clayton: "World Weather Records," *Smithsonian Miscellaneous Collections,* Vol. 105 (1947).

† K. Knoch: "Klimakunde von Südamerika," *Handbuch der Klimatologie,* Band II, Teil G, Berlin, 1930.

dikes prevent the surface water on the land side from draining into this low area. Numerous drainage ditches, which also are used as canals in the sugar estates, carry off by means of pumps the excessive surface water that gathers from the torrential tropical rains. This fresh water, which has leached the sea salt from the soil, is pumped into the ocean through the floodgates during low tide. Empoldered beds are built up to aid further in drainage. Unlike upland laterite soils of the wet tropics, the alluvial and peat soils of the coast, when drained, remain fertile after long, continued cropping. Upland plantation soils were quickly depleted after a few years of cropping, and it was necessary, repeatedly, to clear new areas, while alluvial lands won from the sea by much hard labor have been cropped for years with little evidence of deterioration.

By far the most important factor in sugar production as well as in all other agriculture in Guiana is the labor. The population of the colony is small, and much hand labor is needed, not only in the cultivation of the crops but also to keep the drainage system, which is far from adequate, in repair. In the enervating climate Europeans are of little value as laborers, and the native Indians, who are now outnumbered by the Europeans almost four to one, have deserted the coast entirely for areas in the forested interior. The Dutch, who established the coastal plantations as well as the upland farms, brought in Negro slaves from Africa, a fact that helps to explain the large Negro population in this part of South America. After the freeing of the slaves about a hundred years ago, many of the plantations were divided among the freed men. Thus, the Negro was lost as a supply of valuable labor to the sugar industry, especially since the success of this crop requires large organized plantations rather than small individual holdings. The British have partially solved the labor problem by bringing in people from eastern India, and today 42 per cent of the population are East Indians, 38 per cent Negroes, 5 per cent of European origin (largely of Portuguese descent), 2 per cent Indians, 12 per cent mixed blood, and 1 per cent Chinese. Recognition of the colony's labor conditions is expressed in the colonization schemes that were set forth in 1929 in the land-settlement policy. Four colonies to accommodate 100 families of East Indians each were established in the Essequibo district for the purpose of correcting the paucity of population in the colony.

Rice is the principal staple food crop and the second most important agricultural crop of the colony. Of the 140,000 cropped acres in British Guiana, rice is grown on 30,000 acres, about a third of which produce two crops a year. The alluvial nature of the cultivated coastal plain and the ease with which it can be flooded with fresh water are in keeping with the easy cultivation of rice. Twenty years ago rice was imported, but now a little is exported each year to the West Indies.

Secondary to the dominant sugar and rice agricultural combination of the coastal plain are a number of minor crops, most of which are on the decline. Most important of this group are the coconuts, which occupy almost the same acreage as rice, particularly on the beach ridges of the low coastal plain. Cacao and coffee, both of which were prominent plantation crops at one time, have decreased in importance. About the only other agricultural products are the citrus fruits, especially limes. Local garden crops are, of course, grown on each Negro farm and on each sugar plantation, while the native Indian in the interior produces the characteristic primitive, shifting tropical agriculture of plantains and corn. Manioc is the usual crop grown in little forest clearings by the Indian women. These beds are abandoned for new ones as soon as the soil fertility is depleted and the weeds become too large. Some 150,000 head of cattle and hogs are recorded in the region.

About 80 per cent of the colony's land area is covered with thick, tropical rain forest, of which one-quarter is under some sort of exploitation. Balata is probably one of the most important forest extractions, and small amounts of latex are obtained from the widely scattered rubber trees. Lumber, pulpwood, and ply-wood from the forest are increasing in production. The greenheart is the most frequently cut wood that is brought out to the saw mills on the rivers. Like most tropical forest wood, many of the species are too heavy to float. Punts are constructed to float the heavy lumber to the mills. Although Indian men will not work in the sugar fields, since agriculture is woman's work and therefore degrading to them, they will work in the forest, because the felling of a tree is considered man's work. Thus, much of the forest labor is done by the Indians.

Bauxite, diamonds, and gold are the chief mineral products. Although alluvial gold is widely spread over the entire country, the output of panned gold has diminished to about one-twentieth of the amount produced toward the close of the last century. Recently, interest in the search for gold has been revived. Gold prospecting, however, is carried on with great difficulties because of the tropical vegetation. The best-known diamond field, the Mazaruni, lies just east of the Pakaraima Mountains in the northwestern part of the colony. The bauxite fields are close to the navigable rivers. The most valuable deposit is on the Demerara River, about 75 miles from the coast. During the war, British Guiana and its neighbor, Surinam, were the chief source of the United States and British supply of bauxite. In 1937 the British colony produced 305,000 tons of bauxite, and in 1948 the output was 1,903,000 tons. Canada is the leading market, receiving more than 80 per cent of the Colony's bauxite exports, followed by the United States and the United Kingdom.

British Guiana presents geographically the picture of a sparsely populated tropical colony. It is situated far from the main roads of commerce, and therefore functions only as a minor producer of tropical products for the European and North American markets. The low, wet coastal plain undoubtedly has advantages over the forested, rougher interior, for it is on the plain that the major part of the small population is concentrated.

Georgetown, the capital, population 73,500, and New Amsterdam, the largest cities, are ports situated at the mouths of the Demerara and Berbice Rivers, respectively. Three-fourths of the colony's 80 miles of railroad extends along the coast from Georgetown to the left bank of the Berbice River opposite New Amsterdam. The remaining 20 miles of railroad of the country connects the estuaries of the Essequibo and Demerara Rivers.

BAUXITE PRODUCTION
(Metric Tons)

	1937	*1946*	*1947*	*1948*
Surinam	392,447	857,843	1,809,837	2,148,906
British Guiana	305,533	1,137,990	1,318,190	1,903,230
Brazil	8,770	17,000	17,000	17,000
Haiti	....	300	....	....
United States	446,046	1,121,774	1,221,348	1,480,535
U.S.S.R.	230,000	425,000	475,000	500,000
World Total	3,679,000	4,565,000	6,488,000	8,246,000

Sources: *Mineral Yearbook*, 1939, Bureau of Mines, United States Department of Interior. *Mineral Trade Notes*, Bureau of Mines, United States Department of Interior, Volume 28, No. 4, April, 1949.

Surinam. Dutch Guiana is second in size (54,300 square miles) and importance among colonial possessions in South America. In its broad geographic structure it closely resembles British Guiana, yet in the details of its regional make-up it is quite individual. Paramaribo is the capital, with a population of 59,000.

With a population of 181,000, slightly less than half that of British Guiana, the labor problem is likewise an acute one. The Negro population of 90,000 is by far the largest element in the population. The Negroes were originally slaves on the coastal plantations, but they have been free since a century ago and are no longer bound to the plantations. Plantation labor is carried on chiefly by 32,000 British East Indians and 34,000 Dutch East Indians (Javanese). Other important population elements are approximately 22,000 Chinese, some of whom are merchants, 3,000 native Indians, and 2,000 Europeans.

As in British Guiana, tropical plantation agriculture is the dominant activity of the colony, and it is similarly confined to the coastal region. Sugar cane, the chief crop, is raised on large estates, some of which are protected by dikes, drainage canals, and polders from flooding by the sea. The torrential tropical rains furnish sufficient fresh water to flood the rice fields. Rice is the second crop in importance, followed by coffee. Since some of the coastal land is well drained, coffee is often raised on the same estates with sugar cane.

The great interior upland of the Dutch colony is much less exploited than that in the British colony. The lower Surinam River, 10 miles from the mouth of which is Paramaribo, the capital and chief city, is the life center of the colony. Somewhat over 100 miles up the Surinam River are several bauxite pits operated by the Surinam Bauxite Company, a subsidiary of Aluminum Company of America and a Dutch company. The export of bauxite, the colony's main product, shipped principally to the United States, has increased from 125,000 tons in 1932 to 586,000 tons in 1940, and 673,000 tons in 1945. A railroad, the only one in the colony, extends 107 miles inland from Paramaribo to the bauxite regions.

La Guyane française. In the past, French Guiana was best known in its relation to Devil's Island, a place of confinement for France's dangerous criminals. Now that the insular penal institution has been dissolved, attention is directed to more favorable features of the colony. As in the other colonies, most of the population of about 35,000 lives in the coastal zone. The coastal plain is not so low here as it is in the other colonies, and it has not been necessary to develop an elaborate drainage system. Cayenne, the largest city and the capital, with a population of 12,000, is situated on a low sandstone promontory on the coast. A short stretch of railroad extends for a few miles through the coastal zone. Decadent agricultural activity occupies about 9,000 acres, slightly over 14 square miles, of alluvial lands at the mouths of the rivers. Some attempt to produce cacao and sugar and the subsistence crops–manioc, maize, tobacco, vegetables, and fruits–constitutes the extent of the meager coastal agriculture.

In the interior hill country extractive activities are carried on quite extensively. Gold, balata, and rosewood are taken from this region. Gold mining by placer methods, which is one of the most important industries of the colony, is carried on by scattered individual workers. There are no large-scale workings in the colony.

Thus, French Guiana, with an area of 34,740 square miles, and therefore smaller than the other two colonies, has developed a very different pattern of occupance upon a natural environment strikingly similar to that of the other two colonies.

The inferior position of French Guiana is in part due to the attitude of France toward the colony rather than to environmental conditions. The lack of a constructive colonial policy has done much to break down the normal agricultural use of the alluvial coast. The tendency is for the extractive activities of the interior to predominate. Cayenne probably has the most desirable site of all of the Guiana cities. Its slightly elevated promontory location rises above the low coastal plain, and, unlike the other cities, which are several miles inland, Cayenne is on the seacoast, where it receives any relief the winds might bring. French Guiana, however, has less of the low, wet coastal plain and fewer rivers with alluvial flood plains.

Agriculture, bauxite pits, railroads, boat traffic, and cities center on the lower courses of the rivers in the British and Dutch colonies, while only a small amount of decadent agriculture centers on the rivers in French Guiana.

Summary. The same interior characteristics of highlands, forests, and savanna are present in all three colonies. Alluvial gold is widely scattered over the entire interior region, especially in the river valleys. Only the interior of British Guiana has a diamond region. All of the rivers flowing from the interior highlands descend to the lowlands of the coast by a series of falls and rapids. Transportation by water to and from the interior is thus made difficult. In French Guiana, although the settlements are in the coastal zone, the interior region is the most important economically. Since the mother country does not foster the economic pursuits characteristic of the coast, individuals have found it easier to wander through the interior and pan for gold; this has become the outstanding activity of the colony. In the British and Dutch Guianas, however, agriculture and bauxite production, the principal industries, are carried on mainly in the coastal regions, while the extractive activities in the interior, lumbering and gold mining, hold a less important position. Thus, in the Guiana colonies geographic individuality has resulted from diverse use of regions that are very similar.

SELECTED REFERENCES

Edmundson, C.: "The Relations of Great Britain with Guiana," *Transactions of the Royal Historical Society,* Fourth Series, Vol. VI (1923), London, pp. 1–21.

Holdridge, Desmond: "An Investigation of the Prospect for White Settlement in British Guiana," *Geographical Review,* Vol. XXIX (1939), pp. 622–642.

Manington, George: *The West Indies, with British Guiana and British Honduras,* Scribner, New York, 1925.

Penson, Lillian M.: "The Making of a Crown Colony: British Guiana, 1803–33," Royal Historical Society, Fourth Series, Vol. IX (1926), London, pp. 107–134.

Platt, Raye, and Others: *The European Possessions in the Caribbean Area; a Compilation of Facts Concerning Their Population, Physical Geography, Resources, Industries, Trade, Government, and Strategic Importance,* American Geographical Society, New York, 1941.

Platt, R. S.: "Reconnaissance in British Guiana," *Annals of the Association of American Geographers,* Vol. 29 (1939), pp. 105–126.

Sanderson, Ivan: "A Journey in Dutch Guiana," *Geographical Journal,* Vol. 93 (1939), pp. 469–490.

CENTRAL AMERICA, MEXICO, AND THE WEST INDIES

CHAPTER XX

CENTRAL AMERICA: THE TRANS-AMERICAN LAND

Political divisions. Central America is one of the world's four narrowest crossways between east and west, the others being the Transcaucasian land bridge, the Suez Canal, and the Bosporus and Dardanelles. Within its area are the independent republics of Panama, Costa Rica, Nicaragua, El Salvador, Honduras, Guatemala, and the crown colony of British Honduras, and the Panama Canal Zone. It includes all of the mainland from Mexico to Colombia. The land mass stretches southeast and northwest and varies in width from about 30 miles, at the narrowest point of the Isthmus of Panama, to about 300 miles, across the broadest part of Nicaragua and Honduras. The greatest length of Central America is 1,300 miles. On its eastern and northern side the area is bounded by the Caribbean Sea, on the western and southern side by the Pacific Ocean. The total area has never been determined with exactness, nor has the population been numbered by a census that is any more reliable than a shrewd guess.

AREA AND POPULATION OF CENTRAL AMERICAN COUNTRIES

Country	*Area in Square Miles*	*Population*	*Capital*	*Population of Capital*
Costa Rica	23,000	825,000	San José	90,600
El Salvador	13,176	2,015,000	San Salvador	105,200
Guatemala	48,290	3,706,200	Guatemala City	163,900
Nicaragua	57,143	1,110,000	Managua	124,400
Honduras	46,332	1,230,000	Tegucigalpa	55,800
Panama	34,169	710,000	Panama City	200,000
(British Honduras)	8,867	59,000	Belize	16,000

It is altogether likely that the populations of El Salvador and of Guatemala, in the above table, are exaggerated, although the figures given are estimates by the respective governments concerned. El Salvador, the smallest nation, is also the most densely settled portion of Central America. Nicaragua is the largest country, but Guatemala has the greatest number of inhabitants. The population of Central America as a whole lies between 9 and 10 millions.

Physical landscape. Large areas have never been explored fully because of the heavy growths of unhealthful jungle that spread over the wet lowlands, and because of the thick forests that cover most of the uninhabited highland area.

Central America is located entirely within the low latitudes, the far southern point of Panama being 7° 12′ north of the equator, and the far northern boundary of Guatemala being 18° 3′ north. Climate, however, is influenced not only by latitude but by altitude and other factors.

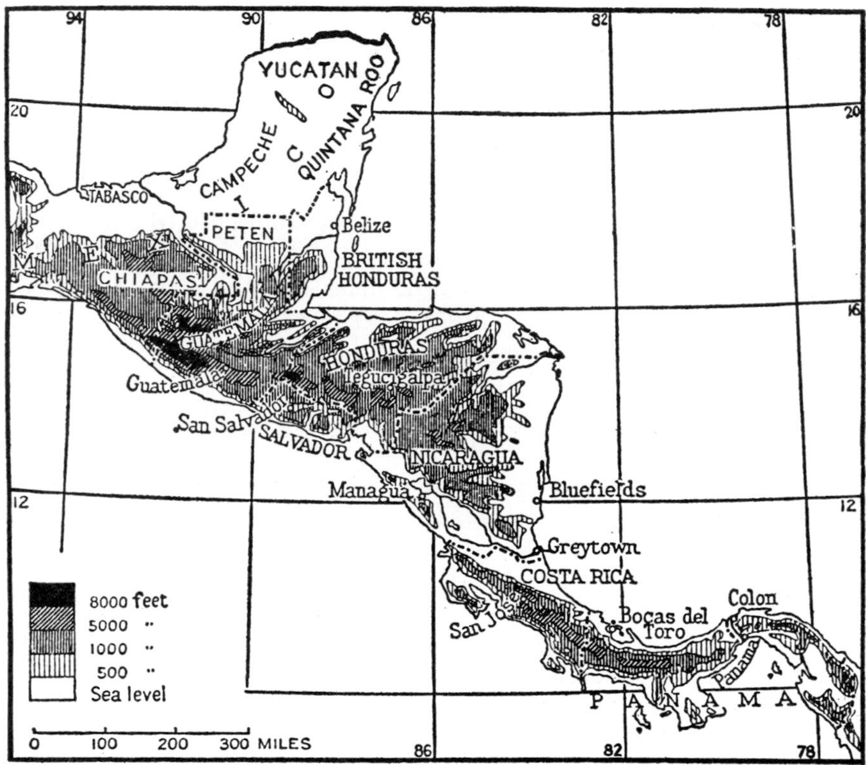

From Geographical Review, Vol. XVIII. Copyright by the American Geographical Society of New York. Reprinted by permission.

Fig. 102. Relief map of Central America.

Along both the west and east coasts extend humid swamps and lowlands that steam with vapor during the wet season. Mosquitoes, biting flies, and other parasitic insects are much more prevalent in the lowlands than on the plateaus. Ants and ticks, on the contrary, seem to prefer land that is better drained. The western band of coastal lowland is narrow, somewhat broader in Guatemala than it is farther south, but entirely overshadowed by the mountains. The eastern plains are also narrow, except in the big elbow of Nicaragua and Honduras. West of these lowlands the altitude increases steadily until, toward the Pacific Coast, plateau highlands culminating in mountain ridges and volcanic cones are the rule. The highlands are interspersed with mountain masses and numerous volcanic cones, some of which attain altitudes of more than 12,000 feet.

There are many short and sharply serrated mountain chains. In places there are flat-topped masses above which volcanic cones extend a few

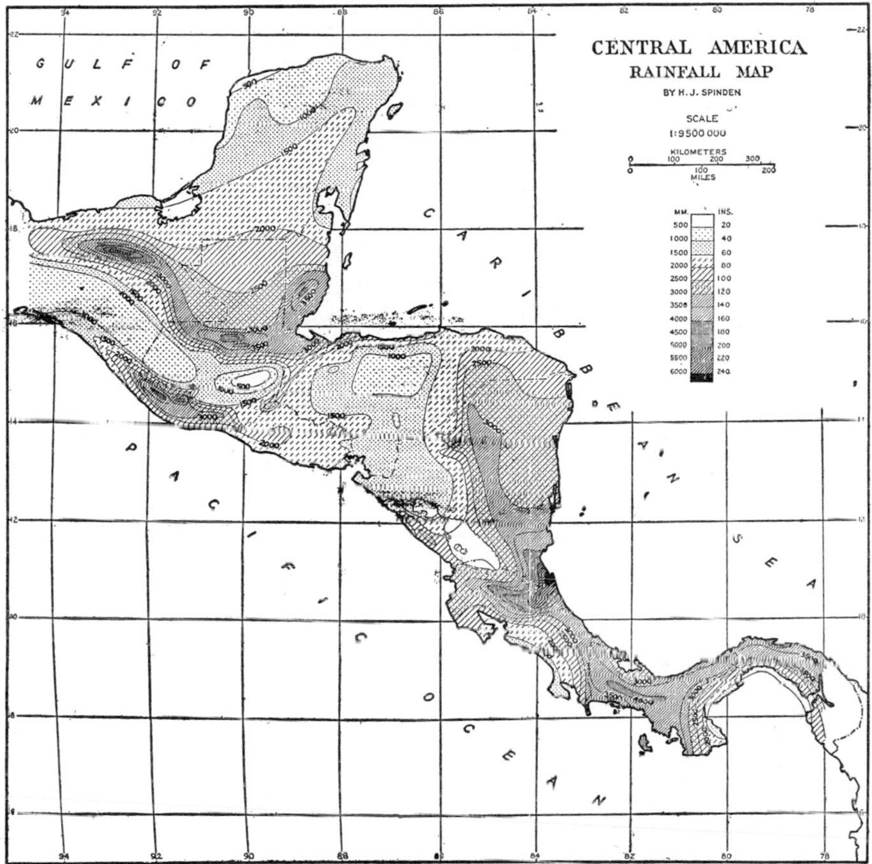

Fig. 103. Annual rainfall map of Central America.

thousand feet. From the central cordilleras cross chains radiate, but these rapidly diminish in altitude. Through the Isthmus of Panama the mountain ranges are about equally distant from the two coasts. Everywhere north of Panama they lie closer to the Pacific Ocean.

Three natural passes discontinuously cross the continent from east to west. The northern one crosses Honduras from the Golfo de Fonseca on the Pacific Coast to the mouth of the Ulúa River on the Caribbean. The middle highland is crossed at a lower altitude than the ones on either side. The second pass is the lake basin of Nicaragua, above which the continental divide rises to an altitude of only 160 feet. Lake Nicaragua itself is 105-110 feet above the sea. On both sides of this lake mountain ranges extend, broken on the western side at a point where a proposed canal was to cross, and on the eastern side by the San Juan River. The third pass occurs in Panama, where the Panama Canal was cut through.

On the highlands of Central America average temperatures are much lower, of course, than they are in the coastal lowlands. In general, an area below 3,000 feet altitude is considered tropical; above 6,000 feet is considered the cold zone; in between is the *tierra templada,* where people generally prefer to live.

In general, the rainfall of Central America occurs primarily during the summer. The driest months are January, February, and March, while the season of heaviest rain is between May and November. In some parts of the Pacific Coast there is a pronounced dry season, one of about three inches of rain. In general the Atlantic side has twice as much rain as the Pacific region. For example in Panama, Cristóbal receives some 127 inches of rain while Balboa on the Pacific side has about 68 inches of rain. The rainfall is more pronounced on the exposed upland slopes than in the lowlands. On the highlands rainfall is much more evenly distributed over the year. Total rainfall varies widely in different areas, from an average of not more than 20 inches to more than 200 inches.

On the uplands drainage is much better than in the lowlands; mosquitoes and other parasites are less obnoxious; plant life can more easily be brought under control for agricultural purposes; temperature is more equable; and both human and animal life are healthier. For these reasons the population of Central America, like that of Mexico and of the Andes nations, tends to concentrate on the highlands.

The volcanoes of Central America are all on the Pacific side of the mountains. Some are still active, and a few of them erupt violently from time to time. As a result of volcanic and tectonic activities, or rather accompanying them, frequent earthquakes occur. Antigua, the old Spanish capital in Guatemala, has been completely destroyed by quakes three times since the establishment of the city more than 400 years ago. Attention of the civilized world was drawn to the severe quake that occurred in 1931, which, with an accompanying conflagration, almost destroyed Managua, the capital of Nicaragua. The fact that Nicaragua is subject to earthquakes and volcanic activity, while on the Isthmus of Panama there are no active volcanoes and no earthquakes of significance have occurred for fifty years, was one of the determining factors in locating the interoceanic canal on the Isthmus. Managua, where quakes do occur, is only 60 miles north of the early proposed canal route in Nicaragua. Two active volcanic cones, Madera and Ometepe, lie near the path of the proposal canal. A canal following this route might be crippled, or even destroyed, by seismic activity.

When volcanic lavas disintegrate, they produce a fertile soil. This has been true in Central America, and the highlands of the volcanic regions have consequently become highly productive agricultural zones. This is a further contributing factor in the density of population on these highlands.

The hundreds of rivers and smaller streams flowing to the Pacific Ocean are, with two or three not very notable exceptions, swift, but they become sluggish ditches as they cross the jungle or sandy wastes along the coast. Generally they are not navigable even for small vessels. The

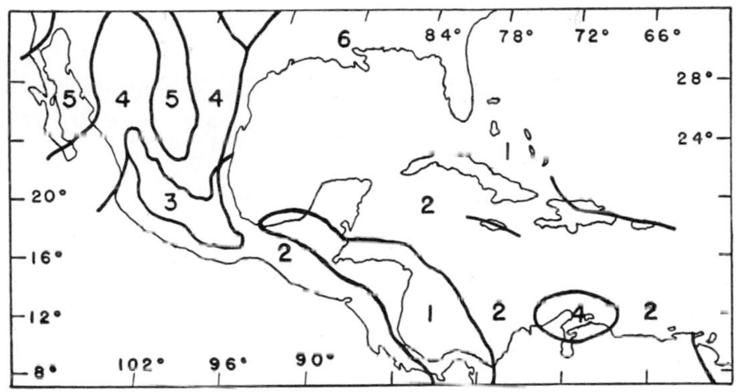

Fig. 104. Climatic regions of Middle America. Major types of climate:

1. Tropical rain forest.
2. Tropical savanna.
3. Tropical highland.
4. Tropical steppe.
5. Tropical desert.
6. Humid sub-tropical.

streams flowing toward the Caribbean are longer, but in the coastal lowlands they become sluggish or merge into marshlands. The longest river is the Segovia, 450 miles long, located in Nicaragua. This and many other eastward-flowing streams are navigable for vessels of small draft. Other principal rivers are the Ulúa in Honduras, the Motagua in Guatemala, the Belize and Hondo in British Honduras, and the San Juan in Nicaragua and Costa Rica.

Only one stream is of potential world significance, the San Juan, which drains Lake Nicaragua. It forms a delta on the Caribbean Coast; the southern arm and main channel of the delta belong to Costa Rica, the other channels to Nicaragua. Small steamers traverse parts of this river regularly. If the Nicaraguan interoceanic canal is ever constructed, this river will form a part of its course. The United States Government in 1916 negotiated with the government of Nicaragua an irrevocable treaty that determines the route of the possible canal and places its construction and control in the hands of the United States. This canal would start at Greytown (San Juan del Norte) on the Caribbean Coast in Nicaraguan territory. After passing up one of the branches of the San Juan River to the main channel, which here is two miles north of the international boundary between Nicaragua and Costa Rica, it would then follow the main channel of the river to Lake Nicaragua, a total distance of some 90 miles from the sea. The route would then pass 60 miles across the southern part of the lake to a point approximately 20 miles from the Pacific Coast, where a channel would be cut to the Pacific. The total

Courtesy Pan American Union.

Fig. 105. A view of the crater of the volcanic cone, Poás, Costa Rica.

length of this canal would be approximately 170 miles, as contrasted with 40 [1] miles for the Panama Canal.

Many lakes are found throughout Central America, but only two are of considerable size, Lake Nicaragua and Lake Managua, both of which are in Nicaragua. They are connected by the Tipitapa Channel. This channel is not, however, navigable. Lake Nicaragua has an area of about 3,500 square miles and contains several volcanic islands. The area of Lake Managua is 575 square miles.

Numerous small mountain lakes are found throughout the entire region, except in Panama. Some of them are of great beauty.

[1] Actual length of the Panama Canal from shore to shore is 40.27 miles. From deep water to deep water, the channel is 50.72 miles.

Several salt-water lagoons are features of the landscape on both the eastern and the western coasts. The largest of these are the Caratasca Lagoon in eastern Honduras and the Pearl Lagoon in eastern Nicaragua. Of the many inlets, bays, and harbors, the one of greatest present significance is the Gulf of Fonseca, on which the three republics of El Salvador, Honduras, and Nicaragua meet. The United States in 1916 acquired from Nicaragua a naval base in this bay, to be used when and if the Nicaraguan canal is constructed. El Salvador and Honduras both protested the ceding of this base by Nicaragua, as also Costa Rica protested the treaty between Nicaragua and the United States, opening the San Juan River to the canal, but the protests went unheeded.

Along the Caribbean Coast are many hundreds of islands or cayos, most of them small and of no great present importance.

Racial heritage and population. The original Indian population has remained basic to all the Central American nations. For three hundred years, and until the beginning of the nineteenth century, immigration was officially limited to citizens of Spain, except in the one area where Britain successfully maintained a colony and exercised a protectorate over the Indians. Spanish blood, therefore, was the only significant European contribution to the racial stock of the entire area until the coming of independence to Central America in the 1820's. At that time immigration from European sources practically ceased. In the last 50 years small colonies of Germans and Italians have settled in certain parts of Guatemala and Honduras, and other European colonies have been encouraged, but with little success. It is probable that two-thirds of the entire population are part Indian, part Spanish ancestry, with the Indian predominating, except in Costa Rica the one "white" nation of Central America—where Spanish blood prevails. In Costa Rica a considerable majority of the population is of pure Spanish descent. This is especially true of the highland area. In the more heavily forested lowland fastnesses are Indian groups that have had only casual contacts with the whites.

Negroes, who originally were imported into the West Indies, were brought to Central America in very much smaller numbers. They settled primarily along the eastern coast, where they mingled freely with the Indian population. They are at present a significant, but not a dominant, element in the population. During the construction of the Panama Canal large numbers of Jamaican and Haitian Negroes came to the isthmus as contract laborers, and numbers of them remained after the canal was finished. Similarly, several hundred East Indian and Chinese merchants settled in the canal cities of Panama.

The population of Central America has suffered numerous vicissitudes. Before the conquest it seems certain that several areas of Central America were densely populated, especially throughout central Honduras and Guatemala and around Lake Nicaragua. After the Spanish conquest two changes occurred. The first was the tendency for the Spanish-Indian population to increase rapidly, for Spanish adventurers brought no women. The second was the tendency for the pure Indian population to decrease under the oppressive labor demands of the conquistadores. Since independence, Indians and mestizos seem to have increased steadily but slowly. At present the birth rate is very high, but infant mortality is also high, and the general lack of sanitary protection has served to keep numbers down. Contacts with the United States and Europe have, within the past 30 or 40 years, deepened the sentiment for better sani-

Courtesy Pan American Union.

Fig. 106. Virgin forest in northeastern Guatemala.

tation and medical care, and the larger cities throughout Central America are decidedly improving in standards of living.

Economy. Coffee is the principal agricultural export commodity from the highlands of Central America, and in world markets it commands a higher price than coffee produced on the Brazilian highlands south of the equator. Prevailing crops, besides coffee, that are produced extensively for local consumption as well as for export are: rice and beans, the staple vegetable foods of Central Americans; tobacco, which is almost universally used in the form of cheroots; maize, which is employed for both animal and human consumption; and cacao and sugar. Many varieties of vegetables and fruits are grown: tomatoes, sweet potatoes, numerous kinds of pumpkins and leafy vegetables, and a dozen different varieties of oranges and bananas. Of all those produced, coffee and bananas are most significant as export commodities, although coconuts and cacao are also exported.

The forests of Central America abound in timber and edible products, of which the best known are mahogany, cedar, balsam, and vanilla. At one time mahogany and cedar were extensively exported, but now the trade has greatly diminished, for the most readily available timbers have been removed. Vanilla, which formerly was gathered wild in the forests, is now produced in plantations, the most productive being found in Mexico. A new market has recently appeared for balsa wood, the lightest timber known; it is used in airplanes. Numerous plantations of balsa trees have recently been developed.

UNITED STATES IMPORTS OF BANANAS

Country of Origin	*Average 1935–38*	*1948*
	In Thousands of Stems	
Mexico	14,815	5,855
Honduras	10,710	13,858
Guatemala	7,967	13,692
Panama (Republic)	6,740	5,572
Panama Canal Zone	———	1,166
Cuba	5,894	2,819
Costa Rica	3,640	7,813
Colombia	3,614	3,690
Nicaragua	2,272	664
Haiti	1,193	2,735
Ecuador	1,159	2,747
British Honduras	637	243
Jamaica	282	46
Dominican Republic	277	1,322
TOTAL	59,256	59,274

The foreign trade of Central America is mainly with the United States and it is carried principally in vessels of American lines, of which there are two types: those in transit between the eastern and western coasts of the United States that stop at Central American ports on the way, and vessels of the fruit companies that carry both passengers and cargo between ports of eastern United States and all of the Caribbean region.

Deposits of useful minerals exist in many locations in Central America, but the known ones are not exceptionally rich. Under Spanish domination some of the gold and silver mines were worked, but with independence these fell into disuse. Only the silver mines of Honduras continued in profitable production, but recently some of the others became active again, principally under the stimulus of North American capital and production methods. Nicaragua, Honduras, and Guatemala are now exporting gold concentrates to the extent of two or three million dollars a year, and small quantities of silver are being shipped from Honduras. Petroleum, a significant product of Mexico to the north and Colombia to the south, is not yet an item in any of the Central American republics. It is believed that deposits exist and concessions are owned by foreign countries, but such deposits seem not to be extensive, and exploitation has not been started.

CENTRAL AMERICAN NATIONS: FOREIGN TRADE

EXPORTS

	1938		*1947*	
	Value (000 dollars)	*United States Percentage of Total*	*Value (000 dollars)*	*United States Percentage of Total*
Costa Rica	10,146	45.6	25,331	76.2
Guatemala	18,234	69.0	52,033	86.5
Honduras	8,166	87.0	17,502	63.7
Nicaragua	5,884	67.3	20,980	77.4
Panama	3,744	89.3	8,520	85.4
El Salvador	10,946	61.7	40,059	77.5
TOTAL	57,120	67.2	164,425	79.1

IMPORTS

	1938		*1947*	
Costa Rica	12,621	49.1	48,069	80.5
Guatemala	20,951	44.7	57,319	83.4
Honduras	10,343	61.4	29,430	77.4
Nicaragua	5,120	59.7	21,086	84.9
Panama	17,651	57.4	75,704	76.6
El Salvador	9,147	46.8	36,933	78.3
TOTAL	75,833	51.9	268,541	79.7

SELECTED REFERENCES

Bengtson, N. A.: "Notes on the Physiography of Honduras," *Geographical Review,* Vol. XVI (1926), pp. 403–413.

Bennett, H. H.: "Agriculture in Central America," *Annals of the Association of American Geographers,* Vol. 16 (1926), pp. 63–84.

Bergsmark, D.: "Geographic Provinces of Costa Rica," *Journal of Geography,* Vol. XXVI (1927), pp. 307–313.

Biesanz, John and Mavis: *Costa Rican Life,* Columbia University Press, New York, 1944.

Carlson, R. E.: "Economic Development in Central America," *Inter-American Economic Affairs,* Vol. II, No. 2 (1948), pp. 5–29.

Castaneda, C. E.: *The Lands of Middle America,* Macmillan, New York, 1947.

Crane, Julian: "Coffee is Gold for El Salvador," *Agriculture in the Americas,* Vol. VII, Nos. 4–5 (1947), pp. 69–72.

Dayton, William A.: "Costa Rica—Land of Forests," *Agriculture in the Americas,* Vol. V, No. 3 (1945), pp. 43–46.

Farringer, Dale E.: "Bananas of the American Tropics," *Agriculture in the Americas,* Vol. VII, Nos. 4–5 (1947), pp. 63–65.

Foscue, Edwin J.: "Land Utilization in Costa Rica," *Scientific Monthly,* Vol. 53 (1941), pp. 427–439.

Governor of the Panama Canal: *Annual Report,* Government Printing Office, Washington, D. C.

Higbee, E. C.: "The Agricultural Regions of Guatemala," *Geographical Review,* Vol. 37, No. 2 (1947), pp. 177–201.

Holdridge, Desmond: "Toledo: A Tropical Refugee Settlement in British Honduras," *Geographical Review,* Vol. XXX (1940), pp. 376–393.

Hoppe, E. O.: "British Honduras," *Canadian Geographical Journal,* Vol. 39 (1949), pp. 18–32.

Jones, C. L.: "Costa Rica and Civilization in the Caribbean," *Studies in the Social Sciences and History No.* 23, University of Wisconsin, Madison, 1941.

Jones, C. L.: *Guatemala, Past and Present,* University of Minnesota Press, Minneapolis, 1940.

Lee, Atherton: "Equatorial Currents—Asset to Middle American Agriculture," *Agriculture in the Americas,* Vol. VII, No. 1 (1947), pp. 3–6.

León, Jorge: "Land Utilization in Costa Rica," *Geographical Review,* Vol. XXXVIII, No. 3 (1948), pp. 444–456.

Lemaire, Minnie E.: "El Salvador," *Economic Geography,* Vol. 22, No. 3 (1946), pp. 193–202.

Marden, Louis: "A Land of Lakes and Volcanoes," *National Geographic Magazine,* Vol. LXXXVI (1944), pp. 161–192.

McBride, G. McCutchen, and McBride, Merle A.: "Highland Guatemala and Its Maya Communities," *Geographical Review,* Vol. XXXII (1942), pp. 252–268.

McBryde, Felix Webster: "Cultural and Historical Geography of Southwest Guatemala," *Publication No. 5,* Smithsonian Institute of Social Anthropology, 1947.

Morley, S. G.: "Research in Middle American Archaeology in 1928," *Bulletin of the Pan American Union,* Vol. LXIII (1929), pp. 230–235.

Morley, S. G.: *The Inscriptions of Petén,* Carnegie Institution of Washington, Washington, D. C., 1938.

Padelford, N. J.: *The Panama Canal in Peace and War,* Macmillan, New York, 1942.

Perkins, D.: *The United States and the Caribbean,* Harvard University Press, Cambridge, 1947.

Platt, R. S.: "An Air Traverse of Central America," *Annals of the Association of American Geographers,* Vol. 24 (1934), pp. 29–39.

Platt, R. S.: "Items in the Regional Geography of Panama," *Annals of the Association of American Geographers,* Vol. 28 (1938), pp. 13–36.

Rands, R. D., and Mackinon, W.: "Small-Farm Rubber Production in Latin America," *Foreign Agriculture,* Vol. 14, No. 3 (1950), pp. 64–67.

Ricketson, O. G., Jr.: "Municipal Organization of an Indian Township in Guatemala," *Geographical Review,* Vol. XXIX (1939), pp. 643–647.

Sapper, K.: "Klimakunde von Mittelamerika," *Handbuch der Klimatologie,* Band II, Teil H, Berlin, 1932.

Schuchert, C.: *Historical Geology of the Antillean-Caribbean Region,* Wiley, New York, 1935.

Shaw, Earl B.: "Recent Changes in the Banana Production of Middle America." *Annals of the Association of American Geographers,* Vol. 32, No. 4 (1942), pp. 371–383.

Stephen, J. L.: "Incidents of Travel in Central America," Rutgers University Press, 1949.

Sterling, M. W.: "Exploring the Past in Panama," *National Geographic Magazine,* Vol. 95, 1949, pp. 373–399.

Spinden, H. J.: "The Population of Ancient America," *Geographical Review,* Vol. XVIII (1928), pp. 641–660.

Vogt, William: *The Population of Costa Rica and Its Natural Resources,* Division of Agricultural Cooperation, Pan American Union, Washington, D. C., 1946.

Von Hagen, V. W.: "The Mosquito Coast of Honduras and Its Inhabitants," *Geographical Review,* Vol. XXX (1940), pp. 238–259.

Von Hagen, V. W.: *Maya Explorer,* University of Oklahoma Press, 1947.

Waibel, Leo: "The Climatic Theory of the Plantation: A Critique," *Geographical Review,* Vol. XXXII (1942), pp. 307–310.

Waibel, Leo: "White Settlement in Costa Rica," *Geographical Review,* Vol. XXIX (1939), pp. 529–560.

Wellman, F. L.: "Balsam of Peru from El Salvador," *Agriculture in the Americas,* Vol. V, No. 5 (1945), pp. 86–87.

Williams, Whiting: "Geographic Determinism in Nicaragua," *The Annals of the American Academy of Political and Social Science,* Vol. CXXII (1927), pp. 142–145.

Wilson, Curtis M.: "El Salvador: A Geographic Reconnaissance," *The Journal of Geography,* Vol. XLVII, No. 5 (1949), pp. 177–196.

CHAPTER XXI

PANAMA AND THE CANAL ZONE

Physical characteristics. The outstanding potential value of the land of Panama has been its favorable location as a crossroad between the two oceans. In earliest times the Spanish authorities constructed a causeway across the isthmus, and practically all of the goods transported overland to the western provinces of South America were carried by this route. In 1903 the people of Panama staged a successful revolution and set up an independent republic. Subsequently the canal was constructed.

The area of Panama is 34,169 square miles, not including the 648 square miles of the Canal Zone. The population is approximately 710,000, and in normal times an additional 52,000 live in the Canal Zone. The population is estimated to be 12 per cent white, 19 per cent Negro, 8 per cent pure Indian, and 61 per cent mestizo. The great mass of Panamanians live simply and humbly, and their wants are few.

Panama is 420 miles long and extends nearly east and west, slightly southeast to northwest. The land mass is shaped like a crescent, with the convex side toward the north. The republic includes all of the territory that might reasonably be called the "isthmus." In width it ranges from 30 miles at the narrowest point to 118 in the widest. The width of the isthmus at the point of the canal is 40 miles. The shores are irregular and are fringed with islands particularly along the Caribbean. Mountain ranges and hilly plateaus extend throughout the isthmus, about equally distant from the shores of the two oceans. There are many fertile plateaus and valleys, and perhaps half the available land is under cultivation. There are no active volcanoes.

Rainfall is heavy, averaging about 120 inches a year on the Caribbean side of the highlands, from which prevailing winds come, and 70 inches on the Pacific side of the mountains. Numerous streams pour down the mountainsides to rather extensive plains and sometimes swampy jungles that border the sea. Of the many rivers, the best known is the Chagres, whose waters serve the locks of the Panama Canal.

Climate is tropical, except in the higher altitudes of the mountains. At the canal night temperatures drop as low as 68°, and day temperatures rise above 90° at times. Since the drainage from the highlands is in general good, and since the sanitation of the entire republic is influenced by the work of North American engineers, the region has become as healthful as any part of Central America. This is especially true of the population centers near the Canal Zone. Away from the cities, it is practically impossible to sanitize the swampy lowlands. At one time all Panama was a veritable pesthole of yellow fever and malaria.

PANAMA: TEMPERATURE AND RAINFALL OF SELECTED STATIONS

	Station	Cristóbal	Balboa Heights
	Elevation (*Feet*)	36	98
Average Temperature (°F.)	*Period of Record*	30 yrs.	25 yrs.
	January	80.9	78
	February	80.9	78
	March	81.5	80
	April	82.4	80
	May	82.1	79
	June	81.7	79
	July	81.5	79
	August	81.5	78
	September	81.3	78
	October	81.1	78
	November	79.8	78
	December	80.6	78
	Annual	81.2	79
	Range	2.6	2.0
Average Rainfall (*Inches*)	*Period of Record*	60 yrs.	30 yrs.
	January	3.5	0.9
	February	1.6	0.8
	March	1.5	0.7
	April	4.3	2.8
	May	12.4	7.8
	June	13.8	8.1
	July	15.7	7.4
	August	15.4	8.0
	September	12.4	7.9
	October	15.4	10.3
	November	21.1	10.2
	December	11.0	4.4
	Annual	128.1	69.3

Source: H. Helm Clayton: World Weather Records. Smithsonian Miscellaneous Collections. Vol. 105, 1947.

Cities. The chief city is Panama, the capital of the republic, located at the southern end of the canal, with a population of about 200,000.

Some five miles east of the present city are the ruins of the old Spanish city that was destroyed in 1671 by the English pirate, Henry Morgan. The old city was well constructed and heavily fortified, and the ruins are still visited by many tourists. Associated with the capital are two cities within the Canal Zone, Balboa, the port, and Ancon, a commercial and residential city. Both Balboa and Ancon are under American jurisdiction, while Panama City and Colón although within the limits of the Panama Canal Zone are excepted from inclusion in the Canal Zone but are subject to certain authority of the United States Government with respect to sanitary measures.

The second city of importance in the republic is Colón, on the Caribbean side of the canal, with a population of 44,000; associated with it is the American port city of Cristóbal. Three other population centers of importance are: Bocas del Toro, a small Caribbean port for the shipment of bananas and the terminus of an extensive network of privately owned banana railways; Portobello, formerly the ancient Spanish port at the Caribbean entrance to the causeway across the isthmus and the most important city of the entire region during the sixteenth century; and David, a city of 10,000 inhabitants near the Pacific Coast at the far western area of the republic.

Transportation and industries. Communications in the area of the canal are good; away from the canal they are poor. One railway parallels the canal and serves the intermediate points. It is owned by the United States Government. A 40-mile railway owned by the government of the republic is operated in Chiriquí province and connects that region with the coast. A highway from coast to coast, in general paralleling the trans-isthmus railway, was recently completed by the United States. Another highway of importance, a section of the Pan-American Highway, extends west from the capital for 325 miles into Chiriquí province near the Costa Rican border. Small coasting vessels carry passengers and produce between the numerous small ports. Air service connects the Canal Zone with the United States and South America.

Mineral resources include deposits of gold, silver, iron, copper, coal, and petroleum, but none of these has been opened for development. The most important mineral deposits are located near the Colombian borders in the territory of the San Blas or Darien Indians. These aborigines are particularly hostile to white men.

Panama, like other Central American republics, produces most of its own essential food requirements, such as rice, beans, potatoes, vegetables, fruits, meat, dairy and poultry products, and coffee. Until recently Panama imported about 60 per cent of its foodstuffs. Today the Republic is self-sufficient in rice and sugar, and produces about 80 per cent of its consumption of potatoes, 95 per cent of its beans, 75 per cent of its coffee, and about 30 per cent of its cattle products.

The leading agricultural exports are bananas, cacao and abacá. These products are produced, primarily, by foreign companies.

Manufacturing in Panama is confined for the most part to light consumer industries whose output is produced in small shops with few workers and small capital investment. Among the leading products are alcoholic beverages, soft drinks, ready-made clothing, ceramics, furniture, shoes, soap, and handicrafts. Recently a number of new enterprises have been established, such as a cement plant and factories utilizing tropical forest resources for the purpose of manufacturing an assortment of wood products. A nail factory has been planned, as well as a number of improvements for the growing business of tourism. Panama has a wealth of tourist attractions.

Panama's principal exports are bananas from the plantations near Bocas del Toro, cacao, abacá, coconuts, hides, ivory nuts, mother of pearl, lumber, and coffee. Considerable difficulty is experienced in getting timber from the interior to the ports of shipment, and this industry has therefore declined. The value of the imports exceeds the value of the exports, and about 75 per cent of the total trade is with the United States. The adverse trade balance is offset to a considerable extent by retail business with visitors who pass through the canal, and by employees of the Canal Zone who are paid by the United States Government.

More than 40 per cent of Panama's national income originates in the Canal Zone. In fact the principal economic activity and export of the Republic since 1914, with few exceptions, has been the sale of services of its citizens to the Canal Zone. "Commerce as related to the Canal Zone is the basic economic activity of Panama."

PANAMA CANAL ZONE

Political geography. Although the Panama Canal Zone is a possession of the United States, it is nevertheless an integral part of the isthmus.

From the earliest times the construction of a canal to join the Pacific and the Atlantic oceans was the subject of speculation and study. Four possible routes were suggested: one through the Isthmus of Darien, a second through the present route of the Panama Canal, a third following the Nicaraguan route up the San Juan River and across Lake Nicaragua, and a fourth through the Mexican Isthmus of Tehuantepec.[1] A canal was actually started through Darien in 1698, and another through the Nicaraguan route in 1889. The French, under the guidance of Ferdinand de Lesseps, a noted engineer, attempted between 1880 and 1889 to construct a sea-level canal at Panama. This project was finally defeated

[1] Read "A Proposed Sea-Level Ship-Canal Across the Isthmus of Tehuantepec" by William H. Hobbs. *Proceedings of the American Society of Civil Engineers for 1948.*

through the combined influences of poor management and yellow fever.

The United States Government became really interested about 1849, when the gold rush to California made the nation keenly conscious of the desirability of facilitating communication between the eastern and western portions of North America. In 1855, as a result of increasing interest, a railway was completed across the isthmus; this was about the

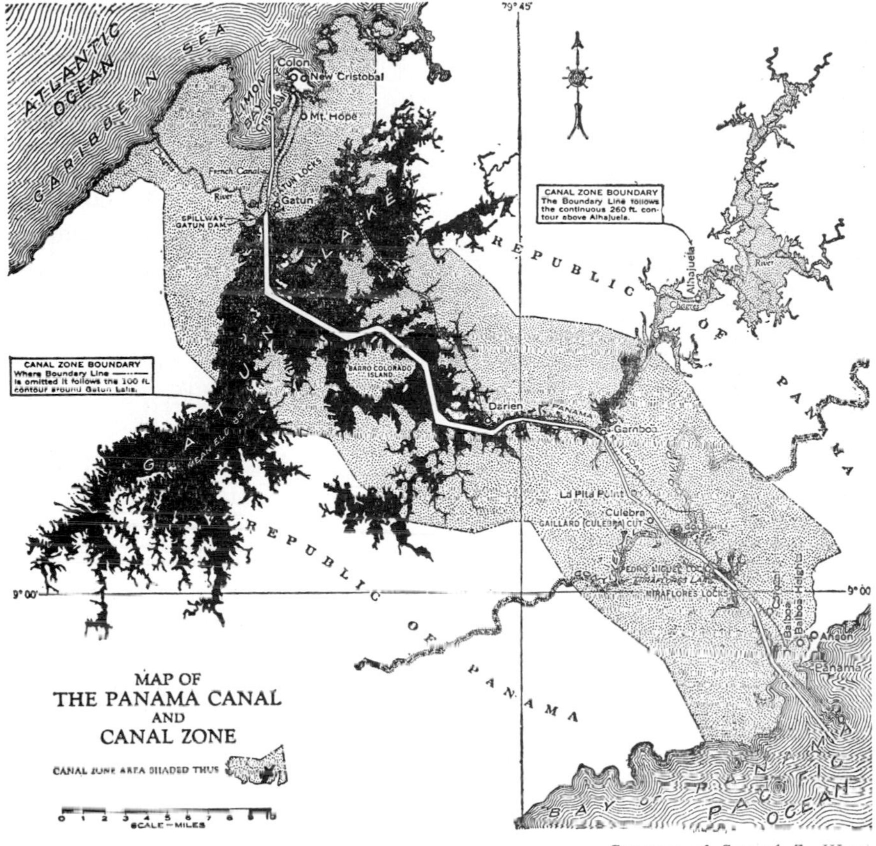

Courtesy of Samuel S. Wyer.

Fig. 107. The Panama Canal and Canal Zone.

period the famous Clayton-Bulwer treaty was made between the United States and Great Britain, under which our government agreed that any canal that might be constructed over either the Panama or the Nicaraguan route should be neutral, and that British shipping should use the canal on the same terms as that of the United States. A new treaty in 1901 gave entire ownership and control to the United States Government and provided that the canal should be open to the vessels of all nations under terms of absolute equality. This treaty makes it impossible to show favors even to shipping concerns moving goods from one side of the United States to the other.

After the United States Government had definitely decided that it could afford to purchase the rights of the French company and undertake to build a canal, it negotiated with the government of Colombia for a concession. After the Colombian congress had adjourned without having ratified or even seriously considered the ratification of the treaty, citizens of the department of Panama revolted. The revolution occurred in 1903, and the Panamanians promptly organized an independent republic and made the desired treaty with the United States.

The concession gave the United States a perpetual lease to a strip of territory five miles wide on either side of the canal route and gave complete authorization to construct, operate, and defend the canal. For the concession the United States Government paid Panama $10,000,000 in cash and in 1923 the United States Senate voted a payment of $25,000,000 to Colombia, technically not as indemnity for justified damages, but in payment for certain property rights and similar items that had been taken over by the United States at the time of constructing the canal. In 1939, a new treaty between the United States and the Republic of Panama was proclaimed, increasing the United States' annual payment to Panama from $250,000 to $430,000.

After three years devoted to making surveys and sanitizing the canal route, construction began. It required ten years of labor under the administration of Colonel G. W. Goethals of the United States Army to complete the canal, and it was finally opened to traffic in 1914. The total cost was $366,000,000. Income from tolls is sufficient to pay operating costs and to yield a nominal return on the investment. According to official records since the opening of the canal in 1914 revenues have exceeded the operating expenses by approximately $271 million amounting to about 2 per cent a year on the net capital investment, now calculated as roughly $516 million.

The Isthmus of Panama extends east and west. The canal is constructed, therefore, on a line, in general, north and south. After entering on the Caribbean Coast, a steamer passes almost directly south for 11 miles, then turns southeast and continues in that direction for the remaining 29 miles to the Pacific Ocean. The Atlantic entrance is, therefore, farther west than the Pacific entrance to the canal.

The length of the canal is 40.27 miles between the shore lines and 50.72 miles from deep water in the Atlantic to deep water in the Pacific. The canal follows the valley of the Chagres River on the Atlantic slope. It passes through the continental divide in the Gaillard (Culebra) Cut and descends to the Pacific down the valley of the Rio Grande. By building a dam across the upper valley of the Chagres, one of the world's largest artificially formed lakes (Gatun Lake) was made to serve for part of the canal. The tops of trees and hills can still be seen above the surface of the lake. Its level, 85 feet above the Atlantic, is reached by the three steps of the Gatun Locks, a mile and one-fifth long, including the approach. A cut known as the Gaillard Cut—8 miles long, 300 feet wide at the base, and about 85 feet deep—was made across the continental divide. The descent to the Pacific is made by three sets of locks, two at Pedro Miguel, and one at Miraflores. The latter has extra depth because of the tidal range on the Pacific side, averaging 12.6 feet, while on the Atlantic side the average tidal range is less than a foot. Each flight of locks has two chambers with a usable length of 1,000 feet, a width of 110 feet, and a depth of 70 feet. The flights are double, enabling ships to pass in opposite directions simultaneously.

Courtesy Pan American Union.

Fig. 108. Panama Canal, Gatun Locks, looking south.

A hydroelectric station at the Gatun Dam supplies electricity for the operation of the gates of the locks, engines, water pumps, lights, and other various uses in the Canal Zone. Eight hours is the usual time required for a ship to pass through the entire length of the canal.

In the section of this chapter dealing with the Republic of Panama, attention was called to the cities of Cristóbal, at the Caribbean entrance to the canal, and Balboa and Ancon, at the Pacific entrance. These cities and a number of other settlements along the route of the canal are under the jurisdiction of the United States Government. The population of the Canal Zone in normal times is approximately 50,000, about 75 per cent whites and the remainder primarily Negroes. There are no commercial enterprises whatever, except commissaries to serve the government employees and their families; dry docks, shops, and similar necessary establishments to serve the canal and steamers passing through it; and barracks for government employees. Administration is vested in a Governor, appointed by the President of the United States. The Governor also is president of the Panama Railroad Company, a United States Government corporation.

Commerce and the canal. The Panama Canal is the most important single factor in the intertransportation of western South America and the United States. It has fostered a close geographical relationship between our country and the western lands of our southern neighbors. The sailing distance from New York to Valparaíso by way of the canal is 3,747 miles shorter than it was through the Strait of Magellan. The saving from New York to Callao is 7,000 miles.

Courtesy Pan American Union.

Fig. 109. Panama Canal, Gaillard Cut, looking north from Contractor's Hill.

PRINCIPAL COMMODITIES SHIPPED THROUGH PANAMA CANAL (1949)

Atlantic to Pacific	*Long tons (2,240 pounds)*
Mineral oils	2,186,777
Coal and coke	1,173,893
Manufactures of iron and steel	1,163,779
Ammonium compounds	448,652
Paper and paper products	393,757
Metals, various	319,386
Flour	307,741
Sulphur	293,626
Cotton, raw	247,931
Machinery	226,429
Tinplate	218,300
Chemicals, unclassified	125,482
Automobiles	120,899
Canned food products	116,301

Pacific to Atlantic	*Long tons (2,240 pounds)*
Ores, various	4,028,279
Lumber	2,005,669
Nitrate	1,445,982
Wheat	1,127,581
Canned food products	733,378
Sugar	668,994
Metals, various	655,312
Food products in refrigeration	601,617
Bananas	480,542
Scrap metal	334,615
Mineral oils	314,527
Coffee	261,870
Wool	228,302
Copra	216,854
Fruits, dried	144,091
Iron and steel manufactures	143,409
Wood pulp	137,998
Flour	133,891
Cotton, raw	123,025

Source: Annual Report of the Governor of the Panama Canal. United States Government Printing Office. Washington, D. C., 1949 (Fiscal year).

REDUCTIONS IN NAUTICAL MILES BY USE OF THE PANAMA CANAL ROUTE

	New York	*New Orleans*	*Liverpool*
San Francisco *	7873	8868	5666
Honolulu *	6610	7605	4403
Guayaquil *	7405	8400	5198
Valparaíso *	3747	4742	1540
Yokohama †	3768	5705	− 694‡
Shanghai †	1876	3813	− 2852‡
Manila †	41	1978	−4421‡
Wellington *	2493	3488	1564‡

* Difference between Panama and Magellan routes.
† Difference between Panama and Suez routes.
‡ Difference in favor of Suez route.
Source: Berglund, Abraham: *Ocean Transportation*, Longmans, Green and Co., New York, 1931, p. 124.

A review of the business of the canal shows that approximately two-thirds of the cargo passes through the canal from west to east. The reason for this eastward movement of cargo is that there is a predominance of heavy raw materials from South America and Western United States. Lighter cargoes, primarily of manufactured goods, move westward. The principal commodities shipped through the canal are listed in the accompanying table.

Lumber and mill products, various ores, nitrate, wheat, mineral oils, canned food products, metals, and sugar are among the leading commodities passing eastward through the canal from the Pacific to the Atlantic. The Pacific-bound cargoes consist, primarily, of mineral oils, manufactures of iron and steel, paper and paper products, various metals, agricultural implements, raw cotton, and machinery.

In 1949, the number of transits was 4,793, as compared to 5,903 in 1939, and 1,058 in 1915. Tons of cargo totalled 25,305,158 in 1949; 27,866,627 in 1939; and 4,888,400 in 1915. The tolls collected in 1949 amounted to $20,541,229.

The segregation of traffic through the Canal by nationality of vessels is as follows:

1949	*Tons of Cargo*	*Percentage*
United States	12,377,506	48.9
British	5,631,876	22.3
Norwegian	1,758,830	7.0
Panamanian	861,448	3.3
Swedish	788,007	3.1
Greek	713,646	2.8
Danish	546,035	2.2
French	519,937	2.1
Honduran	497,580	2.0
Netherland	305,502	1.2
Chilean	300,370	1.1
Others	1,004,421	4.0
TOTAL	25,305,158	100

Source: Annual Report of the Governor of the Panama Canal. United States Government Printing Office. Washington, D. C. 1949. (Fiscal year.)

In 1939, the distribution of traffic according to nationality of vessels was approximately in the same proportion as in 1949, with the exception that German vessels accounted for 6 per cent and Japanese vessels 5 per cent of the total in 1939.

Toll rates. Vessels owned, operated or chartered by the Governments of the United States and Republic of Panama; war vessels of the Republic of Colombia; and vessels transiting solely for the purpose of having repairs made at the Panama Canal shops are entitled to free passage of the Canal. On merchant vessels, when carrying passengers or cargo, the toll rate is 90 cents per vessel-net ton of 100 cubic feet of earning capacity. Vessels in ballast without passengers or cargo pay 80 cents per net vessel-ton. Vessels of war (except those of the United States, Panama, and Colombia, which transit tolls free) and other floating crafts pay 50 cents on displacement tonnage. The displacement tonnage of a vessel is the weight of water displaced by it in floating, expressed in units of long tons (2,240 pounds) or metric tons (2,204 pounds).[2]

[2] A new set of toll rates were proclaimed by the United States Government in 1948 as follows: Merchant vessel-net ton $1.00; vessels in ballast net ton 80 cents; and displacement tonnage 55 cents. At the time of this writing these rates had not been put into effect.

Panama Canal Zone development. Progress in the Panama Canal Zone is a good example of what man can accomplish in the tropics under a sound practice of sanitation and other health measures and with the use of modern equipment.

For additional facts concerning the Panama Canal Zone, confer with Chief of Office, The Panama Canal, Washington, D. C.

CHAPTER XXII

COSTA RICA

The republic of Costa Rica—meaning rich coast—is one of the most interesting countries in Central America. In its area of some 23,000 square miles is a population of about 825,000 inhabitants, of which 80 per cent or more are white. The country has maintained a peaceful and industrious policy, and its development has been outstanding, despite its limited resources. The popular statement that Costa Rica has more teachers than soldiers is at least in principle correct.

Physical features. Mountain ranges pass through Costa Rica from northwest to southeast and are thickly dotted with evidences of past volcanic activity. In places the cordilleras reach altitudes of more than 10,000 feet. The highlands lie closer to the Pacific Coast than to the east. Because of the country's position in the low latitudes and its land extending from lowlands to high altitudes, a diversity of climatic conditions exists, ranging from the tierra caliente regions under 3,000 feet to the tierra templada zone from 3,000 to 6,000 feet and then to the tierra fría, above 6,000 feet. The scale of temperature and elevations on the cooler Pacific Coast is slightly lower than that on the Atlantic side, where higher temperatures generally prevail.

The Caribbean coastline is quite regular and almost harborless except for the one port of Limón. The Pacific Coast, on the contrary, is irregular, with three promontories and a number of bays and inlets. It is served by several small ports, the principal being Puntarenas, the terminus of the nation's transcontinental railway. Many small streams empty into the two oceans, but none of them is navigable, except for small vessels and only for short distances.

In the lower lands, from sea level up to perhaps 3,000 feet, drainage is sluggish; jungle flourishes; and malaria is common. In the more temperate regions, from about 3,000 to 6,000 feet, the climate is much more salubrious. In many places on the plateau malaria is unknown. Seventy-five per cent of the population is concentrated on the plateaus and associated valleys, where the volcanic ash has produced an exceedingly fertile soil.

Population. In 1890 there were perhaps 265,000 inhabitants; in 1904 the number had increased to 330,000; in 1920 to 476,000; and at the present time the population is estimated at 825,000. This steady increase is due in Costa Rica, as in the other Central American nations, to the continually high birth rate and to the reduction in death rate due, in part, to improvement in sanitation and general health conditions.

Costa Rica has few Negroes, probably less than 4 per cent of its total population, and most of these live in the lowland regions. There are some pure-blooded Indians, probably not more than 6,000, according to the recent reports; they live principally in the mountainous regions. Most of the inhabitants are purely Spanish in ancestry, or Spanish mixed with Indian. The proportion of European blood is higher than that of any other Central American nation.

The principal population center is the capital, San José, situated in the uplands at an elevation of 3,724 feet above sea level, with a population of about 90,600. The seaports are Limón on the Caribbean and Puntarenas on the Pacific Coast.

The population of Costa Rica, like that of most other Central American republics, is largely agrarian, but with the difference that most of the inhabitants live on their own small farms, where they raise most of their own necessities and have some to sell. This sturdy Spanish or half-caste farming population looks with disfavor upon political disturbances and insists on a steady, quiet life. This means that revolutions are less frequent in this nation than in others near by. The upper classes, whether living in the cities or in the rural areas, are generally better educated than those of other Central American republics, and they maintain relatively higher standards of living.

AVERAGE TEMPERATURE AND RAINFALL OF SAN JOSÉ, COSTA RICA

(Elevation 3723.7 feet)

	Jan.	*Feb.*	*Mar.*	*Apr.*	*May*	*June*	*July*	*Aug.*	*Sept.*	*Oct.*	*Nov.*	*Dec.*	*Annual*	*Range*
Temperature (°*F.*)	66.0	66.7	67.8	68.7	68.9	68.2	67.6	67.5	67.6	67.3	68.7	65.8	67.5	3.1
(*Period of Record, 1889–1900*)														
Rainfall (*Inches*)	0.2	0.2	0.5	1.1	10.0	11.0	8.3	10.6	14.2	13.3	4.9	1.7	75.9	
(*Period of Record, 1888–1895*)														

Source: K. Sapper: "Klimakunde von Mittelamerika," *Handbuch der Klimatologie*, Band II, Teil H, Berlin, 1932.

Economy. Two principal railways serve Costa Rica. One extends from the port city of Limón to San José, a distance of 102 miles, and serves a number of small cities. The other extends from Puntarenas, on the Pacific Coast, to San José and serves another populous district in its course of 70 miles—the national total is some 500 miles. Within the past few years considerable progress has been made in highway construction in joining all of the important highland cities. Every week in peace times vessels call at the two port cities en route to or from the United States. Steamers of the United Fruit Company serve the east coast, while the Grace Line makes regular stops on the western coast.

Costa Rica is an agricultural nation, and there is very little industrial development. Its leading export commodities are coffee, bananas, and cacao.

The leading agricultural cash crop is coffee, amounting to about 45 per cent of the nation's total exports. Most of the coffee trade is with the United States. Bananas rank second in its foreign trade, making up 30 per cent of the total. In 1948, some 7,800,000 stems were shipped to the United States. The production of bananas has been transferred mainly to the West coast—80 per cent—due to Sigatoka, a leaf-disease, and the Panama root disease, both prevalent on the Atlantic coastal region. Cacao, constituting about 6 per cent of all exports, has replaced the banana industry in some areas in the east. Some vegetables are exported to the Canal Zone.

Mineral deposits exist in the mountains and consist of gold, silver, copper, iron, zinc, and lead. At present only gold is mined, and practically all of it is shipped to the United States.

Approximately 75 per cent of Costa Rica's foreign trade exports and imports in 1947 was with the United States. The United States is the main source of Costa Rica's imports of capital goods; Peru and Cuba are the chief sources of sugar; and India ships jute sacks to Costa Rica, an essential product for coffee exports.

SELECTED REFERENCES

See Chapter XX.

CHAPTER XXIII

NICARAGUA

Physical landscape. The republic of Nicaragua is the largest of the Central American nations, with an area of 57,143 square miles, or about the size of Wisconsin.

The land may be considered as five distinct regions, each with its particular qualities. (1) On the Caribbean side the land is low, flat, tropical jungle, extending inland for 50 to 100 miles from the coast. (2) The lowland gradually rises into a series of broken plateaus, interspersed with frequent mountain ranges, well watered and well wooded. It is possible that at one time this area was a rather flat plateau or peneplain sloping from the mountain chains gradually toward the east, but it has been so cut by streams and weathering that it is now a bewildering mass of hills and valleys. In this area, approximately one-third of the national territory, lie most of the mineral deposits of the nation. (3) The plateaus culminate in a series of mountain ranges paralleling the eastern side of the lake region. (4) Behind the mountains, generally at the foot of steep escarpments, lie the two great lakes, Managua and Nicaragua, in a basin that nearly crosses the continent. The lower lake, Nicaragua, rests at a level of about 105–110 feet above the sea and drains to the southeast through the San Juan River. To the north this lake is joined to Lake Managua by a narrow stream, impassable because of rapids. The lake basin is separated from the Pacific Ocean toward the northwest by a ridge slightly higher than the lakes themselves. It opens into a valley through which flows the Rio Grande. (5) West of the lacustrine basin, bordering the Pacific Coast, is a chain of volcanic peaks, none more than 6,000 feet in altitude, which are separated from each other by valleys and plateaus. These volcanoes are subject to frequent eruptions. Some are constantly emitting vapor and smoke, and earthquakes are frequent. The destruction of Managua by an earthquake and fire in 1931 has already been mentioned.

Because 800,000 of the total population of 1,110,000 live around the lake basin or in the highlands surrounding it, this region is of greatest interest. Lake Nicaragua is about 100 miles long and 45 miles wide at the broadest point. Its total area is about 3,500 square miles, the largest

NICARAGUA: TEMPERATURE AND RAINFALL OF SELECTED STATIONS

	Station	San Ubaldo	Bluefields	Greytown
	Elevation (*Feet*)	108.3	Sea Level (approximately)	Sea Level (approximately)
Average Temperature (°*F.*)	*Period of Record*	1900	3 yrs.	1898–1900
	January	79.5	78.3	77.5
	February	80.8	77.7	77.7
	March	82.9	80.8	78.8
	April	86.4	82.4	80.8
	May	85.8	80.8	80.8
	June	82.9	79.2	80.1
	July	81.3	79.3	79.2
	August	82.9	79.3	79.3
	September	83.1	79.2	80.4
	October	80.6	79.5	80.2
	November	80.2	79.2	78.4
	December	81.1	78.4	77.5
	Annual	82.2	79.5	79.2
	Range	6.9	4.7	3.3
Average Rainfall (*Inches*)	*Period of Record*	1900	1900	1890–1900
	January	1.2	5.7	23.3
	February	0.2	7.0	11.3
	March	0.3	3.5	6.5
	April	0.1	1.1	11.4
	May	7.4	10.4	20.4
	June	9.8	8.9	23.2
	July	24.9	14.6	34.4
	August	5.3	23.5	27.3
	September	14.1	11.2	17.4
	October	8.9	12.3	20.0
	November	1.4	14.9	36.5
	December	0.6	14.5	27.8
	Annual	74.3	127.7	259.4

Source: K. Sapper: "Klimakunde von Mittelamerika," *Handbuch der Klimatologie*, Band II, Teil H, Berlin, 1932.

body of fresh water between Lake Michigan and Lake Titicaca. To the north is Lake Managua, with an area of about 575 square miles. It is some 40 feet higher than its larger neighbor to the south and drains into it through the Tipitapa Channel. Small steamers owned by the government ply these two lakes and serve the numerous villages that surround them. They also navigate the San Juan River to a point close to the

Caribbean, where the channel is obstructed by a series of rapids. The principal river of Nicaragua is the Segovia, navigable for about 150 miles from the Caribbean Coast, through which access is had to several towns and a significant part of the mining section of the eastern half of the republic.

Population centers. The larger part of the population is concentrated in regions around the lakes. These centers have altitudes of 200 to 1,000 feet and are therefore tropical in nature. The capital city is Managua, located on the lake of that name. Other principal population centers are Granada, León, and Chinandega, in the lake basin, or associated lowlands, and Matagalpa, in the highlands. The first four cities have access by rail to the port of Corinto, on the Pacific Coast, the leading Pacific port, located about 87 miles from Managua. Some 70 per cent of the nation's foreign trade passes through El Corinto, consisting mainly of coffee, sugar, hides and wood. El Corinto is on an island with bridge connections to the mainland. Greytown (San Juan del Norte) is the Caribbean port at the mouth of the San Juan River. Bluefields, farther up the Caribbean Coast, at the mouth of the river of the same name, is the chief Atlantic port, and it is particularly known for its banana exports. Highways are fairly good around the region of the lakes, and railway and motor service links the principal population centers. Away from this region, transportation is by pack mule over narrow trails.

As in other Central American republics, the population is increasing, the rise being due almost entirely to the excess of births over deaths. There is little immigration into any Central American nation. The census in 1881 gave the total population as 275,000. In 1900 it had increased to 500,000; now it has attained, according to estimate, a total of 1,110,000. The population is nearly all of mixed blood, Indian strains strongly predominating. Small numbers of German immigrants have come during the past 50 years, and they are engaged in agriculture and commerce. Foreign commerce is largely in their hands.

Agriculture and commerce. Much of the soil of Nicaragua is fertile, and the climate is tropical to semitropical. The nation is, therefore, predominantly agricultural and pastoral. Rice, beans, corn, and vegetable staples are produced for home consumption. Bananas, oranges, and other tropical fruits are produced also, principally for use at home, and vast amounts of fruit are eaten. Bananas, once an important crop, have decreased in trade from 4,000,000 stems in 1929 to 467,000 stems in 1947. This decrease was due to the devastating effects of Sigatoka, a leaf disease, and a root infection known as the Panama disease.

Coffee is Nicaragua's principal cash crop. It is produced in the highlands north and south of Managua and on the plateaus around Matagalpa, northeast of the lake region. Bananas are the nation's second agricultural export. Numerous attempts have been made to grow cotton, for both domestic and export purposes, but without great success as yet. Large numbers of cattle are raised in the southern plateaus. Some are exported alive to neighboring republics. Hides and skins are an important item of export. Attempts have been made to establish rubber plantations, and many thousands of trees have been set out. Rubber, however, has never become an important product. Some hardwood timber is exported each year, but the amount is not significant.

Nicaragua has known mineral deposits in the eastern plateaus. Gold mining is important, and about a half a million dollars a year in bullion finds its way to the United States. Copper, silver, and coal are produced in small quantities.

Approximately 85 per cent of Nicaragua's imports were supplied by the United States in 1947, and 75 per cent of the nation's exports were destined for the United States. Gold is the leading export, accounting for 35 to 40 per cent of the total foreign shipments in 1947. Coffee is the second ranking export, amounting to 25 per cent of the total. Among the other exports are sesame, wood, cattle, rice, ipecac root, and hides and skins. In addition to the United States, Nicaragua trades primarily with Mexico, the United Kingdom, and with other Central American countries.

Costa Rica and Nicaragua in contrast.[1] Before the early days of the twentieth century, Costa Rica and Nicaragua presented a striking difference in their political and social behavior. Costa Rica had national unity, while Nicaragua exhibited pronounced differences within the state. The society of Costa Rica was peaceful, while that of Nicaragua was turbulent. Such dissimilarities in two adjacent states were not uncommon in many other regions of the Americas.

1. Costa Rica had a closely united people, living within a rather limited area. In Nicaragua the inhabitants were distributed in widely separated regions interrupted by lakes and mountains.

2. Costa Rica's population was for the most part homogeneous, whereas that of Nicaragua consisted of many different races and nationalities.

3. In general, Costa Rica had a one-class society with a common economic interest, and one in which small landowners predominated. Nicaragua, on the other hand, had a multi-class society, with resultant conflicts, inequality, and divergent economic interests.

4. The terrain of Costa Rica more or less separated its people from the mother-country, Spain. In Nicaragua the easy transportation from coast to coast served to bring the Spanish influence within the domain. This influence took the form of large land holdings, slavery, and selfish European interests.

5. In Costa Rica there was almost a complete lack of resources of

[1] A résumé of a report prepared by J. L. Busey. Ohio State University. 1946.

significance to foreigners or absentee landowners. The possibilities of an interoceanic canal in Nicaragua, as well as the use of its area for overland journeys from Atlantic to Pacific, instituted international as well as domestic disputes.

6. The climate of Costa Rica in the highland areas favored greater activity and better health conditions. In Nicaragua the greater percentage of the population was distributed in the lowlands of the lake region.

In regional contrasts may be found the fundamental reasons for the early differences in Costa Rica and Nicaragua. Today the two countries in their social, economic, and political affairs do not diverge as greatly as they did years ago. However, the natural regional factors have not completely lost their place in the human pattern of living in Costa Rica and Nicaragua.

SELECTED REFERENCES

See Chapter XX.

CHAPTER XXIV

EL SALVADOR

Physical and cultural characteristics. El Salvador is the smallest Central American republic. Its area is only 13,176 square miles. It is bounded by Honduras on the north and east and by Guatemala on the west. To the south it faces the Pacific Ocean. It has no Caribbean coastline. The republic is only about 160 miles long by 80 miles broad. It is the most densely populated region of Central America, with a total of 2,015,000 inhabitants, or about 153 persons per square mile.

El Salvador has a narrow littoral, tropical in climate during all the year and damp and unhealthful during the season of the rains. Immediately behind the littoral are ranges of mountains separated by wide upland valleys. In these valleys and on the associated highlands most of the inhabitants live. El Salvador, like most of the Central American republics, is subject to earthquakes, probably of volcanic as well as of tectonic origin. A number of large active cones are scattered in various parts of the mountain ranges. The climate on the highlands is healthful, semitropical the year 'round. The wet season extends from May to October.

El Salvador is fairly well provided with railways and motor highways. It is the southern terminus, at present, of the international railways on which one may travel from the southeast corner of El Salvador through that republic, up through Guatemala and Mexico, into the United States. At least 4,000 miles of highways exist in the restricted area of the republic, and perhaps half of them can be used for motor vehicles; the remainder are poor.

Three Pacific ports serve the territory. La Unión is on the far southeast edge of the country, on the Gulf of Fonseca. More than half of the nation's imports and one-third of its exports are handled at La Unión. The port is about 155 miles from the capital city. Acajutla, at the far northwest on the coast, leads in coffee shipments. La Libertad, located midway on the coast, is only 23 miles from San Salvador. La Unión and Acajutla are served by railways; La Libertad with motor transport. The international railway joins with the Guatemalan system, and through this means El Salvador has access to the Guatemalan port of Barrios on the Caribbean Coast.

Population centers are the capital, San Salvador, with a population of 105,200, and Santa Ana, Sonsonate, San Vicente, San Miguel, and Nueva

EL SALVADOR: TEMPERATURE AND RAINFALL

Station	San Salvador	San Salvador
Elevation (*Feet*)	2,238	
	Average Temperature (°*F.*)	Average Rainfall (*Inches*)
Period of Record	1931–40	1931–40
January	72.7	0.5
February	73.0	0.7
March	74.7	0.3
April	75.7	1.3
May	75.6	8.6
June	74.0	10.7
July	74.0	10.4
August	74.3	11.8
September	73.2	12.3
October	73.2	9.7
November	72.3	1.5
December	72.7	0.5
Annual	73.8	74.3
Range	3.4	

Source: H. Helm Clayton. "World Weather Records," *Smithsonian Miscellaneous Collections*, Vol. 105 (1947).

San Salvador; all of them are on the uplands. The population is either Indian, of whom it is estimated that 200,000 remain, or mixed Spanish-Indian. Perhaps 50,000 of the total are of pure European ancestry.

Economy. The principal occupation is agriculture. Rice, beans, corn, sugar, vegetables, and fruits are all produced for local use. Cattle, too, are raised, but entirely for local use, and none are exported. Pigs and chickens are found everywhere, as is true, of course, throughout all Latin America.

El Salvador is a coffee-producing country, and more than 90 per cent of the total value of its exports is in coffee, the nation's only commercial crop of any great importance. Sugar ranks a poor second. El Salvador also exports balsam extract—misnamed "balsam of Peru." The yearly shipment amounts to about 170 tons. Other exports consist of henequen, rice, wood, gold, and silver.

The production of coffee of excellent quality is one of El Salvador's outstanding achievements. Natural conditions, climate, terrain, and soil are most favorable for coffee culture. In addition to these physical attributes, El Salvador has an abundance of cheap labor, good transportation, and efficient methods of cultivating and marketing its leading commercial crop. The nation's prosperity depends largely on coffee.

El Salvador, like all of the other regions in Central America, is lacking in coal and petroleum resources. Charcoal is an essential fuel, and only limited development has taken place in the production of electric power outside of the urban centers.

The foreign trade of El Salvador in 1948 was mainly with the United States—80 per cent of total exports and 75 per cent of all imports.

SELECTED REFERENCES

See Chapter XX.

CHAPTER XXV

HONDURAS

Regions. The republic of Honduras, an area of 46,332 square miles, is mountainous throughout four-fifths of its extent. Along the northern coast is a low plain, ranging from less than 10 to more than 60 miles in width. Behind this plain rise mountains interspersed with plateaus and valleys. Nearly all of the interior is of this highland character and has a semitropical climate. At Tegucigalpa, the capital, the highest usual temperature does not exceed 90° in May, the warmest month, and the lowest does not fall below 50° in December, the coldest month.

AVERAGE TEMPERATURE AND RAINFALL OF TEGUCIGALPA, HONDURAS
(Elevation 3,300 feet)

	Temperature (°*F.*)	Rainfall (*Inches*)
Period of Record	1940	1940
January	79.3	1.8
February	76.6	0.2
March	87.1	0.2
April	86.5	0.5
May	87.1	5.3
June	83.7	6.1
July	81.1	2.0
August	84.4	2.3
September	81.7	13.2
October	78.4	6.0
November	75.7	2.4
December	76.6	0.8
Annual	81.5	40.8
Range	11.4	

Source: H. Helm Clayton: "World Weather Records," *Smithsonian Miscellaneous Collections*, Vol. 105 (1947).

The Caribbean shore line of Honduras is more than 300 miles long. The broad indentation of the Caribbean that is bounded by Honduras, British Honduras, and Guatemala is known locally as the Golfo de

Honduras. (Honduras means "very deep" in Spanish. The name was given first to the waters of the coast and then to the territories adjoining.) Several islands of importance belong to Honduras; these include the Bay Islands on the Caribbean, with the important population center of Roatán, and the island of Tigre, in the Gulf of Fonseca. On the latter island is located the port city of Amapala, which has a customhouse. Passengers for Honduras disembark here and cross by launch to San Lorenzo, on the mainland; freight is lightered across.

Honduras is well watered by numerous rivers, some of them navigable for considerable distances from the coast. The most accessible route across the republic follows the Ulúa River Valley to its tributary, the Humuya, continues along the Humuya Valley to the uplands of Comayagua, then crosses to the valley of the Goascorán River, which extends to the Gulf of Fonseca. In early days it was suggested that a highway from sea to sea should be constructed along this route. Such a highway, suitable for motor vehicles, now exists from San Lorenzo on the Gulf of Fonseca, through Tegucigalpa, located at an elevation of 3,300 feet above sea level, to Potrerillos, a settlement on the headwaters of the Ulúa River. From Potrerillos a national railway now extends to Puerto Cortés, on the Caribbean Coast.

Tegucigalpa is without railway transportation, an exceptional condition for a capital city. However, in addition to the highway, there is a good airport nearby. Amapala is Honduras' only good port on the Pacific. The leading ports on the Atlantic side are Puerto Cortés, the largest, and Tela. Both are important banana shipping centers.

Railway transportation is generally lacking throughout the republic, except along the northern coast, where the banana plantations are served by numerous narrow-gauge lines owned and operated by the banana companies. Between 500 and 600 miles of these commercial lines now exist. Highways, except those for pack mules and ox carts, are entirely inadequate. The national government is aware of this lack and has begun the construction of highways suitable for motor transportation. The one mentioned earlier is the first to be completed. Others are beginning to radiate from the capital city.

Population centers. The 1,230,000 inhabitants of Honduras are primarily Indians or mestizos. The highland Indians seem to be descendants principally of the Mayas or allied races. Most of them have accepted modern culture, but perhaps 100,000 still follow traditionally primitive lines of living and refuse the white man's Christian religion and his modes of life. Along the northern coast are a few small settlements of Caribs, an energetic and active Indian race.

The Spanish-Indian stock tends to concentrate in the highlands toward the south. The chief population center is the capital, Tegucigalpa, with 55,800 inhabitants. Port cities are Amapala, on Tigre Island in the Gulf of Fonseca, and Puerto Cortés, Tela, La Ceiba, Puerto Castillo, and Trujillo on the Caribbean. It is reported that Trujillo is one of the oldest towns in the New World, having been established in 1524. Because of the extensive banana industry, sailings from these points are generally frequent.

Economy. The mineral resources of Honduras are more extensive than those of the other Central American nations. Gold and silver mines were particularly rich during the Spanish regime and were steadily exploited. Honduras exports annually gold and silver valued at more than 2 million dollars.

Like other Central American nations, Honduras is largely and principally an agricultural country. Bananas, coffee, coconuts, plantains, and a little mahogany and cedar are exported. Bananas represent about 46 per cent of the total annual exports, and Honduras leads all countries in the production of this fruit. Its yearly exports of bananas in the past were more than 20,000,000 stems, but recently the production has declined to less than 14,000,000. This reduction is due to the banana-leaf disease, Sigatoka (*Cercospora musae*), the Panama disease, and unseasonal dry weather.

Both the diseases and the necessity of increasing the irrigation have brought about a marked change in the location of the banana industry. Ten years ago less than 10 per cent of all bananas for export in Central America were produced in the Atlantic coastal areas, but that is not true today. For example, in 1930 the total production for the Atlantic side was 38,100,000 stems, that for the Pacific area 2,800,000 stems; in 1940 the records show Atlantic, 23,400,000 stems, and Pacific, 10,000,000. In 1948 reports indicate a continuation of the movement of the banana culture from the Atlantic region to the Pacific. Sigatoka can be controlled by spraying with chemicals, but only at a considerable expense. Consequently, producers are locating in new areas that, at least for the present, appear free from the destructive diseases.[1]

In Honduras the cultivation of bananas is confined mainly to the north coastal area, some 50 miles from the Atlantic. In some of the abandoned banana regions, sugar cane has been introduced. The industry is primarily under the supervision of the United Fruit Company and the Standard Fruit and Steamship Company.

Coffee is not a commercial crop of any importance in Honduras. Some coconuts and copra are exported as well as some forest products.

Second to banana exports is silver, amounting to about 10 per cent of the country's total exports. Gold exports also are significant.

---

[1] For an interesting reference on the banana industry read *Empire in Green and Gold—A Story of the American Banana Trade,* Charles M. Wilson, Holt and Co., New York, 1947.

In 1948, the United States supplied about 75 per cent of Honduras' imports and purchased about 65 per cent of its exports. Among the other regions trading with Honduras are El Salvador, Canada, Cuba, Mexico, Panama, Guatemala, Netherland West Indies, and Peru.

While El Salvador's economy rests on coffee, Honduras depends primarily on its banana industry.

SELECTED REFERENCES

See Chapter XX.

CHAPTER XXVI

GUATEMALA AND BRITISH HONDURAS

GUATEMALA

Regional characteristics. The territory of the republic of Guatemala is divided roughly into four regions. The first is the low coastal plain bordering on the Pacific shores, plains that vary from 20 to 50 miles in width. They are hot, humid, and in general swampy and malarial. Population here is very sparse, except in the few small seaports. The second is a high mountain range with an associated series of plateaus and high valleys, lying directly behind and north of the plains. Climate in this region varies from temperate to cold, and drainage is excellent. In this area are located the great volcanic cones, many of them active, several more than 12,000 feet high. Their detritus has decomposed into an exceedingly fertile soil. Because of the excellent climate and rich soil, the great mass of the population is concentrated in this zone. The third section is behind these plateaus, where the land slopes interruptedly toward the Caribbean Coast. The region is thickly interspersed with mountain ranges and valleys, extending eastward, down which rivers flow. This part of Guatemala is fairly well settled. To the north lies the fourth section, the Plains of Petén, a part of the lowlands including much of Yucatán, and at one time the site of a very populous Mayan civilization. Numerous remains of this civilization still exist, covered with matted jungle. Now this region is thinly settled, with about 12,000 inhabitants mostly primitive Indian tribes. The total area is 48,290 square miles.

Civic centers. Guatemala's population (3,706,200) is largely Indian, with an intermixture of Spanish and Indian. Perhaps 80 to 90 per cent of the inhabitants are predominantly Indian, and 60 per cent of the total population are classed in the census as entirely Indian. Among the most prosperous of the inhabitants of the highlands are several colonies of Italian and German immigrants. These are a stabilizing element and contribute much to the welfare of the republic. They own and manage large acreages set out in coffee and other plantations, and they also form the most significant merchant class in the capital city. Foreign trade is one of their major business activities.

GUATEMALA: TEMPERATURE AND RAINFALL

	Station	Salamá *	Quezaltenango *	Guatemala City †	Quirigua *
	Elevation (*Feet*)	3018.4	7710.0	4888.4	311.7
Average Temperature (°*F.*)	*Period of Record*	1891–1892	1894–1902	6 yrs.	1925–1927
	January	67.8	51.8	63	73.9
	February	69.8	53.4	66	76.5
	March	73.8	57.7	69	77.0
	April	76.6	60.1	70	80.8
	May	77.5	62.4	72	83.3
	June	76.8	61.9	71	81.0
	July	74.5	60.4	69	79.0
	August	73.8	60.1	69	78.6
	September	70.3	60.3	69	79.3
	October	70.7	59.9	68	77.0
	November	71.2	57.0	66	70.2
	December	69.3	52.7	63	71.8
	Annual	72.7	58.3	68	77.4
	Range	9.7	10.6	9	13.1
Average Rainfall (*Inches*)	*Period of Record*	1891–1925	1895–1925	29 yrs.	1918–1927
	January	0.0	0.8	0.3	8.5
	February	0.0	0.1	0.1	6.7
	March	0.5	0.6	0.5	4.0
	April	1.9	1.3	1.2	3.6
	May	3.1	3.9	6.0	4.3
	June	9.2	5.0	10.8	10.5
	July	4.0	3.2	8.0	11.8
	August	3.2	3.8	7.8	12.3
	September	3.1	4.3	9.1	11.1
	October	3.6	3.1	6.8	10.5
	November	1.3	0.6	0.9	11.3
	December	0.2	0.1	0.3	8.4
	Annual	30.1	26.4	51.8	103.0

* K. Sapper: "Klimakunde von Mittelamerika," *Handbuch der Klimatologie,* Band II, Teil H, Berlin, 1932.

† U. S. Weather Bureau, *Technical Paper No. 8,* United States Weather Bureau, Washington, D. C.

The cities of Guatemala are many. Guatemala City, the capital of the nation, is situated on the central plateau. It has a population estimated at 163,900 and is the center of the nation's culture, education, industry, and political activity. Three seaports should be mentioned:

Puerto Barrios, on the Caribbean, and San José and Champerico, on the Pacific. Puerto Barrios is only a four days' sail from New Orleans and five days from New York on the weekly steamers of the United Fruit Company. From the west-coast ports shipping time is six days to San Francisco via the Grace Line's weekly service.

Economy. A narrow gauge railway crosses Guatemala from the Pacific to the Caribbean Coast. It is a section of the International Railways of Central America, a United States company. Originating in the seaport of San José, it penetrates 75 miles through the mountains and plateaus to Guatemala City, and then continues the other 198 miles to Puerto Barrios. A line reaches north from the capital to the Mexican border at Ayulta, 180 miles distant, and there joins with the Mexican railway system. Another line branches south from the main line at Zacapa, to San Salvador in El Salvador, where it joins the system of that nation and makes possible the shipment of Salvadorean products via Puerto Barrios. Fairly good highways of graded dirt or stone radiate from the capital city to other points on the plateau, and motor-truck service is maintained during a considerable part of the year. The eastern part of the country contains navigable streams that support barge and launch traffic.

Guatemala is, primarily, an agricultural country, with more than 70 per cent of its people engaged in farming. The principal export crops are coffee, bananas, chicle, abacá, hardwoods, and vegetable oils. The livestock industry also is important, and serves, principally, domestic demands.

Extensive forests prevail over some 60 per cent of the total area of Guatemala, including such hardwoods as mahogany, lignum vitae, and primavera, and softwoods such as Spanish cedar and balsa.

The Department of Petén, occupying the northern third of the nation, is considered to be Guatemala's greatest potential agricultural land, although at present it is covered largely with dense jungle growth.

Manufacturing is carried on, primarily, for local consumption. The production of textiles and other consumer goods is the leading type of industrial activity.

Approximately 98 per cent of Guatemala's exports consist of farm and forest products, namely, coffee (60 per cent of total export value), bananas, and chicle. About 90 per cent of these are shipped to the United States. Imports are the usual commodities needed by a country that is essentially in an agricultural economy, and include cotton fabrics, yarn, thread, rayon goods, clothing, machinery, tools, petroleum derivatives, chemicals, and others.

In recent years Canada has greatly increased its trade with Guatemala and in Latin America as a whole. Other Western Hemisphere regions trading with Guatemala are Peru, Aruba, Curaçao, and El Salvador.

Exports by ports are as follows: Puerto Barrios (68 per cent), Champerico, San José, Livingston, and others. Imports are received primarily at Puerto Barrios (80 per cent), San José, Champerico, and Livingston.

SELECTED REFERENCES

See Chapter XX.

BRITISH HONDURAS

General characteristics. British Honduras, a crown colony, is located at the northeast corner of Central America. It has an area of 8,867 square miles, including 159 square miles in offshore islands, or *cayos*, and a population estimated in 1946 as 59,000. The colony owes its existence to groups of British from Jamaica who settled on the coast in 1662 for the purpose of extracting mahogany and logwood. Under attacks from the Spanish, these groups tended to assemble along the Belize River, where they finally consolidated their position. Since about 1800 they have been recognized as a settlement of British under the protection of the Crown.

The boundaries of the colony to the north and northwest are limited by Mexico, to the south and west by the Republic of Guatemala. On the east is the Caribbean Sea. In the western part of the territory a number of mountain peaks rise into a chain, from which streams of considerable size descend eastward to the coast. Northward below the mountains is a flat country with many fine areas of grasslands and forests, as well as swamps, lagoons, and sluggish rivers.

The population is composed principally of Jamaica Negroes and Indians who have intermarried both among themselves and with Spanish, Dutch, French, and English adventurers who came in the early days. There may be as many as 2,000 pure English in the colony. The Indians are said to be Mayas and Caribs. The colony embraces what was once a thickly populated part of the Mayan empire, of which many architectural ruins remain.

The principal products of British Honduras are extractions from the forests—mahogany, cedar, chicle, and coconuts. Small quantities of bananas are also exported. Trade is largely with the United Kingdom, although the colony enjoys the maximum freedom in economic matters. The government of the colony realizes the value of its forests and has established a board of conservation that seeks to replant with valuable timber trees the areas which have been exploited.

The capital of the colony is Belize, a city of 16,000 inhabitants situated at the mouth of the river by that name. The coast is subject to tropical storms. In 1932 Belize was practically destroyed by a hurricane, but it

AVERAGE TEMPERATURE AND RAINFALL OF BELIZE, BRITISH HONDURAS

(Elevation, Approximately Sea Level)

	Temperature (°*F.*)	Rainfall (*Inches*)
Period of Record	14 yrs.	22 yrs.
January	74	6.2
February	76	2.3
March	77	1.6
April	79	2.4
May	80	5.2
June	80	7.5
July	80	6.8
August	80	6.6
September	80	10.0
October	78	13.4
November	75	8.9
December	74	7.5
Annual	78	78.4
Range	6	

Source: *United States Weather Bureau Technical Paper No. 8*, United States Weather Bureau, Washington, D. C.

has since been rebuilt. Internal communications are chiefly by coastal steamers, by launches on the rivers, and by pack trail, although the principal population centers are connected by air service, and roads are in process of construction.

SELECTED REFERENCES

See Chapter XX.

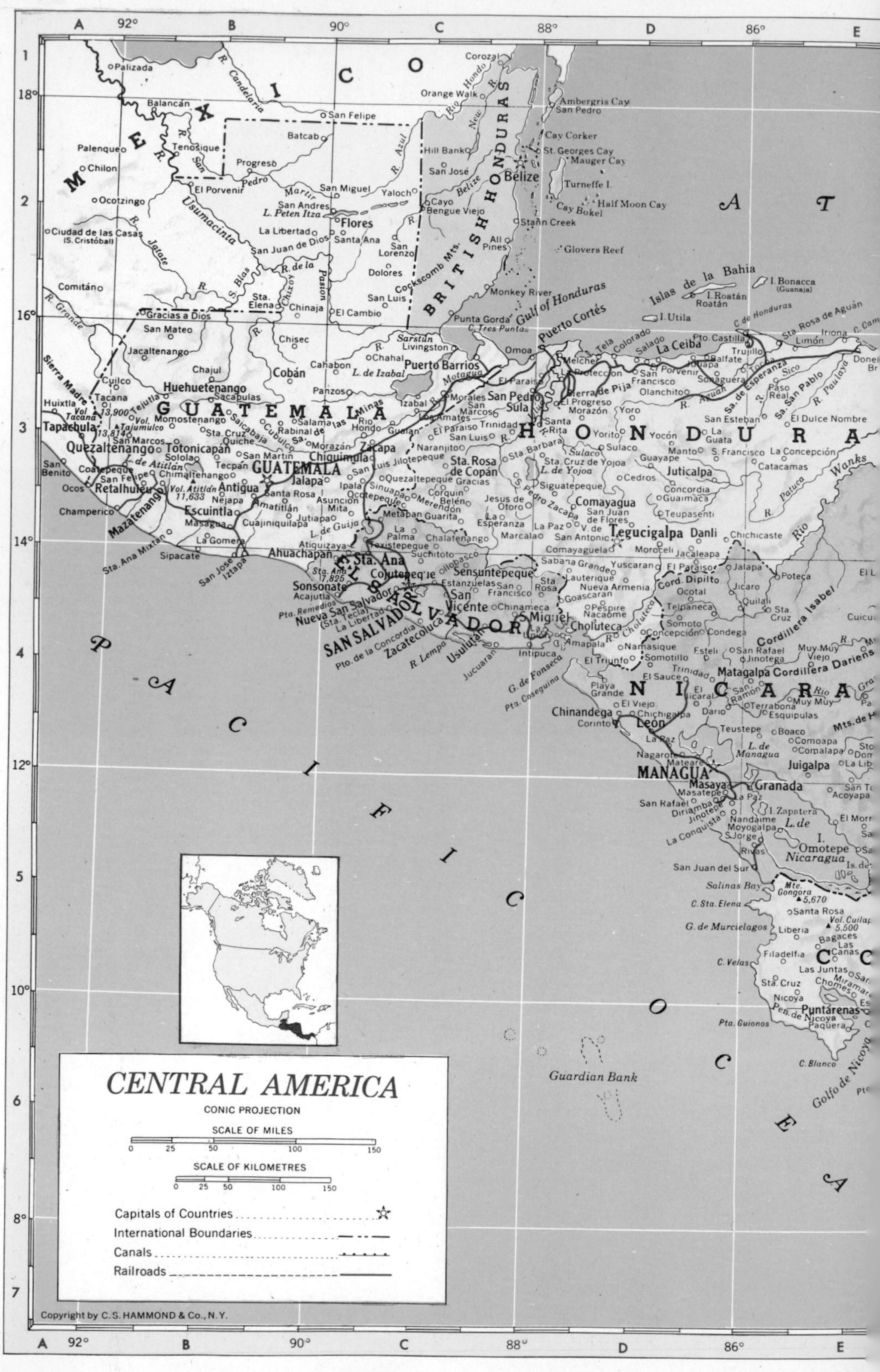
CENTRAL AMERICA
CONIC PROJECTION
SCALE OF MILES
0 25 50 100 150
SCALE OF KILOMETRES
0 25 50 100 150
Capitals of Countries
International Boundaries
Canals
Railroads
Copyright by C.S. HAMMOND & Co., N.Y.
A 92° B 90° C 88° D 86° E
1
18°
2
16°
3
14°
4
12°
5
10°
6
8°
7
MEXICO
GUATEMALA
BRITISH HONDURAS
HONDURAS
EL SALVADOR
NICARAGUA
PACIFIC OCEAN
Palizada
Balancan
R. Candelaria
San Felipe
Corozal
Rio Hondo
New R.
Orange Walk
Ambergris Cay
San Pedro
Cay Corker
St. Georges Cay
Mauger Cay
Belize
Turneffe I.
Half Moon Cay
Cay Bokel
Stann Creek
Glovers Reef
Palenque
Tenosique
Chilon
Batcab
Progreso
R. Azul
Hill Bank
San José
El Porvenir
San Pedro
Martir
San Miguel
Yaloch
Cayo
Bengue Viejo
Ocotzingo
San Andres
L. Peten Itza
Flores
Ciudad de las Casas
(S. Cristóbal)
R. Usumacinta
La Libertad
San Juan de Dios
Santa Ana
San Lorenzo
Dolores
All Pines
R. Jatate
R. de la Pasion
Cockscomb Mts.
Monkey River
Comitán
Sta. Elena
Chinaja
San Luis
El Cambio
Punta Gorda
C. Tres Puntas
Gulf of Honduras
Islas de la Bahia
I. Bonacca
(Guanaja)
I. Roatán
Roatán
I. Utila
Puerto Cortés
R. Grande
Gracias a Dios
San Mateo
Jacaltenango
Chisec
Sarstun
Livingston
Chahal
Cahabon
Puerto Barrios
L. de Izabal
Omoa
Tela
Colorado
Salado
La Ceiba
Pto. Castilla
C. de Honduras
Trujillo
Sta. Rosa de Aguán
Limón
Iriona
Sierra Madre
Chajul
Cobán
Cuilco
Huehuetenango
Sacapulas
Panzos
Izabal
Tacana
Huixtla
Vol. Tacana
13,900
Tejutla
Vol. Tajumulco
13,814
Tapachula
Momostenango
Salama
Rabinal
Minas
Rio Hondo
Morales
San Marcos
San Pedro Sula
El Progreso
Morazán
Yoro
Sierra de Pija
Olanchito
Sonaguera
Balfate
Sa. de Esperanza
Paso Real
Sa. San Pablo
R. Paulaya
San Esteban
El Dulce Nombre
San Marcos
Quezaltenango
Totonicapán
Sta. Cruz
Quiche
Morazán
Zacapa
Gualan
Los Amates
El Paraiso
Trinidad
San Luis
Naranjito
Santa Rita
Yorito
Sulaco
Yocón
La Guata
Manto
S. Francisco
La Concepción
Catacamas
Juticalpa
San Benito
Coatepeque
Sololá
L. de Atitlán
Tecpán
San Martin
Chiquimula
GUATEMALA
Jalapa
Jilotepeque
Sta. Rosa de Copán
Sta. Barbara
Sta. Cruz de Yojoa
L. de Yojoa
Guayape
Cedros
Concordia
Guaimaca
Teupasenti
Ocos
San Felipe
Retalhuleu
Chimaltenango
Vol. Atitlán
11,633
Antigua
Nejapa
Santa Rosa
Ipala
Quezaltepeque
Gracias
Siguatepeque
Comayagua
San Juan de Flores
Champerico
Mazatenango
Escuintla
Amatitlán
Asuncion Mita
Corquin
Belén
Merendón
Jesus de Otoro
Tegucigalpa
Danli
Chichicaste
Masagua
Cuajiniquilapa
Jutiapa
L. de Guija
Metapan
Guarita
La Esperanza
La Paz
Marcala
San Antonio
La Gomera
Sipacate
Sta. Ana Mixtan
San José
Iztapa
Ahuachapán
Atiquizaya
Texistepeque
La Palma
Chalatenango
Suchitoto
Comayaguela
Morocelí
Jacaleapa
Sta. Ana
Sta. Ana
7,825
Sonsonate
Acajutla
Cojutepeque
Sensuntepeque
Sabana Grande
Lauterique
Yuscarán
El Paraiso
Cord. Dipilto
Jalapa
Poteca
Jicaro
Quilali
Sta. Cruz
Cordillera Isabel
Estanzuelas
San Francisco
Sta. Rosa
Nueva Armenia
Goascarán
Ocotal
Pta. Remedios
Nueva San Salvador
(Sta. Tecla)
La Libertad
SAN SALVADOR
San Vicente
Chinameca
S. Miguel
Pespire
Nacaome
Choluteca
Telpaneca
Somoto
Concepción
Condega
Pto. de la Concordia
Zacatecoluca
R. Lempa
Usulutan
Jucuaran
Intipuca
Amapala
Namasique
Estelí
San Rafael
Jinotega
Muy Muy Viejo
Cordillera Dariense
El Triunfo
Somotillo
El Sauce
Trinidad
Matagalpa
G. de Fonseca
Pta. Cosegüina
Playa Grande
El Viejo
San Ramón
El Jicaral
Terrabona
Muy Muy
Esquipulas
Dario
Chinandega
Corinto
Chichigalpa
León
La Paz
Teustepe
Boaco
Comoapa
Comalapa
L. de Managua
Nagarote
Mateare
MANAGUA
Juigalpa
La Libertad
Masaya
Masatepe
Granada
San Rafael
Diriamba
Jinotepe
La Paz
I. Zapatera
Acoyapa
La Conquista
Nandaime
Moyogalpa
S. Jorge
L. de Nicaragua
I. Omotepe
El Morro
Rivas
San Juan del Sur
Salinas Bay
Mte. Gongora
5,670
C. Sta. Elena
Santa Rosa
Vol. Cuilapa
5,500
G. de Murcielagos
Liberia
Bagaces
Las Cañas
Filadelfia
C. Velas
Las Juntas
Sta. Cruz
Chomes
Nicoya
Pen. de Nicoya
Puntarenas
Paquera
Pta. Guiones
C. Blanco
Golfo de Nicoya
Guardian Bank
R. Aguan
Wanks
Rio Patuca
Sico
Mts. de H

JAMAICA
Kingston
Montego Bay
Falmouth
St. Ann's Bay
Port Maria
Annotto Bay
Port Antonio
Ewarton
Savanna la Mar
Black River
Spanish Town
Blue Mountain Pk. 7,388
Morant Point
Portland Point
Walton Bank
Pedro Bank
Pedro Cays (Jamaica)
Morant Cays (Jamaica)
Rosalind Bank
Serranilla Bank
Bajo Nuevo
Cay Gorda
Gorda Bank
Pigeon Cays
Half Moon Reefs
Alargate Reef
Cabo Gracias a Dios
Miskito Cays
Quita Sueño Bank
Serrana Bank
(Claimed by U.S. and Col.)
Puerto Cabezas
Lag. de Karatá
Rio Wawa
Lag. de Wounta
Prinzapolca
Roncador Bank
(Claimed by U.S. and Col.)
I. de Providencia (Col.)
Tyra Cays
King Cays
I. San Andrés (Col.)
Pearl Cays
Little Corn I. (U.S. Lease)
Great Corn I. (U.S. Lease)
Cayos de Albuquerque (Col.)
Bahia de Juan del Norte
Juan del Norte (Greytown)
C A R I B B E A N S E A
O C E A N
Limón
Pta. Blanca
Pta. Cahuita
CANAL ZONE
Colón
Portobelo
Pta. Manzanillo
Miramar
Pta. San Blas
Golfo de San Blas
Archipiélago de las Mulatas
Cristóbal
Gatun L.
Panamá
Balboa
I. Taboga
Cord. de San Blas
Golfo de los Mosquitos
Pen. Valiente
I. de Colón
Bocas del Toro
I. de Bastimentos
Laguna de Chiriqui
Almirante
Escudo de Veragua
Pta. del Rincón
Chiriqui Grande
Vol. Chiriqui 10,991
Boquete
David
Concepción
Puerto Armuelles
Golfo Dulce
Pta. Burica
I. Parida
G. de Chiriqui
Is. Secas
Is. Contreras
Is. Ladrones
I. Coiba
I. Jicarón
G. de Montijo
I. Cebaco
Pta. Mariato
Pen. de Azuero
Tonosio
Pedasi
C. Mala
Morro de Puercos
Las Tablas
Chitre
Santiago
G. de Parita
Golfo de Panamá
ARCH. de las PERLAS
I. San José
I. del Rey
Bahia San Miguel
La Palma
Garachine
Pta. Piñas
Pta. Ardita
Jurado
Golfo de Darién
Golfo de Urabá
Turbo
Nicocli
Acandi
Obaldia
Carreto
C. Tiburón
Pta. Caribana
I. Fuerte
El Real
Riosucio
COLOMBIA
P A N A M A
Greenwich
82° 80° 78° 76°
18° 16° 14° 12° 10° 8°
35120

CHAPTER XXVII

MEXICO

"South of the Border" is the United Mexican States, an American republic rapidly approaching a population of 25,000,000 inhabitants. Its land of infinite diversity in form, culture, and activity embraces an area of 758,258 square miles. You may be one of the several thousands of tourists to have explored the nation's great capital, Mexico, D. F., Xochimilco, the "floating gardens"; the pyramids of San Juan Teotihuacán; the cultural riches of Taxco, Puebla, or the more distant ruins of the Mayan civilization in Yucatán. On your return home, laden with serapes, baskets, and replicas of Aztec culture, what is your impression of Mexico? In all likelihood you will say, "The Mexicans are most interesting people, individualistic, creative, industrious, and patient. They represent many different racial or ethnic groups, who live in villages or small communities. It is certainly a place to return to more than once." While this complimentary answer is not free from qualifications, it is nevertheless a representative characterization of Mexico and its peoples.

A village population. The population of Mexico is today, and always has been, primarily a village population. There are few people living on scattered farms, as in the United States. The workers go to the fields, the mines, and the mills to perform their duties, but at the close of work they return to their homes in villages. This village attraction is not only a Mexican custom but also a Spanish tradition, as shown by the community pattern of Spain. Thus the Spaniards and the Mexican aborigines fused perfectly into the life of the modern Mexican village.

Protection, religion, and government were probably the basis of the early community centers. Along with the development of agriculture, the village became even more completely the center of residences. The large landholdings favored the concentration of workers in definite areas where the overseer might conduct his affairs more effectively than would be possible if the peons were widely distributed over the hacienda. In addition, the aridity of much of the land of Mexico with the scarcity of water for human consumption and agriculture induced a congregation of people in villages. The popular statement that "every Mexican village has its mountain" is in part true. The mountain streams bring water to the dry foothills, the village sites.

The pattern and function of the predominant type of Mexican village have not changed materially from its early characteristics. Somewhere within the village is at least one plaza that in the early days was the geographical center and the most prominent part of the community site. A park provided with shade trees, benches, and a bandstand occupies the center of the plaza. A church built of stone or brick and covered with stucco stands in front of the plaza. On the other sides of the plaza are the municipal offices and private dwellings of size and importance. There are a half dozen streets, some of them unpaved and lined with one-storied adobe or brick buildings, covered with stucco and with tile roofs, that rise directly above the narrow sidewalk. Behind the better houses are spacious *patios*, or yards, with trees and flowers. The street market is the principal trade center. "While the villagers live by agriculture, the village lives by trade."[1]

F. A. Carlson.

Fig. 110. A typical street scene in a small city or village. Orizaba, Mexico. Tiled roofs, one- or two-story stuccoed buildings rising directly from the sidewalk, windows protected by iron gratings, and balconies. The roof projects over the narrow sidewalk and gives protection against the rain or sun.

Ethnic groups. The coming of the Spaniards introduced a new element into the Indo-civilization of early Mexico. To some extent it fused with the culture of the aborigines, and in part it eliminated the civilization of the Indians and established a new culture in its stead. Some of the changes were for the good of the Mexican Indian, while other measures were detrimental. It is true that some of the adventurers were primarily interested in supplying the coffers of Charles V with gold and

[1] Redfield, R.: *Tepoztlan, A Mexican Village,* The University of Chicago Press, Chicago, 1930, p. 19.

silver as well as filling their own strong boxes, but there also were other groups whose benevolence and teachings did much for the Indians. It is sometimes forgotten that the art of the early Mexicans and the artistic qualities of the present Mexican Indians are the result of the instruction of the early Spaniards. The art of colonial Mexico, as viewed today, is comparable if not superior to that of contemporary America or Europe. It is unfortunate that the philosophy of a few of the invaders, whose ambition is found in the quotation, "We have come to get gold, not to till the soil like a peasant," should ring with such lasting reverberations. There is very good reason for believing that the colonial Spaniards of Mexico were not such a bad lot after all and were probably at least as benevolently inclined toward the Indians as were the British colonists of the New England shores.

POPULATION OF PRINCIPAL URBAN CENTERS OF MEXICO *

Mexico, D. F.	1,972,400
Guadalajara	273,400
Monterrey	242,000
Puebla	156,700
Mérida	111,500
Tampico	107,000
Aguascalientes	98,600
San Luis Potosí	94,400
Torreón	75,800
Veracruz	71,700
Saltillo	63,300
Morelia	52,600
Toluca	51,000
Ciudad Juárez	48,800
Orizaba	47,900
Durango	42,400
Querétaro	39,500
Oaxaca	33,200
Guanajuato	28,800
Colima	26,900
Hermosillo	23,700
Campeche	23,300
Zacatecas	21,800
Cuernavaca	17,200
Mazatlán	16,500
Acapulco	9,900
Guaymas	8,800
Manzanillo	6,800
	3,765,900†
Area (Square miles)	758,258

* Population figures are scarcely more than estimates.
† About 15 per cent of a total population of 24,447,649.

During the colonial period very few Spanish women entered Mexico, so that many of the men married Indian women. Thus we have the origin of the mestizo. Since there has been a comparatively small influx of outsiders to Mexico, the mestizos have increased in number and have developed into a distinct group of people. They now constitute half the population of Mexico.

The increase in the numbers of mestizos is shown in the accompanying table. In 1805 the races in Mexico were estimated as follows:

Class	*Numbers*	*Percentage of Total*
Whites	1,000,000	18%
Mestizos	2,000,000	38
Indians	2,500,000	44
	5,500,000	100

In 1910 they were:

Class	*Numbers*	*Percentage of Total*
Whites	1,150,000	7.5%
Mestizos	8,000,000	53
Indians	6,000,000	39.5
	15,150,000	100

Thus, over this period of 105 years the population nearly trebled. The number of whites remained practically stationary; the number of Indians trebled; and there were four times as many mestizos in 1910 as there were in 1805. By now the percentage of whites has undoubtedly diminished further in comparison with the native and mixed stock. It has been estimated that 90 per cent of the people of Mexico are Indians or partly so, including 30 per cent of pure-blooded Indians and 60 per cent mestizos. The remainder of the population consists principally of persons of European descent.

During colonial days Negroes were imported as slaves. Today the Negro type has practically disappeared into the Mexican race. Only occasionally does one see evidences of the black race along the coast of Veracruz and in the Pacific regions of the states of Guerrero and Oaxaca. In the Valley of Mexico there are only a few Negroes.

The economic structure presents most significant contrasts. By far the greater number of the Mexicans live on a low subsistence level, only a few are wealthy, and the middle class, although small at present, is growing. More than two-thirds of the inhabitants are engaged in agriculture.

Physiographic pattern.[2] Mexico's surface forms are extremely complex; it is depicted by high mountains and plateaus, deep valleys or barrancas,

[2] Sánchez, Pedro C.: *Estudio Orogénico de la República Mexicana,* Mexico, D. F., 1929.

steep escarpments, and coastal lowlands of varied width. On the north the land forms are a continuation of those in western United States, while the southern portion of the republic is associated with the lands of Central America. The central part of Mexico is a high plateau, partly without maritime drainage. Two cordilleras enclose this plateau perfectly on the east and west, the Sierra Madre Oriental on the Gulf side and the Sierra Madre Occidental on the Pacific, each separated from the sea by narrow strips of coastal plain. South of the central plateau is another highland region, known as the Sierra Madre del Sur. The most

Courtesy Pedro C. Sánchez, Instituto Panamericano de Geografía e Historia, Mexico, D. F.

Fig. 111. Relief map of Mexico.

prominent lowland is in the peninsula of Yucatán, a natural prolongation of the northern platform of Guatemala. This land extension, separating the Gulf of Mexico from the Caribbean, is a true calcitic formation of horizontal layers with interior slopes. Its shelf extends into the sea below a shallow depth of water (see map, page 386).

Eastern cordillera. The Sierra Madre Oriental is a direct continuation of the highland of Texas; the two come together in the Sierra Guadalupe and the Apaches Mountains. The latter causes the Río Grande—or Río Bravo del Norte, as this international river is known in Mexico—to bend at right angles to cross the range southeast of Presidio, Texas, and the northwestern portion of the state of Coahuila, Mexico. In general, the surface configuration of the Sierra Madre Oriental is one of folded architecture. On the eastward margin are high escarpments. From the international border to about the latitude of Tampico, 300 miles south, the escarpment is steplike and rises to an elevation of some 2,000 feet. The southern and southeastern portion of the escarpment is in the form of a ragged fringe that makes accession very difficult. The western portion of the Sierra Madre Oriental is a series of folds and blocks rising above the Central Plateau.

Western cordillera. The Sierra Madre Occidental, extending in length some 2,000 miles and with a maximum width of 250 miles, is associated with the mountains of southern Arizona. Much of this highland is a tabular volcanic mass that almost completely covers an underlying folded chain. On the west the mountain flanks are clifflike escarpments interrupted by deep canyons. On the east the mountains grade into the features of the Central Plateau.

Central Plateau. The Central Plateau of Mexico is a folded and sunken region, partly filled with water sediment, æolian drift, and volcanic material. It has an average elevation of some 3,000 feet above the sea, being higher to the south, near the large volcanic mountains, and sloping northward. The plateau is very similar to the great central basin of the United States and is evidently its continuation. It is divided into enclosures by longitudinal and transverse ranges, of which the most important is the Valley of Mexico, the site of the nation's capital, Mexico, D. F. The northern portion of *La Altiplanicie,* is known as the northern basin, or *Mesa del Norte.* Its western portion is a region of flat-topped mountains, mesas, and intervening broad, level depressions. In the eastern part the landscape is marked by basinlike hollows known as bolsons. In general, the bolsons are a little below the surface of the surrounding plateau. The southern portion of the central plateau, known as the Mesa Central, rises to an elevation of more than 7,000 feet above the sea. It is a region of volcanic mountains and valleys, some without maritime drainage.

Volcanic zone. On the southern limits of the Central Plateau are a series of transverse cleavages, aligned from west to east and cutting across the east and west cordilleras. Gigantic volcanoes have formed above these dislocations. One may say that this is where North America ends to give way to the entirely different orographic pattern located to the south. Two series of volcanic mountains are characteristic of this east-west zone: first, above the high margins of the plateau are the Volcán Citlaltepetl (18,696 feet), Popocatépetl (17,883 feet), Ajusco (12,956 feet), and Nevado de Toluca (14,950 feet); and the second, at the foot of the immense escarpments, begins with Volcán San Martín Tuxtla (5,084 feet), on the Gulf of Mexico, and continues interruptedly to Colima (14,235 feet), near the Pacific. About midway between the

Central Plateau and the coastal Gulf region is Pico de Orizaba—18,686 feet—the third highest mountain in North America.

Southern cordillera. Facing the volcanic zone, or Eje Volcánico, and south of the Río Balsas, is the Sierra Madre del Sur. It extends in an east-southeasterly direction across the states of Michoacán, Guerrero, Oaxaca, and Chiapas. These mountains have much in common with the Sierra Madre Occidental in having a tabular structure.

Tehuantepec, Yucatán, and coastal lowlands. In the region of the Isthmus of Tehuantepec a low divide separates the broad inland extension of the coastal plain of the Gulf of Mexico from the Pacific. In this Tehuantepec saddle, streams flowing toward the Gulf rise within a few miles of Pacific headstreams. The area as a whole varies from a flat to a slightly undulating terrain dotted with numerous swamps and low hills. A railway crosses the Isthmus from Puerto Mexico to Salina Cruz.

The Yucatán lowlands include much of the northern portion of the peninsula of the same name. This featureless region, rising only a few feet above sea level, is nevertheless one of Mexico's important districts, the site of the sisal and henequén production.

Bordering the Pacific is a narrow coastal plain, interrupted by numerous valleys, lagoons, and offshore bars. On the eastern side of the country the coastal plains are much more extensive and reach from a few miles to more than 100 miles from the Gulf. Inland the coastal plains merge with the lofty escarpments of the eastern cordillera.

Hydrography. Few of the rivers of Mexico are of any importance for navigation. Their chief value is to supply water for irrigation and energy for the generation of hydroelectric power. Both functions are of considerable significance because of the deficiency of rainfall and its seasonality in many regions of the republic, and because of the scarcity of fuel. Among the principal rivers are the Río Grande, or Río Bravo del Norte (1,500 miles), which carries the international boundary between the United States and Mexico from El Paso to the Gulf of Mexico. Two other major rivers are the Río Lerma (540 miles) and the Río Balsas (426 miles). The Río Lerma begins in the swamps of the upper Lerma Valley, about 30 miles from Mexico, D. F. (Distrito Federal), in the state of Mexico, and flows westward to Lake Chapala. From Lake Chapala, the drainage continues north and then west to the Pacific Ocean as the Río Grande de Santiago. It marks the southern extremity of the Sierra Madre Occidental. The Río Balsas, like the Río Lerma, has an east-west course to the Pacific Ocean, and in part it forms a natural division between the volcanic zone and the Sierra Madre del Sur. In its lower course it is known as Río Mexcala. Not far from the headstreams of the Río Lerma rise the headstreams of the Río Pánuco, which flows eastward to the Gulf of Mexico near Tampico, the well-known oil city of Mexico. In the

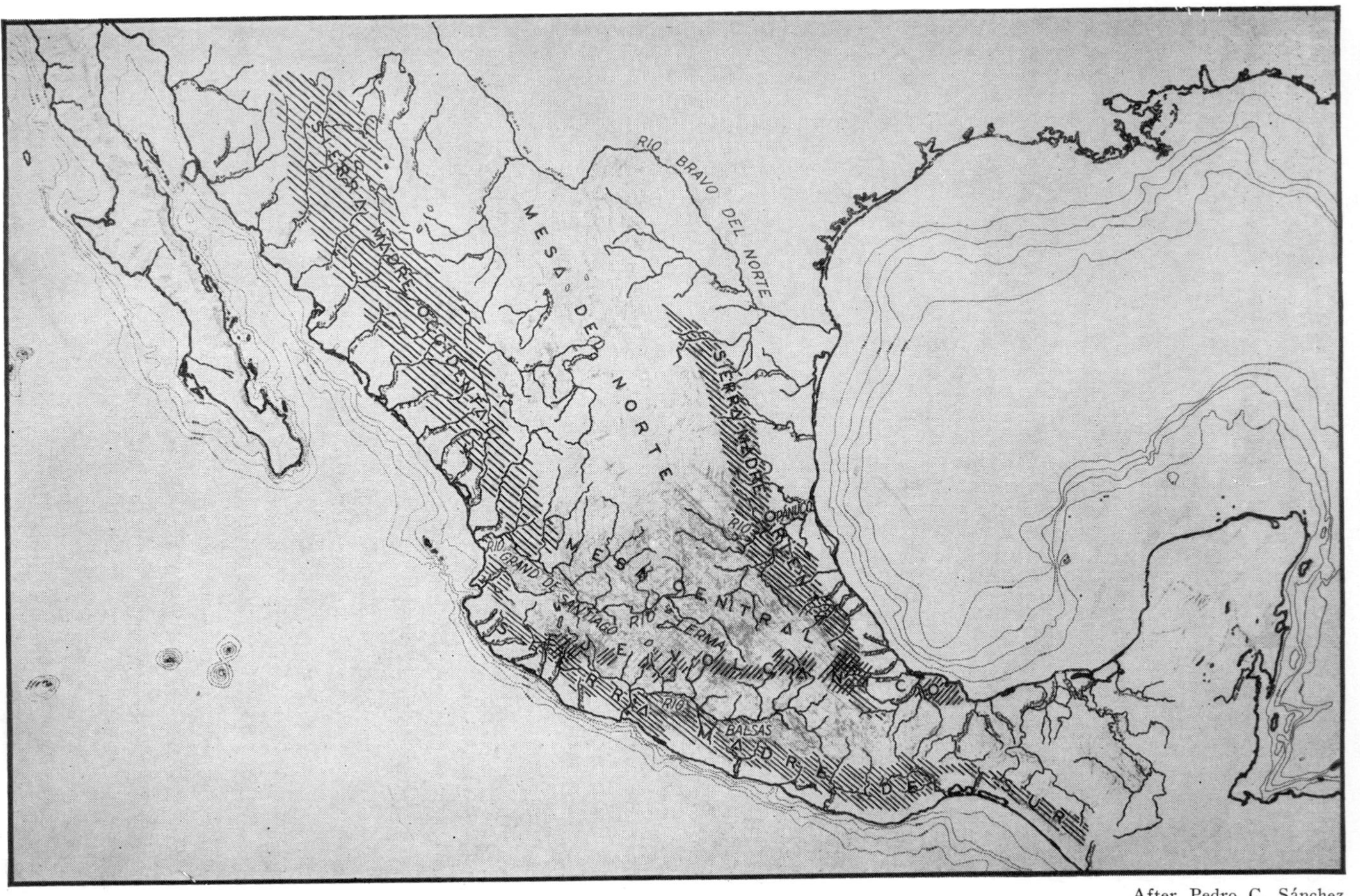

After Pedro C. Sánchez.

Fig. 112. Mexico's physiographic pattern.

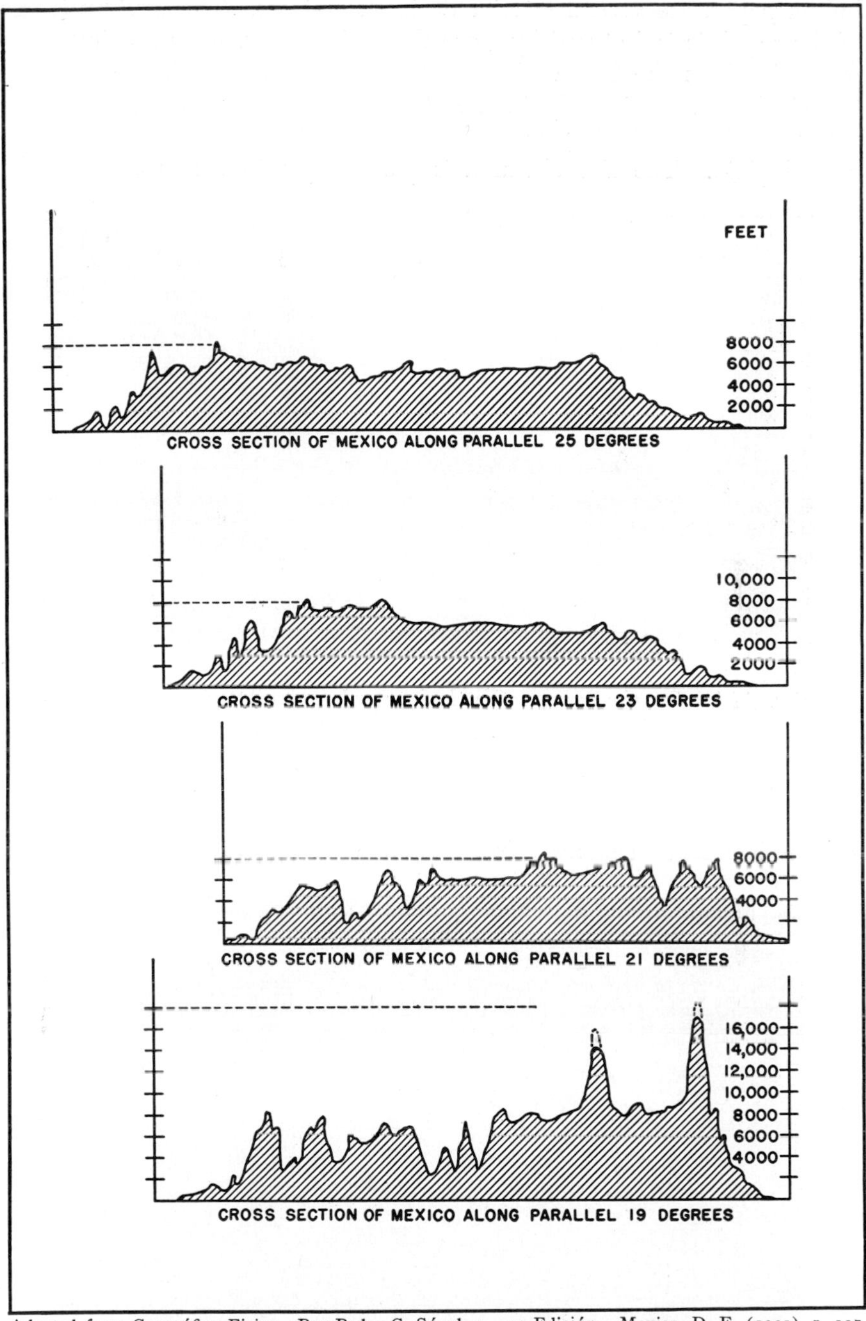

Adapted from Geográfica Fisica—Por Pedro C. Sánchez. 3a Edición. Mexico, D. F. (1931), p. 117.

Fig. 113. Profiles along given parallels, Mexico.

bolson region are several interior drainage systems. The western fringe of the republic is featured by more than 25 streams, some flowing intermittently, from the Sierra Madre Occidental to the Pacific Ocean. On the Gulf side, particularly in the states of Veracruz and Tabasco, are many streams beginning on the highland and cutting across the Gulf coastal plain. The Yucatán area is practically without surface streams

Courtesy H. C. Shetrone.

Fig. 114. On the snow-covered slopes of Ixtaccíhuatl—elevation approximately 16,000 feet above sea level—Mexico.

because of its extremely soluble limestone. An extensive subterranean system exists in this region, and there is a development of sink holes, known locally as *cenotes*. In the Chiapas region is one river system

F. A. Carlson.

Fig. 115. A region of heavy rainfall near Orizaba, Mexico. An Indian hut in the midst of coffee and banana trees.

worthy of note: the Río Grijalva, its tributaries and headstreams flowing into the Golfo de Campeche. The largest lake of Mexico is Lake Chapala, on the boundary line between the states of Jalisco and Michoacán. It is about 70 miles long and 20 miles wide. In the state of Veracruz is the Tamiahua Lagoon, some 60 miles long and 10 miles wide at its maximum. It is used by small vessels en route between Tampico and Tuxpan. In Tamaulipas is another extensive lagoon, the Madre, which continues northward interruptedly to Galveston, Texas.

Temperature and rainfall. Because Mexico lies south of the United States, in the low latitudes, one is inclined to think of her climate as

Courtesy H. C. Shetrone.

Fig. 116. An upland forest and meadow, en route from Mexico, D. F., to Cholula. A Mexican "cowboy" (8 years old) and his "cow-pony" (a ram). Under the folds of his serape he is carrying a lamb.

being hot; but we are reminded that latitude alone does not determine climatic conditions. Other factors must also be considered, such as altitude, nearness to water, atmospheric pressure, rainfall, and ocean currents. One of the most influential determining factors in the temperature of Mexico is altitude, for much of the country comprises high plateaus, ranging from 1,000 to 7,000 feet above the sea, and lofty mountains and peaks.

In general, we may think of Mexico as having three distinct thermal regions: (1) the *tierra caliente,* or hot lands along the coast, to an elevation of about 2,000 feet; (2) the *tierra templada,* or temperate lands extending from 2,000 feet to 6,000 feet; and (3) the *tierra fría*, or cold region rising from 6,000 feet upward. These regions are not constant. Occasional atmospheric disturbances may bring about a marked change in temperature. For example, from November through March, severe winds known as "northers" sweep the coast of the Gulf of Mexico periodically and cause a drop of 40 to 50 degrees. Also, in the dry northern portions of Mexico there is a marked range in temperature between the summer and winter months. On the high portions of the Central Plateau, the temperature is characteristically uniform; it averages from 50 to 70 degrees throughout the year.

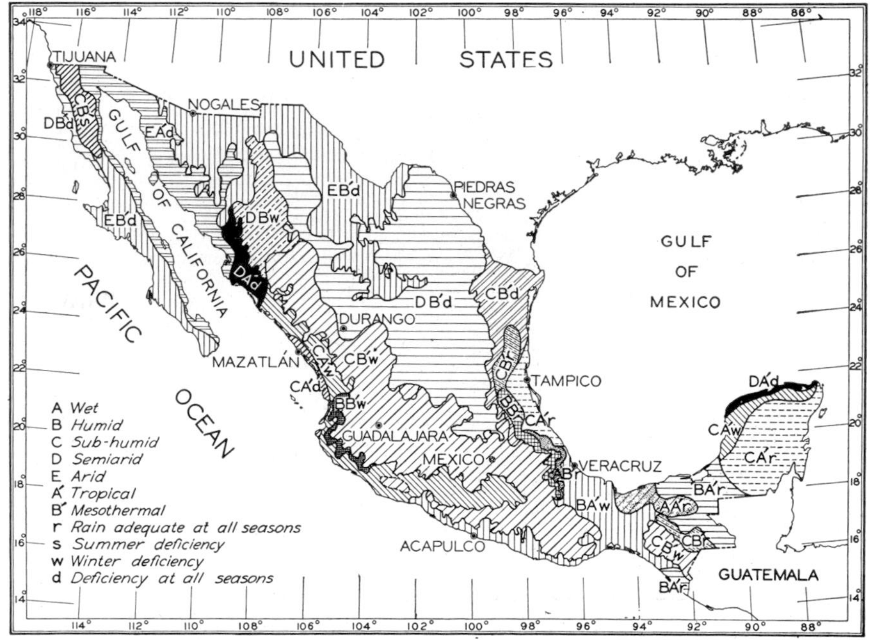

After C. Warren Thornthwaite and others.

Fig. 117. Climates of Mexico. (Example: DA′d indicates semiarid tropical climate with deficiency of moisture at all seasons, as on the northern coast of Yucatán.)

Mexico reveals a wide variation in amount of rainfall and seasonal distribution. Average annual rainfall varies from 2 inches in Sonora to 185 inches in the tropical lowlands of Tabasco. With the exception of the northwestern portion of Lower California, where winter rains occur, the major portion of the precipitation in Mexico falls during the summer seasons. The northwest has winter rains because it comes under the influence of the prevailing westerlies during the winter months, while during the summer months it falls within the dry subtropical belt of high pressure, owing to the migration of the wind belts according to the apparent north-south motion of the sun. North central and northeastern Mexico is a region of slight rainfall because it comes primarily within the subtropical high-pressure zone at all seasons. The northern tip of Yucatán peninsula is tropical, with a deficiency of rain throughout the year. From southwestern Yucatán, and extending along the shores of the Gulf of Campeche, in the vicinity of Veracruz, is an area having adequate rainfall at all seasons. This regularity of rainfall is attributed to northeasterly winds from the Gulf of Mexico and to the decreasing westward barometric gradient. Northward from Veracruz rainfall diminishes in amount but retains its uniform seasonal distribution as far north as Tampico.

The southern portion of the Central Plateau, like most of Mexico, is characterized by summer rainfall, much of it coming during the months of May, June, July, August, and September. Summer rainfall is heavy enough, but the lack of winter rain is a serious difficulty. We are now considering a region that receives from 20 to 25 inches of rainfall annually. It is in this region that less fluctuation is shown for the rainy months than in any other part of the country, the rain being known to fall for 20 days of the month during the rainy months. This region comes under the influence of the trades in summer and the subtropical high-pressure belt in winter. It is during the apparent tour of the sun north that this section is brought within a season of rain. It is in this region that the land, the temperature, and even the rainfall seem to come nearest to helping the Mexican solve his living problems; and it is within this section that more cities appear, and their people show more progress. In fact, this is the real Mexico. But the temperature and rainfall are not ideal, at best. If Mexico could have a better distribution of her rainfall for more months of the year, it would be able to produce more for its people.

SOCIAL AND ECONOMIC AFFAIRS

Agrarian problems. The struggle for land in Mexico is one of long standing. With the Spanish conquest and subsequent depression of the Indian races, feudal estates were organized with Spanish overlords. The peasantry became the slaves of these wealthy domineering invaders. Particularly under the Diaz regime, communal lands of the ejidos were taken over by the hacendados. Until recently this situation had not materially changed.

Under the Spanish sovereign, land concessions were enormous. Vast land grants were given to individuals and groups. As late as 1910, 96 per cent of the rural families owned no land. Furthermore, in 1910, approximately two-thirds of all wealth, resources, and capital belonged to foreigners. But in the past decade Mexico has declared a policy of nationalism, "To keep Mexico for Mexicans and make the Mexicans fit for Mexico." A six-year plan for the period 1934–1940 was instituted by the Mexican National Revolutionary Government, which gave much serious attention to the land problem.[3] The plan has been continued, and more than 50,000,000 acres of land had been expropriated by the government and distributed among 1,500,000 ejidos. This land represents not only that taken from the hacendados but also land taken from foreigners. Former President Cardenas once stated: "We want fewer Indians and more Mexicans."

Courtesy Ben F. Lemert.

Fig. 118. Mexico: Most of the crop land of Mexico must be irrigated. The water supply, both well and stream, diminishes year by year.

The government's policy seems to include greater control over industry and, among many other issues, to accelerate the distribution of agrarian lands. The party in power declares that the chief social problem of Mexico is, without a doubt, the one relative to distribution of lands and their development from a national point of view, connected with the social and economic liberation of farmers. Therefore, the party undoubtedly will continue the struggle of converting the farmers into free and property-owning agriculturists and of enabling them to obtain and enjoy the harvest of their labor. The party realizes that it cannot achieve the social and economic betterment of Mexican farmers solely by providing them with lands; it must also organize agricultural production generally, in order to qualify economically those who work the lands to reap the benefits from them.[4]

Agricultural resources. The agriculture of Mexico is conducted for the

---

[3] "The Mexican Government's Six-Year Plan 1934–1940," *Mexican-American Commerce,* Vol. II, No. 8 (1934), pp. 3–13.

[4] Agrarian Code of the United Mexican States. Translation from the *Diario Oficial* of April 12, 1934—Mexico.

most part under exceedingly adverse physical circumstances. The supply of water is, in general, not sufficient for crop production except by irrigation. In some regions the opposite is true—that is, there is an overabundance of rainfall. Furthermore, the land is broken by mountain ranges, hills, and valleys into rather small regions that are not physiographically suited for large-scale farming. Probably less than 25 per cent of the total area of Mexico is arable—that is, land suited for cultivation—and less than half of this amount can be turned to intensive agricultural use.

The latest available information on the distribution of Mexico's agricultural land follows. The total agricultural land in hectares (2.47 acres)—129,410,076—is classified as

Pasture	43.5	Per Cent
Forest	29.9	" "
Crop	11.5	" "
Agriculturally unproductive	8.4	" "
Productive uncultivated	6.6	" "
	100.0	

In a recent report it was estimated that there are about 14 million cattle, 6 million swine, 5 million sheep, and over 5 million goats in Mexico. The sheep and cattle are found in the States bordering the United States and in the southern portion of the Central Plateau and mountain slopes, while the goats are raised in the drier lands of Nuevo León, San Luis Potosí, and Coahuila.

The cultivated plants of Mexico present a great diversity of products ranging from wheat and corn on the plateau to tropical fruits on the coastal slopes and plains. Along the seaward slopes of the Sierra Madres, particularly in the vicinity of Córdoba, are grown coffee, oranges, bananas, tobacco, sugar cane, mangoes, and pineapples. Corn, the most important grain for domestic use, is extensively grown throughout the southern portion of the Central Plateau and associated slopes and valleys. Kidney beans, known locally as *frijoles*, are another staple. They are grown primarily in the central part of Mexico, south of 21° N. latitude. Most of the wheat is produced in the areas of Coahuila, Sonora, Guanajuato, Michoacán, and Chihuahua. Rice production centers in Sonora, Colima, Morelos, and Veracruz. Cotton is grown, mostly by irrigation, in Coahuila, Durango, and in the Imperial Valley of Mexico. Tomatoes, one of the leading export crops, and other winter vegetables are grown extensively in the valleys along the western coast of the Gulf of Lower California and in areas along the international border of the United States and Mexico, mainly in the states of Sonora, Sinaloa, and Tamaulipas. In the Yucatán area the production of sisal and henequén is the leading agricultural industry. Chicle, a crude gum derived from the Sapodilla tree, is another important product from the southeast and the Yucatán peninsula. During World War II Mexico was one of the leading banana exporters. Most of the plantations are in the southern and coastal states, including Tabasco, Oaxaca, Veracruz, Michoacán, and Chiapas.

While Mexico is not rich in agricultural resources, she possesses an enormous store of human energy in her large rural population. Over 70

Courtesy Ben F. Lemert.

Fig. 119. Mexico: Farming in southern Coahuila, elevation about 4,000 feet. The irrigation water comes from the mountain range in the far background. Except where irrigated, the land produces scant xerophytic vegetation. Daily temperature in summer varies between 50 and 100 degrees, Fahrenheit. For the most part the crops are corn, wheat, grapes, tomatoes, and beans.

per cent of Mexico's inhabitants live in rural communities and gain their livelihood primarily from the "soil." Mexico is capable, under proper guidance, of producing a far greater percentage of the agricultural products needed for domestic consumption than is the case today. It has already made progress in overcoming deficiencies in corn, sugar, and rice, and in the near future hopes to become self-sufficient in wheat.

Mineral resources. Mexico has been one of the leading mineral-producing lands for more than four centuries. Silver, gold, lead, zinc, copper, and petroleum constitute about 50 per cent of her total exports. Other important minerals produced in Mexico are coal, iron, mercury, antimony, arsenic, graphite, tin, and cadmium. In world production

Mexico ranks high in silver, petroleum, and lead; first in the production of silver; third or fourth in lead; and sixth in petroleum.

The mineral districts of Mexico, excluding the petroleum area, roughly comprise the regions of the Sierra Madres and their associated uplands. Pachuca, in the state of Hidalgo, is the largest silver-producing district of Mexico. However, there are hundreds of other silver mines scattered over the country.

The leading lead mines are found in the state of Chihuahua. Formerly the lead ore was sent to New Jersey to be refined, but now most of it is refined at Monterrey. Mexico is the most important foreign source of the United States' imports of lead. In Sonora, about 40 miles southwest of Bisbee, Arizona, lies the Cananea copper district, one of the leading

Courtesy H. A. Radzikowski and Pan American Union.

Fig. 120. The Inter-American Highway about 120 miles north of Mexico, D. F.

copper-producing areas of Mexico. The second most important copper region is on the east coast of Lower California, near Santa Rosalía, the exporting center. The gold output is largely a by-product of silver, copper, and other mines. During the 1930 decade, the period of commercial, industrial, and financial depression, the mining activities of Mexico were in a stage of semi-stagnation although at present there is a marked increase in the mineral industry. But at no time has the social value of mineral resources of Mexico equalled the social value of the agricultural resources.

Silver production. Since the Spanish conquest Mexico has produced 35 per cent of all mined silver, and annually her output of silver is about 40 per cent of the total world production. Practically all of Mexico's silver is exported to the United States, where a price has been paid for silver at a rate generally higher than the world market price, owing to the well-known Silver Purchase Act of 1934. This maintenance of a high price for silver has materially aided Mexico because silver mining has contributed greatly to the tax revenues of the Mexican government. Furthermore, since the bulk of silver mined in Mexico is associated with zinc, lead, and copper, the income for silver has somewhat increased the production of these basic metals. The production of the principal metallic minerals in Mexico—1948—in order of importance based on value is: lead, zinc, silver, copper, gold, and antimony.

Petroleum industry. For more than 50 years Mexico has been one of the leading petroleum-producing countries of the world. The climax of this period occurred in 1921, with a production of more than 193,000,000 barrels, when several petroleum companies brought in gushers in the famous regions of Tampico and Tuxpan, in the state of Veracruz. Since 1921 the production of petroleum in Mexico has declined, until now she occupies sixth place in world production and second in Latin America and produces about one-third of her peak amount in 1921, or a total of about 70 million barrels in 1950.

The oil fields of Mexico are situated, for the most part, in the coastal lowlands, including the southern portion of the state of Tamaulipas, through Veracruz, eastern San Luis Potosí, and Tabasco. The most important producing areas are in the vicinity of Tampico and Tuxpan. Other active fields are located in southern Veracruz, near the port of Puerto Mexico. Another area that has not yet been exploited commercially is situated in the state of Tabasco.

Nearly all of the refineries in Mexico are on the Gulf Coast. One refinery that is not on the coast is located at Atzcapotzalco, a suburb of Mexico, D. F. This plant receives its petroleum from the Tampico district through a pipe line about 140 miles in length, the oil being pumped from near sea level to an elevation of over 7,000 feet by a system of electric pumping stations. The total length of Mexico's pipe lines for delivery of oil and gas is 3,140 miles.

The petroleum industry, with unimportant exceptions, is operated by the government owned "Petroleos Mexicanos." Oil fields and refineries are under the control of the PEMEX. Mexico exports some crude and petroleum products, but also imports fairly large quantities of refined petroleum products. Recently, American companies have been contracted to return to Mexico for exploration and drilling in search of petroleum.

Transportation situation. Until recently Mexico was a country of trails and unimproved roads. Even now the rural areas are for the most part without adequate transportation facilities. Surface irregularities, absence of navigable rivers, vast areas of marginal land too dry or too wet for occupancy, and scattered agricultural and mineral resources have retarded the development of transportation. However, nearly all cities have paved streets and short radii of hard-surfaced highways projecting a few miles beyond the civic center, and in a few cases extending to nearby cities. The urgent necessity is to further the development of interurban communication by good highways. To a limited extent this objective has been accomplished with respect to Mexico, D. F., from which radiate modern highways to the adjacent cities of Puebla, Pachuca, Toluca, Cuernavaca; the Pacific ports Acapulco and Mazatlán; Veracruz, Tampico and other ports on the Gulf; southward to towns beyond Oaxaca; and Brownsville, Laredo, Eagle Pass, and El Paso in the United

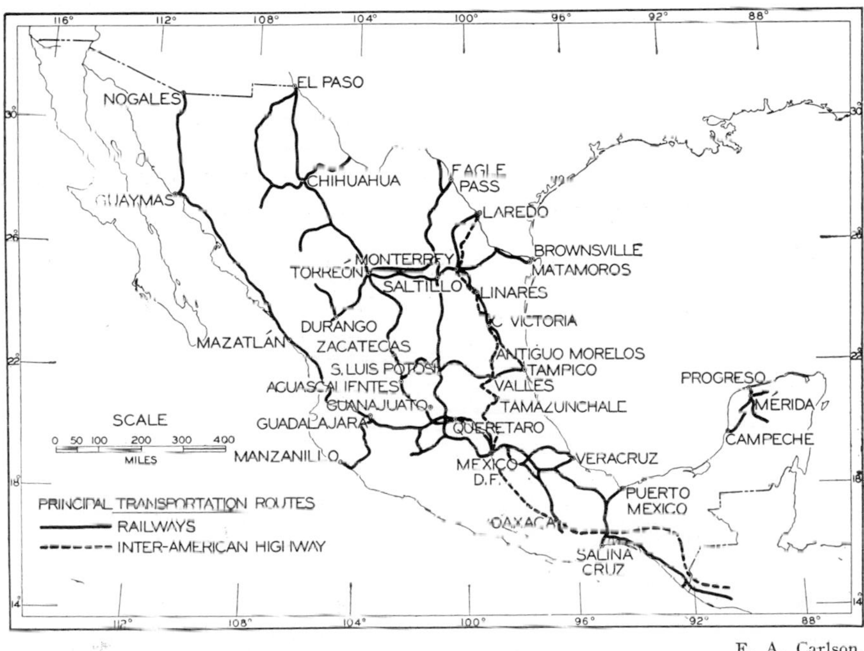

F. A. Carlson.

Fig. 121. Principal land routes of Mexico.

States. Mexico, D. F., also has railway connections with the important coastal, interior, and border towns. Three major railways join Mexico, D. F., and the United States, the border crossings being at Laredo, El Paso, and Nogales.

The most closely watched development of transportation in Mexico, if not in all America, is the Pan-American Highway plan, which calls for the construction of 3,267 miles of motor highway to connect the United States, Mexico, and the Central American republics. One of the routes chosen in Mexico is through Nuevo Laredo, Monterrey, Victoria, Jacala, and Mexico, D. F. From the capital the highway will continue southward through Central America to Panama City and finally on to Buenos

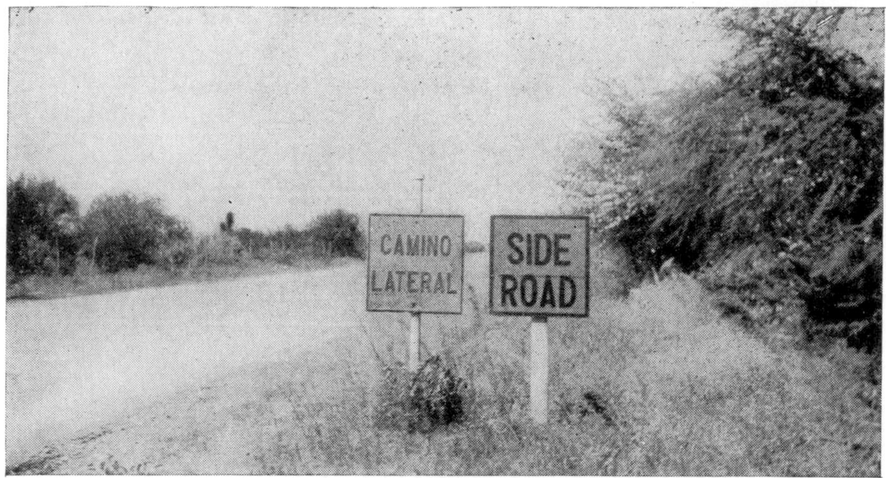

Courtesy H. A. Radzikowski and Pan American Union.

Fig. 122. Inter-American Highway caution signs.

F. A. Carlson.

Fig. 123. En route to Orizaba from their mountain homes, Mexico. In the country and to some extent in the cities, the Mexican dress is distinctively native, having changed very little during the past century. The men wear white cotton trousers, a blouse, and a wide-brimmed straw hat or sombrero. They often go barefooted, but more often wear crude sandals. For protection against cold or rain the men use a blanket-like wrap called a serape. The women wear a white waist and a skirt, ankle-length and very full, fashioned out of one piece of cloth several yards in length. The women do not wear sandals except when walking a long distance. A shawl, or rebozo, is worn over the head or shoulders or may be used as a carrier for the baby, wood, fruit, and the like. A necklace of bright-colored beads or seeds usually completes their dress.

Aires in South America. The portion from the United States to Mexico, D. F., southward to Oaxaca and on to the border of Guatemala, is now open for transportation. Another main highway extends from the border towns El Paso, United States and Ciudad Juárez, Mexico to Mexico, D. F. via Durango, Aguascalientes, and Querétaro. A third international highway has been proposed for western United States and Mexico, to extend southward from Nogales in the state of Sonora, on the American border, to the Guatemalan border.

The principal railways are Laredo–Mexico; Ciudad Juárez–Mexico; Mexico–Veracruz; Mexico–Jalapa–Veracruz; Veracruz–Suchiate, the latter terminus on the Guatemalan border; and the privately operated Southern-Pacific Railway of Mexico, running between Guadalajara and Nogales. The majority of the railways in Mexico are operated by a government agency, the National Railways of Mexico (Ferrocarriles Nacionales de México).

Mexico is adequately served by domestic and international air lines. There are no important navigable rivers within its borders.

Industry. Nearly half of Mexico's manufacturing is concentrated in the Federal District and adjacent territory. Other important industrial centers are: Monterrey–iron and steel, glass, beverages, textiles, furniture, matches, chemicals, enamelware, incandescent lamps, and paper products; Puebla–textiles, railway equipment, cement tiles, ceramics, and railway equipment; León–shoes, clothing, textiles; Guadalajara–iron and steel, textiles, shoes, soap, bricks, tiles, pottery, and glassware; San Luis Potosí–fiber products, leather, soap, flour, beverages; Mérida–cordage. Native handicrafts, including leather goods, silver, fiber, and pottery, are known in many parts of Mexico.

Foreign trade. Mexico exports, primarily, crude and semiprocessed material and imports capital and consumer goods. In 1948 the principal exports were:

	Percentage of Total
Vegetable products	25.3
Common metals	23.9
Foodstuffs, beverages, tobaccos, and products of the chemical industry	11.3
Fuels and derivatives	9.4
Animal products	8.5
Yarn, cloth, felt and manufactures	6.6
Precious metals and coins	5.5
Mineral products	5.0
Securities, arms, explosives, and miscellaneous	2.1
Miscellaneous products	2.3

About 85 per cent of Mexico's total imports were supplied by the United States and some 75 per cent of its exports were shipped to the United States 1948. Among the other countries trading with Mexico are United Kingdom, Canada, Switzerland, and Sweden. If economic conditions in Europe improve it is likely that Germany, France, the Netherlands, and Belgium will become more active in the Mexican trade.

MEXICO: FOREIGN TRADE

	Total Value	*Percentage of Total*					
	(000 Dollars)	United		Latin	United	Continental	All
Exports		States	Canada	America	Kingdom	Europe	Others
1938	195,871	67.4		0.8	9.4	20.0	2.3
1947	443,093	77.0	0.1	9.2	1.8	5.4	6.6
Imports							
1938	115,475	57.7	1.0	0.7	4.1	33.7	2.8
1947	665,441	88.4	1.4	1.2	2.0	5.8	1.2

Exports by customhouses based on value are as follows: Nuevo Laredo, Tampico, Veracruz, Ciudad Juárez, Matamoros, Tuxpan, Progreso, Nogales, Piedras Negras, Puerto Mexico, Campeche, Santa Rosalía, Mexicali, Mazatlán, Tijuana, and others. The leading import centers, arranged according to importance based on value, are: Veracruz, Puerto Mexico, Nuevo Laredo, Tampico, Ciudad Juárez, Manzanillo, Nogales, Piedras Negras, Progreso, Matamoros, and Mazatlán.

Regional characteristics. Mexico's cultural regions will be discussed in the next chapter; emphasis is on the association of natural and cultural features in each region. Students should supplement the text material with extensive collateral reading. This recommendation applies not only to the study of Mexico, but also to the study of each of the Americas.

SELECTED REFERENCES

See Chapter XXVIII.

CHAPTER XXVIII

MEXICO: REGIONS AND CULTURAL CENTERS

VALLEY OF MEXICO

The national focus. For many centuries, the Valley of Mexico has been a social, economic, and political focus of major importance. Within its limits are the pyramids of San Juan Teotihuacán, evidence of an archaic cultural center; the ruins of Tenochtítlan, the capital of the Aztec empire; and Mexico, D. F., the capital of the republic. How many inhabitants occupied the valley in early days is not known. Today the total number of inhabitants in the valley is over 2 million, or approximately 8 per cent of the population of Mexico. That this classic valley should per-

Courtesy Pedro C. Sánchez, Instituto Panamericano de Geografía e Historia, Mexico, D. F.

Fig. 124. The Valley of Mexico.

petuate its dynamic properties, as a cultural center, and not suffer the fate of decadence of Yucatán, the site of the notable Mayan civilization, can be largely attributed to regional features.

Regional delineation. The Valley of Mexico, or the Anahuac Plateau, as this region is also known, is an interior basin almost completely surrounded by highlands. It is located in the southeastern portion of the Central Plateau of Mexico, at an average elevation of 7,238 feet above sea level. Morphologically it is not a rare phenomenon, similar basins being found elsewhere, such as the Sayula Valley in the state of Jalisco,

Mexico; the Pampo Aullagas and Titicaca depressions in Bolivia; and the renowned valley of the Jordan River in Palestine.[1]

The completeness with which the Valley of Mexico is surrounded by mountains is one of its most distinctive features. Toward the north the valley is limited by the Pachuca Mountains and associated hills, formations of Mesozoic limestone, quartz porphyry, and andesite. In general, these highlands are comparatively low in elevation and offer ready accession through natural passes. To the east the valley is bordered by high mountains extending discontinuously from the Pachuca Mountains to the north to the snow-covered Popocatépetl to the south,

Courtesy H. C. Shetrone.

Fig. 125. The east-central portion of the Valley of Mexico—the environs of the pyramids of San Juan Teotihuacán. In the background is the Temple of Quetzalcoatl—a quadrangular court with its four main axes oriented toward the four points of the compass. Within the court are platforms, pyramids, and other monuments of the works of early Americans.

the latter reaching more than 17,000 feet above the sea. The highland lying between the Valley of Mexico and the more eastern valley, Puebla, is commonly called the Sierra Nevada. To these mountains belong the volcanic ranges and cones, the Ixtaccíhuatl, the Telapón, the Tláloc, and the Tlamacas. They form a perfect barrier for more than 20 miles between the Valley of Mexico and the east. To the south, the valley is margined by a portion of the Eje Volcánico, of which the Ajusco Mountain, rising to an elevation of more than 12,000 feet above sea level, is a

[1] The term "Valley" of Mexico is used as a place name. However, physiographically, it is incorrect since the region is not a valley but an interrupted closed basin.

Courtesy H. C. Shetrone.

Fig. 126. The Pyramid of the Sun, San Juan Teotihuacán, is a truncated structure, 216 feet high by about 721 and 761 feet at the base. Its summit is about 59 by 105 feet.

Courtesy H. C. Shetrone.

Fig. 127. The Pyramid of the Moon is about 151 feet high, with a base of 426 feet by 511 feet and a summit about 19 feet square.

part. To the west of the valley is another mountain range, beginning in the Ajusco and including, from south to north, Sierra de las Cruces, Monte Alto, Monte Bajo, Sierra de Tepotznmotlan, and Cerro de Sincoque, all of andesitic rocks.

Surface features. An elliptical contour marks the general outline of the Valley of Mexico, with the longer axis extending north and south and the shorter one east and west. The area is 1,700 square miles. This broad basin, formed by tectonic movements, is partly filled with alluvial, æolian, and volcanic material. Its comparatively level surface is interrupted by numerous hills, largely the summits of partly buried volcanic

Courtesy H. C. Shetrone.

Fig. 128. Details of decorations on wall of the Temple of Quetzalcoatl, showing the plumed or feathered serpents.

masses. On the west-central margin of the valley stands the Sierra de Guadalupe, which connects through the Cuesta de Barrientos with the Monte Bajo to the west. Northeast of the Sierra de Guadalupe is another volcanic hill, the Cerro Chiconautla. These two mountains almost completely divide the valley into two parts, northern and southern. In the southwestern portion of the valley is an extensive basaltic lava formation known as the Pedregal, or bad lands. It covers an area of some 12 square miles and varies in depth from a few feet to more than 50 feet. Under the edges of the lava flow human bones and pottery have been found; this indicates that its origin was at least in part within historical times. Among other conspicuous formations in the valley are the hills of Chapultepec, the site of the famous castle of Chapultepec.

Approximately one-sixth of the total area of the valley is occupied by lakes and reclaimed lake beds. In the northern portion of the valley are Lago de Zumpango, Antiguos Lagos de Zaltócan, and San Cristóbal, while in the southern portion are found Lago Texcoco, Antiguos Lagos de Xochimilco, and Chalco. Formerly these lakes were much larger, and in prehistoric times they occupied much of the valley as one lake. Today Lake Zumpango is confined to a definite basin by means of a retaining wall on the south and by elevated land on the other sides. Lakes Zaltócan and San Cristóbal have been drained, and the reclaimed beds are

Courtesy H. C. Shetrone.

Fig. 129. Beneath the ancient lava flow, 20 feet thick, at the Pedregal, south of Mexico, D. F., are found human skeletons, relics, and remains of houses.

used for pastoral purposes. The basin of Lake Texcoco, which is only partly filled with water, is the largest in the valley, with an area of about 160 square miles. It occupies the lowest portion of the valley, some 10 feet below the level of the other lakes. It is further distinctive in having water of high saline content. The reclaimed lake bed, Chalco, with an area of 38 square miles, is intensively used for agriculture. Lake Xochimilco is probably best known because of its so-called floating gardens. For many years the natives have been digging muck from the lake bed and adding it to the many insular plats. In fact, the entire lake, which covers an area of 40 square miles, is a network of canals and

MEXICO: TEMPERATURE AND RAINFALL OF SELECTED STATIONS IN THE VALLEY OF MEXICO, ADJACENT VALLEYS, AND EASTERN MEXICO

Station	Pachuca, Hgo.*	Teoti-huacán, Mex.*	Tacubaya, D. F.*	Mexico, D. F.†	Xochimil-co, D. F.*	Desierto de los Leones, D. F.*	Cuerna-vaca Mor.*	Toluca, Mex.*	Puebla, Pue.*	Orizaba, Ver.*	Córdoba Ver.*	Veracruz, Ver.*
Elevation (*Feet*)	7,959.3	7,447.5	7,575.4	7,411	7,381.9	10,564.3	5,062.3	8,776.2	7,053.8	4,091.2	2,857.6	52.5
Average Temperature (°F.)												
Period of Record	1921–1934	1921–1934	1921–1934	48 years	1921–1931	1921–1934	1921–1934	1921–1933	1921–1934	1921–1934	1921–1934	1921–1934
January	53.6	52.5	53.1	54	53.2	47.7	65.3	49.8	55.0	59.2	61.9	70.1
February	55.4	55.2	56.1	57	57.7	50.1	67.5	52.0	58.3	61.3	63.9	71.4
March	58.1	57.2	59.9	61	60.3	52.7	70.0	55.4	62.2	63.3	66.9	73.0
April	60.8	60.4	61.9	63	62.2	55.6	70.2	57.7	64.9	68.4	71.4	76.6
May	61.5	62.2	63.1	65	64.2	56.1	73.8	58.8	65.8	69.6	73.6	79.9
June	60.4	61.7	62.1	64	64.9	55.2	70.5	57.9	64.2	68.2	72.5	81.1
July	59.4	61.1	60.1	62	63.1	53.6	68.4	56.1	63.1	66.9	71.1	80.6
August	59.2	60.6	60.1	62	63.7	53.4	68.2	56.1	63.5	67.1	70.9	81.1
September	58.8	60.1	59.8	61	63.3	53.2	67.6	56.1	62.4	67.3	70.7	80.4
October	56.8	58.5	57.9	59	60.6	51.3	68.0	54.9	61.0	65.1	68.7	79.1
November	53.8	55.2	54.9	57	56.7	49.6	66.9	52.3	58.5	63.1	65.1	74.7
December	54.5	53.8	53.4	55	54.3	49.6	66.7	50.5	56.7	60.3	64.2	71.2
Annual	57.7	58.2	58.5	60	60.4	52.3	68.6	54.8	61.3	65.0	68.4	76.6
Days of Frost	22.0	122.8	63.2	....	76.3	66.8	....	68.9	23.8	2.2	0.2	0.0
Average Rainfall (*Inches*)												
Period of Record	1921–1934	1921–1934	1921–1934	48 years	1921–1931	1921–1934	1921–1934	1921–1933	1921–1934	1921–1934	1921–1934	1921–1934
January	0.3	0.3	0.3	0.2	0.5	0.5	0.2	0.5	0.3	1.6	1.8	0.9
February	0.6	0.3	0.3	0.3	0.3	0.7	0.2	0.4	0.3	1.6	1.5	0.6
March	0.6	0.5	0.5	0.5	0.3	0.4	0.1	0.5	0.5	1.1	1.6	0.3
April	0.6	0.9	0.9	0.7	1.3	1.2	0.4	1.2	0.7	1.7	2.1	0.9
May	1.3	2.1	1.9	1.9	2.3	3.2	1.9	2.5	2.9	5.3	4.4	2.0
June	2.8	3.3	4.8	4.1	4.3	8.2	6.7	5.3	5.8	14.0	13.5	9.8
July	2.4	4.5	6.6	4.5	6.0	10.2	8.9	6.6	5.4	15.3	15.8	13.6
August	2.2	4.2	6.0	4.3	5.8	10.8	8.8	5.7	4.4	12.9	14.9	11.6
September	3.0	4.5	6.0	4.1	5.7	9.3	10.1	5.9	7.4	17.3	18.6	13.9
October	1.9	2.0	2.0	1.6	2.0	4.0	3.2	1.9	2.5	7.8	9.7	7.0
November	0.9	0.6	0.8	0.5	0.5	1.1	0.3	0.8	1.0	4.2	3.8	3.8
December	0.2	0.3	0.3	0.3	0.4	0.4	0.1	0.6	0.5	2.3	2.3	0.9
Annual	16.8	23.5	30.4	23.0	29.4	50.0	40.9	31.9	31.7	85.1	90.0	65.3

* Ministerio de Agricultura y Fomento, Departamento de Meteorología, Tacubaya, D. F. Mexico.

† *United States Weather Bureau Technical Paper No. 8*, 1949, United States Weather Bureau, Washington, D. C.

islands. The islands are used primarily for the cultivation of vegetables and flowers. The level of the water is controlled; thus floods or undue draining of the lake is prevented.

Temperature and precipitation. Among the well-known climatic controls—latitude, land and water, ocean currents, altitude and exposure, prevailing winds, and storms—altitude is by far the dominant temperature control in the Valley of Mexico. The high elevation of the valley, some 7,000 feet above sea level, associated with a low latitude, assures the region of not only a cool atmosphere but also one of marked uniformity. The average annual temperature at Mexico, D. F., is 60.1° F., and there is only a slight range from summer to winter. January is generally the coldest month and May the warmest.

In contrast to the uniformity of temperature, the rainfall of the Valley of Mexico is decidedly variable, both in areal and seasonal distribution. The northern half of the valley receives only about half as much rain as the southern portion. For example, the annual average precipitation at Pachuca, located on the northern margin, is 16.8 inches, while Xochimilco, a southern station, is favored with 29.4 inches. Furthermore, approximately 75 per cent of the total rainfall of the valley occurs during the months of June, July, August, and September. Moreover, most of the summer rain takes place during the afternoon or evening.

In the synthesis of the formation and distribution of the rainfall in the valley, it should be noted that: (1) the region has an altitude of more than 7,000 feet above sea level; (2) it is surrounded by high mountains, especially in the east, south, and west, where altitudes as high as 17,000 feet are found; (3) the lowest ranges border the valley on the north and northwest; (4) the strong winds of the valley come largely from the north; (5) the valley is primarily under the influence of the dry, subtropical high-pressure belt in winter and the moisture-bearing air of the northeast trades in summer. In view of these conditions, it can readily be appreciated that the valley receives more rain in summer than in winter and that the origin of the precipitation is primarily of the orographic and convectional types.

The persistent drizzling during certain epochs of the winter occurs during the time that the north continental winds dominate—that is, between October and March. This is also the period when the "northers" take place along the Gulf Coast and which, on many occasions, have their influence over the Central Plateau. These winds come from the northwest or northeast. In the northern portion of the valley there is little or no precipitation, but, as winds rise over the southern mountains, rain may be induced by adiabatic cooling and by contact with the cold highland slopes. This is about the only source of rain during the winter months. It is essentially of the orographic type.

The convectional rains take place primarily during the summer months at the time that the valley as well as most of southern Mexico is under the influence of a low-pressure belt. The convectional circulation of air masses originates in the Gulf or Pacific areas. The rain in the valley at this time has the characteristic of coming in heavy intermittent showers in different places. These unstable showers, which account for most of the precipitation in the valley, also originate in the exterior slopes of the valley, particularly in the region of the high volcanic mountains. In both of these cases there arises from the outside slopes potent cumuliform masses, which, when they acquire their maximum development, are transformed into rain-bearing cumulo-nimbus clouds. If the cloudy formation (*formación nubosa*) is very intense, storms and hail result. Not all the rainfall in the valley conforms to this description, for it should not be forgotten that there also exists, although on a smaller scale—owing to the great extension of the basin—the interior circulation; this at times changes not necessarily the way in which the rain forms but its distribution.

Drainage controls. In early times the marginal rivers flowed into the natural lakes of the valley and frequently caused disastrous floods in the region of Mexico, D. F. On many occasions the nation's capital was partly inundated, with loss of lives and property. The first major project instituted to remove the danger of floods was the erection of dams to control the drainage of Lakes Chalco and Xochimilco and the construction of a series of ramparts or levees around a portion of the capital.

Another defense against floods was the construction of a levee across the narrowest portion of the valley, slightly north of Atzacoalco. The object of this project, known as the Netzahualcoyotl plan, was to prevent the surface water of the north from flowing southward to Mexico, D. F., and its adjacent land. It was not an entirely successful measure, because at different times the levee was broken or the water flowed over it. Now the levee is used as a part of the highway between Mexico, D. F., and Pachuca.

The third major enterprise introduced to prevent floods in the Valley of Mexico was the control of the Cuautitlán River, in the northwestern portion of the valley. Formerly, the Cuautitlán River emptied into Lake Zumpango, and at times, particularly during the rainy season, it added more water to the rather imperfect basin of Lake Zumpango than the latter was able to hold, and thus created an overflow southward to Mexico, D. F. To correct these conditions, an outlet was made for the Cuautitlán River through the upland separating the Valley of Mexico from the lower-lying Mezquital Valley on the north. The drainage of the Cuautitlán River, thus diverted from its former course to the new outlet, called Nochistongo, was the first drainage outlet of the Valley of Mexico. The railway between Mexico, D. F., and El Paso also passes through the Nochistongo cut.

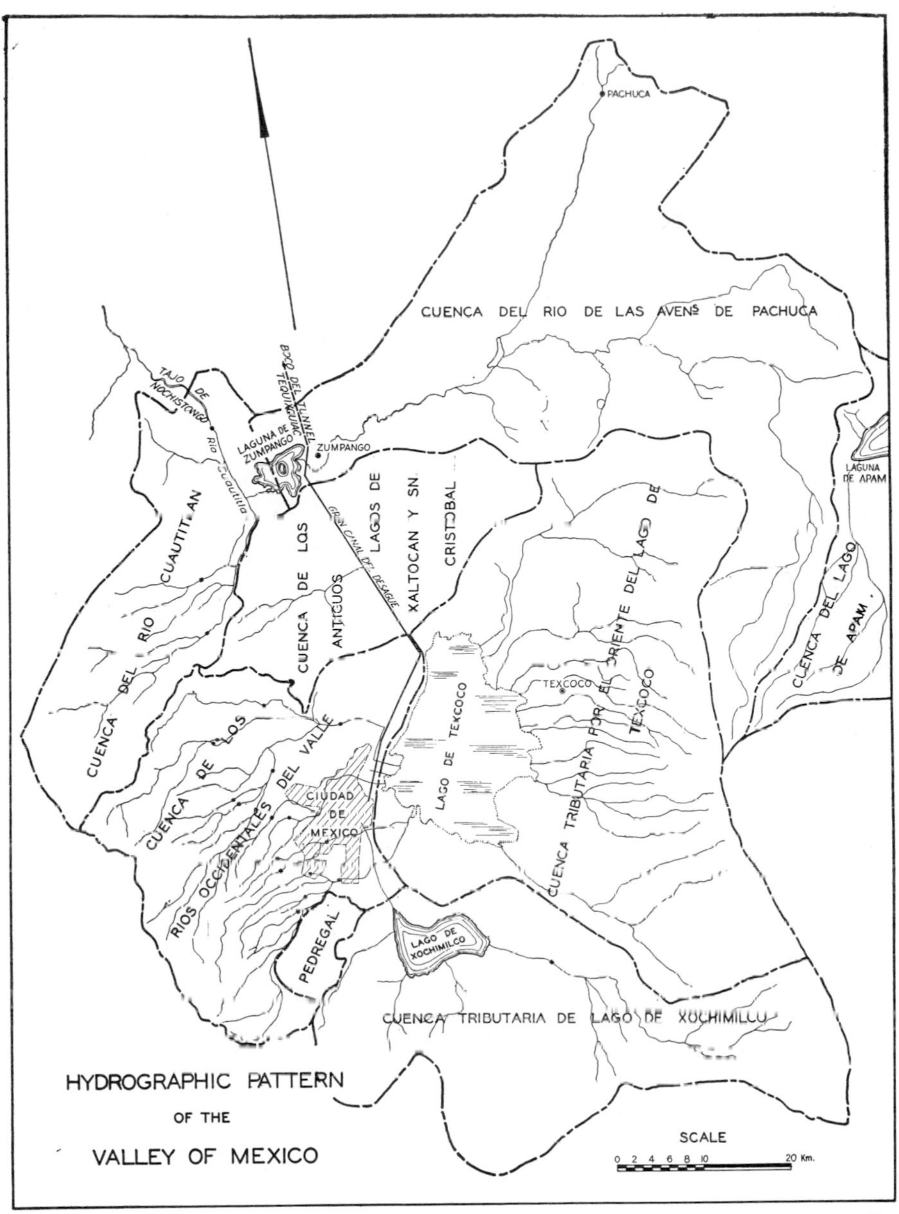

After Carlos Ramírez Ulloa, Departamento de Obras Hidráulicas, Mexico, D. F.

Fig. 130. Hydrographic pattern of the Valley of Mexico.

While the Nochistongo project materially reduced the dangers of floods, it did not completely solve the drainage problem of the valley. In fact, one of the most disastrous floods in the valley occurred after the completion of the Nochistongo cut and inundated parts of Mexico, D. F., to a depth of nearly four feet. On this occasion, however, the flood was primarily due to the uncontrolled drainage in the immediate environment of Mexico, D. F. To remedy this situation the fourth major drainage project, the construction of the Gran Canal del Desagüe, was instituted. The work was started in 1885 and completed 15 years later. The Gran Canal starts at San Lazaro, on the margin of Mexico, D. F., and extends for more than 30 miles to the base of the hills on the northern border of the valley. An outlet, known as the tunnel of Tequixquiac, was made through the hills to the exterior valley on the north to carry the drainage of the Gran Canal to a headstream of the Pánuco River system, which empties into the Gulf of Mexico. By means of the Gran Canal it is possible to regulate the volume of water in all of the lakes in the Valley of Mexico as well as to control marginal drainage. The canal is also used to remove the sewage and surplus water of Mexico, D. F. Without the Nochistongo and Gran Canal projects, the expansion and development in the Valley of Mexico would not have been possible. Both of these enterprises, however, require constant attention. If there were a landslide across the Gran Canal or an obstruction in the Tequixquiac tunnel, the nation's capital would be seriously endangered. Some difficulty is encountered during the rainy season, when the discharge of water into the canal is beyond the capacity of the tunnel; a back flow results and causes the water in the canal to rise and overflow. The Gran Canal solved a problem that occupied the mind of the Aztec at the time of the Spanish conquest.

The most recent plans to improve further the drainage situation in the valley include the construction of a system of dams and canals on the slopes of the western marginal highland. The object is to eliminate rivers and canals passing through Mexico, D. F., which require dredging and numerous bridges, and present an unsightly appearance. By means of storage dams and diversion canals, some of the surface drainage will be carried north to the Nochistongo cut or the Tequixquiac tunnel, and some will be diverted south into the Pedregal volcanic formation to add to the supply of water near Lake Xochimilco. Mexico, D. F., is the only large city of the world supplied almost exclusively with artesian and spring water flowing in quantities sufficient to make extensive storage dams unnecessary.

Another circumstance contributing to the difficulties of controlling surface water in the valley is deforestation. The demand for charcoal in the Valley of Mexico has placed a heavy burden on the original forest resources. The charcoal burner has practically depleted the landscape of forest cover. The deforested slopes accelerate erosion and supply materials for the aggradation of rivers and lakes and the obstruction of canals and tunnels. The natural conservation of moisture and the retardation of surface run-off associated with forests have been lost on the almost barren slopes and hills of the valley. Reforestation, however, is under serious consideration. There are now several tree nurseries in the valley, and a limited area is under reforestation. The most extensive original forests of the region are found in the Sierra Nevada ranges.

The results of the drainage projects in the Valley of Mexico are both beneficial and detrimental. The urban centers are free from disastrous floods, and large tracts of land such as the basins of Lake Chalco, Zaltócan, and San Cristóbal have been reclaimed for agricultural and grazing purposes. By controlling the volume of water in Xochimilco, the insular plats are intensively cultivated, and they produce a large percentage of the vegetables and flowers sold in Mexico, D. F. In general, the Valley of Mexico depicts a striking correlation between its cultural pattern and hydrographic features.

The unfavorable consequences of the drainage enterprises are not serious. The partial draining of Lake Texcoco has exposed extensive areas of silt and clay containing a high percentage of alkalies. At times, particularly during the dry seasons, the northern winds blow the Texcoco dust over Mexico, D. F., and cause all the unpleasant circumstances of our western dust storms. Another significant condition at least partly due to the adjustment of drainage is the sinking of buildings, streets, and sidewalks in Mexico, D. F. The National Theater has sunk nearly four feet into the unstable strata of the valley; Escuela Nacional de Ingenieros, the Church of Nuestra Señora de Loreto, and many other structures show an appreciable degree of subsidence.

Cultural landscape. The Valley of Mexico is not rich in natural agricultural resources. However, through land reclamation, the draining of lakes, the control of surface run-off, and irrigation, large tracts of the valley have been made suitable for the cultivation of crops and for grazing purposes. The basin of former Lake Chalco and the insular plats of Lake Xochimilco are intensively used for the production of vegetables and staple foods, while the reclaimed lands of Lakes Zaltócan, San Cristóbal, and Texcoco provide fair pastures for cattle and goats. Some of the dry land of the northern portion of the valley supports the characteristic xerophyte, maguey, the source of pulque, and an important goat industry for both meat and milk. The goat meat is used in the popular Mexican dish, *Barbacea*.

The principal cattle ranches of the valley are found along the piedmont areas and on the level areas of the more humid southern portion of the valley. The development of the dairy industry is the region's chief contribution to the progress of agriculture of Mexico. Today Mexico,

D. F., and adjacent villages are provided with fresh milk, some of which is pasteurized. Better food, particularly milk, produced and delivered under adequate refrigeration and sanitation, is one of the nation's most urgent needs.

The principal mining industry of the valley is centered in the Pachuca Mountains, along the northeastern border, where silver is the chief mineral. It is among the oldest and most productive silver-mining regions of Mexico. From this area construction stone and other materials are extracted. In near-by places are glass factories, chemical and munition plants, and factories producing chinaware, glazed tile, mosaics, and cement. Salt mining is carried on near Lake Texcoco. An oil refinery and iron and steel smelters are other important industries in the economic life of the valley.

In Mexico, D. F., manufacturing is making some progress. Both native and foreign companies are engaged in the production of paper, furniture, cigars and cigarettes, shoes, soap, and textiles. There are also many semi-household industries for the manufacture of clothing, furniture, pottery, and many other products.

Modern highways and railroads have added much to the development of the Valley of Mexico. National highways lead from Mexico, D. F., to the United States-Mexican border, the Pacific coast, and the Gulf of Mexico. By highway, Mexico, D. F., lies about midway between the Atlantic and the Pacific. The distance from the capital to Veracruz is 282 miles and 284 miles to Acapulco on the Pacific. The principal railroads to the north include the Central Railroad, to El Paso; the National, to Nuevo Laredo; and the Desagüe del Valle, a local railroad to Pachuca. To the eastern port, Veracruz, are two railways: the Interoceanic, via Puebla and Jalapa, and the Mexican Railway, via Orizaba and Córdoba. The latter is the more frequented route. Three important railways extend southward from the national capital to Cuautla, Cuernavaca, and Toluca. The high marginal mountains, having few low passes, and the interior hills and lakes have brought about a concentration of arteries of transportation in limited areas, and there are wide spaces without highways and railroads.

Mexico, D. F. La Ciudad de Méjico was founded early in the twelfth century. When Cortés invaded the Valley of Mexico, the Aztecs' settlement, as already mentioned, was known as Tenochtitlán, which is said to mean "place where the cactus is on the rock." This title, however, appears to have been changed at an early date to Mexico, in honor of the war god, Mexitli.

The pattern of Mexico, D. F., somewhat rectangular in shape, is dominated by the natural features in its environment. Hydrographic and topographic forms have favored an expansion west and south. The Guadalupe Hills to the north and Lake Texcoco to the northeast have checked urban development in those directions.

Most of the highways from east to west are designated as avenues, or *avenidas,* while those running north and south are known as streets, or *calles.* Many adjustments are now being made to improve the traffic facilities to meet new requirements, but even without these changes the plan of the city is comparatively modern. In early days the Plaza de la Constitución, the *Zócalo,* was the geographic center of the city, but now it is far from occupying that position. On the Zócalo stands the national palace, *Palacio Nacional,* and the cathedral, *La Catedral,* the Holy Metropolitan Church of Mexico. This is the largest and most imposing church edifice in the republic and is said to be the largest on the con-

Reprinted by permission of the Compañia Mexicana Aerofoto, S. A.

Fig. 131. Mexico, D. F. (La Ciudad de Méjico). Near the center is the "zócalo," the Plaza de la Constitución or Plaza Mayor. On the north side (left) of the Plaza is La Catedral and on the east El Palacio Nacional.

tinent. One of the most beautiful and spacious avenues of the city is *Paseo de la Reforma,* stretching about three miles from the city proper to the Hill of Chapultepec. It was planned by Maximilian to give ready access from his Chapultepec palace to the municipal center. A double file of trees lines the broad avenue, and it is further beautified by the bordering private lawns and gardens. Parks and plazas are numerous, and attractive suburbs make the nation's capital a delightful city. It is free from coal dust and smoke, since most of the fuel is charcoal or artificial gas. Few of the homes have furnaces but depend largely upon the heat from charcoal burners or electric heaters during the winter months. The electric power and light consumed in Mexico, D. F., are supplied by the Necaxa Hydroelectric Power Plant, located in the state of Puebla, where the Falls of Necaxa, some 540 feet high, have been harnessed.

Adjacent exterior regions. On the exterior of the highlands enclosing the Valley of Mexico are four important contributory regions. To the northward lies the Mezquital Valley, to the east the Puebla Valley, to the south the Cuernavaca Valley, and to the west the Lerma Valley. All of these regions are closely related socially and commercially to the Valley of Mexico.

The principal significance of the Mezquital Valley is in its agriculture, conducted primarily under irrigation. It receives and uses some of the excess drainage from the Valley of Mexico that passes through the Nochistongo cut and the Tequixquiac Tunnel. Some 150,000 acres are irrigated, and alfalfa and corn are successfully grown there, principally for the markets in the Valley of Mexico.

About 30 miles west of the Valley of Mexico is another agricultural region, the Lerma Valley. It is particularly well known for its excellent corn crops. In the upper reaches of the valley is Toluca, a city of about 51,000 inhabitants, and the capital of the state of Mexico. Baskets and pottery that the natives bring to the ready markets of Mexico, D. F., are the chief commercial products of Toluca. Daily the peons may be seen carrying on their backs huge packs of baskets, pottery, earthenware, wood, or charcoal destined for the nation's capital. Climatically, the Lerma Valley is colder than the Valley of Mexico. The low temperature can be attributed to its high altitude, 8,776 feet above sea level.

One of the most delightful regions of Mexico is the Cuernavaca Valley, the site of the famous city of the same name. In this city are the Palace of Cortés—one of the earliest structures built under the Spanish regime—the nation's White House, a home of the late Ambassador Morrow, a cathedral, and many beautiful gardens. It is a tourist's paradise. The city is some 2,000 feet lower than the national capital and enjoys a warm climate. Palm trees, mango trees, and other subtropical plants dot the landscape. An excellent highway marked with beautiful scenery, a favorite afternoon drive, joins Cuernavaca and Mexico, D. F. The warm, balmy air of Cuernavaca is at times a welcome change from the cool and even penetrating atmosphere of Mexico, D. F.

In a broad valley, east of the snow-capped mountains Popocatépetl and Ixtaccíhuatl, stands Puebla, the fourth largest city of Mexico. It is about 130 miles from Mexico, D. F., to Puebla, the city of churches and tile. Puebla is also known as the Manchester of Mexico, because of its textile industries. It is an important railway center, where connections may be made to Veracruz, Tehuacán, Cuautla, Oaxaca, and Mexico, D. F. Puebla is an upland city with a climate quite similar to that of Mexico, D. F. Within its immediate environs are grown temperate crops, while only a short distance at lower elevations to the east and south are subtropical and tropical plants.

MEXICO'S YUCATAN

General characteristics. Three political entities share the peninsula of Yucatán: namely, Mexico, Guatemala, and the crown possession, British Honduras. The Mexican portion of the peninsula is divided into Yu-

Courtesy Pan American Union.

Fig. 132. Yucatán, Mexico. Chichén Itzá—Temple of the Warriors, or Temple of a Thousand Columns.

catán, Campeche, and Quintana Roo. From 1902 to 1931 the eastern portion of the land was known as the Territory of Quintana Roo, but in 1932 the territory, as a political division, was abolished. In 1935 a federal decree became effective, restoring the territorial boundary of Quintana Roo. The total area of Mexico's Yucatán is about 54,000 square miles, and the population is some 500,000, mostly of Mayan Indians and mestizos. In the sixteenth century the number of inhabitants was considerably larger than today. It was even greater in the thirteenth than in the sixteenth century. Famines, pestilences, and civil wars are supposed to have reduced the population in numbers as well as in national power before the arrival of the Spaniards. Before this decadence, however, Yucatán had reached a high degree of civilization of the time, as exemplified today by the many ruins of temples, citadels, and other civic structures. While Yucatán has lost much of its early significance, it still maintains an important place in Mexican affairs. From its lands come agave and chicle, products of international importance.

Land and climate. The Mexican portion of Yucatán is low in both relief and latitude. In the state of Yucatán the flat land rises slightly from the coast to about 28 feet above sea level in the interior. The state of Campeche is also comparatively flat, but its uniform surface is broken by numerous hills and ridges reaching as high as 1,000 feet above the sea. The limited information available about the underlying structure shows that the upper strata consist primarily of soluble limestone. Because of the soluble nature of the surface stratum, with resultant fissures, caves, and underground channels, the rainwater quickly runs in and disappears. Consequently, there are few surface streams and lakes, except in the southern and eastern portion of the state of Campeche. The best-known hydrographic features are Lake Chichancanab, containing brackish water; Lake Bacalar; Laguna de Largartos; and Laguna de Términos, with its numerous streams.

While there is little surface water in the northern portion of the peninsula, nature has blessed the inhabitants with an abundance of underground water rising to the level of the sea. Thus by artificial wells conspicuously marked by American windmills, by natural wells, and by rainwater collected from the roofs of houses and stored in cisterns, Yucatán obtains its supply of water for domestic use. However, very few dwellings in Yucatán have running water.

Climatically, Yucatán may be characterized as a tropical region with fairly uniform temperature throughout the year and a variable amount of rainfall. The range in temperature from summer to winter is 11.2° F. at Campeche and 7.6° F. at Progreso. However, between the absolute lowest and the absolute highest during all months, the range is much greater, 40–50° F. between winter and spring. January is the coldest month and May is the warmest. The greatest variations in rainfall are between that of the northern portion of the state of Yucatán and that of the southern portion of the state of Campeche. There is also more rainfall in the interior than in the coastal regions. The greater rainfall in the interior is probably due to higher wind velocity along the north coast, which interferes with convection, and to the higher temperature and stronger convection in the interior. Summer is the rainy season, as in nearly all parts of Mexico, the major portion of the precipitation occurring from May to October. June is generally the rainiest month. The annual precipitation at the three most important urban centers is as follows: Mérida, 34.6 inches; Progreso, 17.8 inches; and Campeche, 37.4 inches. The southern portion of the peninsula has over 80 inches of rain a year. Another significant characteristic of the region is the destructive tropical hurricanes that occur occasionally in summer and fall.

MERIDA: Elevation, 72 feet above sea level

Period of Record 1931–1940													
Temperature (*°F.*)	*Jan.*	*Feb.*	*Mar.*	*Apr.*	*May*	*June*	*July*	*Aug.*	*Sept.*	*Oct.*	*Nov.*	*Dec.*	*Annual*
	73.6	75.0	77.2	80.1	81.5	81.3	80.8	81.1	80.6	78.6	74.7	73.4	78.2
Rainfall (*Inches*)	0.9	0.6	0.8	1.4	3.3	5.1	5.4	5.6	6.1	3.0	1.1	1.3	34.6

Source: H. Helm Clayton: "World Weather Records," *Smithsonian Miscellaneous Collections,* Vol. 105 (1947).

Fibers and chicle. The cultivation of agave, from which sisal and henequén, two closely related species, are produced, is the chief industry

Courtesy Pan American Union.

Fig. 133. Henequén harvest. The leaves are severed from the plants, the terminal and lateral spines removed, and the "pencas" or leaves corded together to be hauled by tramway to the stripping machines. The central leaves are left as a nucleus for future cutting.

of the northwestern portion of the state of Yucatán.[2]. The agave belongs to the cactus family; its fibers are used extensively in the manufacture of binder twine and other cordage. Most of the fiber, comprising over 90

[2] Agave sisalina is the source of sisal, and agave fourcroyles yields henequén. Sisal is used chiefly in the manufacture of wrapping twines and small rope, and henequén, principally in the manufacture of binder twine.

per cent of the total exports to the state of Yucatán, is shipped to the United States. The eastern and southern portions of this state are not well suited to the cultivation of the agave, and, in consequence, much of this land is unproductive and overgrown with low, scrubby "bush." The bush merges gradually into the forested lands of southeastern Yucatán and the southern half of the state of Campeche. Some general farming, including the production of sugar cane, corn, beans, pigs, and a few cattle, is conducted in a rather primitive manner in these more humid lands. The chief product of this region, however, is chicle. The shipment of crude chicle from this area to the United States has reached as high as 2,500,000 pounds in a single year. From the rain forests come other important products, particularly mahogany, fruits, and coconuts.

Trade centers. The principal civic centers of the Mexican Yucatán are Mérida, Progreso, and Campeche. Mérida, having a population of about 111,500 inhabitants, is the only large city of the entire peninsula. It is an orderly city, with yellowish, stuccoed houses rising directly from the sidewalk. Similar to most of Latin America, the houses, particularly those of the better class, have large windows protected with iron gratings; and during the daytime and evening, when the great windows are open, one may see spacious patios and trees and flowers within.

Progreso is the seaport of Mérida. The two cities are joined by a railway and an excellent automobile road of 28 miles. Progreso has no harbor and the water along the sandy shore is very shallow. Vessels drawing more than 12 feet of water must anchor offshore, and all cargo and passengers must be transported in lighters. A narrow channel, however, enables small steamers to come to a pier for loading and discharging cargo. The town of Progreso (15,000 population) has a dilapidated and neglected appearance. Probably the most attractive part of the site is its excellent bathing beach, which attracts many Yucateos from Mérida and near-by villages.

On the west coast of the peninsula is Campeche, capital of the state of Campeche. A railway joins Campeche and Mérida and Tenosique in the state of Tabasco. Like Progreso, Campeche is without a harbor, and lighterage is necessary. Campeche, in its small way, is a shipping point for products of the northern part of that state and handles some of the traffic between Mérida and central Mexico.

In many respects the whole Mexican Yucatán is commercially closer to the United States than to the cultural and trade areas of the central plateau of Mexico. It is without overland transportation means with the heart of Mexico and depends primarily upon the United States for its exterior trade. The establishment of airway service between Veracruz and Mérida has greatly reduced Yucatán's isolation and has brought it closer to central Mexico's affairs.[3]

---

[3] For reference to the Mayas in Yucatán see Chapter I.

EASTERN MEXICO

Physical setting. Eastern Mexico comprises physiographically the Gulf Coastal Plain and associated highlands, and politically the state of Tamaulipas, the southeastern portion of the state of San Luis Potosí, the state of Veracruz, and the state of Tabasco. It is an area of striking contrasts, including coastal lowlands, steep escarpments, deep valleys, and lofty mountains. The coastal lowlands vary in width from a few to more than 100 miles. Above these lowlands rise a series of mountain ranges and valleys varying in elevation from a few feet above sea level to more than 8,000 feet. The highest mountain is Orizaba, also known as Citlaltepetl, towering far above the surrounding landscape to an elevation of more than 18,000 feet above sea level. It is the third highest mountain in North America, surpassed only by Mount McKinley in Alaska and Mt. Logan in Canada. The snow-capped Orizaba presents a lasting impression when viewed from the subtropical regions in the midst of coffee trees, palms, and banana groves.

Along the Gulf Coast the climate is hot and humid in the summers but mild and quite delightful during the winter, except when the north winds or "northers" bring about an abrupt drop in temperature. In the highland region the climate is subtropical to temperate. The annual rainfall on the lowlands varies from a few inches in the north to about 40 inches at Tampico and 65 inches at Veracruz. In the mountains the rainfall is decidedly variable and depends upon the position and height of the ranges. Approximately 75 per cent of the rainfall occurs between June and the end of October.

Veracruz to Mexico, D. F. The rugged mountains lying between the Gulf Coast and the Central Plateau make transportation between Mexico's leading port, Veracruz, and the nation's capital exceedingly difficult. The railway route from Veracruz to Mexico, D. F., via Córdoba and Orizaba over the Mexican Railway extends from a few feet above sea level to more than 8,000 feet. In the first 50 miles, Veracruz to Paso del Macho, the ascent is 1,500 feet. At Paso del Macho the diesel engines are replaced by two great electric locomotives that pull the train to an elevation of 8,050 feet above the sea at Esperanza, a climb of 6,550 feet in about 64 miles. It is a land of steep escarpments, deep barrancas, waterfalls, high bridges, and tunnels. One of the major engineering accomplishments of the route is the Metlac Bridge, built on a curve of 335-feet radius, a 3-per-cent grade, and 92 feet above a raging river. From Esperanza the grade again permits the use of steam engines. The highest point on the route is at Acocotla, 8,320 feet above sea level. From here there is a gradual descent to the nation's capital, on the way passing fields of maguey, corn, and grazing cattle, and with the Pyramids of San Juan Teotihuacán and the shrine of Guadalupe to be seen in the distance.

The highway between Veracruz and the central plateau follows more or less the route of the Spanish conquistadores in their invasion of the lands of Montezuma. From Veracruz a road passes to the capital via Jalapa and Puebla and en route or near by are many interesting Indian villages, churches, and pyramids (particularly outstanding are the ruins of Cholula).

Industries and commerce. On the highland slopes, particularly in the vicinity of Orizaba, Córdoba, and Jalapa, are grown coffee, oranges, sugar cane, mangoes, pineapples, and numerous staple food crops. The mountain slopes are covered with valuable forests, probably the most

F. A. Carlson.

Fig. 134. A young banana plantation near Córdoba, state of Veracruz, Mexico. Mt. Orizaba is in the distance.

extensive in Mexico. Many streams await the development of hydroelectric power. Some progress in this respect has been made at Tuxpango, near the city of Orizaba, where a modern hydroelectric plant provides power for that part of the Mexican Railroad between Esperanza and Paso del Macho as well as for near-by towns, and even for the more distant plateau city of Puebla. The development of the textile industry at Santa Rosa, Nogales, and Río Blanco, located a few miles west of Orizaba, can be mainly attributed to the presence of water power in this area.

On the coastal lands, the production, refining, and exportation of petroleum constitute the most important industry. Approximately 75 per cent of Mexico's total oil production, 72 per cent of its petroleum exports, and 61 per cent of its oil refinery output come from the Tampico and Tuxpan regions.

The principal coastal plain cities are Matamoros, Tampico, Veracruz, Puerto Mexico, and Alvaro Obregon. Veracruz ranks first, it being the leading Mexican port. It has a deep and well-protected harbor and adequate wharfage and warehouses. It is the chief port for clearing merchandise from Europe and the United States and is the port of arrival for European passengers. Most of the freight arriving at Veracruz by water is distributed by rail to interior points. There are four railways leading out of Veracruz: two go to Mexico, D. F., one via Orizaba and Córdoba, and one via Jalapa and Puebla; the third line goes to Alvarado, about 20 miles south on the coast; and the fourth is to the

F. A. Carlson

Fig. 135. A cover of banana trees and coffee trees and a profusion of wild vegetation in the warm humid lands near Córdoba, Mexico.

Isthmus of Tehuantepec. The principal exports from Veracruz are coffee, bananas, vanilla, and chicle.

The port of Tampico, located on the Pánuco River, about seven miles from its mouth, is accessible to ocean vessels. Rail transportation exists between Tampico and Texas border points via Monterrey, and to Mexico, D. F., through the city of San Luis Potosí.

The coastal plain settlements of Puerto Mexico, Alvaro Obregon, and Matamoros have little importance. Puerto Mexico is practically limited to the shipment of small quantities of oil, while Alvaro Obregon exports some bananas. Although Matamoros is a coastal plain town, it is discussed elsewhere, under the subject of border settlements, because its trade relations are closer with the northern than eastern portion of Mexico.

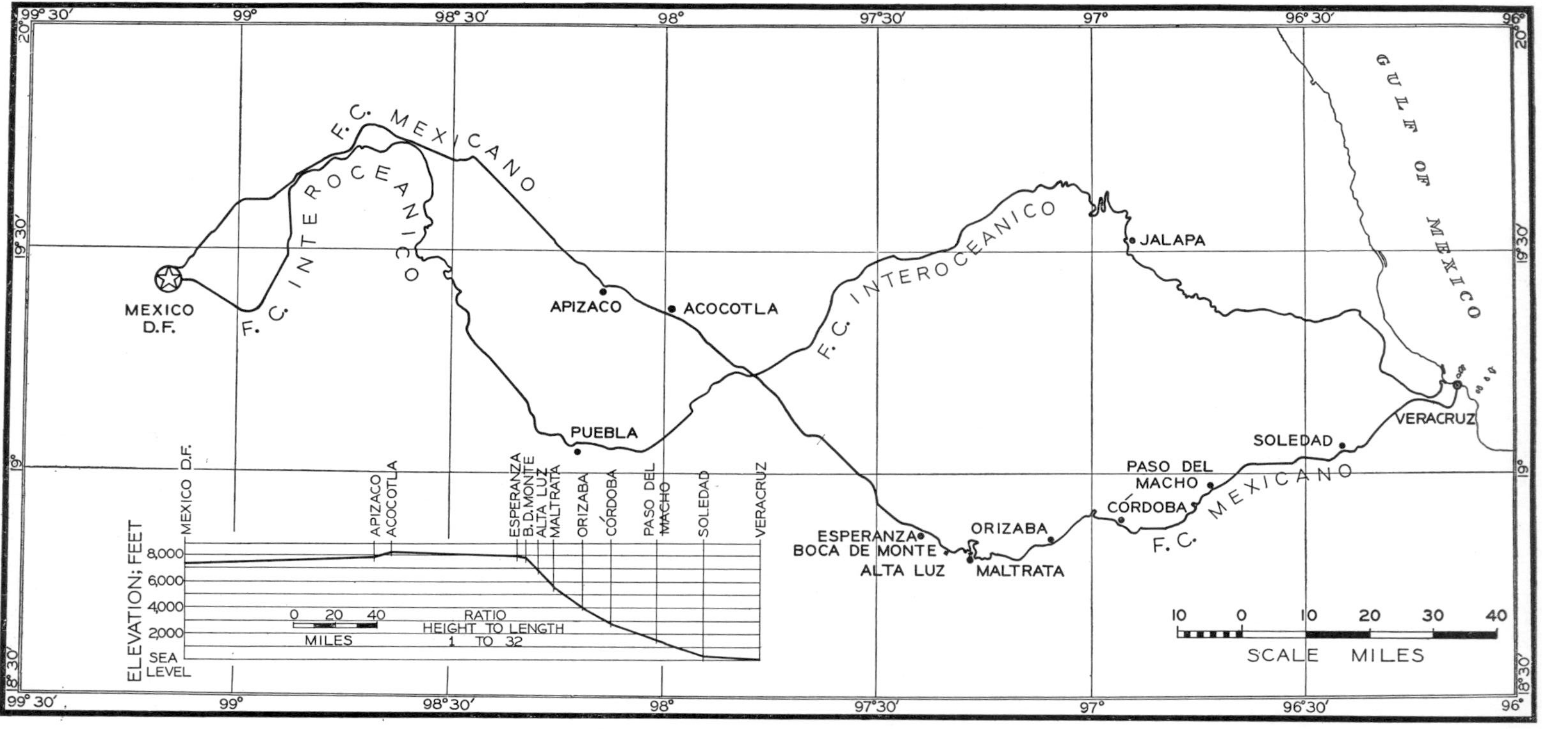

F. A. Carlson.

Fig. 136. The Mexico, D. F., and Veracruz railway routes.

WESTERN MEXICO

Extent of region. Western Mexico embraces the southern territory of Lower California; approximately the southern half of the state of Sonora; and the Pacific coastal states, Sinaloa, Nayarit, Jalisco, Colima, Michoacán, Guerrero, Oaxaca, and Chiapas. Portions of the area are rich in mineral, forest, and agricultural resources. The principal centers of trade are Guaymas, Mazatlán, Manzanillo, Guadalajara, and Colima. The first three are ports; the others inland cities.

Guaymas district. The southern territory of Lower California is best known for its mining activities. The principal mineral center is Santa Rosalía, where there are important copper mines and smelters. Small boats sailing from Guaymas, Sonora, and Mazatlán, Sinaloa, connect Santa Rosalía and other points in the Territorio Sur de la Baja California with the Mexican mainland. Baja California has no inland transportation facilities.

The upland of the Guaymas district includes two important river valleys, the Yaqui and the Mayo, each extensive and having considerable agricultural development. The eastern part of Sonora is composed of hills mostly suitable for cattle raising, with an occasional small valley adaptable for dry farming. The rest of the region is chiefly arid lowlands and hills.

Relatively mild winters and long, hot summers are prevalent in the lower altitudes of the Guaymas district. The daily temperature at Guaymas in midsummer usually ranges between 95° and 107° F. Midwinter temperatures rarely drop below 50° and usually are closer to 70°. The average annual rainfall at Guaymas is about 12 inches, and most of it comes between July and October.

Agriculture is by far the most important occupation in the vicinity of Guaymas. Considerable quantities of winter tomatoes and peas are produced in the irrigated Yaqui and Mayo River valleys. These valleys also produce appreciable quantities of wheat, rice, garbanzos, corn, beans, and alfalfa. Some gold and silver mining is also carried on in this region.

Guaymas is connected by rail with points in the United States via Nogales, Arizona, and with the interior of Mexico via Guadalajara. Occasionally freight vessels from Los Angeles and San Francisco call at Guaymas and Yavaros, Sonora, and at Santa Rosalía and La Paz, Baja California. The chief exports of Guaymas include winter tomatoes and green peas for the United States, garbanzos for Spain, and some gypsum and amorphous graphite for the United States.

Region of Mazatlán. The Mazatlán district consists primarily of the states of Sinaloa and Nayarit. The climate is semitropical, with cool winters. The average annual temperature is about 75° F.; the average annual rainfall is 36 inches, most of which falls in the rainy season, from

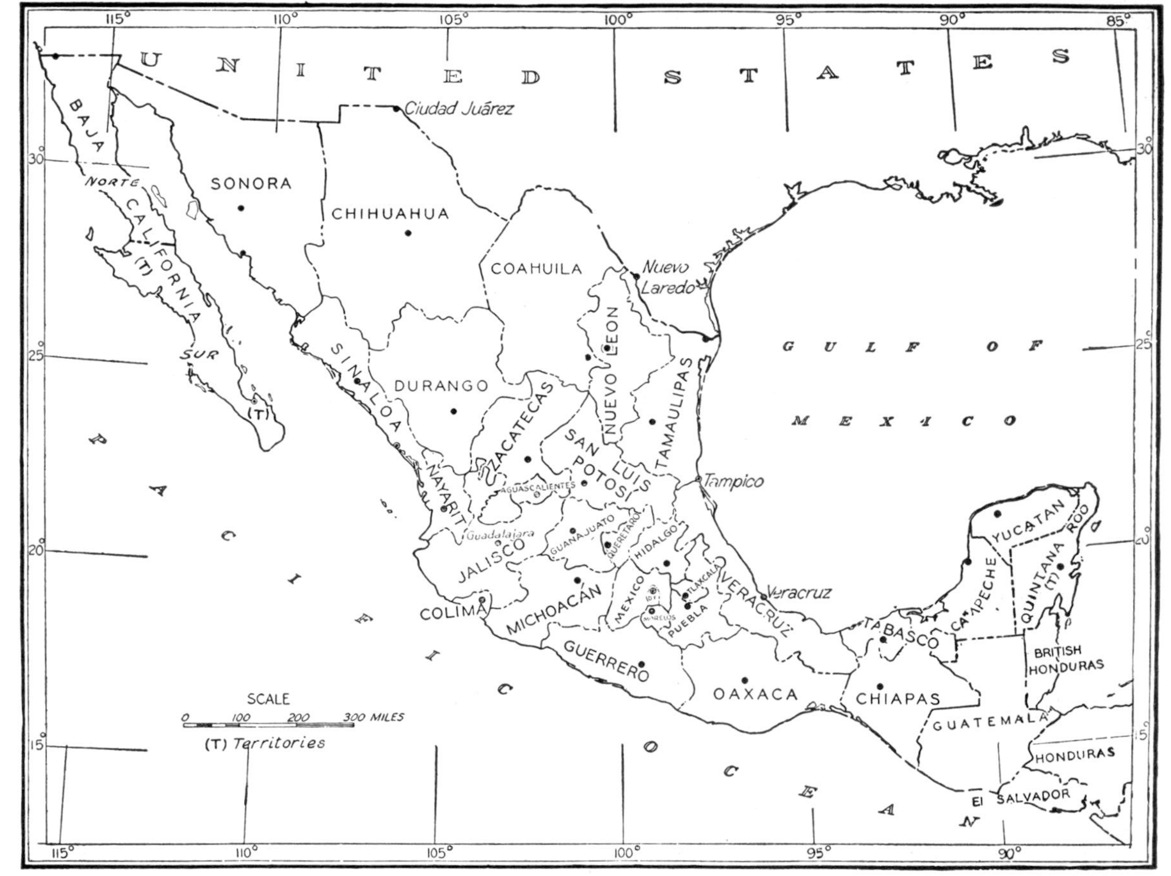

F. A. Carlson.

Fig. 137. Political divisions of Mexico.

Mexico now has 29 states and 2 territories. The latter are Baja California, South District, and Quintana Roo, on the Yucátan Peninsula.

July to September. An extensive coastal plain comprises the western portion of the district, while the eastern part includes the highland of the Sierra Madre Occidental.

MAZATLAN: Elevation, 256 feet above sea level

Period of Record 1931–1940													
Temperature	*Jan.*	*Feb.*	*Mar.*	*Apr.*	*May*	*June*	*July*	*Aug.*	*Sept.*	*Oct.*	*Nov.*	*Dec.*	*Annual*
(°*F.*)	66.2	66.4	68.5	71.6	75.4	80.1	81.9	81.3	81.1	75.4	69.8	75.0	74.4
Rainfall (*Inches*)	0.5	0.3	0.0	0.1	1.1	1.3	8.8	11.2	11.5	0.8	0.6	0.7	36.9

Source: H. Helm Clayton: "World Weather Records," *Smithsonian Miscellaneous Collections,* Vol. 105 (1947).

Agriculture is the leading industry of the Mazatlán district, the principal crops being fresh vegetables—including tomatoes, peas, and peppers—garbanzos, sugar cane, tobacco, coffee, cotton, corn, and beans. Mining is of considerable significance, and valuable deposits of gold and silver ore are being worked, chiefly by American capital.

Courtesy H. C. Shetrone.

Fig. 138. Vendors at a Mexican village railway station.

Mazatlán, the principal port in the Sinaloa-Nayarit area, is an open roadstead, and all water shipments must be lightered. The Southern Pacific Railway of Mexico passes through Mazatlán and offers service to United States and Mexico, D. F.

Other trade centers. The states of Colima and Jalisco comprise another important trade district, bordering the Pacific Ocean for more than 260 miles and projecting inland to include a portion of the high Central Plateau. The climate varies primarily according to altitude. The temperature in summer is 94° F., and in winter it seldom reaches 38°. The annual rainfall varies from 20 to 28 inches. Agriculture and mining are of equal importance.

Manzanillo is the chief port of the Pacific and has a well-protected harbor. Deep-draft vessels may anchor in the inner harbor. The Mexican Railways join the port of Manzanillo with Guadalajara, a distance of about 230 miles.

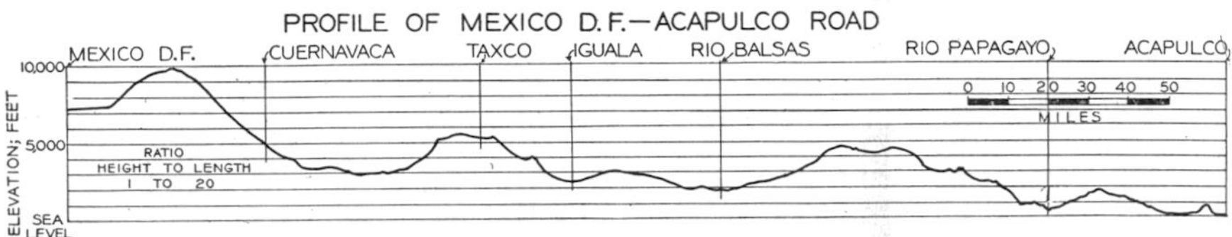

Fig. 139. Profile of the road between Mexico, D. F., and Acapulco.

Guadalajara, the capital of the state of Jalisco and the second largest city of the republic (273,400), is one of the finest population centers in Mexico. It is a modern city, clean and well lighted, and located in a rich agricultural area and important mining region. Although within the low latitudes, its elevation of more than 5,000 feet makes the climate delightful and agreeable. It has rail connections with Mexico, D. F. (318 miles), El Paso (1,169 miles), Laredo (865 miles), and Nogales (1,100 miles). A highway extends to Guadalajara via Toluca through a picturesque region. Plans call for the projection of this highway up the west coast to Nogales, Arizona.

Colima, the capital of the state of the same name, occupies a beautiful spot in the fertile valley of the Río Colima. Its tropical aspect presents a striking contrast with the cold snows of the twin volcanoes in the distance. The Mexican Railways join it with Manzanillo, Guadalajara, and points north.

Nearly due south of Mexico City lies the beautiful harbor of Acapulco, one of the finest water havens on the Pacific. Unfortunately a broken and high terrain separates Acapulco from the cultural centers on the great Central Plateau. This ideal harbor and port are without railway transportation, but a good highway joins it with Mexico, D. F., 284 miles away.

The harbor of Acapulco is nearly completely enclosed, the longer axis extending northwest and southeast for more than five miles, and the shorter axis running east and west for about three miles. The open side to the Pacific is divided and protected on the north by islands. But few ships enter this spacious harbor, and only an occasional freighter or passenger-cargo carrier makes it a port of call to discharge goods for local consumption, or tourists en route to Mexico, D. F. The port is a growing communal center, one of the leading resorts in Mexico. Many vacationists make trips to Acapulco to enjoy the ocean bathing and fishing.

The state of Chiapas, the most southern portion of Mexico bordering the Pacific, is rapidly becoming an important coffee region. It also ranks high in natural forest resources. Much of the region, however, has not been explored.

INTERIOR MEXICO

Trade centers. The interior of Mexico embraces the southern portions of the states of Nuevo León, Coahuila, and Chihuahua; the western and central parts of San Luis Potosí; and the entire states of Durango, Zacatecas, Aguascalientes, Guanajuato, and Querétaro. Approximately 75 per cent of the interior's total population lives within 100 miles of the city of San Luis Potosí, almost the geographic center of Mexico. The cultural districts of the interior are marked by San Luis Potosí, Durango, Torreón, Saltillo, Monterrey, and Chihuahua. All of these focal centers have rail transportation with Mexico, D. F., and the United States.

The San Luis Potosí district has an average elevation of 6,000 feet above sea level. However, certain valleys in the eastern portion of the state of San Luis Potosí are not over 1,000 feet above the sea, while the area occupied by the city of Zacatecas is over 8,000 feet above the sea. The elevation of the city of San Luis Potosí is 6,100 feet; Guanajuato, 6,800; León, 6,100; and Aguascalientes, 6,500. Practically the whole district of San Luis Potosí has a light rainfall, varying between 12 inches annually, in San Luis Potosí, and 25 inches at Aguascalientes and portions of Guanajuato. Extensive drought is common. The summers are not excessively hot, and the winters are mild. Snow, however, occurs occasionally in the mountains of Zacatecas and northern San Luis Potosí.

Agriculture and mining are the most important industries in the San Luis Potosí district. There are large smelters at San Luis Potosí and Matehuala. The arsenic plant in San Luis Potosí is said to be one of the largest in the world. The chief agricultural products are corn, beans, wheat, sugar, tobacco, coffee, fruit, alfalfa, and maguey. Cattle and goats are the principal livestock, and their number is rapidly increasing.

The Torreón district lies in the arid portion of the Central Plateau, with elevations ranging from 3,779 feet at the city of Torreón to 5,000 feet in outlying parts of the district. The annual range of temperature is from 50° to 100° F. The average annual rainfall is about 6 to 8 inches, most of which falls between June and September. Precipitation is not sufficient to support crops, and the employment of irrigation is necessary. The principal sources of water are the Nazas and Aguanaval rivers.

Water from these rivers is conveyed to the fertile plains of the Laguna area. Cotton production is the leading industry in the district, the average crop being somewhat in excess of 275,000 bales per year. Other agricultural products are wheat, corn, beans, alfalfa, and grapes. In former years the mining and smelting of silver was an important industry, as were also the mining of lead, gold, zinc, and arsenic. The principal exports to the United States are goatskins, zinc concentrates, and cotton linters.

About 200 miles from the border at Laredo is Saltillo, another cultural center of the interior. Much of its district, a mile above the sea, is semiarid and dotted with cacti and other desert plants. Mining and farming are the leading industries. The principal ores are copper, lead-silver, and zinc. Winter wheat is the chief commercial crop, with corn and beans next. Istle fiber, used for cordage and brushes, is taken from a wild plant that is prevalent here and in other parts of the interior. Another interesting product is Candelilla wax, also taken from a plant, *Pedilánthus pavonis,* and used in shoe, floor, and furniture polishes.

MONTERREY: Elevation, 1,732 feet above sea level

Period of Record 1931–1940													
Temperature	*Jan.*	*Feb.*	*Mar.*	*Apr.*	*May*	*June*	*July*	*Aug.*	*Sept.*	*Oct.*	*Nov.*	*Dec.*	*Annual*
(°*F.*)	59.7	61.9	68.4	72.5	77.2	81.1	81.0	80.8	76.6	72.3	63.9	59.2	71.2
Rainfall (*Inches*)	1.3	0.5	0.5	0.9	2.1	1.8	3.7	6.5	9.6	2. 9	1.1	1.2	32.1

Source: H. Helm Clayton: "World Weather Records," *Smithsonian Miscellaneous Collections,* Vol. 105 (1947).

Monterrey is another important interior center. It is located in a progressive mining area of high mountains and some fertile valleys where irrigation is possible. The elevation of Monterrey is about 1,700 feet above the sea. Its climate is very hot during the summer. Monterrey has become primarily an industrial city, the site of the largest iron and steel plant in Mexico. There are also argentiferous lead smelters and refiners. All ores and fuel used, except natural gas, are of Mexican origin. The gas, which is piped from Texas, is slowly replacing other fuel in the industries as well as for domestic purposes.

The northwestern portion of Mexico's interior is served by the city of Chihuahua. Its surroundings are mountainous, with great areas of tablelands. The summers are warm and the winters mild, with freezing temperatures but no snow. The average rainfall is about 16 inches. Agriculture, mining and smelting, stock raising, and lumbering are the chief occupations of the district.

The west-central portion of the interior includes largely the mountainous state of Durango. East of its focal center, the city of Durango, is a comparatively flat terrain that supports a sparse agricultural population. In the highland areas the chief industry is mining. The city of Durango, located at an elevation of about 6,200 feet above sea level, has a temperature of 73° F. in the summer and of 55° F. during the winter. The rainfall amounts to about 15 inches annually, and most of the precipitation occurs during the summer.

NORTHERN BORDER ZONE

Border towns and trade. For the most part the international boundary between the United States and Mexico lies in a region of light rainfall, fairly mountainous country with a few fertile valleys, and sparse population. The major activities focus about ports of entry, including the Mexican border towns of Tijuana, Mexicali, Nogales, Ciudad Juárez, Piedras Negras, Nuevo Laredo, and Matamoros. A vast expanse of waste land separates these northern towns from the populous centers of the great Central Plateau, and for many years they were without transportation means to the nation's capital. The first railway in Mexico that connected Mexico, D. F., with the border and the United States was not built until 1884. Because of this isolation, which still exists somewhat, the Mexicans along the border were much more dependent upon the United States than on the rest of Mexico. To prevent undue emigration and lessen the burden of tariff duties, the "Free Zone" was established some 12½ miles wide on the Mexican side. Imports from the United States were admitted at a rate that amounted to only 11½ per cent of the regular Mexican tariff. This free zone was maintained from 1851 to 1905, or until the special problems of the border people disappeared, upon the completion of adequate transportation facilities. However, even today special privileges are extended to the border population. Free zones have been established in the border towns, into which may be imported, without payment of customs and duties, practically all articles not manufactured locally, if for consumption within those zones. Also, special border-crossing privileges are extended to the local residents and visitors.

The northwestern portion of the Mexican border zone, marked by the major focal centers of Tijuana and Mexicali, is semiarid and somewhat mountainous, with fertile valleys. The climate is similar to that prevailing in the southwestern portion of the United States, with an extremely hot season from May to October and mild winters. A light rainfall occurs primarily during the winter months.

In this northwestern portion of Mexico is the famous Imperial Valley of Mexico, consisting of more than 1,000,000 acres, of which 300,000 have been reclaimed for cultivation by irrigation. Vegetables, cotton, and wheat are the principal crops. Fresh vegetables and fruits are grown in large quantities and shipped mostly to the United States. The acreage planted to wheat has been constantly increased during the past several years.

Tourism is another important industry, one that is welcomed by all the border towns. It is the principal source of income for Tijuana and other border resorts.

Tijuana is joined to the United States by rail and highway. A highway, a portion of which is paved, also extends to the Pacific port, Ensenada. The greater percentage of the foreign imports and exports of these border towns is carried in motor vehicles.

Nogales is the principal trade center of the northwestern part of the state of Sonora and the port of entry for the Southern Pacific, which extends from Nogales southward to Mexico, D. F. The lands surrounding Nogales are largely mountainous and hilly and contain a limited area of river valleys with fertile soil and water for irrigation. The chief occupations of the area are mining—for copper, silver, gold, antimony, and other metals—and cattle raising and farming. As an exporting center, Nogales ranks first among the border ports. A large part of the food products and some of the metals exported from Nogales originate in areas south of the border region.

Across the border from El Paso, Texas, is Ciudad Juárez, one of the important distributing centers of northern Mexico. It is the northern terminus of two Mexican railway lines and an international highway. The Mexican National Railways operate daily trains from Ciudad Juárez to Chihuahua City and points immediately beyond. Connections are also made with transcontinental American railways for all parts of the United States and Canada. Reference has previously been made to the new highway joining Ciudad Juárez and Mexico, D. F.

Approximately the northern third of the state of Chihuahua comprises the hinterland of Ciudad Juárez. The region presents a rolling to a

CHIHUAHUA: Elevation, 4,669 feet above sea level

Period of Record 1936–1940

Rainfall (*Inches*)	*Jan.*	*Feb.*	*Mar.*	*Apr.*	*May*	*June*	*July*	*Aug.*	*Sept.*	*Oct.*	*Nov.*	*Dec.*	*Annual*
	0.6	0.6	0.2	0.1	0.3	1.7	3.9	2.7	3.8	0.4	0.9	0.5	15.7

Source: H. Helm Clayton: "World Weather Records," *Smithsonian Miscellaneous Collections,* Vol. 105 (1947).

rugged mountainous terrain. The altitude averages from 2,000 to 7,000 feet above the sea. The city of Juárez has an altitude of about 3,800 feet. The climate is semiarid, with occasional showers occurring during the summer months. During the winter there may be frost and snow. Irrigation is necessary for the production of cultivated crops, but there are good natural pasture lands, and the high mountain section has abundant rainfall that supports without irrigation crops of corn and wheat for local consumption. The leading exports from the region are lumber; silver and gold bullion; lead, silver, and gold ore; cattle products; cotton; and vegetables.

The northern half of the state of Coahuila is represented by Piedras Negras. This border town is a terminal of the Mexican National Railways. There is connection by bridge with the Southern Pacific System at Eagle Pass, Texas. An excellent asphalt-paved highway joins San Antonio and Eagle Pass, Texas, which adds to the importance of Piedras Negras. More people enter Coahuila from San Antonio and adjacent points via Piedras Negras than over any other route. In the Mexican trade region of Piedras Negras, agricultural, stock raising, zinc smelting, and coal production comprise the chief industries. A high grade of bituminous coal is mined in this region. A large zinc smelter is located at Rosita. Practically all business of a commercial nature is done with Eagle Pass, Del Rio, and San Antonio, Texas.

Nuevo Laredo is the principal northeastern border port of entry and shipment for goods destined for the populous sections of the Central Plateau of Mexico. Its adjacent land is a gentle rolling plain covered with mesquite, chaparral, and cactus, and is of little importance either as a consuming or producing region. The significance of Nuevo Laredo's participation in Mexico's trade is due primarily to its accessibility to Central Mexico and to the Mississippi Valley and the eastern manufacturing centers of the United States. It is a terminal of the National Railways of Mexico and the chief artery of rail communication between Mexico, D. F., and the central and eastern portions of the United States. There is a paved highway between Nuevo Laredo and Monterrey, a portion of the Pan-American Highway, which projects southward to Mexico, D. F. The distance by rail from Nuevo Laredo to Mexico, D. F., is about 800 miles, and by highway 763 miles.

The border town Matamoros warrants mention because of its location with respect to Brownsville, Texas. The latter is the site of one of the chief airports of the Pan American Airways, which daily maintains service between Brownsville and points in the United States and Latin America. The National Railways of Mexico connect Matamoros with Monterrey and other interior cities. A plan has been proposed to make Brownsville a deep-water port, which would make Matamoros a leading port of entry for goods destined to northeastern Mexico.

Summary. Northern Mexico consists of deserts, barren mountains, saline basins, and inaccessible valleys. The hostile nature of the terrain is fully emphasized by the prevalent cactus and mesquite. To a limited degree irrigation has made possible the cultivation of crops, including primarily winter vegetables and cotton. Minerals are by far the chief natural resources of this northern land. One of the most profitable business enterprises is tourism. The southern portion of the Central Plateau is the heart of Mexico, the leading agricultural, mining, and industrial center of the republic. On the seaward slopes of the coastal highland are the principal areas of tropical and subtropical agriculture.

Water is the most significant factor of deficiency in Mexico's natural environment. From time immemorial, Mexico has struggled to control water for agriculture and urban purposes. It has been the motive for worship and combat.

Since 1934, Mexico has pursued a policy of greater control of its natural resources and the establishment of communal lands or ejidos. This national social program awaits evaluation. Mexico's needs include more capital, more modern technology, greater agricultural production, and an improvement in the standards of living, particularly of its rural inhabitants. Health, nutrition, and sanitation should and undoubtedly will receive greater attention. Mexicans, however, are deterministic, and Mexico as a nation is progressively moving forward.

SELECTED REFERENCES

Atlas Geográfico de la República Mexicana, Tacubaya, Mexico, 1932.

Catálogo de Datos Numéricos, Geográficos y Topográficos de la República Mexicana, No. 8, 2d Ed., Tacubaya, Mexico, 1933.

Chamberlain, R. S.: "The Conquest and Colonization of Yucatán, 1517–1550," *Publication 582,* Carnegie Institution of Washington, Washington, D. C., 1948.

Cushing, S. W.: "The Distribution of Population in Mexico," *Geographical Review,* Vol. XI (1921), pp. 227–242.

Dicken, S. N.: "Corn and Wheat in Mexico's Changing Economy," *Journal of Geography,* Vol. 38 (1939), pp. 99–109.

Dicken, S. N.: "The Basin Settlements of the Middle Sierra Madre Oriental, Mexico," *Annals of the Association of American Geographers,* Vol. 26 (1936), pp. 157–178.

Dicken, S. N.: "Cotton Regions of Mexico," *Economic Geography,* Vol. XIV (1938), pp. 363–371.

Dicken, S. N.: "Monterrey and Northeastern Mexico," *Annals of the Association of American Geographers,* Vol. 29 (1939), pp. 127–158.

Foscue, Edwin J.: "Tasco, Mexico's Silver City," *American Resort Series, No. 2,* Southern Methodist University, Dallas, 1947.

Garlock, Lorene A.: "Cotton in the Economy of Mexico," *Economic Geography,* Vol. 20 (1944), pp. 70–77.

Garrison, Dorotha J.: "Reclamation Project of the Papaloapan River Basin in Mexico," *Economic Geography,* Vol. 26 (1950), pp. 59–64.

Gómez, Ana W.: "Mexican Agrarian Policy—Postwar Development," *Foreign Agriculture,* Vol. XII, No. 10 (1948), pp. 221–224.

Huntington, E.: "The Relation of Health to Racial Capacity: The Example of Mexico," *Geographical Review,* Vol. XI (1921), pp. 243–264.

Kniffen, F. B.: "The National Landscape of the Colorado Delta," *University of California Publications in Geography,* Vol. 5 (1932), pp. 149–245.

Lemert, Ben F., and Lemert, Rose V.: "Mexico: Rural Life in the Northeastern Coastal Plain," *Journal of Geography,* Vol. XXXIV, No. 8 (1935), pp. 318–324.

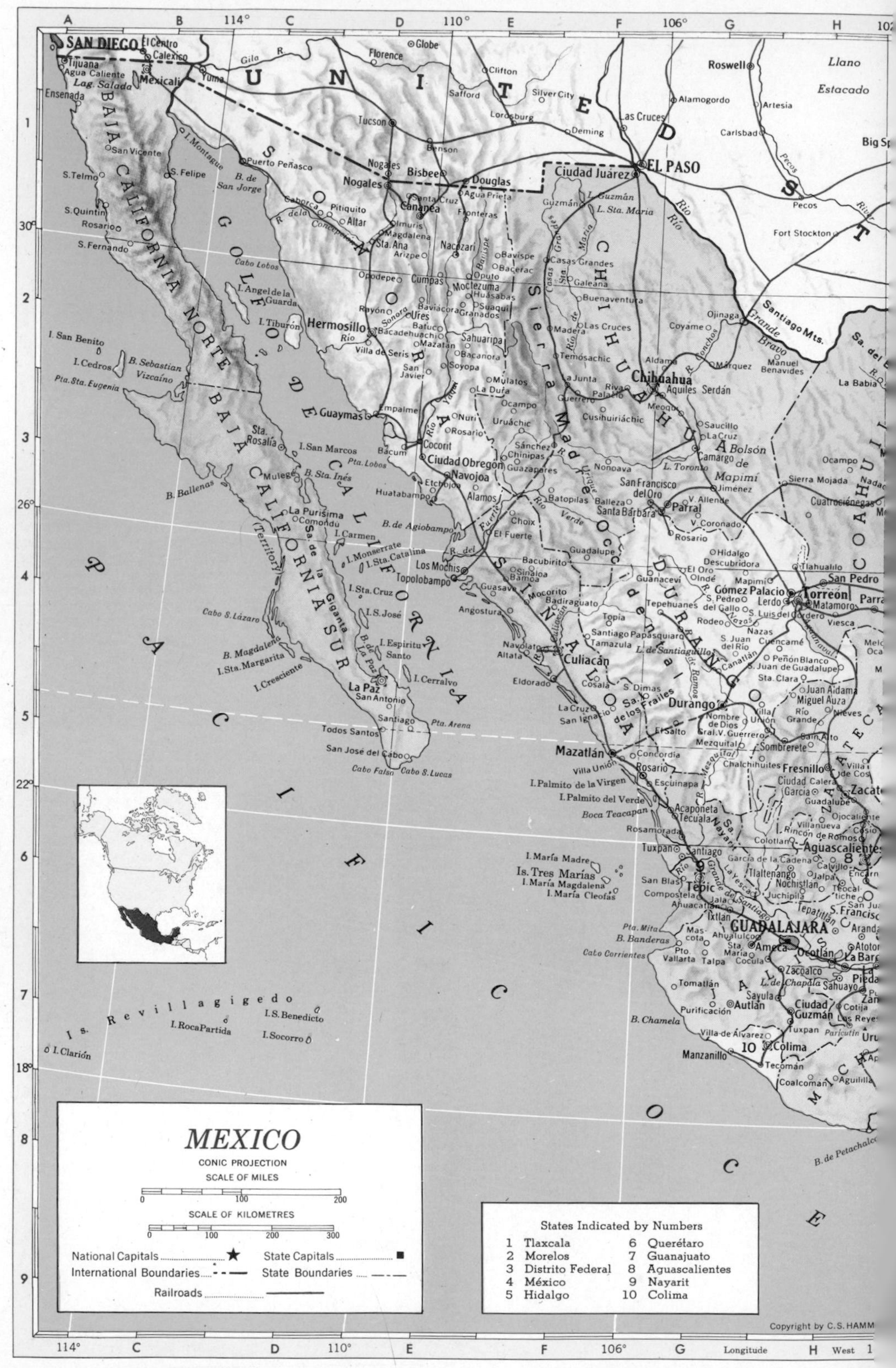
MEXICO
CONIC PROJECTION
SCALE OF MILES
0 100 200
SCALE OF KILOMETRES
0 100 200 300
National Capitals
State Capitals
International Boundaries
State Boundaries
Railroads
States Indicated by Numbers
1 Tlaxcala
2 Morelos
3 Distrito Federal
4 México
5 Hidalgo
6 Querétaro
7 Guanajuato
8 Aguascalientes
9 Nayarit
10 Colima
Copyright by C.S. HAMM
Longitude West
UNITED STATES
SAN DIEGO
El Centro
Calexico
Tijuana
Agua Caliente
Lag. Salada
Mexicali
Yuma
Ensenada
Gila R.
Florence
Globe
Clifton
Safford
Silver City
Tucson
Lordsburg
Deming
Las Cruces
Alamogordo
Roswell
Artesia
Carlsbad
Llano Estacado
Benson
Bisbee
Douglas
Nogales
Ciudad Juárez
EL PASO
Pecos
Fort Stockton
Big Sp
Santiago Mts.
Río Grande
Río Bravo
BAJA CALIFORNIA NORTE
BAJA CALIFORNIA SUR
(Territory)
GOLFO DE CALIFORNIA
SONORA
CHIHUAHUA
SINALOA
DURANGO
COAHUILA
ZACATECAS
JALISCO
Sierra Madre Occidental
San Vicente
S. Telmo
S. Quintín
Rosario
S. Fernando
S. Felipe
I. Montague
Puerto Peñasco
B. de San Jorge
Caborca
Pitiquito
Altar
R. de la Concepción
Cananea
Santa Cruz
Agua Prieta
Fronteras
Imuris
Magdalena
Sta. Ana
Arizpe
Nacozari
Bavispe
Bacerac
Cabo Lobos
I. Angel de la Guarda
Opodepe
Cumpas
Moctezuma
Opoto
Huásabas
Suaqui
Granados
Rayón
Ures
Baviácora
Río Sonora
I. Tiburón
Hermosillo
Batuco
Bacadehuachi
Mazatán
Sahuaripa
Villa de Seris
Bacanora
Soyopa
San Javier
I. San Benito
I. Cedros
B. Sebastian Vizcaíno
Pta. Sta. Eugenia
Guaymas
Empalme
Mulatos
La Dura
Ocampo
Nuri
Rosario
Uruáchic
Río Yaqui
Sta. Rosalía
I. San Marcos
Pta. Lobos
Bacum
Cocorit
Ciudad Obregón
Navojoa
Mulegé
B. Sta. Inés
B. Ballenas
Etchojoa
Huatabampo
Alamos
La Purísima
Comondú
I. Carmen
B. de Agiobampo
I. Monserrate
I. Sta. Catalina
Los Mochis
Topolobampo
I. Sta. Cruz
I. S. José
Cabo S. Lázaro
B. Magdalena
I. Sta. Margarita
I. Creciente
I. Espíritu Santo
I. Cerralvo
La Paz
San Antonio
Santiago
Pta. Arena
Todos Santos
San José del Cabo
Cabo Falso
Cabo S. Lucas
Sa. de la Giganta
PACIFIC OCEAN
Guzmán
L. Guzmán
L. Sta. María
Casas Grandes
Galeana
Buenaventura
Madera
Las Cruces
Temósachic
La Junta
Guerrero
Riva Palacio
Cusihuiriáchic
Chihuahua
Aquiles Serdán
Ojinaga
Coyame
Aldama
Márquez
R. Conchos
Manuel Benavides
La Babia
Meoqui
Saucillo
La Cruz
Camargo
Bolsón de Mapimí
L. Toronto
Nonoava
Sánchez
Chinipas
Guazapares
San Francisco del Oro
Parral
Santa Bárbara
Balleza
Batopilas
Jiménez
V. Allende
V. Coronado
Rosario
Choix
El Fuerte
Río Fuerte
Río Verde
Guadalupe
Bacubirito
Sinaloa
Bamoa
Guasave
Mocorito
Badiraguato
Angostura
Hidalgo
Descubridora
El Oro
Indé
Guanaceví
Mapimí
Gómez Palacio
Torreón
Lerdo
Matamoros
San Pedro
Viesca
Tlahualilo
Sierra Mojada
Ocampo
Cuatrociénegas
S. Pedro del Gallo
S. Luis del Cordero
Tepehuanes
Rodeo
Nazas
Topia
Santiago Papasquiaro
Tamazula
L. de Santiaguillo
S. Juan del Río
Cuencamé
Canatlán
Peñón Blanco
S. Juan de Guadalupe
Sta. Clara
Juan Aldama
Miguel Auza
Río Grande
Nieves
Navolato
Altata
Culiacán
Cosalá
Eldorado
S. Dimas
Sa. de los Frailes
Durango
Villa Unión
Nombre de Dios
Gral. V. Guerrero
Mezquital
El Salto
La Cruz
San Ignacio
Mazatlán
Concordia
Rosario
Escuinapa
Villa Unión
Chalchihuites
Sombrerete
Fresnillo
Sain Alto
Ciudad García
Calera
Zacatecas
I. Palmito de la Virgen
I. Palmito del Verde
Boca Teacapan
Acaponeta
Tecuala
Rosamorada
Tuxpan
Santiago
Villanueva
Ojocaliente
Guadalupe
Rincón de Romos
Aguascalientes
Colotlán
I. María Madre
Is. Tres Marías
I. María Magdalena
I. María Cleofás
San Blas
Tepic
Compostela
Ahuacatlán
Jala
Ixtlán
García de la Cadena
Tlaltenango
Nochistlán
Juchipila
Jalpa
Calvillo
Teocaltiche
Tepatitlán
S. Francisco
Pta. Mita
B. Banderas
Mascota
Ahualulco
GUADALAJARA
Ameca
Sta. María
Cocula
Ocotlán
Atotonilco
La Barca
Cabo Corrientes
Pto. Vallarta
Talpa
Zacoalco
L. de Chapala
Sahuayo
Tomatlán
Sayula
Autlán
Ciudad Guzmán
Cotija
Los Reyes
Purificación
B. Chamela
Villa de Alvarez
Tuxpan
Paricutín
Manzanillo
Colima
Tecomán
Coalcomán
Aguililla
B. de Petacalco
Is. Revillagigedo
I. S. Benedicto
I. Roca Partida
I. Socorro
I. Clarión
114°
110°
106°
30°
26°
22°
18°

Lemert, Ben F., and Lemert, Rose V.: "Rural Life in the Mountains Between Mexico, D. F., and Acapulco," *Journal of Geography,* Vol. XXXIV, No. 9 (1935), pp. 357–363.

Lemert, Ben F., and Lemert, Rose V.: "The United States and Mexico," *Journal of Geography,* Vol. XXXIV, No. 7 (1935), pp. 261–266.

Lemert, Ben F.: "Cities of Mexico," *Journal of Geography,* Vol. XLVI, No. 3 (1947), pp. 287–295.

Lemert, Ben F.: "Parícutin," *Journal of Geography,* Vol. XLVII (1948), pp. 267–275.

McBride, G. M.: "The Land Systems of Mexico," *Research Series No. 12,* American Geographical Society, New York, 1923.

McClarren, J. K.: "Foot-and-Mouth Disease Control in Mexico—Third Year," *Foreign Agriculture,* Vol. 13, No. 7 (1949), pp. 147–152.

Morley, S. G.: *The Ancient Maya,* Stanford University Press, Stanford, 1946.

Pough, Frederick H.: "The Geologic History of Parícutin," *Transactions of the New York Academy of Sciences,* Ser. 2, Vol. 2, No. 2 (1948), pp. 28–33.

Redfield, R.: *Tepoztlan, a Mexican Village,* University of Chicago Press, Chicago, 1930.

Redfield, R.: *The Folk Culture of Yucatán,* the University of Chicago Press, Chicago, 1941.

Sanders, E. M.: "Natural Regions of Mexico," *Geographical Review,* Vol. XI (1921), pp. 212–226.

Sauer, C. O.: "The Personality of Mexico," *Geographical Review,* Vol. XXXI (1941), pp. 353–364.

Shattuck, G. C.: *The Peninsula of Yucatán,* Carnegie Institution of Washington, Washington, D. C., 1933.

Sterling, H. S.: "The Changing Face of Rural Mexico," *Geographical Review,* Vol. XXXIX (1949), pp. 139–143.

Spinden, H. J.: *Ancient Civilizations of Mexico and Central America,* American Museum of Natural History, New York, 1917.

Tannenbaum, F.: *Mexico,* Alfred A. Knopf, New York, 1950.

Thornthwaite, C. W.: "The Climates of North America According to a New Classification," *Geographical Review,* Vol. XXI (1931), pp. 633–655.

Vivó, Jorge A.: *Geografía de Mexico,* Fonda de Cultura Económica, Mexico, D. F., 1948.

Vogt, William: *Mexican Natural Resources—Their Past, Present and Future,* Report on activities of the Conservation Section, Division of Agricultural Cooperation, Pan American Union, Washington, D. C., 1946.

West, R. C., and Parsons, J. J.: "The Topia Road: A Trans-Sierran Trail of Colonial Mexico," *Geographical Review,* Vol. XXXI (1941), pp. 406–413.

Whetten, Nathan L.: *Rural Mexico,* University of Chicago Press, Chicago, 1948.

Whitaker, A. P., ed.: "Mexico Today," *Annals of the American Academy of Political and Social Science,* Vol. 208 (March, 1940).

CHAPTER XXIX

THE WEST INDIES: AN INSULAR PATTERN OF MANY COUNTRIES

GENERAL CHARACTERISTICS

Political pattern. The insular chain known as the West Indies begins near the coast of Florida and extends eastward until it curves sharply southward to the shores of Venezuela. Three major groups of islands comprise this chain: (1) the Bahamas, (2) the Greater Antilles, and (3)

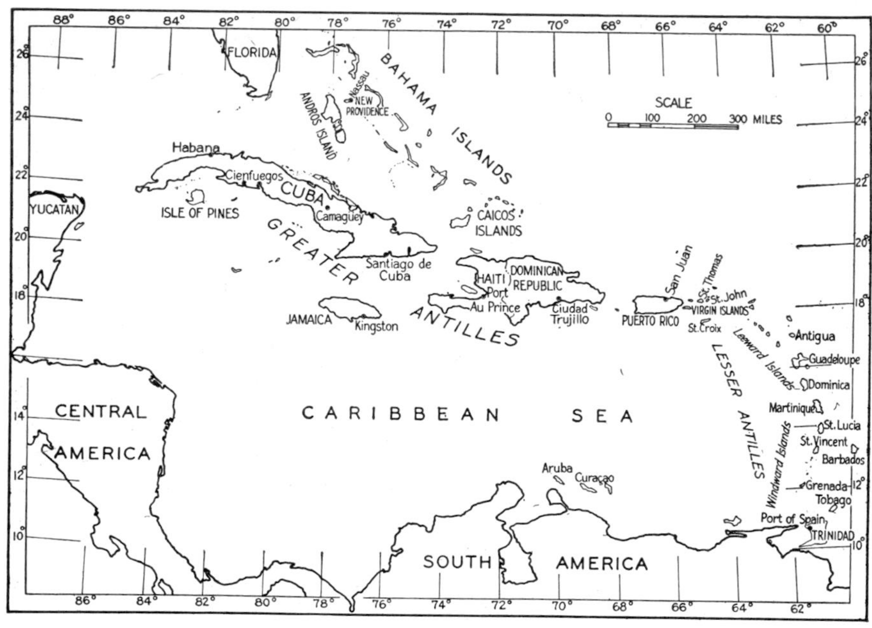

F. A. Carlson.

Fig. 140. The West Indies.

the Lesser Antilles. The Bahamas, a British archipelago of more than 300 islands, extend southeastward of Florida for some 700 miles. Within the Greater Antilles are three nations, Cuba, Haiti, and the Dominican Republic, and possessions of the United States and European countries. Southeast of the Greater Antilles are the small islands of the Lesser

Antilles. This latter group is classified into (1) the Leeward Islands, located in the turn of the chain toward South America; and (2) the Windward Islands running directly south, and along the coast of Venezuela. They consist of British, Netherland, and French possessions.

West Indian population—distribution and heritage. The total population of the West Indies is estimated—there is no accurate census available—at some 15 million. Approximately 90 per cent of the inhabitants live on the four largest islands: Cuba, Hispaniola, including the republics of Haiti and Dominica; Puerto Rico, and Jamaica.

AREA AND POPULATION OF PRINCIPAL WEST INDIAN ISLANDS

Island	*Area in Square Miles*	*Population*	*Capital*	*Population of Capital*
Cuba	44,164	5,052,000	Habana	850,000
Dominican Republic	19,325	2,245,000	Ciudad Trujillo	116,000
Haiti	10,700	3,500,000	Port-au-Prince	142,000
Jamaica	4,411	1,238,000	Kingston	109,000
Puerto Rico *	3,421	2,205,308	San Juan	209,000
Trinidad	1,862	568,000	Port of Spain	95,000

* Puerto Rico and its islands of Mona, Vieques, and Culebra have a total area of 3,421 square miles.

The density of population and the fact that specialized agriculture is the chief industry clearly indicate an overpopulation. Puerto Rico is overcrowded, with approximately 644 persons per square mile; Jamaica, 278; Haiti, 327; Barbados, 1,163; Cuba, 113; and the Dominican Republic, 116. The normal rate of increase is high, far above that of continental United States and Europe. Since immigration to the islands has practically stopped, the increase represents the number of births over deaths; and this is a significant addition to the already overpopulated areas.

How many Indian aborigines occupied the insular lands at the beginning of colonization in the sixteenth century is unknown. Some writers have placed the number at 6 million, which is probably far too high. In any case the original inhabitants were nearly all destroyed or absorbed into the racial complex of European and African settlers during the early colonial days. It is reported that there are still a few groups of Indians of pure descent in the Virgin Islands, Puerto Rico, and the Dominican Republic.

Three stocks—the Indian aborigine, the European, and the African Negro—constitute the racial heritage of the West Indies. With respect to physical characteristics, the African stock was apparently the dominant factor, because today, with the exception of Cuba and Puerto Rico, there is a marked tendency for the Negro population to be the prevalent one of the islands. In Jamaica there are 60 Negroes to 1 white; in Haiti there are practically no white people; the Dominican Republic reports 25 per cent white, 50 per cent mixed (largely mulattoes), and 25 per cent

Negro; Cuba has 27 per cent Negro and mixed, and the remainder white; and Puerto Rico has not more than 35 per cent Negro. Both Cuba and Puerto Rico have shown, in the course of the past century, an increase in the percentage of whites over Negroes, while in the other islands, particularly the smaller ones, the increase is one of Negroes over whites.

Early in the sixteenth century Negroes were imported for work in the sugar plantations—in part to replace the rapidly disappearing Indian and in part to meet the growing demand for additional labor. The importation of African Negroes for local labor and for shipment either to the United States or to South America continued until the abolition of slavery in the West Indies and on the American mainland. The suitability of the Negro for life in the West Indies and other tropical regions is widely recognized. He is able to do hard work in a hot, humid climate and to live, apparently satisfied, with the bare necessities of life. Not that he does not want a high standard of living, good wages, and the like, but his background and general philosophy of life seem to make it easier for him than for the white man to meet the adversities of the tropics. In nearly every case the Negro can underlive the white, and this makes it almost impossible for whites to compete with the blacks in general labor in the tropics.

It is seldom that a Negro is elected to high office except in Haiti, or attains to high standing in the governmental service. Of course, there are many of mixed blood holding high office, but they are predominantly white. Usually the higher officials are members of the old aristocratic families of Spanish extraction, with occasionally some admixture of Indian blood. They acquired their estates under the old imperial, aristocratic regime by gift of the crown. They have remained the large landlords, the settled aristocracy, to this day. Their Negro tenants and less prosperous neighbors would not think of running for office, even if they had the education and ability necessary to hold it.

The personnel in the business offices and the clerks in the larger stores are almost always white, and the administrative officials in the industrial world are also white. Industrial capital is to a considerable extent supplied by European or American capitalists, who have their own representatives to manage it, and who normally select white subordinates. The darker skinned natives occupy the humbler walks of life, as operatives and mechanics in the factories, laborers in the cities, or hands or tenants on the farms.

Climates in general. The West Indies has an insular, tropical climate, with a slight range in temperature and an abundant rainfall in nearly all of the islands.

Near sea level the average annual temperature is between 77.5° and 79.5° F. At greater elevations temperatures are naturally lower; they average about 70° at 1,500 feet and 60° at 4,900 feet above sea level.

July or August is generally the warmest month, with an average temperature of between 78° and 84° at sea level, 75° at 1,500 feet, and 65° at 4,900 feet. The lowest temperatures occur in January or February; near sea level the readings are as a rule between 75° and 77°, while for the higher elevations they are 70° at 1,500 feet and 58° at 4,900 feet. The average annual range in temperature—that is, the average difference between absolute maximum and absolute minimum—decreases somewhat from north to south, with about 41° in the Bahamas and Cuba and 35° in Barbados and Grenada.

The islands lie within the northeast trades, the prevailing winds coming from the northeast and east. These winds are remarkably steady and, when associated with highlands, play a significant role in the distribution of rainfall.

A considerable difference in the amount of rainfall occurs over the windward and leeward slopes. The contrast is particularly marked between high windward and low leeward regions, even within comparatively short distances. One of the most striking contrasts is in Jamaica, where there is a variation of 192 inches between Mooretown and Kingston in a distance of 30 miles. Another marked difference in rainfall is found in Dominica, where Roseau on the western coast, at an elevation of 25 feet, has an average annual precipitation of 78 inches, while Shawford, only some three miles to the northeast, at an elevation of 560 feet, has an average annual rainfall of more than 150 inches.

As a whole, the West Indies have two periods of maximum rainfall: May to June, and September to November. The seasons of minimum rainfall come in middle or late autumn and in middle or late winter. In nearly all the islands the greatest monthly rainfalls are over 10 inches, and at some places they exceed 20 inches; while the lowest monthly averages fall below one inch.

In late summer and autumn, tropical cyclones or hurricanes occasionally visit the West Indies. They come from the east or southeast, and usually move to the west, northwest, and then northeast along the Atlantic Coast of the United States. Sometimes they travel westward across the northern portion of Mexico. These storms are most frequent in the northern and eastern islands; the more southern islands are less frequently visited by hurricanes. The more violent storms such as the ones in 1917 and 1926 cause loss of life, destruction of property and crops, and disasters at sea.

Strategic and economic importance. In time of peace or war, the significance of the West Indies has been demonstrated. Located near the approach to the heart of the Western Hemisphere, the West Indies are of vital importance as sites for war bases. The insular pattern of the West Indies can be penetrated by sea only through rather narrow passages. Cuba and the northern peninsula of Haiti are separated by the Windward Passage (about 45 miles wide); the Dominican Republic and Puerto Rico by the Mona Passage (60 miles wide), but midway in this water lie the Mona Islands, a possession of the United States; the Virgin Islands and the Anguilla Island by the Anegada Passage (70 miles wide)—30 miles from the Virgin Islands to the lighthouse on Sombrero, located in the Anegada Passage; and the unnamed southern passages between Grenada and Tobago (about 85 miles wide) and Tobago and Trinidad (21 miles wide). These passages act as knotting points or areas of ship concentration where enemy craft are likely to ply for their attack. One of the most difficult passages to patrol, because of its width, is the Strait of Florida between Cuba and the state of Florida, an expanse of sea some 100 miles wide.

Economically, all of the West Indies are of importance as sources of strategic materials. Trinidad produces about 20,000,000 barrels of oil annually, and off the coast of northern South America lie the islands of Aruba and Curaçao, where some 80 per cent of Venezuela's 500,000,000 barrels of oil are refined or stored for foreign shipment. In normal times 40 per cent of the sugar consumed in the United States is imported from the Caribbean Islands, as well as large quantities of tobacco, fruits, vegetables, fibers, and manufactured goods. Cuba is a leading source of chrome ore or chromite, and other essential minerals are produced in Cuba as well as in other islands of the West Indies. With respect to trade, the Caribbean Islands constitute one of the major regions in terms of United States' exports and imports.

Summary. The economy of the West Indies, like all of Latin America, centers primarily in the production of raw materials. In the West Indies the leading raw materials are largely agricultural; they include sugar, tobacco, coffee, cacao, coconuts, spices, and fruits. Among the important mineral and forest products are petroleum, asphalt, iron and chrome ores, logwood, and mahogany. The most important product from an international viewpoint, however, is sugar.

In general, standards of living are low; health, nutrition and sanitation conditions are not extensively supervised; land is owned by a few, mostly absentee owners; overpopulation prevails; the ethnic trend is toward a group consisting of mixed races, Negro and white; and interinsular transportation facilities are inadequate.

A decided improvement in these West Indies affairs may be instituted through: (1) a greater development of forestry and livestock, (2) a greater diversification of agriculture, (3) a greater production of foodstuffs for home consumption, (4) a greater number of self-sustaining farmers, (5) a greater variety of products for foreign markets, and (6) a greater development of minor manufacturing industries.

SELECTED REFERENCES

Arnold, Edwin G.: "The Expanding Economy of Puerto Rico," *Think,* Vol. 13, No. 11 (1947).

Beard, J. S.: "The Natural Vegetation of Trinidad," *Oxford Forestry Memoirs, No. 20,* Oxford University Press, 1946.

Bennett, H. H.: "Some Geographical Aspects of Cuban Soils," *Geographical Review,* Vol. XVIII (1928), pp. 62–82.

Billmyer, James H. S.: "The Cayman Islands," *Geographical Review,* Vol. XXXVI, No. 1 (1946), pp. 29–43.

Blanshard, Paul: *Democracy and Empire in the Caribbean,* Macmillan, New York, 1948.

Boyer, Helen M.: "Distribution of Sugar Cane Production in Cuba," *Economic Geography,* Vol. XV (1939), pp. 311–325.

Canet, Gerardo A., and Raisez, Erwin: *Atlas of Cuba,* Harvard University Press, Cambridge, 1949.

Carlson, F. A.: "American Settlement in the Isla de Pinos, Cuba," *Geographical Review,* Vol. XXXII (1942), pp. 21–35.

Chamberlin, T. W.: "Rainfall Maps of Cuba," *Monthly Weather Review,* Vol. 68 (1940), pp. 4–10.

Chapman, Charles E.: *A History of the Cuban Republic; A Study in Hispanic American Politics,* Macmillan, New York, 1927.

Clark, V. S., and associates: *Porto Rico and Its Problems,* The Brookings Institution, Washington, D. C., 1930.

Crist, R.: "Static and emerging cultural landscape on the Islands of St. Kitts and Nevis, B. W. I.," *Economic Geography,* Vol. 25, No. 2 (1949), pp. 134–145.

Crist, R.: "Sugar Cane and Coffee in Puerto Rico," *American Journal of Economics and Sociology,* Vol. 7, No. 2 (1948), pp. 173–184.

Evans, L. H.: "Unrest in the Virgin Islands," *Foreign Policy Reports,* Vol. XI (1935), Foreign Policy Association, New York, pp. 14–24.

Evans, L. E.: *The Virgin Islands,* Edwards, Ann Arbor, 1945.

Gottman, Jean: "The Isles of Guadeloupe," *Geographical Review,* Vol. XXXV, No. 2 (1945), pp. 182–203.

Gordon, W. W.: "Race Patterns and Prejudice in Puerto Rico," *American Sociological Review,* Vol. 14 (1949), pp. 294–301.

Gunther, J.: "Hispaniola," *Foreign Affairs,* Vol. 19 (1941), pp. 764–777.

Haas, W. H.: "Puerto Rico: An Interpretation," *Journal of Geography,* Vol. 45, No. 5 (1946).

Harrison, Lucia Carolyn: "Dominica: A Wet Tropical Human Habitat," *Economic Geography,* Vol 11 (1935), pp. 62–76.

James, P. E.: "The Climate of Trinidad, B. W. I.," *Monthly Weather Review,* Vol. LIII (1925), U. S. Department of Agriculture, pp. 71–75.

James, P. E.: "A Geographic Reconnaissance of Trinidad," *Economic Geography,* Vol. III (1927), pp. 87–109.

Koeller, Harold L.: "Our Increasing Agricultural Trade with Cuba," *Foreign Agriculture,* Vol. XII, No. 7 (1948), pp. 149–152.

Massip, Salvador: *Introducción A La Geografia De Cuba,* La Habana, Cuba, 1942.

Meyerhoff, H. A.: "The Texture of Karst Topography in Cuba and Puerto Rico," *Journal of Geomorphology,* Vol. 1 (1940), pp. 279–295.

Milstead, H. P.: "Cacao Industry of Grenada," *Economic Geography,* Vol. XVI (1940), pp. 195–203.

Nelson, Lowry: "La Zafra—Cuba's Sugar Cane Harvest," *Agriculture in the Americas,* Vol. VII, No. 2 (1947), pp. 34–36.

Perkins, Dexter: *The United States and the Caribbean,* Harvard University Press, Cambridge, 1947.

Picó, R.: "Land Tenure in the Leading Types of Farming of Puerto Rico," *Economic Geography,* Vol. XV (1939), pp. 135–145.

Puerto Rico and Virgin Islands: *Industrial Development of Puerto Rico and the Virgin Islands of the United States,* Report of the United States Section, Caribbean Commission, Port-of-Spain, Trinidad, 1948, pp. 268–300.

Puerto Rico: *Annual Report of the Governor of Puerto Rico.*

Puerto Rico: *Information on Puerto Rico,* prepared by the Insular Government and the Department of the Interior, Washington, D. C., 1948.

Senior, Clarence: "Puerto Rico Is Overpopulated," *News Letter of the Institute of Ethnic Affairs,* Vol. 3, No. 2 (1948), pp. 1–7.

Senior, Clarence: "Population Pressure and the Future of Puerto Rico," *Journal of Heredity,* Vol. 38, No. 5 (1947), pp. 131–134.

Shaw, E. B.: "Population Adjustments in Our Virgin Islands," *Economic Geography,* Vol. XI (1935), pp. 267–279.

Shaw, E. B.: "St. Croix: A Marginal Sugar Producing Island," *Geographical Review,* Vol. XXIII (1933), pp. 414–422.

Shaw, E. B.: "St. Thomas: The Keystone of the Antilles," *Journal of Geography,* Vol. XXXII (1934), pp. 131–139.

Shaw, E. B.: "The Balanced Economy of St. John Island," *Economic Geography,* Vol. IX (1933), pp. 160–166.

Starkey, O. P.: *The Economic Geography of Barbados; A Study of the Relationships between Environmental Variations and Economic Development,* Columbia University Press, New York, 1939.

Stovall, Rollo P.: "Cibao Valley—Food Basket of the Dominican Republic," *Agriculture in the Americas,* Vol. VII, No. 405 (1947), pp. 73–75.

Tugwell, Rexford G.: *The Stricken Land: The Story of Puerto Rico,* Doubleday and Co., New York, 1947.

United States Weather Bureau, *Climatic Summary of the United States,* Section 106, "Puerto Rico and the U. S. Virgin Islands," United States Department of Commerce.

Van Royen, W.: "A Geographical Reconnaissance of the Cibao of Santo Domingo," *Geographical Review,* Vol. XXVIII (1938), pp. 556–572.

Ward, R. De C., and Brooks, C. F.: "Climatology of the West Indies," *Handbuch der Klimatologie,* Band II, Teil I (1934), Berlin, pp. 111–147.

CHAPTER XXX

REPUBLICS IN THE WEST INDIES

CUBA

Largest West Indian island. The republic of Cuba, located directly south of Florida, consists of the island of Cuba, the Isle of Pines, and several other small islands. The area is about 44,000 square miles, and the population is over 5,000,000. Habana, the capital of Cuba, is 324 nautical miles from Tampa, Florida, and 1,166 from New York.[1] From Key West to Habana the distance is only some 100 nautical miles.

Nearly all parts of the island can be reached from Habana over the republic's 3,000 miles of railway. In addition to public service railways, a considerable mileage is maintained by the sugar companies; the henequén growers, and other industries. Only 200 miles of the public railways are narrow gauge. The remainder is standard gauge. The industrial lines include standard and various widths of narrow gauge.

A concrete highway extends across the island from Santiago de Cuba in the east to Pinar del Río, at the western extremity, a distance of about 700 miles. In addition, there are some 2,000 miles of improved roads.

Isle of Pines. Almost due south of Habana, and about 60 miles across the Gulf of Batabano, is the Isle of Pines, an integral part of Cuba. Its political status was not clearly defined until 1925, when the United States relinquished all claim to this Cuban satellite. A few Americans have settled on the island and are primarily engaged, somewhat successfully, in the growing of grapefruit and winter vegetables. The area of the island is 860 square miles, and the population is about 4,000. Its chief port and city is Nueva Gerona.

Climatic conditions. Moderately high and uniform temperatures prevail in Cuba. The average temperature is about 80° F. in summer and approximately 70° F. in winter. In the interior the temperature is usually higher than along the insular margins. The island is free from damaging frosts, and snow is unknown. Occasionally, during winter, cool north winds blow over the island.

The most significant statement that can be made about the rainfall of Cuba is that it is dependable and sufficient during the usual crop-growing

[1] *Habana* is the Spanish way of spelling the name of the Cuban capital; *Havana* is the English word.

CUBA: TEMPERATURE AND RAINFALL OF SELECTED STATIONS

Station	Camajuani*	Camagüey *	Cienfuegos	Habana†	Nueva Gerona Isle of Pines*	Pinar del Río *	Preston*	Santiago de Cuba†
Elevation (*Feet*)	328.1	344.5	98.4	78.7	196.9	180.5	16.4	114.8
Average Temperature (°F.)								
Period of Record	1900–1919	1900–1919	1911–1921	60 yrs.	1899–1920	1899–1927	1899–1927	16 yrs.
January	67.5	71.8	71.8	72	73.4	71.8	74.3	75
February	68.5	73.8	71.2	72	71.8	72.5	74.3	75
March	70.5	76.1	73.2	74	75.4	75.0	75.2	77
April	72.9	77.5	75.4	77	78.1	77.9	77.0	78
May	75.6	79.5	77.5	79	80.2	80.6	79.3	80
June	77.0	80.4	78.8	81	81.0	81.9	80.6	81
July	77.5	81.7	80.2	82	81.9	82.8	81.1	82
August	77.7	82.0	80.6	82	81.7	82.8	81.3	82
September	76.6	80.6	79.5	81	80.8	81.5	81.1	81
October	75.4	79.0	78.4	79	79.2	79.3	80.4	80
November	71.2	75.4	74.5	75	76.3	75.0	77.7	76
December	69.1	73.2	72.7	72	73.9	72.9	75.2	79
Annual	73.2	77.5	76.3	77	77.7	77.7	77.9	79
Range	10.2	10.2	9.4	10.0	10.1	11.0	7.0	7.0
Average Rainfall (*Inches*)								
Period of Record	1900–1920	1900–1921	1911–1921	72 yrs.	1911–1927	1899–1927	1908–1927	21 yrs.
January	2.0	1.5	0.7	2.8	1.6	1.9	3.9	1.2
February	1.2	1.5	0.9	1.9	2.3	1.9	2.2	0.7
March	1.4	2.4	0.9	1.9	2.2	2.2	1.3	1.5
April	3.0	3.7	1.5	2.2	4.0	2.6	3.1	2.8
May	6.3	7.5	4.1	4.5	8.4	6.7	5.4	6.0
June	9.4	10.7	5.9	6.6	11.1	10.1	2.2	5.1
July	5.2	5.5	5.0	4.8	7.4	6.5	1.3	2.2
August	5.4	5.4	4.9	5.4	8.0	7.6	1.6	3.8
September	6.5	7.4	5.9	5.8	10.6	10.5	3.8	6.0
October	7.0	5.4	5.4	6.5	10.0	7.7	6.4	8.5
November	5.0	3.1	2.3	3.0	2.0	2.4	8.6	3.9
December	2.8	1.9	0.9	2.3	1.5	1.2	5.5	1.2
Annual	55.2	56.1	38.7	47.7	70.6	63.4	47.1	42.9

* R. De C. Ward and C. F. Brooks: "Climatology of the West Indies," *Handbuch der Klimatologie,* Band II, Teil I, Berlin, 1934.

† *United States Weather Bureau Technical Paper No. 8,* United States Weather Bureau, Washington, D. C., 1949.

months from May to November. In accord with the general distribution of rainfall in the West Indies, Cuba has two periods of maxima, in May to June, and in September to November, while the periods of minima occur in middle or late autumn and winter. The average annual precipitation is usually from 60 to 70 inches in the extreme western province of Pinar del Río, in the southern part of the province of Habana, and at Nueva Gerona, on the Isle of Pines. In the provinces of Matanzas, Santa

Clara, and Camagüey, it is about 50 to 55 inches, while in the province of Oriente the amounts are generally 40 to 50 inches.

Cuba lies in the belt of hurricanes and on several occasions has experienced the menace of these destructive storms. The western end has suffered more than the central and eastern portions because of the fact that the average path of these storms lies close to the western end of the island. Unfortunately the hurricane season coincides with the stage of crop harvest, from July to October.

Topographical features. About 60 per cent of the land of Cuba is flat to gently rolling and well adapted, as far as relief is concerned, to the use of modern farm machinery. The remaining 40 per cent of the island consists of a rugged hilly to mountainous terrain, of which about one-half is suitable for cultivation. Practically all of the distinctly mountainous country is found in the eastern portion of the island, in the province of Oriente. Here one range, the Sierra Maestra, located along the southern shore of Oriente, rises to an elevation of 7,872 feet above sea level. Approximately 80 per cent of this area is mountainous and hilly. At the other end of the island, in the province of Pinar del Río, the western portion of Cuba, there are also areas of strong relief. The Guaniguanico Mountains, comprising the western portion of the highlands of Pinar del Río, are most peculiar topographical features. Huge blocks and mesas, known as magotes, rise from a slightly rolling plain to heights of a thousand feet. The third highland area of the republic is in the central province of Santa Clara. A discontinuous low divide occupies the major east-west axis of the island, and from this numerous streams flow either to the north or to the south, except in the highland region of Oriente.

An extensive submarine shelf projects in places beyond the insular shores, and over this the water is not very deep. In these shallow waters are numerous cayos, or mangrove islands, and obstructive reefs.

The coast of Cuba is high and rocky in some places, particularly along the seaward margins of the provinces of Habana, Matanzas, and Oriente. In other places the coast is flat and frequently merges into swamps. Much of it is inundated during the wet seasons, and great damage is done to crops. Some of these coastal lowlands are utilized only for pasturing stock. Along the northern coast and associated islands are extensive mangrove swamps.

Cuba has many excellent harbors, located for the most part at the mouths of rivers. They are deep and landlocked, and nearly all have a distinctive pouch shape, particularly those on the northern coast. The most important ones are Habana, Cienfuegos, Santiago de Cuba, Nuevitas, and Matanzas. A free trade zone has been established at Matanzas, which should have a national importance. Most of the ports are connected with railways giving ready access to sugar centrals and other

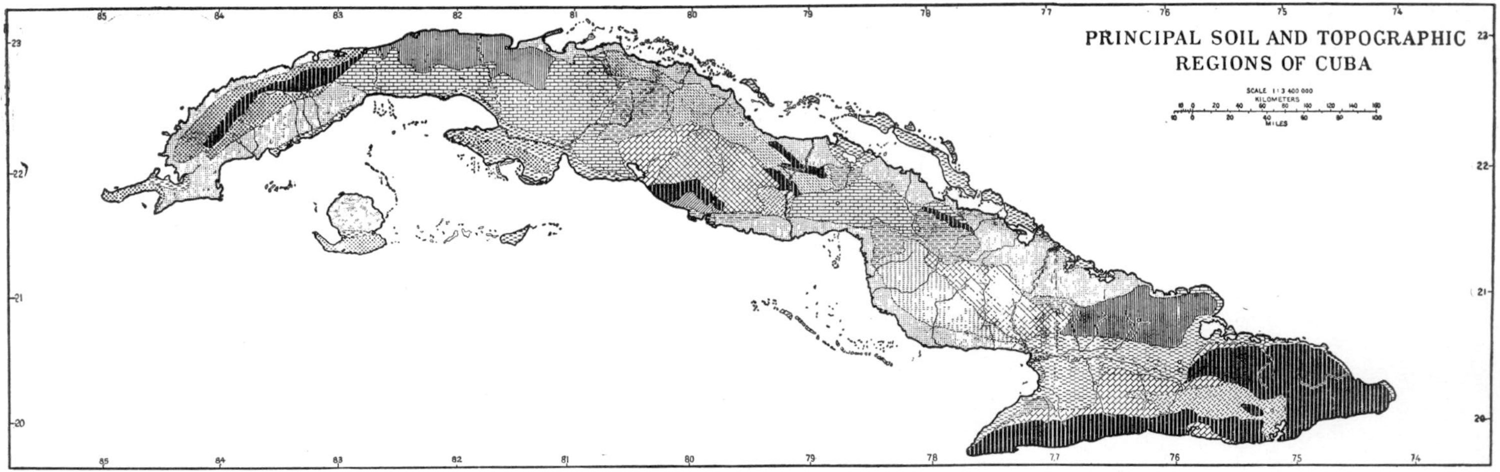

PRINCIPAL SOIL AND TOPOGRAPHIC REGIONS OF CUBA

From the Geographical Review, Vol. XVIII. Copyright by The American Geographical Society, New York. Reprinted by permission.

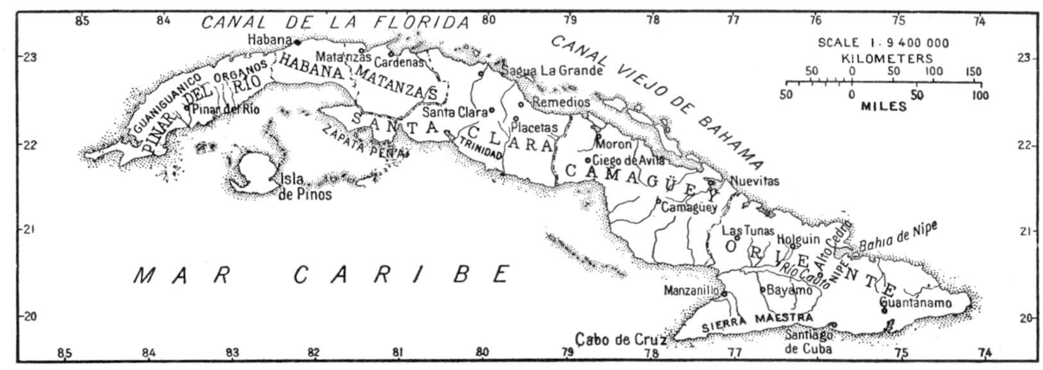

1. Coastal Plains. Mainly flat and frequently merging into swamp: much land inundated in wet season. Large variety of soils chiefly clays of stiff, impervious subsoils: brown over yellow (*Júcaro*); brown over yellow, gray, and red (*Herrera*); black over yellow (*Zapata*); and *Truffin*. In northwestern Camagüey much stiff, gray alluvial clay (*Yaguajay*); in northeastern Camagüey and northwestern Oriente much black and gray clay over greenish, stiff clay (*Lugareño* and *Tunas*); in northwestern Oriente considerable brown, friable clay of purplish cast (*Chaparra*). The *Chaparra* is nearly all in cane, giving good yields: other clays often have hummocky surface (hogwallow), difficult to keep in good tilth. Much cane grown with rather poor yields on the *Júcaro, Herrera*, and *Zapata*, and also on local salty areas. In Pinar del Rio flat and often wet near sea; undulating to rolling and well drained toward interior. Predominantly sandy and gravelly soils of acid reaction and low fertility. Many types like those of southeastern United States. The better drained of these, especially those with reddish, friable sandy clay subsoils (*Greenville, Orangeburg, Ruston;* and *Pinar del Rio*), produce with fertilizers a fine grade of tobacco. Some good cane on alluvial soils. Considerable hardwood forest locally in east. Some infertile savanas.

2. Limestone red lands. Mainly flat plains. Deep, red clay (*Matanzas*) friable and highly permeable; little change from surface downward. Excellent soil, largely used for sugar cane. Locally shallow and stony, better suited to pasture. Considerable red and brown clays (*Perico* and *Truffin*) with tough clay subsoils, highly desiccated and stone-like in the dry season, but on which yields can be greatly increased by deep subsoil tillage.

3. Rio Cauto-Alto Cedro Plain. Low and flat; some areas imperfectly drained. Mostly heavy clay of black (*Bayamo*) and gray (*Alto Cedro*) color, difficult to keep in good tilth. Extensively used for cane. Some limestone hills, consisting chiefly of *Santa Clara* soils. In places injurious amounts of salt.

4. Savanas. Flat, locally undulating. Mainly grass, with palms and small trees locally abundant. Sandy soils and shallow clay over rock, usually of low productivity. Liberally fertilized, well-drained deep sandy lands (*Estrella types*) produce fair crops of cane. The dominant shallow soils, including the peculiar *Mocarrero* sandy types with ironstone hardpan, best suited to grazing: henequen probably could be grown. Little cultivation except on associated patches of limestone. Many small savanas not shown.

5. Sandy peneplain, northern part Isle of Pines. Mainly grayish, acid sandy soils, locally containing abundance of angular quartz, over yellow and red clay (*Santa Barbara*); brown sandy soils, with abundance of iron concretions over reddish and yellowish clay (*Nueva Gerona*). Well drained, giving good results with citrus fruits where fertilized. Vegetables grown commercially on moister flats. Vegetation chiefly pine and palmettos. Basal rocks largely quartz schist: several isolated limestone mountains and schist hills.

6. Southern Interior Camagüey Plain. Flattish to undulating, with low isolated hills. Some flats covered with water in wet season, but generally fair to good drainage. Principal soils; black clay over chalk (*Oriente*), black clay over yellow, limey clay (*Camagüey*), and *Santa Clara, Truffin*, and *Matanzas* clays. On the hills some gravelly and stony *Habana* and *Matanzas* clays. Much good cane land. Considerable hardwood forest in places.

7. Trinidad Plain. Undulating to rolling, with some hills. Well drained, with considerable good soil extensively used for cane. Predominantly brown clay loam over yellow clay, with gravel and soft sedimentary lime rock beneath (*Palmarita*); chocolate-colored clay and clay loam over red, friable clay, representing old alluvium on beaches (*Caracusey*) *Santa Clara* clay and stony clay on the higher positions.

8. Guantanamo Valley Region. Undulating and rolling with some hills, good drainage. In western part chiefly brown clay and clay loam overlying interbedded sandstone, conglomerate, and chalky lime (*Palma types*) with considerable *Santa Clara, Habana*, and stony clay. In eastern part chiefly brown clay overlying greenish clay derived from greenish shale, with considerable good alluvial soil. Much good cane land. Exceptionally dry climate about Guantanamo Bay; some desert vegetation.

9. Gently rolling to hilly. Well-drained brown (*Santa Clara*), ashy-gray (*Habana*), black (*Camagüey*), and red (*Matanzas*) limestone clays. Locally shallow and stony. Deeper types of smoother areas productive and extensively used for sugar cane and locally for tobacco. Some quite stony areas of *Havana* clay produce good cane.

10. Sagua-Moron rolling to hilly. Chiefly *Habana, Matanzas, Santa Clara, Truffin*, and *Camagüey* clays, gravelly clays, and stony clays. Some exceedingly stony hills in north-central Santa Clara Province. Soils highly varied. Many deep favorable areas used for cane. Much tobacco grown in *Remedios* district on all types of clay, including quite stony lands. Considerable stony land best suited to pasture.

11. Gently rolling to hilly. Well-drained brown (*La Largo*) and red (*Limones*) clays derived from igneous rocks, chiefly serpentine hard when dry. Smoother areas of deeper soil produce fairly good cane. Some heavy tobacco grown. Many shallow and stony areas, now farmed, give low yields and should be turned to pasture. Cattle raising very important in Camaguey-Las Tunas area.

12. Foothills or Piedmont Region of Western Cuba. Rolling to hilly peneplain of thin gravelly and sandy soil of low productivity. Little used except for pasture. Pine and wire grass. Tobacco on alluvial soils. Some isolated hills, 1500 feet elevation.

13. Habana-Matanzas Hill Region. Higher elevations 900 to 950 feet altitude. Mainly *Habana, La Largo, Limones, Matanzas*, and *Truffin* clays and stony clays. Considerable deep soil locally, on which fair to good sugar cane is grown. Some trucking and dairy farming. Stony areas generally used for pastures. Some stony soil of the *Habana* type used for fruit, while some exceedingly stony land of the *Matanzas* type gives good yields of henequen.

14. Holguin Hill Region. Shallow, gravelly, and stony land underlain by sedimentary and igneous (mostly serpentine) rocks. Much rolling land with deeper soil derived from limestone and serpentine. The more stony soils, as the red serpentine clay (*Holguin*) and the shallower (*Matanzas, La Largo* and *Limones*) types, droughty, of low crop value, and best suited for pasture, although henequen might be introduced. Some good cane on deeper soils and fair yields from occasional limey gravelly areas. Some very poor savana, with chalk near the surface and thick growth of palm. Region exceedingly variable in soil, topography, and agricultural value.

15. Mountains, including Maestra Range (maximum elevation about 8000 feet); the great massif of extreme eastern Cuba, including Nipe and other mountains; Trinidad Mountains; Organ Range, Guaniguanicos. These highlands are rough and include much excessively stony and steeply sloping land of value only for forestry. Many strips in valleys and coves and patches on shouldering positions cultivated by small farmers. The deep, friable, red serpentine soil of the Nipe Mountains, mined for iron ore is exceedingly poor but supports pine forest and wire grass. In parts of the eastern mountains considerable hardwood forest.

16. Piedra Hueca. Shallow soil over cavernous limestone. Mainly forested and only useful for timber.

17. Swamp Lands. Chiefly mangrove swamp (saline clay); deep and shallow peat, as in Zapata Peninsula region, and marl. Peat and marl areas support mainly a growth of saw grass. Permanently saturated and very little used except for wood cut for charcoal.

Fig 141. Principal soil and topographical regions of Cuba.

industrial enterprises. Ordinarily about 70 per cent of the imports and 25 per cent of the exports of the republic pass through the port of Habana.

Natural vegetation. Before the extensive cultivation of sugar cane, the lowlands of Cuba—except the savannas, swamps, and excessively stony areas—were heavily forested. In the wasteful rush to make more room for cane plantation, valuable timber was destroyed. The regions unsuited for crop culture still retain much of the original forest cover. There are tracts of pine in Pinar del Río, in the Nipe Mountains of eastern Cuba, and in portions of the Isle of Pines. The eastern mountains have a fairly good stand of timber, although there are extensive areas of mountain country that support only small trees because of the exceedingly stony surface. The native lowland forests contain many species of hardwoods, palms, and shrubs that vary considerably according to soil and drainage conditions. The widely distributed royal palm is one of the most conspicuous features of the Cuban landscape.

In some of the drier regions of the islands, such as the lower Guantánamo Valley, are found small trees—stunted palms, cacti, and semidesert brush growth. On the mangrove swamps are small trees that have little use except for charcoal making. The savanna regions, located primarily in eastern Camagüey and western Santa Clara, are largely covered with grasses, palmettos, bushes, and small trees. They are regions of infertile sandy soil and shallow clay over rock, being used, primarily for pastures.

Cuban economy. Agriculture is the principal industry in Cuba; it includes the production of sugar cane, tobacco, henequén, bananas, pineapples, coffee, and winter vegetables. Cattle raising and apiculture are also important. The growing of sugar cane is by far the predominant type of agriculture and forms the base for the leading manufacturing industry—the preparation of sugar and its by-product, molasses. Sugar is the "king" product of Cuba, and upon it depends the prosperity of the republic. It is grown in every province from Oriente to Pinar del Río.

Among other important resources of the island are chromite, copper, iron, manganese, fish, sponges, and hardwoods. The mining operations are confined primarily to chromite, iron, manganese, gold, lead and zinc. No coal is produced in Cuba, and only a small amount of natural naptha and a light-gravity oil.

Sugar industry. The development of the sugar industry in Cuba as well as in all of the early Spanish West Indies was very slow. Up to the middle of the eighteenth century the potentiality of sugar production in Cuba and Puerto Rico had not been recognized. By the middle of the nineteenth century, however, the Spanish dominated the sugar industry of the New World. Production at that time totalled some 368,000 metric tons—300,000 in Cuba and 68,000 in Puerto Rico. This amount was more than the total production of sugar of all the remainder of the Caribbean region. The yield of sugar, particularly in Cuba, continued to increase, and totalled more than 1,197,587 short tons in 1894. Then came the War of Independence, which brought a marked reduction in the sugar production, the amount in 1898 being about 300,000 short tons. Later, with few exceptions, Cuba increased her production of sugar, and reached a prewar climax in the year 1924–1925 with some 5,800,000 short tons. From 1925–1939 Cuban sugar products declined from 5,800,000 to 2,720,000 tons. In 1949 the production of raw sugar amounted to 6,126,000 short tons. Cuba is by far the world's leading producer of

PRODUCTION: Centrifugal Sugar *
In 1,000 short tons

	1935–39 Av.	*1948*	*1949*	*1950 †*
Cuba	3,183	5,763	6,126	6,300
Puerto Rico	974	1,277	1,286	1,275
Hawaiian Islands	980	956	960	1,085
Philippine Islands	1,058	720	680	1,000
United States (cane)	414	477	520	525
(beet)	1,518	1,370	1,564	1,950
Brazil	786	1,549	1,500	1,550
India ‡	1,300	1,319	1,251	1,560
World Total (cane)	17,310	20,208	20,430	21,889
(beet)	11,827	11,154	11,625	13,499
Grand Total	29,137	31,362	32,055	35,386

* Centrifugal sugar includes cane and beet sugar produced by the centrifugal process which is the principal kind moving in international trade.

† Preliminary.

‡ India's output is primarily non-centrifugal sugar called gur. India's production of gur (sugar) in 1950 was estimated at 3,125,000 short tons. World's production of non centrifugal sugar in 1950 was approximately 5,700,000 short tons.

Source: United States Department of Agriculture. Office of Foreign Agricultural Relations. *Foreign Crops and Markets,* Vol. 61, No. 22, November, 1950, pp. 541–543.

high-grade refining sugar but is surpassed by India in the total production of all kinds of sugar. However, most of that produced in India is a low grade of unrefined sugar, known as "gur."

The leading sugar regions are Oriente, Camagüey, Santa Clara, and Matanzas. In all, more than 1,500,000 acres are under sugar-cane cultivation. The greatest amount of Cuba's sugar is exported to the United States, and the large part is shipped unrefined. In 1931, the total shipment of raw and refined sugars to the United States amounted to 2,085,491 tons; in 1932, 1,701,618 tons; in 1933, 1,390,669 tons; in 1941, 1,959,947 tons; and in 1948, 3,110,000 tons. The amount of sugar that Cuba is permitted to ship to the United States is governed by the United States Sugar Act of 1937.[2]

---

[2] Sugar quotas are listed in Chapter XXXIV, Inter-American trade, page 509.

The chief reasons for Cuba's supremacy in the production of sugar are: (1) favorable climatic, topographic, and soil conditions for the cultivation of cane, (2) the large amounts of capital invested in the sugar industry by Americans, (3) the proximity and demand of United States markets, (4) trade agreements with the United States, and (5) technical improvement in the preparation of refined sugar.

Other leading agricultural products of Cuba, with production for 1948, are:

Leaf tobacco	56,000,000 lbs.
Coffee	72,884,000 lbs.
Henequén fiber	28,000,000 lbs.
Pineapples	372,000,000 lbs.
Rice (milled)	88,000,000 lbs.
Beans	100,000,000 lbs.
Peanuts	23,000,000 lbs.

Citrus fruits, avocados, bananas, tomatoes, and a variety of vegetables add to Cuba's economy, not only for domestic consumption but also for exportation. Although Cuba imports dairy products and meat, primarily from the United States, its cattle industry is expanding.

Industrialization. In addition to the manufacture of sugar from cane, Cuba's leading industry, a great many other industries are in operation, including the production of cigars and cigarettes, matches, cement, cotton piece goods, rayon piece goods, beverages, automobile tires and tubes, paper, vegetable oils, soap, paint, leather footwear, rubber goods, furniture, glass, chemicals, cosmetics and perfumes, brick and tile, clothing and hats, canned vegetables and meats, and dairy products.

Foreign trade. The principal exports of Cuba are sugar, raw and refined; molasses; leaf tobacco and cigars; bananas; copper and iron ore; chrome ore (chromite); manganese; rum; sponges; coffee; pineapples; henequén; and vegetables. In general, sugar and sugar products amount to about 78 per cent, and tobacco and manufactures 10 per cent of Cuba's total foreign shipments. The United States takes about 65 per cent of Cuba's total sugar exports, chiefly in the raw form to be refined in the United States.

Cuban imports consist principally of food products—rice, wheat flour, lard, edible oils, beans and peas, potatoes, meat, and canned milk—machinery, instruments, and vehicles; chemicals, drugs, and dyes; metals and manufactures; paper and paper products; and cotton and rayon textiles.

In 1948, the United States supplied 79.7 per cent of Cuba's total imports and purchased 51.6 per cent of its total exports. In 1938, a prewar year, the United States furnished 70.9 per cent of all imports and absorbed 75.9 per cent of Cuba's exports.

CUBA: FOREIGN TRADE

	Total Value (000 Dollars)	*Percentage of Total* United States	Canada	Latin America	United Kingdom	Continental Europe	All Others
Exports							
1938	142,678	75.9	0.2	1.6	13.7	7.2	1.2
1947	746,592	66.7	3.1	1.9	17.8	7.6	2.9
Imports							
1938	106,007	70.9	0.8	2.3	4.2	14.1	7.7
1947	519,890	84.0	0.9	4.6	1.3	5.0	4.3

Cuban problems. In common with nearly all of the islands of the West Indies, Cuba does not have an adequate diversification of industries and depends too much upon foreign markets for staple food products. Cuba possesses suitable soils, a favorable climate, and good workers, and she could substantially improve her economic situation if she so desired. Much land that is not fit for sugar cane should be used for the increased production of hogs and cattle. There are also opportunities to give more attention to the growing of corn, sweet potatoes, manioc, rice, tropical yams, and fruits for local consumption. The dairy industry, likewise, awaits greater development. Grass and forage can be grown nearly everywhere, and the market for dairy products gives assurance of success under efficient management. In addition, coffee and cacao, formerly extensively grown, again should be given serious consideration and would probably become important exports.

The need, however, is not only for greater diversification of agricultural crops but also for the improvement of present methods of farming. Some of the ills of Cuban agriculture, particularly in the growing of sugar, can be attributed to: (1) the use of marginal lands for agriculture, (2) inadequate preparation of the fields before planting, (3) failure to cultivate and control weeds, (4) failure to use enough fertilizers to prevent impoverishment of soil, (5) failure to correct imperfect drainage, (6) failure to control or eradicate plant diseases, and (7) the complexities known as economic ills.[3]

Cuba, however, has made some appreciable progress toward greater agricultural and commercial diversification. Coffee, the production of which has been almost entirely neglected since the colonial period, has increased. In the past Cuba imported large quantities of corn and corn flour. Now her production of corn not only meets the domestic demand, but there is also a substantial surplus for foreign markets. This is a significant improvement because corn is used as feed for livestock and as flour for human consumption. Cattle and dairy products also have been increased to satisfy the local demand. At present there are some 4,000,000 head of cattle on the island—the major portion being in the province of Camagüey—some 1,700,000 hogs, and between 150,000 and

[3] Bennett, H. H.: "Some Geographic Aspects of Cuban Soils," *Geographical Review,* Vol. XVIII (1928), p. 76.

200,000 sheep and goats. Chickens and eggs are other farm products in which production has greatly increased.

Although Cuba's economy has become more diversified and greater attention is being directed to the domestic food problem and to other national deficiencies, "sugar" is the big business in Cuba. In 1948 the crop was valued at approximately $625,000,000. The prosperity level in Cuba is, largely, determined by the economic status of the sugar industry.

HAITI AND THE DOMINICAN REPUBLIC

Political background. Considerable confusion has arisen in the use of the words "Haiti," "Santo Domingo," and "Hispaniola." Each name has been applied to the island now occupied by Haiti and the Dominican Republic. At the present time, however, most standard sources of geographic information give preference to the word Hispaniola as the name of the entire island.

The republic of Haiti occupies the western end of the island of Hispaniola, and the Dominican Republic the eastern portion. Haiti has an area of 10,700 square miles and a population estimated at 3,500,000. The Dominican Republic's area is nearly twice as large—19,325 square miles—but her population is more sparse—2,245,000.

Haiti differs in many important respects from the other nations to the south of the United States. First, immediately before independence, it was a French, not a Spanish, possession. Second, the official language is French, and not Spanish, as in many of the other West Indies. Third, it is a Negro republic. The proportion of whites has always been very small and the population of blacks very large. A century ago there were only 30,000 whites and more than 500,000 Negroes. Fourth, Haiti was the first of the Caribbean countries to acquire independence. Uprisings began in 1790, and by 1795 independence from France had been achieved. Under Napoleon Bonaparte an effort was made in 1802 to reconquer the island, but yellow fever conquered Napoleon's armies. In 1804 it was declared free, under the aboriginal Indian name of Haiti. Fifth, the population was so consciously and proudly Negro that for a hundred years whites were not permitted to become citizens or to hold property, and their very presence was discouraged. Thus Haiti has had a real opportunity to show the capacity for self-government possessed by Negroes under conditions of modern life.

The early leadership was devoted and strong. After this had disappeared, Haiti fell into the "insurrection habit." It continued as a disorganized and inefficient nation until the inception of foreign influence. Of course, Haiti contracted foreign debts. Early in 1914, France and Germany, to whom she owed large sums, planned to intervene, seize control of the customhouses, and thus guarantee repayment of their loans. At the same time the National City Bank of New York, whose subsidiary, the Bank of Haiti, held the government funds, had to appeal to the United States for aid. Help was granted, and European intervention was prevented. At first the government of Haiti refused the offer of the United States to supervise its finances. Within a year, however, after a particularly atrocious massacre, the United States effectively intervened. Under pressure, the Haitian authorities signed a treaty under which the United States was to supervise their political and financial structure for ten years. This treaty has been abolished, the Americans having withdrawn from both customs and military control.

Under efficient American guidance, reconstruction at once began. As earlier in Cuba, Puerto Rico, and the Philippines, sanitation and education were the potent needs, and these received immediate attention, with glowing success. If public health can be guaranteed, and if people can be educated in knowledge and in self-control, the future should be brighter. Hospitals and dispensaries have therefore been constructed and public health has improved amazingly. Primary schools have been introduced everywhere, and there are secondary schools in all principal centers. Particular attention has been given to agricultural schools for adults.

Governmental finances have been stabilized, and most of the foreign debt paid. The United States has withdrawn its marines, has changed its foreign representative from a military official to a civilian one, and has given Haitians control of their government.

Here again the United States has come in for much unjust criticism. In spite of the absolute necessity for help from a civilized nation, an intensive campaign was levelled against the United States for her "intervention in the internal affairs of a weaker nation."

The majority of the Dominicans are of mixed Negro and Spanish ancestry. Perhaps they lean a little toward the Negro, but they are more white than the Haitians. Some, of course, are entirely white.

Beginning in 1822, the dictators of Haiti hungered to rule the Dominican area also, and succeeded in doing so for a considerable part of the time. Numerically, Haiti was much the stronger republic, and it suffered from a militaristic psychology. It was proudly Negro, while the Dominican Republic was white. Feeling between the east and west ran high, and there was constant strife.

As early as 1850 the Dominicans invited the United States to annex their country, but they were not at that time encouraged. They felt that under protection of the United States the need for fear of Haiti would vanish. In 1866 the idea of annexation again arose. The United States sought to obtain a naval base on Samaná Bay in exchange for a loan but did not succeed at that time. Three years later the Dominicans again requested the United States to take possession of their country, but President Grant was unable to bring it about. By a popular vote the Dominicans formally registered their desires, and Grant presented the matter to the Senate, which, however, refrained from taking the decisive step of accepting the offer.

In 1874 the fear of conquest by Haiti was removed by the signing of a treaty of friendship, and for 25 years matters moved smoothly. Just at the close of the century, however, after a period of extravagance by the governing group, which brought the national finances to a deplorably low ebb, President Heureaux asked the United States to intervene and establish a protectorate, a petition that was refused. Finally, in 1907, after threats of intervention by France, and at the request of the Dominican authorities, a treaty was signed with the United States by which our government did assume direction of public finances. Of course, this meant that the funds collected would be applied wisely, and the republic soon discovered itself practically out of debt. In politics, however, one revolution continued to follow another, until in 1916 our government landed marines and assumed direction of the entire government. Criticisms were levelled against the American military officials, however, for mistreating Dominican citizens, and a Congressional investigation was ordered. Finally, in 1924, our marines were withdrawn and the republic returned to the control of its own citizens.

Climate and topography. In the republic of Haiti, the average annual temperature is 81° in the western portion, 77° in the south, and 76° in the elevated interior. Limited records in the Dominican Republic show an average annual temperature of 78° near sea level.

Comparable with the West Indies as a whole, the rainfall of the island of Haiti varies considerably within remarkably short distances. It averages from 59 inches to 78 inches over much of the northern coast and valleys, the southern coast, and the mountainous areas of the interior, but only 20 inches over the leeward or western portion. The eastern and southwestern portions of the Dominican Republic and the northwestern portion of the republic of Haiti have less than 40 inches. In the latter, north of Port-au-Prince, the yearly rainfall along the coast is about 20 inches. The monthly precipitation is greatest from April to May and from September to November in Haiti, and from May to November in the Dominican region. The lowest amounts occur as a rule in January or July in Haiti, and in February and March in the Dominican Republic.

Mountains and valleys, in general extending west northwest to east southeast, dominate the landscape of Hispaniola. The major axis of the island is marked by the Gran Cordillera Central, or Cibao Mountains.

HAITI: TEMPERATURE AND RAINFALL OF SELECTED STATIONS

	Station	Bayeux *	Les Cayes *	Ganthier *	Port-au-Prince †
	Elevation (*Feet*)	36.1	23.0	229.7	123
Average Temperature (°F.)	*Period of Record*	6 yrs.	1906–1921	1906–1921	1931–40
	January	72.3	75.7	74.8	77.0
	February	72.3	75.6	76.5	77.4
	March	73.6	76.3	77.4	78.8
	April	75.7	77.2	79.0	80.1
	May	77.4	78.4	80.6	80.2
	June	79.0	79.9	81.7	81.9
	July	80.2	80.1	82.6	83.0
	August	80.2	80.4	82.8	82.4
	September	79.9	80.2	81.9	81.3
	October	79.0	79.5	80.4	80.1
	November	76.3	78.8	78.6	78.8
	December	73.6	76.8	76.5	77.4
	Annual	76.6	78.3	79.3	79.9
	Range	7.9	4.8	8.0	6.0
Average Rainfall (Inches)	*Period of Record*	18 yrs.	1906–1926	1899–1927	1931–40
	January	6.5	3.1	0.5	1.0
	February	5.0	3.8	0.9	1.8
	March	4.5	6.6	1.6	2.7
	April	7.4	7.0	4.6	5.4
	May	8.1	10.7	4.7	9.5
	June	4.4	6.2	1.9	4.0
	July	1.8	4.6	1.2	3.3
	August	3.5	7.7	2.6	6.4
	September	5.6	8.9	4.8	6.9
	October	8.6	12.7	5.4	6.7
	November	15.4	7.7	2.6	3.0
	December	10.9	3.0	0.7	1.0
	Annual	81.7	80.4	31.2	51.7

* R. De C. Ward and C. F. Brooks: "Climatology of the West Indies," *Handbuch der Klimatologie,* Band II, Teil I, Berlin, 1934.

† H. Helm Clayton, "World Weather Records," *Smithsonian Miscellaneous Collections,* Vol. 105 (1947).

On the northeast is the Cordillera Setentrional, separated from the Cibao ranges by the Río Yaque del Norte Valley and the upper reaches of the Camu Valley, known collectively as the Cibao Valley. Its eastern portion is highly fertile, and the valley as a whole is the most important agricultural region in Hispaniola. Along the southern margin of the republic of Haiti and the southwestern portion of the Dominican Republic is another prominent sierra, known by different names in different places. Between these southern ranges and the more central mountain masses is a structural depression called Cul de Sac, which extends from Port-au-Prince, the capital and the most important city of the republic

DOMINICAN REPUBLIC: TEMPERATURE AND RAINFALL OF SELECTED STATIONS

	Station	Puerto Plata *	Sanchez *	Ciudad Trujillo †
	Elevation (*Feet*)	39.4	49.2	59.1
Average Temperature (°*F.*)	*Period of Record*	1906–1926	1886–1924	26 yrs.
	January	74.8	73.9	75
	February	74.5	74.1	75
	March	75.4	75.2	76
	April	77.0	76.3	77
	May	78.6	78.1	79
	June	80.6	79.3	80
	July	81.1	79.0	80
	August	82.0	79.7	81
	September	81.3	79.5	80
	October	80.8	79.5	79
	November	77.7	77.4	78
	December	75.6	75.0	76
	Annual	77.9	77.4	78
	Range	7.5	5.8	6
Average Rainfall (*Inches*)	*Period of Record*	1905–1926	1886–1927	25 yrs.
	January	6.7	5.2	2.4
	February	7.0	3.7	1.4
	March	4.0	3.9	1.9
	April	5.2	7.4	3.9
	May	3.1	7.6	6.8
	June	1.8	8.6	6.2
	July	3.0	8.0	6.4
	August	3.0	8.0	6.3
	September	4.7	6.0	7.3
	October	4.5	5.8	6.0
	November	13.4	9.8	4.8
	December	9.5	5.4	2.4
	Annual	65.5	77.3	55.8

* R. De C. Ward and C. F. Brooks: "Climatology of the West Indies," *Handbuch der Klimatologie,* Band II, Teil I, Berlin, 1934.

† *United States Weather Bureau Technical Paper No. 8,* United States Weather Bureau, Washington, D. C., 1949.

of Haiti, to the Neiba Bay in the Dominican Republic. In this valley are important lakes. This lowland was, undoubtedly, at one time an arm of the sea separating the lands of southern Haiti from the rest of the island. The southeastern portion of the Dominican Republic consists principally of low elevation and relief. Monte Trujillo in the central axis is 10,417 feet above sea level and is the highest peak in the West Indies.

Courtesy Raymond E. Crist.

Fig. 142. Haiti: On the trail to Furcy. The women are carrying produce. Massif de la Selle is in the background. Corn grows on the steep slopes to the left foreground.

The higher mountains are fairly heavily timbered with pine trees, while the lower slopes support palms, mahogany, logwood, and mimosas. On the mountain slopes and hills, the production of coffee is the important activity, while in the valleys and plains, sugar cane, cotton, cacao, and tobacco are the principal products.

Haitian economy. The republic of Haiti has been referred to as the land of "thousands of small farms." Individually owned farms dominate the agricultural landscape of Haiti. The chief cash crop is coffee, representing about 35 per cent of the republic's total exports. Sugar ranks second among the export crops. For many years cotton held second place, but it has recently dropped to a low position because of the destructive boll weevil. The production of henequén and sisal fibers has been increased. Export crops of lesser importance are bananas, cacao, castor beans, mahogany, and handicrafts. Owing to the semiarid conditions in portions of Haiti, irrigation is necessary to assure crop production, particularly sugar cane. Most of the banana planting also requires irrigation. The coffee is grown on the humid mountain slopes and the cotton on the drier uplands and plains.

Dominican Republic. In the eastern portion of Hispaniola, the Dominican Republic, the main crop is sugar cane, as it has been since the days of Spanish dependence. It supplies more than half of the value of the country's exports. Much of the lowlands is well suited for the growing of sugar cane, and the republic is increasing its acreage and production. Cacao and coffee are second and third, respectively, among Dominican exports. Cacao warrants special attention as a source of national income. At one time tobacco was grown extensively in the Cibao Valley, but in recent years, owing to low market prices, the production has declined.

In both Haiti and the Dominican Republic there is a need for capital to improve and increase transportation facilities, to introduce new industries, and to bring about a greater diversification of agricultural production.

Foreign trade. Haiti's principal exports consist of coffee, amounting to about 35 per cent of the total value; bananas, 20 per cent; sisal, 18 per cent; and sugar (raw), 9 per cent. Other exports are cacao, castor beans, and shoes and slippers made of sisal. Cotton textiles make up over one-fourth of Haiti's imports. These consist principally of yard goods, and about 90 per cent come from the United States. Foodstuffs constitute 15 per cent of the value of all imports, and include wheat, flour, fish, and lard. Chemicals and pharmaceutical products, machinery, and various other manufactures follow in importance.

Exports by ports, based on value, are as follows: Port-au-Prince, 40 per cent of total exports; Fort Liberté, 12 per cent; Les Cayes, 8 per cent; Cap-Haïtien; Jacmel; Saint Marc; and others. Imports enter primarily at Port-au-Prince, 85 per cent; Cap-Haïtien; Fort Liberté; Saint Marc; and Les Cayes.

HAITI AND DOMINICAN REPUBLIC: FOREIGN TRADE

HAITI

	Total Value (000 Dollars)	*Percentage of Total*					
		United States	Canada	Latin America	United Kingdom	Continental Europe	All Others
Exports							
1937–38	6,946	42.8	0.2	0.1	13.6	39.9	3.5
1946–47	31,498	59.6	0.1	0.6	9.3	28.8	1.5
Imports							
1937–38	7,595	54.3	2.4	1.2	15.5	17.5	9.1
1946–47	27,230	87.8	3.2	2.1	0.7	2.5	3.7

Dominican Republic							
Exports							
1938	14,347	32.1		0.4	20.9	36.1	10.5
1947	83,206	25.3	10.4	9.2	41.4	5.3	8.3
Imports							
1938	11,342	53.5	1.1	1.0	3.3	18.8	22.3
1947	53,448	78.3	3.2	6.0	1.7	3.3	7.6

Sugar makes up more than 50 per cent of the Dominican Republic's exports. Other leading products shipped overseas are cacao, coffee, rice, molasses, starch, leaf tobacco, bananas, and cattle hides. The nation's imports are quite similar in composition to those of Haiti.

The leading exporting centers are San Pedro de Macorís, 34 per cent of total exports based on value; La Romana, 17 per cent; Ciudad Trujillo, 15 per cent; Barahona; and others. Imports reach the Dominican Republic primarily at Ciudad Trujillo, 60 per cent; Puerto Plata, 10 per cent; San Pedro de Macorís; and La Romana.

SELECTED REFERENCES

See Chapter XXIX.

CHAPTER XXXI

THE UNITED STATES IN THE WEST INDIES

PUERTO RICO[1]

General characteristics. The Commonwealth of Puerto Rico, including the three offshore islands of Vieques, Culebra, and Mona, has an area of 3,421 square miles, 1,000 square miles less than the area of Jamaica, or about the size of the combined area of the states of Rhode Island and Delaware.[2] The population of this comparatively small island is over two million or about 644 persons per square mile, one of the world's most thickly populated areas. Its inhabitants are practically all descendants of either Spanish settlers or Negroes, or both. The ratio of whites to colored is nearly three to one. Since Puerto Rico is a part of the United States, a vast majority of her people are American citizens. There are some 2,000 continental Americans in residence on the island, and more than half of these are located in the metropolitan area of San Juan.

POPULATION OF PUERTO RICO

Year	Population
1765	44,883
1800	155,426
1815	220,892
1846	447,914
1899	953,243
1910	1,118,012
1920	1,299,809
1930	1,543,913
1935	1,723,534
1940	1,869,249
1950	2,205,398

The terrain of Puerto Rico consists of rugged hills and mountains, rising to an average elevation of 2,500 feet above sea level in the interior. A few peaks project above the central sierra, such as El Yunque (The Anvil), 3,532 feet above sea level, located at the northeastern corner of

[1] For a basic reference on Puerto Rico see "The Geographic Regions of Puerto Rico" by Rafael Picó, University of Puerto Rico Press, Río Piedras, P. R., 1950.

[2] The area of Puerto, including only land, is 3,418 square miles. Outlying Puerto Rico, consisting of the islands of Vieques, 50.7 square miles; Culebra, 10.4 square miles, and Mona, 21 square miles, had a total population of 11,719 in 1948. About 93 per cent of the inhabitants is in Vieque Island. Mona is practically uninhabited and Culebra occupants number only 738.

the island; and Pico de Jayuya, 4,398 feet in elevation, found near the center of the island. A narrow belt of coastal lowlands extends around the entire island, and above it rises rather abruptly the complex interior highland. There are numerous streams, but no navigable rivers. The shoreline is distinctively straight and regular and free from the fringing keys and deep indentions so extensively developed on the Cuban coast.

The northern portion, comprising over two-thirds of the entire island, has an abundant rainfall in all seasons of the year; while along the southern side the rainfall is not only comparatively light, but is also unevenly distributed through the year, and irrigation of crop land is necessary. The average annual rainfall is 20 inches for the drier sections

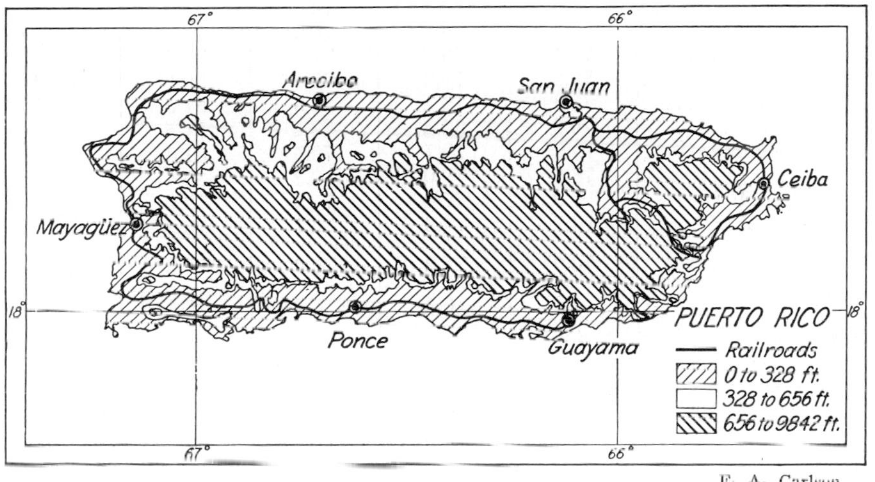

Fig. 143. Puerto Rico.

of the southern coast, 90 inches in the northern portion of the island, and more than 180 inches on some of the higher mountains.

There are no well-defined wet and dry seasons in Puerto Rico. In the winter the rains are comparatively light and reach a minimum in January, February, or March, the months varying according to the location. A rather steady increase in precipitation occurs through the spring and summer months, until a maximum is reached in September, October, or November. A secondary maximum occurs in summer over the mountainous interior. In general, the rainfall is torrential in character and occurs in short durations of 10 to 12 minutes in the afternoon. The hours of 12 to 4 P.M. are the rainiest, with twice as much rainfall per hour as from 8 to 11 A.M., the least rainy hours.

The average annual temperature is about 78° for the coastal lowlands, that of the higher elevations being naturally lower, as, for example, 73° at Cayes, 1,350 feet, and 69° at Toro Negro Dam, 2,275 feet. The range

PUERTO RICO: TEMPERATURE AND RAINFALL OF SELECTED STATIONS

	Station	Comerio Falls *	Humacao *	Mayagüez *	Ponce *	San Juan †
	Elevation (*Feet*)	492	98.4	78.7	78.7	98
Average Temperature (°*F.*)	*Period of Record*	1899–1929	1899–1927	1899–1927	1899–1927	1931–1940
	January	73.0	73.8	74.7	75.4	75.0
	February	73.2	73.9	74.1	75.4	74.8
	March	73.6	74.8	74.5	75.9	75.8
	April	75.4	76.3	75.9	77.5	76.8
	May	78.1	78.3	77.5	79.5	79.0
	June	78.8	79.2	78.6	80.6	80.0
	July	78.8	79.7	78.8	81.0	80.4
	August	79.2	80.2	79.2	81.5	80.8
	September	79.2	79.7	79.5	81.3	80.8
	October	78.6	79.0	79.2	80.4	80.2
	November	77.0	77.4	77.5	79.0	78.6
	December	74.7	74.8	76.1	76.8	76.7
	Annual	76.6	77.2	77.0	78.6	78.2
	Range	6.2	6.4	5.4	6.1	5.6
Average Rainfall (*Inches*)	*Period of Record*	1899–1927	1899–1927	1899–1927	1901–1927	1931–1940
	January	6.5	4.1	1.9	1.1	4.8
	February	5.0	3.8	2.4	1.1	2.6
	March	4.9	3.5	3.2	1.4	2.3
	April	6.1	4.8	5.6	2.2	4.2
	May	5.6	8.2	7.5	3.0	7.6
	June	4.8	8.9	9.3	3.6	6.1
	July	8.4	8.3	11.5	3.0	5.3
	August	8.0	8.4	11.0	4.1	7.1
	September	7.3	10.1	10.5	4.9	6.4
	October	6.5	9.6	9.6	6.4	5.8
	November	8.9	9.1	6.2	4.0	5.1
	December	7.0	4.8	2.5	1.1	5.5
	Annual	79.2	83.7	80.9	35.8	62.8

* R. De C. Ward and C. F. Brooks: "Climatology of the West Indies," *Handbuch der Klimatologie,* Band II, Teil I, Berlin, 1934.

† H. Helm Clayton: "World Weather Records," *Smithsonian Miscellaneous Collections,* Vol. 105 (1947).

in monthly average temperature from August and September to January and February is from 5° to 7°. San Juan is not only the most important city of the island, but it is further distinguished by possessing the most equable temperature of any portion of the island. This advantage is primarily due to the fact that the city is almost surrounded by water. Frost has never been reported at the weather stations, although the natives speak of the "rigors of winter" and thus indicate the significance of the so-called "sensible" temperature.

Hurricanes, or tropical storms, have caused considerable damage in Puerto Rico. Not less than ten destructive storms have visited the island within the past 30 years. Most of these West Indian hurricanes occur in August, September, and October.

Puerto Rican economy. Sugar dominates the agricultural and industrial life of the people of Puerto Rico and to a large degree affects the welfare of a large proportion of her inhabitants. Approximately 30 per cent of the island's cultivated area is in sugar cane, and 14 per cent of the workers are directly engaged in producing sugar. Of the capital invested on the island, more than 50 per cent is in sugar, and most of the investments have been made by continental Americans. The exports in sugar and molasses make up about 50 per cent of Puerto Rico's total exports. Furthermore, the sugar-cane lands are conceded to be the best on the island. They lie in the coastal area and the fertile valleys.

PUERTO RICO: GENERAL LAND USES

	Cuerdas *	*Per Cent of Farm Land*
Total land area	2,255,684	
Land area in farms	1,885,874	100.0
Cropland	1,053,314	55.9
Harvested	739,751	39.2
Sugar cane	229,750	
Tobacco	28,584	
Other field crops	298,178	
Coffee	181,106	
Vegetables	6,860	
Fruits (except coffee)	83,085	
Not harvested	313,563	16.7
Pasture	618,871	32.8
Clear (plowable)	300,266	
Woodland and other	318,605	
Other land	213,689	11.3
Woodland not pastured	131,911	
All other	81,778	

* One cuerda is equivalent to 0.9712 acre.

Other basic crops of the island are tobacco, pineapples, citrus fruits, cotton, coffee, and vegetables. Tobacco ranks next to sugar in value of agricultural exports. Among the fruits, grapefruit and pineapples are the outstanding products. Coffee is referred to as the small man's crop. Although falling far below sugar cane, tobacco, and fruit production in total value, coffee is of peculiar significance to the Puerto Ricans since it is grown primarily by native agriculturists, many of whom are small landholders. However, unless the coffee industry receives greater marketing attention, the business will be ruined. Some sea-island cotton is produced, and in recent years the growing of fresh vegetables has become important.

Puerto Rico has a number of manufacturing establishments engaged in the utilization of agricultural and mineral products, such as sugar mills, tobacco factories, distilleries, canning factories, and chemical plants. Other forms of manufacturing include the needlework industry, straw-hat making, the manufacture of shell buttons, and the cutting and polishing of jewels.

Courtesy Bureau of Insular Affairs, United States War Department.

Fig. 144. View at Boca de Cangrejo, near San Juan, Puerto Rico.

Neither coal nor petroleum is found in Puerto Rico, and the available water power is not extensive. At present hydroelectric sources provide 33 per cent and steam-electric sources about 67 per cent of electric energy. Power lines serve some 97 per cent of all communities of more than 1,000 inhabitants and 50 per cent of those with 250 to 1,000 persons. Approximately 37 per cent of all homes consume electricity. Because of the small number of impounding sites still available in the hills, it is quite likely that the development of steam-powered electric plants will increase.

Puerto Rico's population is essentially rural. Most of the inhabitants live in towns and villages of less than 10,000 people. There are only three or four cities with more than 50,000 inhabitants. San Juan is the largest city in the island, with a population of 230,000 persons; Ponce is second, with 75,000; followed by Mayagüez with 60,000. The San Juan metropolitan area embodying the cities and towns of San Juan, Río Piedras, Catano, Bayamon, Carolina, and Guaynabo, has a population of 368,700 and it is increasing by over 15,000 persons annually.[3] San Juan and Ponce are the leading ports of the island.

The only railway is a narrow-gauge (one-meter) line that nearly encircles the island—all but the southeastern margin—and serves such important cities and towns as San Juan, Arecibo, Mayagüez, Ponce, and Guayama. Transportation, however, is chiefly by automobile and bus. There are about 2,000 miles of macadamized highway reaching nearly all quarters of the island, and an equal mileage of dirt roads serves the interior.

Changes, trends, and summary. Since the time of the early Spanish settlers, the most valuable land of the island, the coastal plain, has been held in large haciendas. When the Americans took possession in 1898, these large landholdings were bought by a few individuals and corporations, in whose hands the property still remains. Consequently the majority of the Puerto Ricans are without land, and they work as laborers on the sugar plantations or live in the cities, where there is little employment.

On the rugged marginal lands of the interior are some small landholdings. The occupants carry on a rudimentary form of subsistence agriculture and live in dilapidated shacks. Most of these mountaineers are white or nearly white.

What to do with the landless Puerto Ricans is one of the island's major problems—in other words, how to correct the evil of unequal distribution of land.

In part as a result of the unequal distribution of land and consequent high prices for life's necessities, and the low standard of living, Puerto Rico has one of the world's highest incidences of malaria, tuberculosis, and hookworm. Puerto Rico awaits economic and social adjustments. All public lands were disposed of by 1929, with the exception of the Luquillo National Forest, covering the highlands of the eastern end of the island. This region is not only unsuited for agriculture, but is needed for conservation purposes. Some attempt has been made on the part of the United States to buy land in the interior and assign it to Puerto Ricans at a low annual payment. This scheme may offer partial solution to the problem of the overpopulated cities and the consequent unem-

[3] Between July 1940 and mid-1949, the Puerto Rican population increased about 310,000—from 1,870,000 to 2,180,000. The number of deaths per thousand population was 18 in 1940, 12 in 1948, and 10 in 1949. Births were about 40 per thousand people in 1949.

ployment. Moreover, the introduction of greater diversification of agriculture will eventually improve economic conditions. Its ultimate result will be that more Puerto Ricans will have farms of their own, will accept greater responsibilities, and will have a higher standard of living. At least it will partly remove the pressure of ever-growing economic and social problems.

Another attempt to solve the land problem embodies the establishment of cooperative farms. Some of the former large sugar estates have been placed under a "share alike" policy. The object is to maintain the efficiency of large scale production, and to share any profits among workers and employers in proportion to the length and importance of their service.

Puerto Rico also is trying to improve its economy through greater industrialization. In order to attract continental and insular capital, the Puerto Rican Development Bank was established to make available long-term and low interest loans to be used for construction or expansion of industries. Also, the Island Legislature passed the Tax Holiday Act in 1947, exempting all new industries from property, excise, and income taxes for 15 years. Since the United States tax on corporate income does not apply to Puerto Rican business, it means that new industries established on the Island are practically free from taxes.

A number of new factories have been built and others have been planned for the near future. This new industrial development includes the production of textiles, ceramic ware, glass, fertilizers, beverages, and petroleum products. It represents a much needed addition to the Puerto Rican economy.

In trade, Puerto Rico is one of continental United States' best markets. Substantial quantities of foodstuffs, textiles, machinery, vehicles, chemicals, paper, and many other items are listed in our commerce to Puerto Rico, amounting in value to about $337,256,000 in 1947–1948. Our imports from Puerto Rico consist, primarily, of sugar, needlework products, tobacco, rum, fruits, molasses, and coffee, totalling approximately $185,745,000 in 1947–1948. More than 90 per cent of Puerto Rico's overseas trade is with continental United States. It is estimated that nearly 50 per cent of Puerto Rico's income is based on the export of sugar and sugar products.

Puerto Rico wants lower-cost overseas transportation. Puerto Ricans pay transportation charges on a great many imported commodities. In addition, the island's producers have to absorb costs of shipments of goods to continental United States because they must sell their products in competition with producers nearer those markets.

Considerable emphasis has been placed on the slums and other regions in Puerto Rico where living conditions are deplorable. It is unfortunate that so many continental Americans view the island only in terms of its

IMPORTS OF PRINCIPAL ARTICLES INTO PUERTO RICO *

Value in Thousands of Dollars

Fiscal Year	Edible Products (Not Including Fodders and Feeds) Value	Per Cent of Total Imports	Machinery and Vehicles (All Kinds) Value	Per Cent of Total Imports	Cotton (Unmanufactured and Manufactured) Value	Per Cent of Total Imports	Cigarettes Value	Per Cent of Total Imports	Footwear (Including Rubber Footwear) Value	Per Cent of Total Imports	Fertilizers and Fertilizer Material Value	Per Cent of Total Imports	Total Value of Imports
1920–21	32,993	31.3	4,922	4.7	15,128	14.3	.....	...	.....	...	3,166	3.0	150,480
1927–28	29,142	31.6	7,643	8.3	11,576	12.5	1,497	1.6	3,479	3.8	3,273	3.5	92,301
1937–38	28,585	30.6	8,691	9.3	10,048	10.8	3,168	3.4	3,216	3.5	3,521	3.8	93,315
1945–46	83,590	34.5	16,562	6.9	26,608	11.0	3,929	1.6	9,995	4.1	4,732	2.0	242,040
1946–47	75,704	25.0	34,508	11.4	30,056	10.0	4,348	1.4	11,956	4.0	7,836	2.6	302,411

EXPORTS OF PRINCIPAL ARTICLES FROM PUERTO RICO †

Value in Thousands of Dollars

Fiscal Year	Sugar and Molasses Value	Per Cent of Total Exports	Tobacco (Unmanufactured and Manufactured) Value	Per Cent of Total Exports	Rum Value	Per Cent of Total Exports	Needlework Value	Per Cent of Total Exports	Fruits, Fresh and Prepared or Preserved Value	Per Cent of Total Exports	Coffee Value	Per Cent of Total Exports	Total Value of Exports
1920–21	73,835	65.8	21,690	19.3	......	...	2,333	2.8	3,144	2.8	5,353	4.8	112,279
1927–28	55,441	55.6	20,779	20.1	......	...	8,984	8.7	6,818	6.6	2,597	2.5	103,535
1937–38	51,361	62.6	8,484	10.3	3,1[illegible]7	3.8	11,616	14.2	1,760	2.1	111	0.2	82,077
1945–46	80,220	49.7	21,407	13.3	12,497	7.7	25,551	15.9	3,771	2.3	†	†	161,459
1946–47	88,535	49.6	16,295	9.1	7,033	4.0	39,269	22.0	3,562	2.0	†	†	178,561

* Prepared by the Insular Government of Puerto Rico in cooperation with the Department of the Interior, Washington, D. C., 1948.

† Exports of coffee amounted only to $132, $200, $170, and $985 in the fiscal years 1943–44, 1944–45, 1945–46, and 1946–47, respectively.

weakness, and completely fail to recognize the fact that Puerto Rico has many modern and sanitary urban centers as well as places of natural beauty, such as El Junque, coastal areas, and other sites of attractiveness.

Now that the Governor of Puerto Rico is elected by its insular citizens, greater progress is anticipated.[4] The excellent work of the Planning, Urbanizing, and Zoning Board, under the efficient guidance of a geographer, Dr. Rafael Picó, should do much to improve housing conditions. Expansion in tourism, also, should be a means of increasing the island's income and employment. Puerto Rico's importance as an air base is another asset. Practically all of the commercial planes flying between the United States and eastern South America stop at Puerto Rico. Puerto Rico is a region where Latin American and Anglo-American culture meet on common ground, the United States of America.

EXTERNAL TRADE OF PUERTO RICO

Fiscal Years. Figures in Dollars *

Imports from	*1939–40*	*1946–47*	*1947–48*	*1948–49*
United States	100,517,184	279,322,773	337,255,714	326,135,198
Foreign countries	6,513,298	23,088,266	23,191,014	24,208,953
Total	107,030,482	302,411,039	360,446,728	350,344,151
Exports to				
United States	99,902,156	170,622,490	185,745,350	195,843,645
Foreign countries	1,445,086	7,938,696	6,280,475	8,281,381
Total	101,347,242	178,561,186	192,025,825	204,125,026

* Source: Puerto Rico: Information on Puerto Rico. Prepared by the Government of Puerto Rico in cooperation with the Department of the Interior. United States Government Printing Office, Washington, D. C. 1948. Annual Report of the Governor of Puerto Rico. 1949.

THE VIRGIN ISLANDS

The Virgin Islands of the United States are a group of small islands east of Puerto Rico. In the past they have been held by Spain, Great Britain, and Denmark.

In 1867 the United States began negotiations with Denmark for the purchase of the Danish West Indies, as these islands were called. The three principal ones are St. Thomas, St. Croix, and St. John. Finally in 1917 the negotiations came to a head, and the purchase was completed, the consideration being $25,000,000. The population of the islands is around 26,000, of whom more than 90 per cent are Negro or mulatto.

The significance of these islands, and the reason the United States desired them, lies in their strategic position and in the exceptionally fine harbor of St. Thomas, one of the best in the entire region. This island is 1,442 miles from New York and 1,029 miles from Panama. The harbor has long been used as a fueling station. Fear that it might be fortified

[4] See *Notes and Comments on the Commonwealth of Puerto Rico*. Washington, D. C., 1952.

by some European power and thus become a naval base led the United States to purchase it.

POPULATION

Year	*St. Thomas*	*St. Croix*	*St. John*	*Total*
1773	4,371	21,809	2,402	28,582
1835	14,022	26,681	2,475	43,178
1917	10,191	14,901	959	26,051
1930	9,834	11,413	765	22,012
1940	11,265	12,902	722	24,889
1950	13,811	12,096	747	26,654

Courtesy Robert S. Matthews.

Fig. 145. Looking over the port of St. Thomas, Virgin Islands.

Like all the smaller Caribbean islands, the Virgin Islands are economically dependent, primarily for the want of human energy. Some efforts have been made to discover some source of productive agriculture or industry that will make the islands more adequately self-supporting than they now are. Some attempts have been made to influence wealthy Americans to establish winter homes on the islands, which are very healthful, for the climate is inviting even in summer. The view overlooking the harbor from the hills behind and to one side of St. Thomas is exquisite.

In the past century the total population of the Virgin Islands has decreased very nearly 50 per cent. In 1835 there were 43,178 inhabitants on the islands, and today the number is about 26,000. This decline in population can be largely attributed to economic changes. In the early part of the eighteenth century St. Croix and St. Thomas were important sugar-producing regions. At the present time this industry is of little significance. The production of sugar has become progressively an uncertain undertaking because of competitive regions, and the general irresponsible attitude of many of the natives since our purchase of the islands. A marked decline has also taken place in the harbor business of St. Thomas. New developments in shipping have brought about an increasing shift from coal to oil as fuel and have thus reduced not only the need for labor but also the relative importance of St. Thomas as a port of call. Furthermore, the introduction of loading cranes, electrically equipped to load coal in ships with little hand labor, has also lessened the demand for workers. In the past many ships called at St. Thomas for orders, but this has become unnecessary since the world-wide use of radio communication. In every direction there are other evidences of the growing dependence of these insular plots upon Continental United States.

The seat of the government of the Virgin Islands is located at Charlotte Amalie, St. Thomas, whose population of 10,000 makes it the largest community of the islands. Frederiksted and Christiansted are the main centers of St. Croix. There are no towns on St. John.

St. Thomas presents a rough hilly terrain with steep slopes ending abruptly at the sea. St. Croix and St. John are less irregular in their surface features. Rainfall occurs usually in the form of light showers with a maximum precipitation in September, October, and November. Brush-forests and grasses constitute the natural vegetation cover. Some of the trees produce edible fruits, and there is the tree or bush from which the extract bay rum is obtained—the barber's delight of the gay nineties. Charcoal is another important use of the vegetation, because it is the principal fuel used in most of the insular homes.

The industries of the islands may be summarized as follows:

St. Thomas—Transportation services, manufacture of bay rum, production of rum, cattle raising, handicrafts, and tourism. (It operates as a free port.)

St. Croix—Sugar cultivation and cattle raising.

St. John—Production of charcoal, cultivation of bay trees, limited cattle raising, and tourism.

Exports of the islands consist, mainly, of raw sugar, rum, beef, handicrafts, and bay rum.

THE UNITED STATES' DEFENSE BASES

For defense of the Americas in World War II the United States leased a number of bases in British possessions in the West Indies, including locations in the Bahamas, Jamaica, Antigua, St. Lucia, and Trinidad. In the Bahamas the United States leased a site in Mayaguana, a small island located in the waters of Abraham Bay. The defense sites in Jamaica include a fleet anchorage in Portland Bight, near-by land areas for landing fields, and the right to develop the Port Royal dockyard in Kingston Harbor for joint use by British and United States forces. The Antigua site is on Parham Sound on the northeast side of the island and the narrow Crabs Peninsula that encloses Parham Harbor on the east. In St. Lucia the defense site includes a part of Gross Islet Bay for a seaplane base. (The Trinidad base is located in the region of the Gulf of Paria. In British Guiana bases have been secured on the Demerara and Essequibo Rivers.) Of course, the United States also has bases at Guantánamo Bay, Cuba; San Juan, Puerto Rico; and St. Thomas, Virgin Islands.[5]

SELECTED REFERENCES

See Chapter XXIX.

[5] G. S. Bryan: "Geography and the Defense of the Caribbean and the Panama Canal." Annals of the Association of American Geographers, Vol. XXXI, 1941, pp. 83–94. Also Earl B. Shaw: "United States Atlantic Defense," in *America at War*, edited by S. Van Valkenburg. Prentice-Hall, Inc., New York, 1942. Pp. 200–232.

CHAPTER XXXII

EUROPEAN POSSESSIONS IN THE WEST INDIES

BAHAMA ISLANDS

Extending southeastward off the coast of Florida are many small islands known collectively as the Bahamas, a British archipelago. Twenty of these islands are inhabited, either permanently or intermittently, with a total population of about 68,000. Nassau, on the island of New Providence, the capital of the colony, is the most important settlement. Its population is estimated as 20,000. Because of its climate and location,

NASSAU, BAHAMAS

15-Year Record Temperature	*Jan.*	*Feb.*	*Mar.*	*Apr.*	*May*	*June*	*July*	*Aug.*	*Sept.*	*Oct.*	*Nov.*	*Dec.*	*Annual*
(*°F.*)	71	72	73	75	78	80	82	82	82	80	76	73	77
59-Year Record Rainfall (*Inches*)	2.2	1.7	1.5	2.4	5.9	6.6	6.0	6.6	7.0	6.6	2.8	1.4	50.7

Source: *United States Weather Bureau Technical Paper No. 8*, United States Weather Bureau, Washington, D. C., 1949.

near Miami, Florida, Nassau has become an attractive winter resort for Americans. Until 1925 the chief Bahaman exports were sponges and sisal. Owing to a sponge disease and competitive synthetic products, these commodities have declined in the role of exports. Now the leading items in the Bahamas' limited foreign trade are cascarilla bark, hardwoods, shell and straw handicrafts, marine curios, turtle shell, and vegetables and fruits. More than half of the exports are shipped to the United States.

The total area of the Colony is about 4,000 square miles. The best land, some 600 square miles, is privately owned, while the remainder, consisting largely of swamps and barren terrain, is in the hands of the British Government.

JAMAICA AND DEPENDENCIES

Cultural evolutions. In the eighteenth century Jamaica was regarded as one of the richest colonies of the British Empire. At that time it was one of the leading sugar-producing regions of the world. There were large estates on which hundreds of Negro slaves worked, producing the "sweet gold" so highly valued in Europe. Beet sugar was unknown; preferential tariffs were yet to be drafted; and free entry was the general practice. Consequently the demand for cane sugar was beyond supply and gave a handsome profit to the producer. But, with the advent of beet sugar, the development of new sugar-cane regions, the abolition of slavery, and the introduction of trade restrictions, the cane industry of Jamaica fell into a deplorable state.

Adjustments followed, however, and again the production of sugar and its by-products is Jamica's leading industry. The annual output of sugar averages about 175,000 tons.

Banana culture is another significant activity in the Island. However, the lack of transportation for shipments overseas during the war, diseases affecting the banana plant, and the hurricane of 1944 greatly reduced production. In 1939, Jamaica supplied 18 million stems of bananas for exportation, as compared with less than 6 million stems in 1946. The British Commonwealth, particularly the United Kingdom and Canada, import more than 90 per cent of Jamaica's total banana exports.

While Jamaica may be designated as a sugar-banana country, nevertheless the island is not suffering from the one-crop specialty to the same extent as are Cuba and Puerto Rico. Many other agricultural products, including coconuts, coffee, cacao, oranges, grapefruit, pimento (allspice), ginger, logwood, breadfruit, mangoes, and cattle products, add to the economic welfare of the island. Special tribute should be given to the Jamaicans for their Blue Mountain coffee, which is said to rank among the highest grade coffee produced anywhere.

Land features and climate. In spite of the importance of Jamaica's agriculture, only 10 per cent of the land is under cultivation.

AREA OF LAND AT VARIOUS ELEVATIONS

Elevation	*Square Miles*	*Percentage*
Below 1,000 feet	2,250	51%
Between 1,000–2,000 feet	1,521	35
Between 2,000–3,000 feet	458	10
Between 3,000–4,000 feet	89	2
Between 4,000–5,000 feet	55	1
Above 5,000 feet	39	1
Total	4,450	100

The island is extremely mountainous. Of Jamaica's 4,411 square miles, only some 600 square miles, or 14 per cent, are classed as land in low relief, and much of this land is unsuited for cultivation.

A highland known as the Blue Mountains occupies the eastern third of the island. It is an ancient mass of complex folds, reduced to a stage of maturity, and rising to an elevation of over 7,000 feet above sea level.

JAMAICA: TEMPERATURE AND RAINFALL OF SELECTED STATIONS

	Station	Hill Gardens *	Kingston †	Morant Point *	S. Negril Point *
	Elevation (*Feet*)	4921.2	23.0	6.6	32.8
Average Temperature (°F.)	*Period of Record*	1908–1923	33 yrs.	1908–1925	1908–1925
	January	59.4	76	77.4	76.3
	February	59.2	76	77.2	75.7
	March	60.3	77	77.2	76.3
	April	61.2	78	78.3	77.9
	May	62.6	80	80.1	79.0
	June	63.9	81	81.7	79.9
	July	65.1	81	82.2	80.4
	August	64.9	81	82.2	80.2
	September	64.4	81	81.9	80.2
	October	63.1	79	80.8	79.9
	November	61.7	78	79.3	78.4
	December	60.4	77	78.4	77.5
	Annual	62.2	79	79.7	78.4
	Range	5.9	5	5.0	4.7
Average Rainfall (*Inches*)	*Period of Record*	1899–1927	53 yrs.	1899–1927	1899–1927
	January	7.4	0.9	4.2	1.9
	February	4.7	0.7	3.0	2.1
	March	4.0	1.0	2.6	2.8
	April	4.8	1.2	3.2	2.8
	May	8.0	4.2	6.2	5.9
	June	6.5	4.0	5.2	5.9
	July	2.7	1.5	2.9	5.6
	August	6.5	3.4	4.7	6.6
	September	9.4	4.4	6.3	7.3
	October	13.5	7.0	10.1	7.9
	November	19.7	2.8	9.3	4.1
	December	8.6	1.6	4.7	2.0
	Annual	93.2	32.7	62.6	55.0

* R. De C. Ward and C. F. Brooks: "Climatology of the West Indies," *Handbuch der Klimatologie*, Band II, Teil I, Berlin, 1934.

† *United States Weather Bureau Technical Paper No. 8*, United States Weather Bureau, Washington, D. C., 1949.

Surrounding, and projecting westward over, the greater part of the island is a highly dissected limestone plateau, above which rise residual knobs to an elevation of 3,000 feet above the sea. In this plateau are deep valleys and broad basins covered, for the most part, with fertile limestone soils that support some of the best agricultural communities in the island.

Margining the island is a discontinuous coastal plain that varies in width from practically nothing to more than five miles. The most extensive coastal lowland is the Liguanea Plain, embodying an area of 200 square miles, located north and west of Kingston.

The island of Jamaica shows a striking control of altitude over temperature. Near sea level the average annual temperature is 79° and decreases to 62° at an elevation of 5,000 feet. For the warmest month the range is from 82° to 65°, and for the coldest, from 77° to 59°, at these elevations.

The amount of precipitation varies considerably in different parts of the island, the high windward slopes receiving much more rainfall than the low leeward areas. At Kingston, to leeward of the high Blue Mountains, the average annual rainfall is about 30 inches; while in the windward regions north and northeast of Kingston the amounts are much greater, totalling some 222 inches at Mooretown, in the Valley of the Río Grande. The period of maximum rainfall occurs from October to November, and the drier season is from January to March. The monthly averages for these periods are 7 and 1 inches at Kingston, and 35 and 10 inches at Mooretown. The island is in the region of destructive storms and in the summer of 1951 Kingston suffered its most devastating hurricane of all time.

Land utilization. Jamaica is large enough and possesses a sufficiently varied terrain and climate to produce any of the tropical crops and many that are associated with higher latitudes. However, the island is so mountainous that after more than four centuries only 10 per cent of it is cultivated. But the highlands are not entirely waste lands; they are used for pastures, for the growing of coffee, and as sites for homes. The Blue Mountains are rather densely populated up to 4,000 feet, and coffee fields are numerous at elevations between 2,000 and 4,000 feet above sea level. On the slopes of the northeast, a region of heavy rainfall, and also on the drier lands northeast of Kingston, principally under irrigation, the banana is grown extensively. Sugar cane is grown mostly on the level land near the coast.

Population. Nearly one-half of the population of the British possessions in the West Indies live in Jamaica, with an estimated number of 1,237,000. Seventy-five per cent of the Jamaicans are classified as Negroes, 18 per cent mixed white and Negro blood, less than 2 per cent white, and the remainder East Indians and Chinese. The largest city is the capital, Kingston, with a population of about 109,000. Other important centers are Spanish Town, Port Antonio, and Montego Bay.

Dependencies. Islands directly subject to the governor of Jamaica are the Cayman Islands, the Turks, the Caicos Islands, and the Morant and Pedro Cayos. Of these dependencies Grand Cayman Island is the most important.

Prosperity and depression. Like most of the West Indies, Jamaica has enjoyed prosperity and experienced the discontent of depression. As a whole, there has been more depression than prosperity. Nevertheless, there are concrete evidences of progress, even though it may not be associated with prosperity. All-weather roads have been constructed to nearly all parts of the island. Railways extend from Kingston to Port Antonio and Montego Bay, and, together with two short spurs, total 222 miles of track. The port cities, Kingston and Port Antonio, have harbors accessible to ocean-plying vessels. There are many more landowners, a condition made possible by banana culture, which is better suited for small-farm production than sugar cane. Unlike the other West Indies, Jamaica has a more favorable agricultural diversification, and this is a matter of considerable significance, for there are comparatively no mineral resources and little manufacturing in this British colony.

The trade of Jamaica is primarily with Canada, the United Kingdom, and the United States. In order of importance the leading exports are sugar, rum, bananas, coffee, cigars, pimento, ginger, citrus pulp, fruit juices, dyeing and tanning materials, and goat and kid skins.

THE LESSER ANTILLES

Characteristics and value. The insular arc extending from Puerto Rico to Venezuela, known as the Lesser Antilles, includes some 25 inhabited islands and many without human occupants. In this group of the West Indies are the United States' Virgin Islands, all of the Dutch and French colonies in the Caribbean, and numerous British islands. The largest and most important is Trinidad. Although it falls within the line of the Lesser Antilles, Trinidad is physically as well as commercially more closely related to South America than to the West Indies.

Physiographically, the Lesser Antilles may be classified into two groups: (1) those primarily volcanic, and (2) those consisting largely of limestone. Among the more conspicuous volcanic islands are Martinique, the scene of the terrible eruption of Mt. Pelée that caused the loss of 25,000 lives in 1902; the majestic Dominica; and the symmetrical cones of Saba, St. Eustatius, and Nevis. Of the islands composed primarily of limestone, Barbados is best known. Unlike the volcanic islands, the limestone areas are low in relief, have few surface streams, and are generally intensively cultivated and densely populated.

Each of the inhabited islands has one important city, in every case a port, located on the western side for protection against the prevailing northeast winds and hurricanes. Only two of the islands, St. Thomas, one of the Virgin Islands of the United States, and St. Lucia, a British possession, have good harbors. The St. Thomas harbor is a deep and well-protected embayment and is undoubtedly one of the major attractions that led the United States to the purchase of Denmark's Virgin Islands. Other equally important factors are proximity to Puerto Rico and to trade routes toward Panama.

Sugar is the leading export in more than half of the Lesser Antilles. On the whole the sugar estates are small and the mills only semimodern. The European colonies are practically excluded from selling in the sugar market of the United States by a high tariff and quotas, although they can enter their product at a preferential rate in their mother countries.

The nonsugar-specializing islands are known economically primarily in terms of a limited number of export items. These include arrowroot from St. Vincent; unground nutmegs from Grenada and St. Vincent; essential or distilled vegetable oils from Grenada and St. Vincent; and cacao beans from Dominica, Grenada, St. Lucia, and St. Vincent. The Dutch islands, Curaçao and Aruba, as explained in the chapter on Venezuela, are important oil-refining and shipping centers. As a whole, in normal times, the French colonies trade with France, the British colonies with the British Commonwealth and particularly with Canada, and the United States possessions with the United States.

Barbados. The British colony Barbados consists of a small island of 166 square miles. Its terrain is largely a flat to rolling limestone surface with the highest hills some 1,000 feet above sea level near the center of the island. The average annual rainfall is about 60 inches. June to November is the rainy season and March to May the dry period. Like nearly all of the islands in the West Indies, a remarkably uniform temperature and a high humidity prevail throughout the year. The trades bring about some modification of the temperature during the winter months. August is the hottest month (81.0°) and February the coolest (77.8°).

The population of Barbados is about 193,000, of which Negroes constitute 70 per cent, mixed races 23 per cent, and whites 7 per cent. Sugar cane and sea-island cotton are the island's chief money crops. Other profitable crops are arrowroot, ginger, and vegetables. Most of the land under cultivation is in estates amounting to 52,000 acres out of a total crop acreage of 68,000. The remainder, 16,000, is divided in small holdings, of which there are some 14,000 one-acre plots. Bridgetown, population 15,000, located in Carlisle Bay, is the center of the island's urban life and the chief port. Since only vessels of shallow draft can dock at its wharves, lighters are used in the transportation of cargo between port and larger ships.

The chief exports of Barbados are sugar, molasses, rum, and cotton, and more than 90 per cent of its total overseas trade is with the British Commonwealth.

Trinidad and Tobago. On the basis of commercial products, Trinidad is the most valuable British colony of the West Indies. Among the island's important exports are cacao, coconuts, sugar, tropical timber, petroleum, and natural asphalt. Sugar and cacao are the chief crops of Trinidad, as they have been for many centuries. The island's natural asphalt is a phenomenal deposit of world significance.

PORT-OF-SPAIN, TRINIDAD

31-Year Record

Temperature	*Jan.*	*Feb.*	*Mar.*	*Apr.*	*May*	*June*	*July*	*Aug.*	*Sept.*	*Oct.*	*Nov.*	*Dec.*	*Annual*
(°*F.*)	78	78	79	80	81	80	80	80	80	80	80	79	80
Rainfall													
(*Inches*)	2.3	1.2	1.4	1.3	2.8	6.4	7.8	7.6	6.9	5.6	6.5	4.7	54.5

Source: *United States Weather Bureau Techniocal Paper No. 8*, United States Weather Bureau, Washington, D. C., 1949.

Regionally, Trinidad is closely related to the coastal land of eastern Venezuela. It is located only a short distance from the mainland, near the mouth of the Orinoco River, and constitutes a fragment of South America. A moderately high uniform temperature prevails over the lowlands, with a slight decrease at the higher elevations. In the mountainous areas of the north there is a rainfall of more than 150 inches, while on the shores of the Paria Gulf the average annual amount is less than 60 inches. Almost all other portions of the island have a precipitation of 60 inches or more. Cacao is produced in the rainy eastern regions and sugar cane in the drier western districts.

Comparatively little of the area of Trinidad is flat, high relief predominating in the north, central, and south portions. Between these belts, somewhat parallel to each other, are areas of moderate relief, dissected plains, and level lands and swamps. Approximately 40 per cent of the island is suitable for cultivation; the remaining 60 per cent is forest or waste lands.

The area of Trinidad is 1,862 square miles, and the population is estimated at 568,000. The drier areas of the west and the regions of low relief between the mountain belts are most densely settled. Comparatively few people occupy the rainy eastern and northeastern portions of the island. The most important city is Port-of-Spain, which has a population of some 95,000, and which serves the most productive and most densely populated area of the island. San Fernando ranks second in importance with some 14,000 inhabitants.

Petroleum is Trinidad's leading product, with a value in commerce almost twice that of any other export. Shipments increased from 8,907,298 barrels in 1933 to 16,417,056 barrels in 1938 and more than 20,000,000 barrels in 1950. Trinidad is internationally known for its asphalt from the famous Pitch Lake. The production in 1946 amounted to about 100,000 tons. Recently shipments have declined. Petroleum and asphalt, both important exports, contribute much to the economic welfare of the island, but, in common with the West Indies as a whole,

Trinidad is primarily an agricultural region. Her leading crops and agricultural exports are sugar and cacao, and these commodities are surpassed in export value only by petroleum. Other Trinidad exports are grapefruit, coconuts and coconut products, limes and lime products, angostura bitters, bananas, and rum.

Trinidad, located on the southern route from Europe to northern Venezuela, Colombia, and the Panama, serves as a center of redistribution, the chief trade center being Port-of-Spain. In addition, Trinidad is a major base on air routes between the United States and South America.

Tobago. Tobago holds the status of a ward in the colony of Trinidad. It lies about 22 miles northeast of Trinidad. An estimated population of 27,000 occupies its land of 116 square miles. Only one-seventh of its area is utilized for agriculture, in part because of its mountainous terrain. The chief exports from Tobago are cacao, copra, coconuts, lime extract, and staple foodstuffs.

SELECTED REFERENCES

See Chapter XXIX.

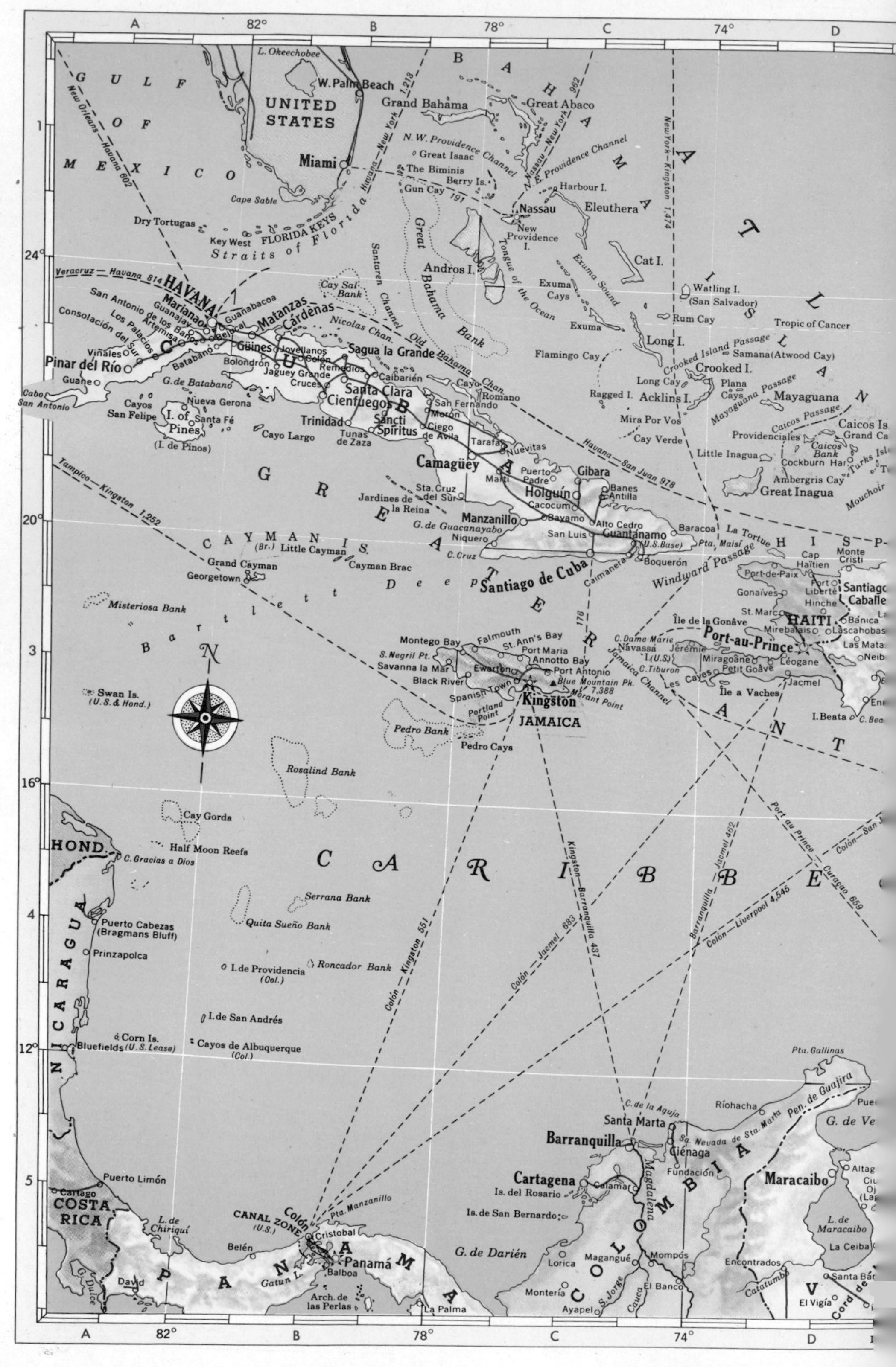

A
82°
B
78°
C
74°
D
1
24°
20°
3
16°
4
12°
5
GULF OF MEXICO
New Orleans—Havana 602
L. Okeechobee
W. Palm Beach
UNITED STATES
Miami
Cape Sable
Dry Tortugas
Key West
FLORIDA KEYS
Straits of Florida
Havana—New York 1,213
BAHAMA
Grand Bahama
Great Abaco
Nassau—New York 962
N.W. Providence Channel
N.E. Providence Channel
Great Isaac
The Biminis
Berry Is.
Gun Cay
Harbour I.
Nassau
Eleuthera
New Providence I.
Great Bahama Bank
Santaren Channel
Tongue of the Ocean
Andros I.
Exuma Sound
Cat I.
Exuma Cays
Exuma
New York—Kingston 1,474
ATLANTIC
Watling I. (San Salvador)
Rum Cay
Tropic of Cancer
Long I.
Crooked Island Passage
Samana (Atwood Cay)
Crooked I.
Flamingo Cay
Long Cay
Acklins I.
Plana Cays
Mayaguana Passage
Mayaguana
Ragged I.
Mira Por Vos
Cay Verde
Caicos Passage
Caicos Is.
Grand Ca
Providenciales
Caicos Bank
Turks Isl
Little Inagua
Cockburn Har
Ambergris Cay
Great Inagua
Mouchoir
Veracruz—Havana 814
HAVANA
Cay Sal Bank
Guanabacoa
Marianao
Matanzas
Cárdenas
San Antonio de los Baños
Guanajay
Artemisa
Consolación del Sur
Los Palacios
Bejucal
Nicolas Chan.
Old Bahama Chan.
CUBA
Viñales
Güines
Jovellanos
Colón
Sagua la Grande
Pinar del Río
Batabanó
Bolondrón
Remedios
Jaguey Grande
Caibarién
Guane
G. de Batabanó
Cruces
Santa Clara
Cayo Romano
Cabo San Antonio
Cayos San Felipe
Nueva Gerona
Cienfuegos
San Fernando
I. of Pines
Santa Fé
(I. de Pinos)
Trinidad
Sancti Spíritus
Morón
Cayo Largo
Tunas de Zaza
Ciego de Avila
Tarafa
Nuevitas
Havana—San Juan 978
Camagüey
Puerto Padre
Gibara
Banes
Antilla
Marti
Holguín
Sta. Cruz del Sur
Jardines de la Reina
Cacocum
Bayamo
Alto Cedro
Manzanillo
G. de Guacanayabo
Niquero
San Luis
Guantánamo
Baracoa
La Tortue
Tampico—Kingston 1,252
CAYMAN IS.
(Br.)
Little Cayman
C. Cruz
(U.S. Base)
Pta. Maisí
Grand Cayman
Cayman Brac
Boquerón
Windward Passage
HISP
Cap Haïtien
Monte Cristi
Georgetown
Bartlett Deep
Santiago de Cuba
Caimanera
Port-de-Paix
Gonaïves
Fort Liberté
Hinche
Santiago
Caballe
GREATER ANTILLES
Misteriosa Bank
St. Marc
Île de la Gonâve
HAITI
Bánica
Mirebalais
Lascahobas
Las Matas
Neib
176
C. Dame Marie
Port-au-Prince
Montego Bay
Falmouth
St. Ann's Bay
Port Maria
Navassa I. (U.S.)
Jérémie
Miragoâne
Léogane
S. Negril Pt.
Annotto Bay
Savanna la Mar
Ewarton
Port Antonio
C. Tiburon
Petit Goâve
Jamaica Channel
Black River
Blue Mountain Pk. 7,388
Les Cayes
Île a Vaches
Jacmel
Swan Is. (U.S. & Hond.)
Spanish Town
Kingston
Morant Point
Portland Point
JAMAICA
I. Beata
C. Bea
N
Pedro Bank
Pedro Cays
Rosalind Bank
Port au Prince
Colón—San J
Cay Gorda
HOND.
Half Moon Reefs
C. Gracias a Dios
CARIBBEAN
Kingston—Barranquilla 437
Barranquilla—Jacmel 452
Curaçao 659
Serrana Bank
Colón—Liverpool 4,545
Puerto Cabezas (Bragmans Bluff)
Quita Sueño Bank
Colón—Kingston 551
Colón—Jacmel 683
Prinzapolca
I. de Providencia (Col.)
Roncador Bank
NICARAGUA
I. de San Andrés
Corn Is.
Bluefields
(U.S. Lease)
Cayos de Albuquerque (Col.)
Pta. Gallinas
C. de la Aguja
Ríohacha
Pen. de Guajira
Santa Marta
Sa. Nevada de Sta. Marta
G. de Ve
Barranquilla
Ciénaga
Fundación
Puerto Limón
Cartago
Cartagena
Calamar
Maracaibo
Altag
COSTA RICA
Is. del Rosario
Magdalena
COLOMBIA
CANAL ZONE (U.S.)
Colón
Pta. Manzanillo
L. de Chiriquí
Is. de San Bernardo
L. de Maracaibo
Cristobal
Belén
PANAMA
Panamá
G. de Darién
Magangué
Mompós
Encontrados
La Ceiba
G. Dulce
David
Gatun L.
Balboa
Lorica
Arch. de las Perlas
Montería
S. Jorge
Cauca
El Banco
Catatumbo
Santa Bár
La Palma
Ayapel
El Vigía
Cord de

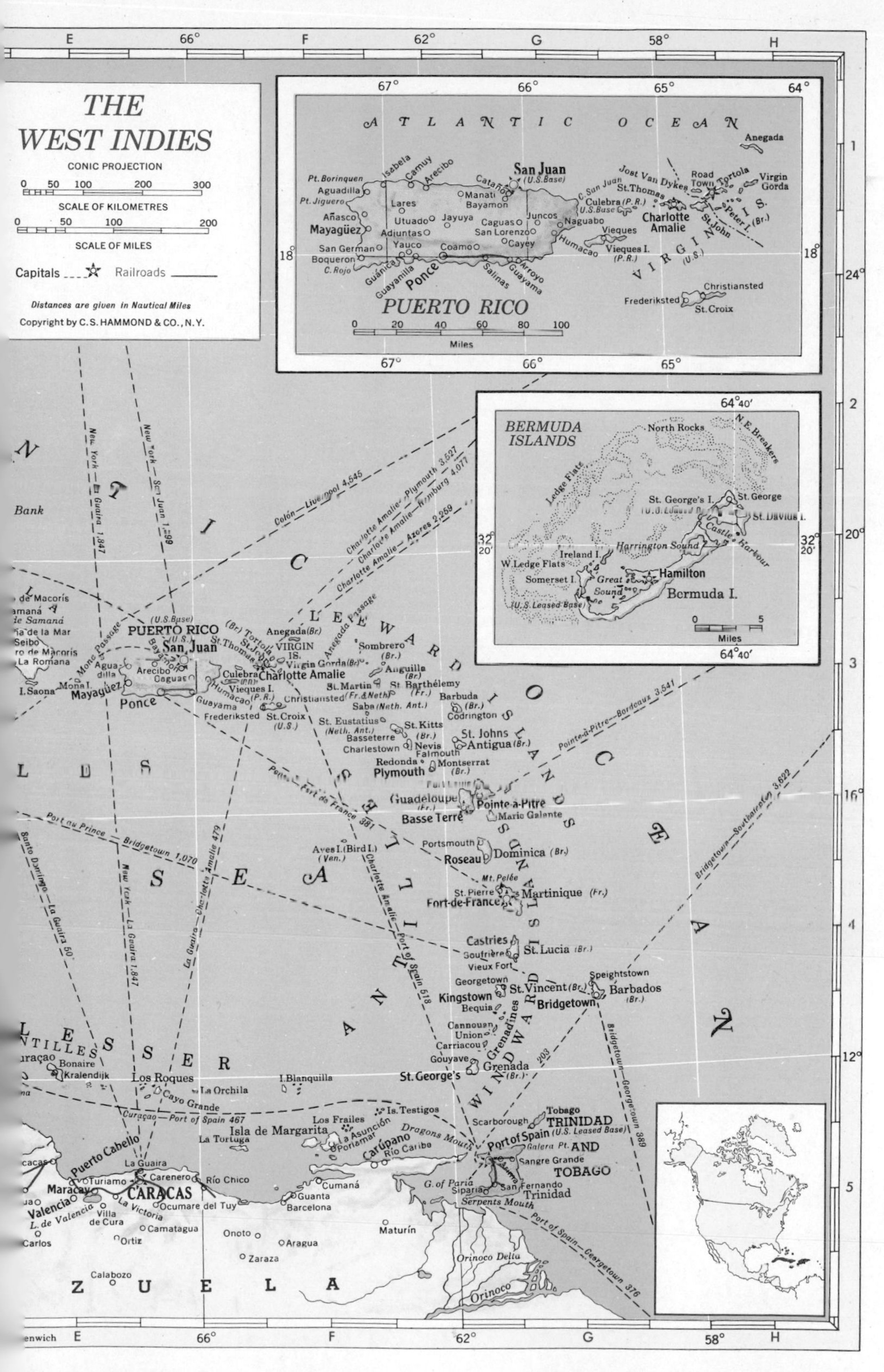
THE WEST INDIES
CONIC PROJECTION
SCALE OF KILOMETRES
SCALE OF MILES
Capitals
Railroads
Distances are given in Nautical Miles
Copyright by C.S. HAMMOND & CO., N.Y.
PUERTO RICO
ATLANTIC OCEAN
San Juan
Mayagüez
Ponce
Charlotte Amalie
VIRGIN IS.
St. Croix
Christiansted
Frederiksted
BERMUDA ISLANDS
Hamilton
Bermuda I.
St. George
LEEWARD ISLANDS
WINDWARD ISLANDS
Guadeloupe
Pointe-à-Pitre
Basse Terre
Dominica
Roseau
Martinique
Fort-de-France
St. Lucia
Castries
St. Vincent
Kingstown
Barbados
Bridgetown
Grenada
St. George's
TRINIDAD AND TOBAGO
Port of Spain
CARACAS
Valencia
Maracay
Puerto Cabello
La Guaira
Cumaná
Barcelona
Isla de Margarita
Los Roques
Orinoco
CARIBBEAN SEA
LESSER ANTILLES
ATLANTIC OCEAN
VENEZUELA

INTER-AMERICAN AFFAIRS

CHAPTER XXXIII

INTER-AMERICAN TRANSPORTATION

PAN-AMERICAN HIGHWAY

The plan. Hemispherical solidarity of the Americas has received the sanction of nature in the form of the unbroken continuity of land that stretches from Alaska to the Strait of Magellan, but unfortunately this geographical bond has never been fully utilized. Until comparatively recent years few of the American nations were linked by international highways; in fact, before 1930 the road between the United States and the capital of Mexico was little better than a trail. The lack of adequate land-transportation facilities was made very conspicuous shortly after December 7, 1941. While the conflict served the salutary purpose of bringing the Americas closer together in a common front against their enemies, the actualities of war did much to separate the nations of the Western Hemisphere because inter-American transportation was made more difficult. Ships in the inter-American sea lanes were the constant prey of the enemy, and many were destroyed. The effectiveness of ocean commerce in supplying the needs of the Americas was reduced. It is clear that if adequate land-transportation facilities had been available, some of the hardships of war could have been reduced, for land shipping could, in part, have replaced ocean transportation. Official wartime reports reflect the recognition of the need for better and more extensive highways, particularly those of international importance.

However, the dreams of some progressive thinkers and planners have not been altogether without result. The goal of such men has been the realization of a 10,000-mile highway, stretching from Fairbanks, Alaska, to Buenos Aires, Argentina, and on to Cape Horn; and the major part of this highway has already been constructed and is in use. It is called the Pan-American Highway System. At present, the 1,600 miles in the Alaskan-Canadian section have been completed, and, of course, good roads cover the entire 1,500 or more miles between Canada and the Mexican border. Approximately 80 per cent of the 3,267 miles between Laredo and Panama City are traversed by an all-weather highway. The stretch between Panama City and northwestern Colombia remains difficult, for an area of some 300 miles has not been surveyed. However, more than 90 per cent of the 3,500 miles of the Pan-American Highway between Colombia and Argentina is passable, at worst—and excellent in many places—throughout the year.

A policy, or probably one should say a past policy, of isolationism, prevalent in the Americas, had much to do with the failure to get an earlier start on the Pan-American Highway, but other factors of equal significance should not be overlooked.

The topography of the land, the weather conditions, the spottily concentrated commercial interests—all contributed their retarding effect. A high and broken terrain, swamps and rapidly flowing intermittent streams, and deserts and regions of constant, heavy rains are formidable obstacles in the construction and maintenance costs of highways. In many places the expense of construction and maintenance of an international highway would have been far in excess of any profit to be derived from traffic. A more detailed examination of the Pan-American Highway will illustrate these points.

Inter-American Highway.[1] The section of the Pan-American Highway system between Laredo and Panama City, covering 3,267 miles, is generally referred to as the Inter-American Highway. Passing over this highway, the traveller may see an unexcelled geographical traverse, or cross section, of the land and life of Mexico and the Central American nations. The highway begins at the international bridge over the Río Bravo del Norte and extends for some 100 miles at an imperceptible grade to the Mamaulipas Pass. Through this region the landscape is dominated by a broad expanse of small trees and shrubs, including mesquite, cactus, acacia, and other desert or semiarid plants. En route, 150 miles from Laredo, is Monterrey, Mexico's most important industrial city, located at an elevation of 1,769 feet above sea level and almost completely surrounded by mountains. Westward from Monterrey a highway leads to Saltillo, and the Inter-American Highway descends southward between the Saddle Back Mountains on the east and the Sierra Anáhuac on the west. Fields of corn and groves of fruit dot the landscape. The highway crosses Trópico de Cancer 348 miles south of Laredo, and the country, coincidentally, becomes distinctively tropical. At Ciudad Victoria, a branch road runs eastward 100 miles to Tampico, the well-known oil center of Mexico; and the plateau city of San Luis Potosí, to the west, can be reached from Antiguo Morelos. The town of Valles, lowest point of elevation on the route, lies 90 feet above sea level about halfway between Laredo and Mexico, D. F. From Ciudad Valles the highway ascends to an elevation of more than a mile and a half before it reaches Mexico, D. F., an elevation of 7,458 feet above sea level. As the elevation increases, one notices a marked change in the

[1] For further reference to highways between the United States and Mexico see chapters on Mexico.

vegetation. From the distinctly tropical, the vegetation becomes intermediate and in some places even sub-arctic. Forests of pine, scrubs, and grasses abound. About 40 miles from Mexico, D. F., the highway enters the valley of Mexico, a comparatively flat land surface marked with the

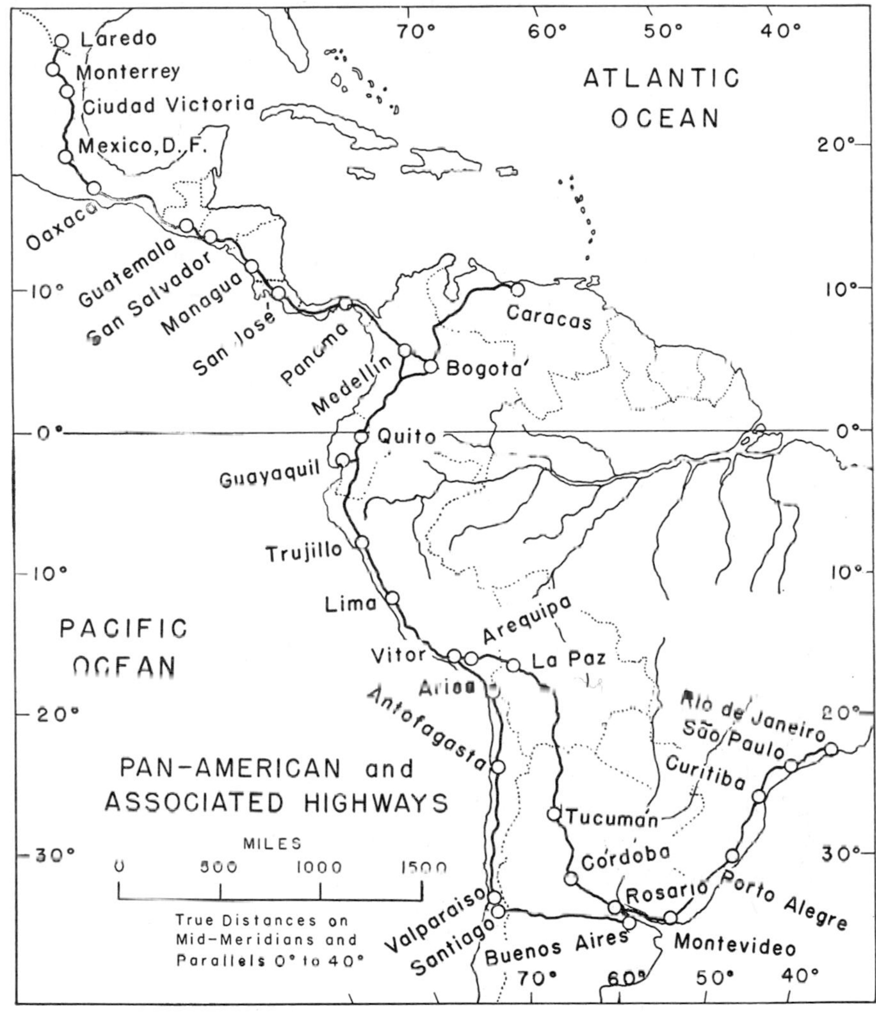

Goode's Homolosine Equal-Area Projection. Courtesy University of Chicago Press and Rand McNally and Company.

Fig. 146. Routes of Pan-American and Associated Highways.

conspicuous maguey, tuna cactus, and many other plant varieties. The total distance from Laredo to Mexico, D. F., is 763 miles.

Mexico, D. F., is linked with the country's leading port, Veracruz, by a highway that extends some 282 miles eastward; the Pacific port of Acapulco lies approximately the same distance by highway to the west.

The International Highway winds eastward, then southward, from the capital to the Isthmus of Tehuantepec, a low, hot, tropical region. From the Isthmus one travels across the little-known state of Chiapas, some 400 miles to Ciudad Cuauhtémoc, on the Guatemalan border. From Ciudad Cuauhtémoc the route extends to Tapachula, near the border. This section has not been completed. From Tapachula a road connects with the Inter-American Highway in Guatemala which leads to the fascinating highland towns of San Marcos, Quezaltenango, and Guatemala City itself. The Guatemalan capital's elevation is some 5,000 feet. However, from the lowlands to the uplands the highway reaches altitudes of about 10,000 feet above sea level.

Immediately to the south of Guatemala lies the nation of El Salvador, the first Central American country to complete her section of the Inter-American Highway. The route leads southward from Guatemala City to the border. In El Salvador proper the route leads about 205 miles over comparatively flat terrain through Santa Ana, San Salvador, the capital, and other important centers, such as San Vicente and San Miguel.

The next country crossed is Honduras. It has only about 90 miles of the Inter-American Highway and is the only country en route in which the highway does not reach the nation's capital (Tegucigalpa). At San Lorenzo, on the Inter-American route, an inter-oceanic highway leads northward to Tegucigalpa, and Lake Yojoa, where a ferry transports traffic across to where the road goes on to San Pedro Sula, where railway facilities extend to the coast. This north-south route carries more local traffic than the east-west section of the Inter-American Highway.

One may follow on the map the course of the highway as it traverses Nicaragua through the national capital, Managua, to the border of Costa Rica. For a hundred miles south of the Nicaragua-Costa Rica boundary line there is no road that can be traveled safely by passenger vehicles. In central Costa Rica the highway continues through San José for a distance of some 85 miles, but in the southern portion of the country—and as far south as Volcan, Panama, a distance of 125 miles—there is no road of any sort. Travel in any type of motor vehicle is practically impossible. Here lofty, rugged mountains, deep canyons, and treacherous streams have thus far combined to form an impenetrable barrier in the path of highway construction.

In Panama, the road from Volcan to Panama City, a distance of 338 miles, is open at all times. The road passes through the Pan-American city of David, a center of importance, and on to the Panama Canal, where ferry service is available to Balboa, Panama City, and to a highway leading to the Caribbean port of Cristóbal.

The Darien peninsula is one of several bottlenecks in the progress of the Inter-American Highway. The Republic of Panama has continued the road some 50 miles south of the Canal Zone, but from that point on to the Colombian frontier no construction has been made. Cars are shipped to Puerto Cabello or La Guaira, Venezuela, or to a west-coast port on the Pacific to continue their southward journeys. It is not probable that any attempt will be made in the near future to join Panama and Colombia by road; thus the gap will remain until the traffic demand is sufficient to justify the large outlay of capital that will be necessary to close it.

Simón Bolívar Highway. The portion of the Pan-American Highway extending through northern South America is generally known as the Simón Bolívar Highway, named for one of the famed revolutionary heroes. Cars shipped from Panama to Venezuela by sea usually land at La Guaira. A most picturesque highway runs from La Guaira over a mountainous terrain to Caracas, Venezuela's capital. The distance is 22 miles, and it involves a climb of some 3,000 feet. From Caracas one passes over the Simón Bolívar Highway to the international border of Colombia and Venezuela by way of Maracay, Valencia, Taborda, Barquisimeto, Valera, Mérida, and Cristóbal in Venezuela, to the Colombian town Cúcuta. From Cúcuta the route passes southward to Bogotá and on to the border of Ecuador by way of Ibaqué, Popayan, and Pasto, a distance of 1,075 miles. From La Guaira, Venezuela, to Bogotá, Colombia, the distance is about 1,800 miles. From Pasto, Colombia, to the Ecuador boundary, the road traverses high mountains at an elevation of 10,000 feet above sea level. If the Inter-American Highway is completed through the Republic of Panama and on into Colombia, the route will project to Medellín and join the Simón Bolívar Highway in the vicinity of Sevilla. In Ecuador, the highway has been completed through and some miles south of the Highland capital, Quito. The nation's southern portion, however, has only links of highways that await connection.

Coastal route. The Pan-American Highway extends along or near the entire coast of Peru. In the vicinity of Camana, southern Peru, the highway ascends to Arequipa, the largest city in south Peru, which lies in a beautiful mountain valley at an elevation of 7,500 feet above sea level. Leaving Arequipa, the road climbs to an elevation of 14,000 feet before descending to Lake Titicaca, which is at an elevation of 12,000 feet. From here the route continues to La Paz, Bolivia, and then turns diagonally to the distant capital of Argentina, Buenos Aires.

Another road leads from the Peruvian boundary to Santiago, Chile, a distance of 1,440 miles, and serves the important ports of Arica and Antofagasta, Chile. Here, as in Peru, much of the coastal route extends over desert lands. From La Serena and Coquimbo, southward to Santiago, the road passes through a region climatically classified as mediterranean.

Transcontinental route. Reference has been made to the Trans-Andean route between Peru and Argentina by way of Bolivia. A second route extends from Valparaíso to Santiago, over the Andes by way of the Uspallata Pass (12,800 feet above sea level) and then eastward to Buenos Aires.

Unfortunately, the pass is blocked by snow at times from May through December. When the pass is obstructed, cars can be shipped by rail to the Argentine side of the Andes. This is possible because the railroad uses a two mile tunnel located 2,300 feet lower than the pass. Leaving Uspallata, the road climbs to an elevation of 10,000 feet and then winds down to Mendoza, Argentina, located at the foot of the Andes at an elevation of 2,500 feet above sea level. The distance from the Chile border to Mendoza is 126 miles. From Mendoza to San Luis, a distance of 165 miles, the road runs through a dry area and then into a region of wooded hills. From the vicinity of San Luis, the well-known Pampa of Argentina extends to the Atlantic. It includes Buenos Aires, the metropolitan center and capital of Argentina.

Eastern international routes. The principal routes from Buenos Aires to Brazil include one via Sante Fé and the Paso de los Libres Bridge, and another along the coast via Montevideo, Uruguay. By the coastal route, connection with the Uruguay road system is by ferry from Buenos Aires to Colonia, Uruguay. From Colonia, an all-paved highway extends to Montevideo. From Montevideo, the route passes northward to the Brazilian boundary at Acegua.

The distance from the Uruguay border to Rio de Janeiro via Acegua is 1,464 miles, and from the Argentine boundary—Paso de los Libres Bridge—it is 1,653 miles. Road construction and maintenance along these eastern South American routes do not face the difficulties that they would in the rainy tropics. In fact, highway expansion in the eastern parts of South America—particularly in Argentina, Uruguay and portions of south Brazil—has been favored by climate and terrain. Here highway development has progressed rapidly in the past decade.

Summary. Highway construction in the other Americas has made considerable strides, but much remains to be done. At present, travel is largely from farm to market or between adjacent towns and cities. International transportation by highways is possible between most of the countries, but sections of the highway are passable only in the dry season. Approximately two-thirds of the Pan-American Highway System in the other Americas is open to automobile travel at all seasons of the year. Eventually all gaps will be closed, and the dream of continuous automobile travel from Alaska to Argentina will be realized. In all probability, the gap between Panama and Colombia will not be closed for many years to come.[2]

---

[2] See W. E. Rudolph: "Strategic Roads of the World," *Geographical Review*, Vol. XXXIII, 1943, pp. 124–129.

AIRWAYS

Pioneers. The remarkable development of inter-American airlines is still too recent for us to realize the historical importance of the pioneers who made it possible. Thirty-five years ago air travel in the Americas was largely in the barnstorming stage. Today, through the pioneer work of such men as Bauer, Faucett, Harris, Yerex, Musick, Wells, Dumont, Rihl, Rickenbacker, and others, the Western Hemisphere is covered by a network of commercial airlines serving all the Americas.[3] It does not seem too much to expect that eventually the efforts of such men will rank in importance with the feats of early exploration by Columbus, Magellan, and Clark; for, just as those early explorers blazed new trails by sea and land through the wilderness of a new continent, these later heroes of the air found the way and laid the groundwork for a transportation system that has done a great deal to bring the Americas closer together.

The first commercial airline in the Western Hemisphere, and the second in the entire world, was established in Colombia in 1919. In 1921 the United States granted the first airmail contract, linking our country with Cuba.

Prior to 1927 inter-American transportation was measured almost entirely in terms of sea traffic. Even as late as 1929, airmail service between the United States and South America required three days from Miami to Panama, four days to Buenaventura, six days to Lima, eight days to Santiago, and ten days to Argentina via the West Coast and across the Andes. In less than ten years, however, the flying time between the United States and Latin America had been reduced by 50 per cent.

At the beginning, the task of establishing dependable air transportation was an enormous one. Practically unexplored lands and seas had to be mapped; airway charts had to be prepared from scratch; landing fields had to be built and radio and weather stations established; ground crews had to be organized and trained; and other innumerable details essential

---

[3] Edwin C. Musick: Pioneer pilot, blazed the trail across the Pacific. Hugh I. Wells: Another World War I pilot, pioneer, surveyed courses in Latin America. Charles Lindbergh: Initiated early airlines between the United States and Latin America. Peter von Bauer: Founder of the first commercial airline in the Western Hemisphere, Austrian pilot and organizer of Colombia's Scadta, now nationalized as Avianca. Elmer C. Faucett: Founder and president of Compañía de Aviación Faucett, domestic airline of Peru. Harold R. Harris: Founder in 1928 of Peruvian Airways, now Pan American-Grace Airways (Panagra). Juan T. Trippe: Organizer and president of Pan American Airways system, 90-mile route in 1927 between Key West and Havana, now flying over 60,000 route miles in Latin America. George Rihl: Organizer in 1924 of Compañía Mexicana de Aviación, a domestic network of Mexico. Lowell Yerex: New Zealand-born founder in 1931 of Transportes Aéreos Centro-Americanos (Taca), covering Central America, except Guatemala. Santos Dumont: Pioneer of aviation in Brazil.

to the smooth and safe working of an airway had to be worked out. The planes that were available in the beginning were not designed for long-distance flights and could not fly at high altitude. The amphibian plane had not yet been constructed. Against such odds the first inter-American airway development began.

One of the first important contributions to the new enterprise was the introduction of the Fokker ship, a tri-motor plane with a cruising speed of 90 miles an hour; it was built by the Dutch designer Anthony H. G. Fokker. In 1927, Edwin C. Musick, who later opened a route across the Pacific, took a Fokker from Key West across the 90 miles of open sea between that point and Cuba. In 1928 this route was extended to include Haiti and Puerto Rico, but there development stopped temporarily because the danger of attempting to continue southward over the greater expanses of sea, relieved only by small islands whose broken terrain forbade safe landing, was too great. A new type of plane was needed, one that could land safely on the sea. Again inventive genius was equal to the task, and Igor Sikorsky, originally a Russian but now a well-known American builder of planes, designed his multi-engined seaplane. Lindbergh, using Sikorsky's new invention, inaugurated the first United States airmail route to the Canal Zone in 1929 and later completed the link between Puerto Rico and the mainland of South America. Thus development of inter-American air transportation was well under way.

Pan American Airways system. The Pan American Airways system has reached the point where it may be regarded as one of the greatest institutions of international transportation the world has yet known. It is, by far, the most extensive of the air systems of the Americas. More than 60,000 miles of the Americas, reaching every one of the 21 nations, are covered now by Pan American.

Two major routes lead southward from the United States; the division is caused by the geographical distribution of land and water. One major base is located at Miami, Florida, and the other lies at Brownsville, Texas. Planes regularly leave Brownsville for Mexico, D. F., Central America, and Balboa in the Canal Zone, where connections are made with Pan American west-coast service. From Miami regularly scheduled flights are made to Nassau; to Cuba and on to Haiti, Puerto Rico, and Trinidad; or from Cuba or Haiti to Colombia. Alternate routes from Cuba lead via Jamaica to the Canal Zone, or from Cuba to Yucatán.

From Trinidad one may now fly southward either to the Guianas or westward to Venezuela. If the Guianan route is chosen, the traveller may continue to Belém, Brazil, and thence down the east coast of Brazil to Uruguay and Argentina. Also from Belém it is possible to cut across the great eastern bulge of Brazil directly south to Rio de Janeiro. These eastern routes are all connected at strategic points with the company's own or affiliated lines along the west coast of the continent. Thus Pan

American comes close to serving all the important points in the continent of South America, and it is constantly improving and enlarging its service.

Avianca. The Avianca, or Aerovías Nacionales de Colombia, is one of the oldest commercial lines in the Americas. One Peter von Bauer started the company in 1919, with an operation between Barranquilla and Bogotá. That was the origin of the old Scadta Company. Within a few years German interests had developed Bauer's original venture into the Sociedad Colombo Alemana de Transportes Aéreos, or Scadta, and

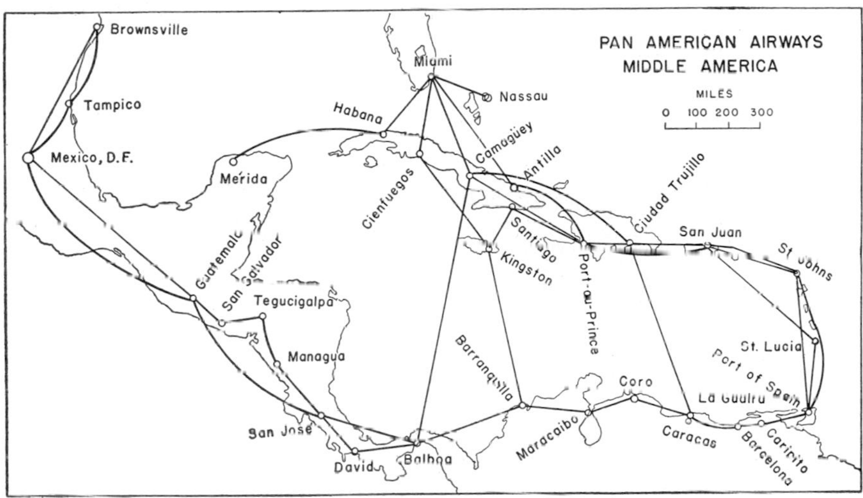

Fig. 147. Routes of Pan American Airways in Middle America.

Miami to Camagüey	343 miles	Kingston to Barranquilla	497 miles
Camagüey to Port-au-Prince	372 miles		
Port-au-Prince to San Juan	410 miles	Brownsville to Mexico, D. F.	464 miles
San Juan to Port-of-Spain	765 miles	Mexico, D. F. to Balboa	1626 miles
Port-of-Spain to Belém	1287 miles	Balboa to Cali	434 miles
Belém to Recife	1234 miles	Cali to Lima	1244 miles
Recife to Rio de Janeiro	1286 miles	Lima to Arica	638 miles
Rio de Janeiro to Buenos Aires	1238 miles	Arica to La Paz	193 miles
		Arica to Santiago	1036 miles
Miami to Cienfuegos	[illegible]18 miles	Santiago to Buenos Aires	797 miles
Cienfuegos to Kingston	376 miles		

(Distances represent commercial air miles and not necessarily Great Circle mileage.)

had built up a network of lines in Colombia to within a few hundred miles of the Panama Canal. By 1931 the controlling interest in the Scadta was acquired by Pan American Airways, but the lines themselves continued to operate largely under German interest and direction until 1939 when, because of the increasing prospect of United States involvement in the world crisis, the Scadta was disbanded and a new company was formed. In the resulting reorganization 60 per cent of the stock was acquired by the Colombian government and citizens and 40 per cent was held by a foreign company—undoubtedly the Pan American Airways. The new organization is called the Avianca, and at the present time its operation is strictly in the control of companies and interests of the Americas.

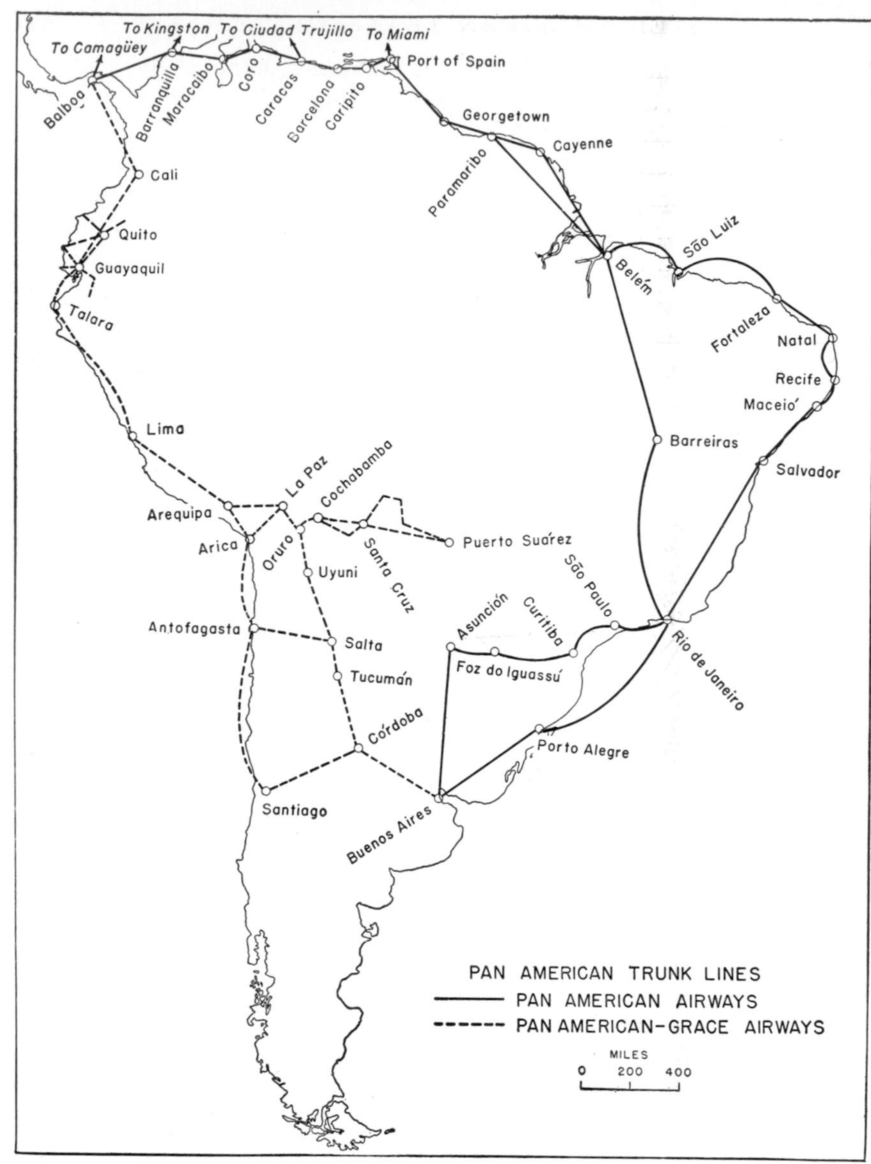

Fig. 148. Pan American Airways–South America.

(Great Circle distances in statute miles and flying time at a speed of 300 miles per hour—approximate)

Miami to Barranquilla	1082 miles	3 hrs., 36 min.
Miami to Natal	3720 miles	12 hrs., 24 min.
Natal to Buenos Aires	2350 miles	7 hrs., 50 min.
New York to Rio de Janeiro	4850 miles	16 hrs., 10 min.
New York to Panama	2190 miles	7 hrs., 18 min.
Panama to Buenos Aires	3310 miles	11 hrs., 2 min.
Natal to Dakar	1868 miles	6 hrs., 12 min.
New York to Belfast	3158 miles	10 hrs., 32 min.
New York to Moscow	4651 miles	15 hrs., 30 min.
San Francisco to Unalaska (Dutch Harbor)	2351 miles	7 hrs., 50 min.
San Francisco to Honolulu	2402 miles	8 hrs.
Honolulu to Sydney	5075 miles	16 hrs., 55 min.
Sydney to Tokyo	4860 miles	16 hrs., 12 min.
Unalaska to Tokyo	2836 miles	9 hrs., 27 min.

Taca. The development of the Taca, or Transportes Aéreos Centro-Americanos, illustrates in a striking manner the courage and ingenuity with which the early airmen in the Americas went about the task of building up a transportation system. The story of Taca has never been recorded in detail, but it forms one of the most remarkable adventures in commercial aviation. Lowell Yerex, a New Zealander by birth, took a rather rickety plane on a barnstorming tour of Honduras. He saw the need for air transportation and by a great deal of hard work, coupled with imagination and determination, built up an organization that in 1940 consisted of more than 50 modern planes, 60 or more airports, and 600 employees. Just before the outbreak of war in 1941 Taca's annual traffic amounted to more than 60,000 passengers, and cargoes that varied

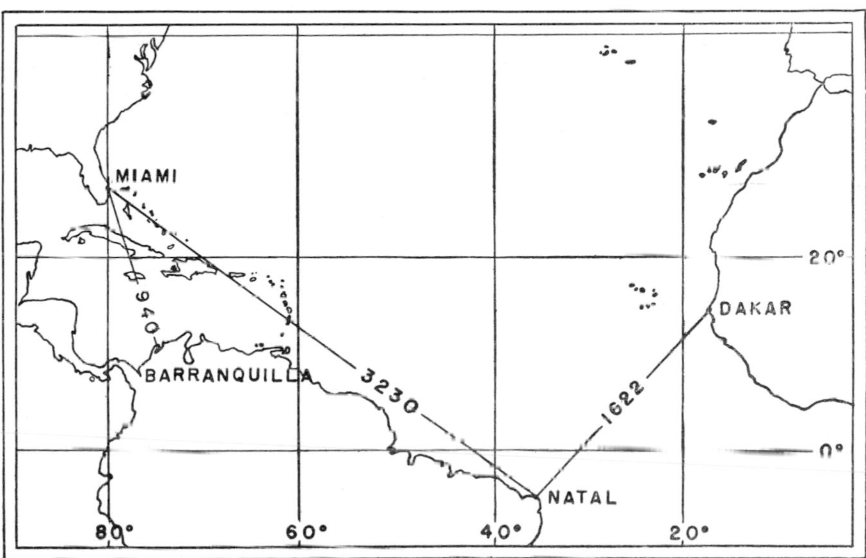

Fig. 149. Great Circle distances expressed in nautical miles.

from live poultry to oil tankers were carried. Yerex, until very recently, remained the sole owner of the company he had founded.

Panagra. The Pan American-Grace Airways owes its development to the pioneering efforts of Captain H. Harris, a war pilot of 1918. Harris went to Peru to fulfill a contract to dust cotton plants. As others were doing, he visualized the opportunities for commercial aviation in a country where the terrain has made land transportation exceedingly difficult, and his plans resulted in the inauguration of the Peruvian Airways Corporation, which later became a holding of the Panagra. The operation expanded, and by the outbreak of World War II, Panagra had a fine fleet of airships and regularly flown routes totalling more than 5,000 miles. The field of operation included flights between Balboa, in the

Panama Canal Zone, to Santiago, Chile; thence across the Andes to Buenos Aires. Other points served are Lima, in Peru; Quito, in Ecuador; most of western Peru; and La Paz, in Bolivia. Panagra has the distinction of operating the world's highest airport, 13,500 feet above sea level, near La Paz, Bolivia.

Prewar European airlines. Italy, France, and particularly Germany have been active in promoting or developing airlines in South America. Before the Second World War an Italian line, the Lati, operated between Rome and Buenos Aires, via Dakar, Africa, and Natal, Brazil. A French line followed much the same course.

Reference has already been made to the former German Scadta organization in Colombia. Other German lines operated by the Deutsche Lufthansa included a mail service between Germany and Brazil, Argentina, and Chile. The Lufthansa either controlled or owned outright such lines as the Sindicato Condor in Brazil, the Lloyd Aéreo Boliviano in Bolivia, the Sedta in Ecuador, and the Varig in Rio Grande do Sul in Brazil. Germany not only extended her air operations over thousands of miles, in fact throughout South America, but she also built airplane plants and repair shops such as the Focke-Wulf factory at Rio de Janeiro and the Lufthansa's repair shops at Buenos Aires. It is undoubtedly true that Germany made an extensive survey in the form of maps and photographs of strategic areas throughout Latin America. However, since the Rio Conference in 1942, and to some extent previously, all German airlines in Latin America have been disbanded or absorbed by the local governments.

Present international airline operations. North American, South American, and European air carriers include Latin America on their scheduled routes. Among the well-known companies of the United States are Pan American, Panagra, Braniff, Chicago and Southern, Eastern, National, and American. The number of non-United States carriers or companies operating between the United States and Latin America or within the other Americas is extensive.[4] Some of these carriers are more or less recognized as subsidiaries of United States companies.

National airway policies. Recently the governments of the Americas have taken a great deal more interest in airlines than they did formerly.

---

[4] A partial list is as follows:

Argentina—Línea Aérea de Transporte Nacional (LATN)
Brazil—Emprêsa de Transportes Aerovias Brasil, S.A. (Aerovias Brasil)
Colombia—Aerovías Nacionales de Colombia, S. A. (AVIANCA)
Cuba—Aerovías "Q," S. A. (Aerovías "Q")
Compañía Cubana de Aviación, S. A. (Cubana)
Expreso Aéreo Inter-Americano, S. A. (Expreso)
El Salvador—TACA, S. A. (TACA El Salvador)
Mexico—Aeronaves de México, S. A. (Aeronaves)
Aero-Transportes, S. A. (ATSA)
Compañía Mexicana de Aviacion, S. A. (CMA)
Líneas Aéreas Mexicanas, S. A. (LAMSA)

The present trend is toward the nationalization of Latin American lines and toward increased government supervision of lines engaged in international operation. Each of the Americas now has its own local airlines. With the tremendous development of the aircraft industry there is likely to be a corresponding increase in the number of commercial planes, marked expansion of airlines, and by far a greater national control of air activity. Certainly the operation of foreign airways in Latin America will be under more careful scrutiny than it has been in the past.

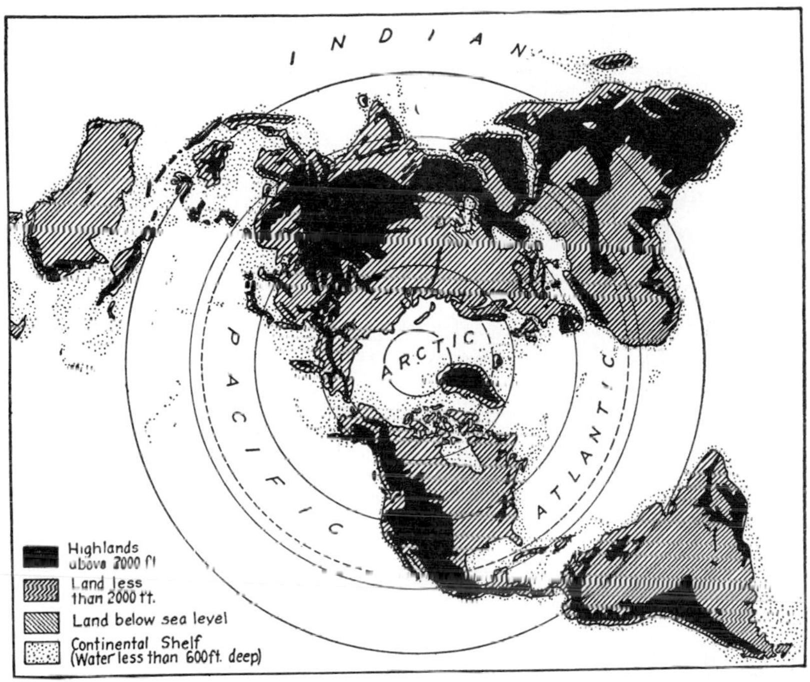

From Huntington and Carlson, Geographic Basis of Society. *Prentice-Hall, Inc., 1933.*

Fig. 150. Latin America's global position.

SEAWAYS

Merchant marine. Although a great deal of progress has been made in other methods of transportation, the sea—the age-old carrier of freight and men, and the method by which the Americas were discovered—still

Venezuela—Línea Aeropostal Venezolana (LAV)
Belgium—S. A. Belge d'Exploitation de la Navigation Aérienne (SABENA)
France—Campagnie Nationale Air France (Air France)
Italy—(*Alitalia*)
Netherlands—Koninklijke Luchtvaart Maatschappij N. V. (KLM)
United Kingdom—Bahamas Airways, Ltd. (BAL)
British Caribbean Airways, Ltd. (BCA)
British Overseas Airways Corporation (BOAC)
British South American Airways Corporation (BSAA)
Caribbean International Airways, Ltd. (CIA)

bears the brunt of the transportation of all heavy or bulky commodities in inter-American trade. Communication by sea has developed to the point where modern fleets of merchant vessels flying flags of the Americas are one of the strongest ties in American solidarity.

In the early days of American independence the United States merchant marine was unexcelled by any other nation, and our clipper ships sailed the seven seas with prize cargoes. However, the development was not continued, and during the nineteenth century our shipping industry passed from stagnation to decadence. At the beginning of the First World War, in 1914, the merchant marine of the United States was practically nonexistent and certainly carried no great weight in foreign trade. In fact, our own ships carried less than 10 per cent by value of our own foreign commerce, and inter-American trade was completely at the mercy of European and Asiatic powers. Records show that in 1914 the United States had 20 ocean-going vessels registered in overseas trade; of these, 6 were operating to Europe, 7 to the Orient, 4 to the west coast of South America, and 3 to Australasia. We did not have a single line under our flag to the important east coast of South America, although one line, plying between the United States and the west-coast nations via Cape Horn, offered limited service to eastern South America.

The outbreak of World War I and the consequent withdrawal of shipping from peacetime routes made very evident our need for a more adequate merchant marine. As a result of this emergency, our inter-American shipping was improved. However, during the period from 1920 to 1936 the public interest in a merchant marine waned in the United States, and thus the development that had begun during the war years largely went for naught. Our shipping lost heavily in quality and prestige.

Again emergency, this time an anticipated one, caused a revival of interest in American shipping. Affairs in Europe seemed to point to an outbreak of war long before the Second World War really began, and, with the realization of the impending danger, interest in shipping was revived, and American lines were generally improved. The Maritime Commission, created under the Merchant Marine Act of 1936, was charged with the task of rehabilitating our merchant fleet. A 10-year construction program was instituted, calling for 50 new ships a year, and a minimum of 500 vessels. With the actual opening of hostilities this program was greatly expanded.

As evidence of the particular part that the new program of development plays in inter-American trade, one may cite the establishment of the "Good Neighbor Fleet," which operated between New York, Brazil, Uruguay, and Argentina—with calls at Barbados and Trinidad en route. In this service the Maritime Commission spent over 2 million dollars in equipping three of the finest ships of their type—the *Argentina*, the

Brazil, and the *Uruguay.* Even before the outbreak of war these ships materially added to the increase of passenger and cargo movements between the United States and the eastern seaboard of South America.

The emphasis here has been placed on the development of shipping along the east coast of South America, for that was where development was so sorely needed. However, the west coast of South America and the Caribbean countries have had fairly adequate shipping facilities for many years.

The merchant marines of the other American republics have also expanded and are aiding in inter-American trade. Brazil, Argentina, Chile, Mexico, Peru, and Venezuela all operate commendable lines of merchant vessels. During the early days of the Second World War the fleet of the Republic of Panama was greatly increased by the change of many vessels from United States to Panamanian registry. Brazil, perhaps, has done more than any other of our sister republics to keep her merchant fleet up to date. At present, fleets of all of the Americas are being enlarged.

Trade routes. The first all-water route between the Atlantic Coast and the Pacific regions of Latin America was by way of the long and tortuous Cape Horn, or Magellan, route. When a railway was built across the Isthmus of Tehuantepec, in Middle America, the east-west routes, including both sea and land transportation, were greatly shortened. The culmination of seaway development in routes, however, came in 1914 with the opening of the Panama Canal, which provides a shorter all-water route between the Atlantic and Pacific Coasts.

In normal, peaceful times the principal inter-American seaways include routes:

(1) Between Atlantic ports and the east coast of South America.

(2) Between Gulf of Mexico ports and the east coast of South America.

(3) Between Atlantic ports and the west coast of South America.

(4) Between Pacific ports in the United States and the west coast of Latin America.

(5) Between Pacific ports and the east coast of South America.

(6) Between Atlantic ports and the north coast of South America.

(7) Between Gulf ports and the West Indies and north coast of South America.

(8) Between Gulf ports and Mexico and east-coast ports of Central America.

(9) Between Atlantic ports and northern South America and the west coast of Central America.

In 1889 the trip by steamship from the United States to Brazil required 24 days; to Chile the time consumed was two months. Now one may travel from New York to Rio de Janeiro in 12 days and on to Buenos

Aires or Valparaiso in a total of 17 days. The journey from New Orleans to Rio de Janeiro requires 18 days.

Development along the lines that we have been discussing is by no means complete. Taken all together, the airlines and the seaways are making great strides toward the goal of a closer-knit Western Hemisphere, and the Pan-American Highway will some day no longer be an interrupted reality but a unity in the support of a stronger and a better understanding of Inter-American affairs.

SELECTED REFERENCES

American Merchant Marine, *Proceedings,* Annual Publication.

Anderson, R. E.: *The Merchant Marine and World Frontiers,* Cornell Maritime Press, New York, 1945.

"Civil Aviation Program in Latin America," *Bulletin of the Pan-American Union,* Vol. 82, No. 4 (April, 1948), p. 231.

Coulter, J. W.: "Wings over the Atlantic. Time-Place Factor in Geography," *Journal of Geography,* Vol. 47, No. 8 (1948), pp. 313–325.

Franck, H. A., and Lanks, H. C.: *The Pan American Highway, from the Rio Grande to the Canal Zone,* Appleton-Century, New York, 1940.

Hager, Alice R.: *Wings over the Americas,* Macmillan, New York, 1940.

Lanks, H. G.: *By Pan American Highway Through South America,* Appleton-Century, New York, 1942.

Pearcy, G. Etzel: "The Air Age: Facts or Fantasy?" *Journal of Geography,* Vol. 46, No. 8 (1947), pp. 304–312.

Pearcy, G. Etzel: "Air Transportation World Coverage," *Journal of Geography,* Vol. 48, No. 3 (1949), pp. 105–112.

Pollog, C. H.: "Commercial Aviation in the American Mediterranean," *Geographical Review,* Vol. XXVII (1937), pp. 255–268.

United States Department of Commerce: Pan-American Highway System. *World Trade in Commodities,* Vol. VII, Part 1, No. 9 (July, 1942).

Van Zandt, J. P.: *The Geography of World Air Transport,* Brookings Institution, 1944.

Van Zandt, J. P. (Ed.): *World Aviation Annual,* Aviation Research Institute, Washington, D. C. and James Jackson Cabot Professorship of Norwich University, Washington, D. C., 1948.

CHAPTER XXXIV

COMMERCIAL RELATIONS

Latin American foreign trade. The Latin American countries are primarily exporters of raw materials and foodstuffs and importers of manufactured goods and food products. Among the principal exports are minerals, coffee, meats, sugar, cereals, vegetable oils, bananas, and cacao. Minerals are dominant in the foreign trade of Mexico, the west-coast countries of South America, and Venezuela; sugar in the West Indies; bananas and coffee in Central America; coffee and cacao in Brazil, Colombia, and Ecuador; and animal products and cereals in Argentina and Uruguay. The leading Latin American imports are the essentials, normally required in any land of limited domestic manufacturing, including textiles and manufactures, machinery, tools, vehicles and accessories, chemicals, pharmaceutical products, and scientific instruments.

TRADE WITH THE UNITED STATES

(Expressed as a percentage of total Latin American trade)

	Exports to U. S.	*Imports from U. S.*
1910	34.5%	23.5%
1932	32.1	32.3
1934	29.4	30.1
1935	32.8	31.7
1936	32.8	31.5
1937	31.0	34.0
1938	32.3	34.6
1939	35.2	40.6
1940	44.1	52.7
1941	57.3	62.1
1942	54.6	56.0
1943	52.6 *	54.2
1944	50.9 *	59.2
1945	49.2	58.5
1946	41.3 †	60.3
1947	39.1 †	65.9

* Country of destination of large shipments of petroleum not specified, and percentage probably understates shipments to United States for these periods.

† Estimate for year based on data shown for individual countries.

Source: *Foreign Commerce Weekly*, Vol. 31, No. 3, April 17, 1948, p. 4.

Based on value, the total foreign trade of the 20 Latin American nations for the year 1947 amounted to more than 10 billion dollars, against 3 billion in 1938, or approximately one-half of the foreign trade of the United States. About 50 per cent of Latin America's trade is with the United States.

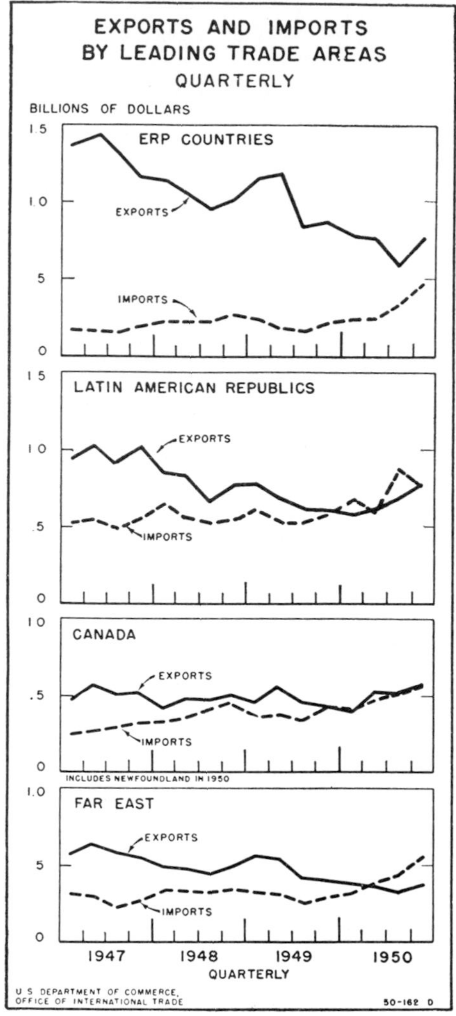

Fig. 151. Destination and origin of the Foreign Trade of the United States.

The other leading commercial nations trading with Latin America in prewar years were the United Kingdom, France, Germany, Italy, and Japan. In 1910 the United Kingdom's share of Latin American trade was 20.9 per cent of exports and 26.0 per cent of imports. These percentages were reduced in 1940 to 16.1 and 11.1, respectively. Germany's part in Latin American exports declined from 11.1 per cent in 1910 to an insignificant figure for the year 1940. Imports for the same years were

15.6 and 1.2 per cent, respectively. Prior to 1940 Germany had increased its share of Latin American business, whereas the United Kingdom's trade with the 20 nations had decreased.

Until recently, inter-American trade was almost wholly between the United States and Latin America, but now an increasing degree of commerce is taking place among the Latin American countries. The policy of the Latin American countries to trade with Europe or the United States, rather than with one another, dates back to colonial days when, as colonies, they were limited in their commercial relations to their mother country or its selected regions. Of course, the lack of adequate inter-American transportation facilities, the similarity of much of their production, and the need for manufactures and capital are among other

LATIN AMERICAN REPUBLICS: PERCENTAGE PARTICIPATION OF LEADING COUNTRIES AND GEOGRAPHICAL AREAS IN TOTAL TRADE

Exports to	*1938*	*1946*	*1947*
United States	32.3	41.3	30.1
Canada	1.1	1.5	1.4
Latin American Republics	6.3	13.0	10.7
United Kingdom	17.5	12.2	14.8
Continental Europe	30.6	20.2	22.0
U. S. S. R.	..	0.8	0.3
Others	...	...	...
Imports from			
United States	34.6	60.3	65.9
Canada	1.0	2.2	2.0
Latin American Republics	9.2	18.1	12.0
United Kingdom	12.1	6.2	5.4
Continental Europe	35.9	9.6	12.5
U. S. S. R.	.. *	...	...
Others	...	...	...

* Less than 0.1 per cent.

Source: *Foreign Commerce Weekly*, Vol. 35, No. 2, April 11, 1949, p. 12.

important reasons for the paucity of inter Latin American trade in the past. Consequently these producers of raw materials for foreign markets sought trade with the industrial nations of the world. Some of the early obstacles in the path of inter-Latin American trade have been overcome and, stimulated by the lack of overseas shipping during the war, the Americas to the south are finding new markets among themselves. For example, the inter-Latin American export trade has increased from about 7 per cent in 1938 to 10 per cent of the total in 1947. In terms of imports, the records show about 9 per cent in 1938 and 12 per cent in 1947.

Latin America as a source of raw materials. Latin America is the principal, and in many instances the only, source of many important United States imports. Approximately one-half of our imports of cacao, cattle hides, graphite, tungsten, and wool originate in Latin America. It also supplies all or nearly all of our imports of antimony, bauxite, beryllium, copper, vanadium, zinc, sodium nitrate, quartz crystals, iodine, babassú nuts, castor beans, coffee, flaxseed, henequén, and quebracho extract. It is true that the United States is a producer of some of these commodities—particularly cattle hides, flaxseed, wool, bauxite, copper, nitrates, and zinc—but we depend upon imports to supplement our output, especially in times of abnormal demands. Latin America is likewise a source of limited amounts of such essentials as chrome ore, manganese, mica, tin, platinum, titanium, zirconium, industrial diamonds, sheep and goat skins, flax, hemp, copra, jute, palm oil, kapok, and cinchona bark. The production of some of these raw materials, notably the forest and agricultural commodities, may be increased.

Rubber. In 1938 Latin America produced about 2 per cent of the world's total output of rubber, and practically the entire production of this region was obtained from wild trees in South America and in Mexico from a desert shrub known as guayule. British Malaya and the Netherlands East Indies, the two principal rubber-producing regions, accounted for 97 per cent. The world's exports of crude rubber amounted to about 895,000 long tons, of which Asia supplied about 865,000; South America, principally Brazil, 15,000; Mexico, 3,000; and the remainder, largely from Africa. The year of greatest production of crude rubber in South America was 1912, when the output was 49,000 long tons. With the development of rubber plantations in Asia and accompanying low market prices for crude rubber, South America's wild-rubber output declined rapidly. The production of rubber on plantations in South America has not been particularly encouraging because of a leaf disease, high cost of labor, and other physical and economic limitations that do not affect production in the East.

Before the actual beginning of hostilities in the Pacific, the United States, in coöperation with Latin American countries, had started a careful survey of the possibilities of increasing rubber production in the tropical regions of the Americas. Planting materials had been brought from the East and Africa, where the growers have had considerable experience in selecting high-yielding and disease-resistant varieties. More than 15,000,000 rubber trees have been planted in Latin America, 10,000,000 of them under coöperative arrangements between the United States Department of Agriculture and 12 Latin American countries, and the other 5,000,000 or more by United States commercial interests. Among the selected sites are agronomy experiment stations located in Guatemala, Honduras, Costa Rica, Panama, Colombia, Ecuador, Venezuela, Haiti, and Brazil. Efforts are being made to get farmers operating small farms to produce rubber. Rubber production, however, is a long-term project, and Latin America could hardly be expected to materially increase her rubber production within the next ten years. From 6 to 10 years are required for a rubber tree to reach its production stage.

As previously stated, Latin America will continue to supply a small percentage of the world's production of rubber, and in all probability the greater percentage of its output will come from the wild rubber trees in the Amazon region and not from plantations.

Abacá. Abacá, commercially known as manila hemp, is the principal fiber used for making rope. More than 95 per cent of the world's supply of abacá fiber has been produced in its indigenous land, the Philippines. Recently a limited amount has reached the United States from the republic of Panama, and it is reported that abacá can be grown successfully in other Latin American countries.

Babassú nuts. The babassú nuts, the kernels of a species of oil palm grown in Brazil, are imported into the United States for the production of babassú oil. It can be used as a substitute for coconut oil in the manufacture of soap and in the production of margarine and other edible products. Brazil is the only important source of babassú nuts.

Cacao beans. Although the cacao bean is a native of Latin America, more than two-thirds of the world's exports have been supplied by Africa, particularly the Gold Coast, Nigeria, and the Ivory Coast. The failure on the part of Latin American growers to meet the past competition can be attributed to poor management in producing and shipping. With the control or eradication of plant diseases affecting the cacao trees and the improvement in harvesting, grading, and shipping, the possibilities for increased production of cacao beans in Latin America are excellent.

Castor beans. The oil of the castor bean is used in the preparation of sulphonated or soluble oils for the textile industry; in the production of synthetic resins as lubricants for high-speed engines; in the preparation of leather, linoleum, paints, varnishes, and lacquers; and for medicinal purposes. Latin America has increased substantially its output and now produces approximately one-half of the world's supply. Brazil and Argentina are the leading producers of castor beans in Latin America.

Cinchona bark. The bark of various species of cinchona trees is the raw material for the production of quinine and its related alkaloids. In normal times the Netherlands East Indies have produced 90 per cent of the world's output of cinchona bark and Latin America and British India the remainder. The production in the East Indies, largely on the island of Java and in India, is from cultivated plantation, whereas in Latin America the output is principally from wild cinchona trees. Cinchona trees are indigenous to Latin America, growing here and there on the eastern slopes of the Andes, from Colombia through Bolivia. About 1850 the cinchona tree was introduced into India and Java, and, with their improved cultivation, the Latin American supply was practically eliminated from the world's market. However, in recent years Latin America has increased its output. The leading regions of production are in Bolivia and Peru.

Copra. The dried meat of the coconut is commercially known as copra and from it is obtained coconut oil, used in the manufacture of soap and in the preparation of shortening, oleomargarine, and other edible products. Copra and coconut oil have come chiefly from the Philippines, Ceylon, British Malaya, the Netherlands East Indies, and India. Latin America has produced very little copra or coconut oil. However, extensive regions of coconut palms are found in Brazil and in other tropical areas in Latin America, and, if the demand for coconut products continues, it is likely that Latin America may utilize more effectively its coconut resources.

Kapok. Kapok is a vegetable down obtained from the seed pod of a tropical tree. Its physical properties of being light in weight and resilient make it especially suitable for use as a filler in mattresses, pillows, and life preservers. Kapok is an excellent insulation material. Kapok is a native of southern Asia and the Netherlands East Indies, the principal centers of the present commercial production. In Latin America, Brazil and Ecuador are the leading exporters of kapok. An effort is being made to increase kapok production in Latin America. In 1940 some 500 thousand seedlings were planted in private nurseries in Guatemala and El Salvador. It takes about six years before a planting reaches a commercial stage of production.

With the restoration of normal shipping facilities, Latin America is finding it increasingly difficult to compete with other tropical regions. During the war our only available source of some tropical products was Latin America, but now we are again turning to Africa and the East Indies. It is generally accepted that Latin America lost its position in the production of a number of products that originated within its area, such as rubber, cacao, and cinchona, either because taxes and restrictions limited development, or because its primitive methods of production could not compete with plantation culture as practiced in Africa and the East Indies. Colonial regions also were favored with political stability, which in some Latin American countries did not exist.

Foreign trade of the United States with the 20 Latin American Republics. In 1948 the value of the United States imports from Latin America reached $2,508,000,000 and our exports totaled $3,359,000,000, as compared with $554,275,000 in imports and $503,751,000 in exports in 1938. For three consecutive years, 1946–48, exports exceeded imports in value, a contrast to our prewar import balance except in 1939 and 1940. In 1949, the gap between the United States exports and imports with Latin America was reduced to the difference between our exports valued at 3.1 billion dollars and our imports valued at 2.3 billion dollars. However, in 1950, the records of trade between the United States and the other Americas gave Latin America a favorable balance of about 239 million dollars. The marked increase in the dollar value of the trade of the United States with Latin America can in part be attributed to higher prices and an increased volume of a few items, particularly petroleum, sugar, coffee, and metals. The value of trade between the United States and Latin America exceeded the value of our trade with any other large geographic area. Approximately 35 per cent of total United States imports comes from Latin America, and 27 per cent of its total exports are marketed in the other Americas. In the prewar period, the southern Republics accounted for about one-fourth of our total imports and one-sixth of exports.

Three-fourths of the United States' trade with Latin America is with Brazil, Cuba, Venezuela, Mexico, Argentina, and Colombia. Our leading sources of imports are, generally, Brazil, Cuba, and Venezuela, whereas our chief markets for exports are Mexico, Venezuela, Brazil, and Cuba. The order of importance, based on value, may change from year to year.

Our major imports from the Latin American Republics are coffee, cane sugar, crude petroleum, and copper. Other significant imports are tin, wool, sisal and henequén, cacao, inedible vegetable oils and oilseeds, bananas, and hides and skins. The list of exports from the United States to the other Americas includes, primarily, industrial machinery, automobiles, parts, and accessories, vegetable food products, textile manufactures, chemicals, iron and steel mill products, and electrical machinery. For more detailed information concerning the composition of the United States' trade with Latin America, examine the accompanying tables.

UNITED STATES TOTAL MERCHANDISE TRADE WITH LATIN AMERICAN REPUBLICS

(Value in thousands of dollars)

	Exports	*Imports*
1936	395,045	501,610
1937	578,203	672,611
1938	503,751	554,275
1946	2,013,343	1,845,927
1947	3,669,243	2,304,944
1948	3,358,673	2,507,616
1949	2,721,000	2,303,828
1950	2,668,000	2,907,000

Source: United States Department of Commerce, *International Reference Service*, Vol. VI, No. 32 (1949).

United States Department of Commerce, *Foreign Commerce Weekly*, Vol. 43, No. 3, 1951.

TRADE OF THE UNITED STATES WITH LATIN AMERICAN TRADE REGIONS AND COUNTRIES

(Value in thousands of dollars)

General Imports

Trade Regions	*Countries*	*1938*	*1947*	*1948*	*1949*	Per Cent Distribution *1949*
Mexico, total		**49,030**	**246,689**	**246,447**	**244,200**	**10.6**
	Mexico	49,030	246,689	246,447	244,200	10.6
Caribbean, total		**214,658**	**1,058,592**	**1,069,611**	**1,092,200**	**47.5**
	Costa Rica	4,102	20,688	22,938	22,400	1.0
	Guatemala	9,529	44,042	44,080	43,300	1.9
	Honduras	5,692	11,577	13,031	15,200	0.7
	Nicaragua	2,478	8,993	11,698	6,700	0.3
	Panama, Republic of	3,352	6,710	8,998	11,200	0.5
	El Salvador	5,672	27,468	31,136	40,200	1.7
	Cuba	105,691	509,624	374,209	387,500	16.8
	Dominican Republic	5,745	30,228	35,211	25,600	1.1
	Haiti	2,967	20,144	18,849	19,800	0.9
	Colombia	49,398	205,628	236,398	241,500	10.5
	Venezuela	20,032	173,490	273,063	278,800	12.1
East, South America, total		**144,729**	**640,327**	**755,782**	**709,200**	**30.8**
	Brazil	97,933	445,669	513,850	551,900	24.0
	Uruguay	4,751	37,753	57,725	54,100	2.4
	Argentina	40,709	154,637	180,116	97,500	4.2
	Paraguay	1,336	2,268	4,091	5,700	0.2
West, South America, total		**44,530**	**221,976**	**282,132**	**258,400**	**11.1**
	Ecuador	2,584	18,470	18,887	17,100	0.7
	Peru	12,813	41,701	35,288	40,300	1.7
	Bolivia	865	39,505	48,840	48,500	2.1
	Chile	28,268	122,300	179,117	152,500	6.6

General Exports, Including Reexports

Trade Regions	*Countries*	*1938*	*1947*	*1948*	*1949*	Per Cent Distribution *1949*
Mexico, total		**62,016**	**629,898**	**520,364**	**462,400**	**17.0**
	Mexico	62,016	629,898	520,364	462,400	17.0
Caribbean, total		**213,909**	**1,536,424**	**1,459,337**	**1,399,500**	**51.6**
	Costa Rica	5,449	35,053	28,047	27,000	1.0
	Guatemala	6,861	41,377	44,817	44,900	1.7
	Honduras	6,292	29,901	26,777	33,600	1.2
	Nicaragua	2,807	17,403	20,577	15,700	0.6
	Panama, Republic of	10,165	172,162	91,902	115,700	4.3
	El Salvador	3,526	28,433	25,792	25,800	1.0
	Cuba	76,331	491,843	440,927	380,300	14.0
	Dominican Republic	5,696	49,324	46,981	38,300	1.4
	Haiti	3,642	25,214	20,204	23,800	0.9
	Colombia	40,862	218,931	196,875	175,900	6.5
	Venezuela	52,278	426,783	516,438	518,500	19.0
East, South America, total		**154,454**	**1,406,307**	**942,809**	**553,300**	**20.5**
	Brazil	61,957	643,225	497,559	381,900	14.1
	Uruguay	5,060	75,491	60,132	34,600	1.3
	Argentina	86,793	679,851	378,959	129,100	4.8
	Paraguay	644	7,740	6,159	7,700	0.3
West, South America, total		**50,201**	**285,187**	**238,241**	**297,000**	**10.9**
	Ecuador	3,311	39,996	30,748	32,400	1.2
	Peru	16,892	91,561	66,319	86,200	3.2
	Bolivia	5,395	28,290	35,706	36,200	1.3
	Chile	24,603	125,340	105,468	142,200	5.2

Source: United States Department of Commerce, International Reference Service, Vol. VI, No. 32, 1949. *Foreign Commerce Weekly,* Vol. 39, No. 2, 1950.

PRINCIPAL COMMODITIES IN UNITED STATES TRADE WITH THE LATIN AMERICAN REPUBLICS *

Imports

	Quantity		Value (000)	
	1938	*1948*	*1938*	*1948*
Coffee (1,000 lb.)				
Brazil	1,200,253	1,530,673	67,426	352,595
Colombia	452,890	703,391	45,830	206,259
El Salvador	71,266	115,940	5,550	29,686
Guatemala	59,910	100,118	4,094	27,239
Venezuela	23,951	73,131	1,963	20,028
Mexico	49,946	63,205	4,302	17,357
Costa Rica	13,733	42,365	1,222	11,815
Nicaragua	15,568	29,217	959	7,594
Cane sugar (1,000 lb.)				
Cuba	3,757,876	5,761,372	76,828	283,163
Peru	111,537	87,151	1,127	3,732
Crude petroleum (1,000 bbl.)				
Venezuela	23,563	93,622	16,541	222,962
Colombia		8,649		22,148
Mexico	2,484	4,060	2,058	6,443
Copper, crude and semimanufactured (1,000 lb. copper content)				
Chile	130,530	636,252	11,747	133,024
Mexico	71,958	114,806	6,175	23,075
Peru	76,062	33,517	7,132	7,425
Cuba	19,349	29,911	1,470	4,964
Tin, mainly ore (long ton)				
Bolivia	25	20,337	22	37,817
Wool, unmanufactured (1,000 lb.)				
Argentina	22,528	198,194	6,273	79,247
Uruguay	2,043	60,244	834	49,683
Brazil	85	4,880	9	3,228
Sisal and henequén (long ton)				
Mexico	48,387	49,902	3,971	15,394
Haiti	6,184	25,042	481	7,802
Vegetable oils and oilseeds				
Brazil			8,486	46,908
Argentina			18,596	295
Mexico			257	4,325
Bananas (1,000 stems)				
Honduras	9,888	13,796		
Guatemala	9,175	10,692		
Costa Rica	4,074	7,813		
Mexico	15,497	5,855		
Panama	6,353	5,572		
Colombia	3,751	3,690		
Cuba	4,227	2,819		
Haiti	1,443	2,735		
Ecuador	1,160	2,747		
Hides and skins				
Argentina			4,583	23,209
Brazil			2,872	10,255
Uruguay			236	1,370
All vegetables and preparations				
Mexico			1,243	25,716
Brazil			6	6,347
Chile			439	2,766
Cuba			1,395	2,087

PRINCIPAL COMMODITIES IN UNITED STATES TRADE WITH THE LATIN AMERICAN REPUBLICS *

IMPORTS

	Quantity		(Value (000)	
	1938	*1948*	*1938*	*1948*
Tomatoes, natural state (1,000 lb.)				
Mexico	20,807	230,442	623	21,780
Cuba	44,494	25,483	818	1,383
Sodium nitrate (short ton)				
Chile	575,841	720,764	10,689	23,400
Tobacco, unmanufactured (1,000 lb.)				
Cuba	12,673	18,709	7,810	23,299

* Imports for consumption.

Source: United States Department of Commerce, *International Reference Service,* Vol. VI, No. 32, 1949.

LEADING COMMODITIES IN TRADE OF THE UNITED STATES WITH THE LATIN AMERICAN REPUBLICS

(VALUE IN MILLIONS OF DOLLARS)

	1948	*1949*	*Per Cent Distribution 1949*
Total exports	3,358.7	2,721.0	100.0
Machinery total	795.9	665.8	24.7
Industrial	464.3	403.7	15.0
Electrical	238.1	182.6	6.8
Tractors	63.1	53.7	2.0
Agricultural	30.4	25.8	1.0
Automobiles, parts and accessories	364.1	262.4	9.7
Iron and steel-mill products	228.5	230.1	8.5
Chemicals and related products	241.3	225.5	8.4
Rice, flour, and vegetable food products	258.3	199.2	7.4
Textile manufactures	245.6	187.3	7.0
Meats, fats, milk, and other edible animal products	105.1	104.9	3.9
Merchant vessels	100.7	103.3	3.8
Petroleum and products	97.7	97.6	3.6
Iron and steel advanced manufactures	95.9	80.3	3.0
Other	———	———	20.0
Total imports	2,507.6	2,303.8	100.0
Coffee	685.2	780.6	34.0
Cane sugar	290.0	322.0	14.0
Metals and manufactures	296.2	297.0	12.9
Copper, crude and semimanufactured	170.8	155.2	6.8
Lead	47.4	65.4	2.8
Tin	38.0	38.1	1.7
Petroleum and products	254.5	295.4	12.9
Crude petroleum	249.5	280.2	12.2
Textile fibers and manufactures	194.7	148.5	6.5
Wool unmanufactured	135.9	94.3	4.1
Sisal and henequén	28.7	20.5	0.9
Cocoa or cacao beans	85.9	53.5	2.3
Bananas	48.7	51.4	2.2
Vegetable oils and oilseeds (inedible)	57.7	51.2	2.2
Sodium nitrate	23.4	26.0	1.1
Vegetables and preparations	38.0	24.7	1.1
Tobacco unmanufactured	23.3	24.0	1.0
Hides and skins	39.7	16.4	0.7
Other	———	———	8.9

Source: United States Department of Commerce, *Foreign Commerce Weekly,* Vol. 39, No. 2, 1950.

Factors affecting trade. In 1934 the Congress of the United States authorized the President to enter reciprocal trade agreements with foreign countries:

> For the purpose of expanding foreign markets for the products of the United States (as a means of assisting in the present emergency in restoring the American standard of living, in overcoming domestic unemployment and the present economic depression, in increasing the purchasing power of the American public, and in establishing and maintaining a better relationship among various branches of American agriculture, industry, mining and commerce) by regulating the admission of foreign goods into the United States in accordance with the characteristics and needs of various branches of American production so that foreign markets will be made available to those branches of American production which require and are capable of developing such outlets by affording corresponding market opportunities for foreign products in the United States. . . .

At the time of the passage of the Trade Agreements Act, the United States as well as the whole world was in the folds of an economic depression. The unemployment in the United States totalled more than 12,000,000; national income had been reduced from $79,631,000,000 in 1929 to $44,745,000,000 in 1933; the foreign trade of the United States declined from $9,640,336,000 in 1929 to $2,983,790,000 in 1934; our trade with Latin America fell from $1,925,876,000 to $518,303,000 in the same period; and Germany was engaged in a vicious barter system with some of the Latin American nations.

The Smoot-Hawley Tariff Act of 1930 had established high import duties which, in the opinion of some economists, had the effect of "setting up artificial trade barriers which tended to choke the normal channels of trade." In order to meet the growing competition and to improve commercial relations, the Trade Agreements Act was put into operation.

The first reciprocal trade agreement was negotiated between the United States and Cuba in 1934. Since that date, all but two Latin American countries have entered into a trade agreement with the United States. The agreements embody not only the lowering of tariffs and the fixing of some commodities on the free list but they also include, with minor exceptions, the unconditional most-favored-nation clause. This means that if either nation reduces any customs duty applicable to foreign importation, either autonomously or in connection with a trade agreement with a foreign country, the like article of the other country will immediately get the benefit of the reduced rate. The practical importance of this assurance is that exporters in each country will continue to be able to compete in the other country on a parity with other foreign producers and that the concessions which each country has granted to the other will not be impaired through the granting of greater concessions to any third foreign country.

Owing to the complexity of world affairs, it is impossible to measure accurately the specific effects of the program. However, some justification exists for concluding that the Reciprocal Trade Agreements have been one of many factors contributing to an improvement of commercial relations between the United States and Latin America.

On the supposition that world affairs can be improved through the *expansion of international trade* and that an increase in trade among nations, in part, depends on *the lowering of trade barriers,* a number of conferences and organizations have been instituted. The entire reciprocal trade agreement program is being modified by the participation of various countries in the General Agreement on Tariffs and Trade (GATT) under the International Trade Organization (ITO) activities.[1]

Quota system. Another factor governing trade is the limitation placed on quantity of imports or exports. For example, under the Sugar Act the Secretary of Agriculture of the United States annually announces quotas for domestic and foreign sugar-producing areas. In 1950 these quotas were established on the basis of (1) the determination that 7,500,000 short tons of sugar were needed to meet the needs of the continental United States and (2) a deficit of 300,000 short tons in the statutory quota for the Philippines. The basic quotas, proration of Philippine deficit, and adjusted quotas for 1950 are shown in the accompanying table.

Many commodities are under the quota system. However, a restriction on quantity of selected imports is a common practice not only in the United States but also in the other Americas.

Export-Import Bank. Owing to the increase of United States exports over imports in trade with Latin America, the debtor nations have found it a mounting difficulty to meet their financial obligations. In general, the Latin American nations obtain, through the sale of products abroad, the credit by means of which they buy foreign goods and discount in-

[1](1) The following American countries are contracting parties to the General Agreement on Tariffs and Trade, signed at Geneva, October 30, 1947:

(a) Original signatory countries: Brazil, Chile, Cuba.

(b) Signatories to the Annecy Protocol (1949): Dominican Republic (effective May 19, 1950), Haiti (effective January 1, 1950), Nicaragua (effective May 28, 1950).

Existing bilateral trade agreements between the above countries and the United States were suspended or terminated upon their accession to GATT.

(2) Bilateral trade agreements remain in force between the United States and the following countries: Argentina, Costa Rica, Ecuador, El Salvador, Guatemala, Honduras, Mexico, Paraguay, Peru, Uruguay, Venezuela.

Of these 11 countries two—Guatemala and Peru—have accepted invitations to participate in the forthcoming 1950 GATT negotiations at Torquay, England.

(3) There are *no* bilateral trade agreements between the United States and the following countries: Bolivia, Colombia (1936 Agreement was terminated November 30, 1949), Panama.

terest payments, shipping services, and many other requirements. With the growing disruption of European trade in 1938 and later of United States trade, owing to world hostilities, the need for a more favorable medium of trade in Latin America became increasingly apparent.

BASIC QUOTAS, PRORATION OF PHILIPPINE DEFICIT AND ADJUSTED QUOTAS, 1950
(Short tons, raw value)

Production area	*Basic quota*	*Proration of deficit in quota for Philippines*	*Adjusted quota*
Domestic beet sugar	1,800,000		1,800,000
Mainland cane sugar	500,000		500,000
Hawaii *	1,052,000		1,052,000
Puerto Rico *	910,000		910,000
Virgin Islands	6,000		6,000
Philippines *	982,000 ‡	(300,000)	682,000
Cuba *	2,219,400	285,000	2,504,400
Other foreign countries †	30,600	15,000	45,000
TOTAL	7,500,000		7,500,000
Proration of quota for other foreign countries:			
Belgium	180.6	88.7	269.3
Canada	346.2	170.0	516.2
China and Hongkong	176.8	86.8	263.6
Czechoslovakia	161.6	79.3	240.9
Dominican Republic	4,092.3	2,009.1	6,101.4
Dutch East Indies	129.7	63.7	193.4
Guatemala	205.5	100.9	306.4
Haiti	565.6	277.7	843.3
Honduras	2,106.5	1,034.2	3,140.7
Mexico	3,701.6	1,817.3	5,518.9
Netherlands	133.7	65.6	199.3
Nicaragua	6,272.4	3,079.4	9,351.8
Peru	6,820.5	3,348.4	10,168.9
El Salvador	5,037.4	2,473.1	7,510.5
United Kingdom	215.2	105.6	320.8
Venezuela	178.0	87.3	265.3
Other countries	26.4	12.9	39.3
Unallotted reserve	250.0	100.0	350.0
TOTAL	30,600.0	15,000.0	45,600.0

* The following quantities may be entered as direct-consumption sugar: Hawaii, 29,616 tons; Puerto Rico, 126,033; Philippines, 59,920; Cuba, 375,000.

† Prorations of basic quota may be filled with direct-consumption or raw sugar. Prorations of Philippine deficit may be filled with raw sugar only.

‡ Regardless of deficit proration, by reason of Sec. 204 (c) of the act, the Republic of the Philippines retains its basic quota.

In an attempt to improve the purchasing power of the Latin American countries, the United States made available through the Export-Import

Bank a considerable amount of money or credit. By 1941, of the total $500,000,000, appropriated to "facilitate and to aid in financing exports and imports and the exchange of commodities between the United States and foreign countries," a disbursement of more than $40,000,000 had been made to Latin American nations with some $230,000,000 more under authorization. For example, in the period 1939–1941, Brazil received through the Export-Import Bank some $65,000,000 for use in the stabilization of her exchange rates and to help finance the construction of a steel plant and purchase of merchant ships. Loans also have been made to other Latin American countries, to be used in the development of a variety of industrial and commercial enterprises.

EXPORT-IMPORT BANK OPERATIONS, BY COUNTRIES
(In thousands of dollars)

Country	Total credits authorized from Feb. 12, 1934 to June 30, 1949	Balances outstanding as of June 30, 1949	
		Undisbursed authorizations	Outstanding loans
LATIN AMERICA			
Argentina *	93,690	....	184
Bolivia	20,998	1,050	17,704
Brazil	283,696	10,714	98,833
Chile	112,681	28,596	46,001
Colombia	65,279	21,254	20,464
Costa Rica	8,723	....	6,619
Cuba	90,367	....	10,897
Dominican Republic	3,300	....	534
Ecuador	20,617	7,992	9,478
Haiti	17,350	4,000	5,470
Honduras	2,700	....	344
Mexico	155,659	38,365	73,285
Nicaragua	5,235	....	1,648
Panama	6,500	1,794	206
Paraguay	7,800	....	4,044
Peru	37,450	....	329
El Salvador	1,726	....	1,031
Uruguay	43,727	329	13,568
Venezuela	47,339	3,041	3,275
Various	118,983	19,605	....
Total Latin America	1,143,820	136,740	313,914

* In 1950, a loan of 125 million to Argentina was approved by the directors of the Export-Import Bank.

World Bank. Another lending agency is the International Bank for Reconstruction and Development. It was founded in 1944 at Bretton Woods for the purpose of financing reconstruction and economic development in order to stabilize currencies and promote world progress. The United States is one of its many members. In the course of its operation the World Bank has loaned about one billion dollars. Nearly 25 per cent of this amount went into a single pre-Marshall Plan reconstruction loan to France. With the growing dependency of the United States on Latin America the World Bank may offer a source of financial aid in the development of its strategic raw materials.

Investments. Owing to constant fluctuation in value, only a general estimate of the amount of American investments in Latin America is known.

Total United States investments in Latin America at mid-1948 were estimated at $5,720,000,000, of which $4,240,000,000 represents long-term private investments, $700,000,000 short-term private investments, $380,000,000 holdings of dollar bonds, and $400,000,000 government loans. This compares roughly with a total of $5,200,000,000 in 1930, $3,500,000,000 in 1936 and $3,700,000,000 in 1941.

The leading localities of our total direct investments in Latin America by 1950 were in Cuba, Chile, Mexico, Venezuela, Brazil, Argentina, Peru, and Colombia.[2] However, in the 1946-49 period, about 60 per cent of the billion dollars of new United States direct investments in Latin America went to Venezuela, mainly, in the petroleum industry. In fact Latin America has received 40 per cent of the total new United States direct investments abroad since World War II.

While the American investment has increased, the British investment has declined drastically. Several Latin American countries have used the sterling accumulated during the war years to repatriate British investments in railways and utilities. The British-owned Mexican Railway was sold to the Mexican government. The Brazilian government has purchased or expropriated a number of British properties. Argentina has liquidated most of its public debt in sterling, and there have been debt readjustments in other countries. British long-term investments in Latin America as a whole declined from about $4,500,000,000 in 1939 to $2,600,000,000 in 1947.

The composition of our direct investments in Latin America is as follows:—approximately—petroleum, 37 per cent of total; public utilities, 18 per cent; manufacturing, 16 per cent; agriculture, 12 per cent; mining and smelting, 10 per cent; distribution, 6 per cent; and miscellaneous, 1 per cent.

---

[2] Direct investments include such enterprises as mining, public utilities, manufacturing, selling organizations, and the stocks and bonds of United States controlled companies. They are made for the purpose of owning or controlling the foreign located establishments. Another type is known as the portfolio investments which include some equity or security in foreign-controlled companies or foreign government affairs. The United States direct investments in Latin America are about three times the value of the portfolio investments.

Among the business pioneers of the United States in the location of direct investments in Latin America are the United Shoe Machinery Company, 1903; the Singer Sewing Machine Company, 1904; Swift and Company, 1907; fruit companies, 1914; and a number of mining companies. Today many more well-known United States concerns are represented in Latin America, including the International Telephone and Telegraph, American and Foreign Power, Standard Oil and associates, United Fruit, W. R. Grace and Company, Cuban-American Sugar Company, the National City Bank, the First National Bank of Boston, the Cerro de Pasco Mining Corporation, the Pan American Airways System, Goodyear, General Motors, the Ford Company, the Guggenheim, Mellon, and Du Pont interests, and many others.

An effective trade barrier. A lack of geographic information and its application is an effective trade barrier, and one that is fully as significant as tariffs, purchasing power, short-term credit, and fluctuation in the rate of foreign exchange. The failure to appreciate the vast area of Latin America, the great distances between commercial centers, the problems of transportation, and the nature of the climates have caused many business ventures to fail. The excessive and long-continued heat and the unremitting humidity in some of the tropical lowlands are particularly severe on many articles of trade. Unless this fact is understood so thoroughly that the exporter takes complete precautions about his shipment, losses are likely to occur. An illustration may be cited with reference to shipping. Many of the ports of Latin America, particularly those on the western coast of South America, are located on open roadsteads. Ships anchor a mile or more offshore, and cargoes are loaded and discharged from lighters. Unless utmost care has been executed in the preparation of cargo for such treatment, losses and damages may occur. Packing for foreign market is, in general, different from packing for domestic shipment. These requirements, however, apply not only to Latin America but also to nearly all foreign markets. However, in general, there are no unusual conditions in Latin America that require business methods different from those applicable in any other part of the civilized world.

Trade trends in Latin America. The Americas exhibit a growing diversification in goods for exportation. Since many of the products of Latin America are produced almost entirely for foreign markets, the economy of the countries is dependent to a large extent upon commodity prices and the demand for their export products. Consequently, it is essential to have a variety of products for shipment abroad to meet changes in prices and demands.

Another pronounced development in Latin America is in processing, or manufacture before export. For example, Argentina and Uruguay have expanded their oilseed crushing facilities, thus shifting the exports from flaxseed to linseed oil. Brazil has increased the processing of castor beans and cacao beans. In part, the purpose of Brazil's expanding industrialization is to have finished or semi-finished commodities for exportation, such as pig iron and steel plates, cotton cloth, rubber tires and tubes, and various chemical manufactures. In Venezuela, the government requires the petroleum companies to refine a given percentage of crude oil in the country. Bag and cordage plants in Mexico, Cuba, and El Salvador, and the copper rolling mill and copper tube and pipe industries in Chile are other examples of manufacture before export.

In order to encourage domestic manufacture and an adequate supply of materials, as well as to conserve local capital, the Latin American Republics have placed various restrictions, in the form of quotas, taxes, and exchange control measures, on some imports and exportable goods. These government policies indicate the trend toward greater emphasis on internal markets.

Exports of certain minerals from Latin America are quite likely to increase. Since prewar 1938, petroleum exports have increased nearly 30 per cent, based primarily on the Venezuelan output. Other minerals in growing demand are copper from Chile, zinc from Mexico, bauxite from the Guianas, manganese and iron ore from Brazil. Iron ore from the new developments in Venezuela and Mexico will probably be in great demand.

If restoration continues in Europe, the trade between Europe and Latin America will continue to expand. For example, over 75 per cent of the Argentine exports normally go to the United Kingdom and Continental European countries. This is equally true for Uruguay. Peru normally sells much of its sugar and cotton in Europe, and Chile is dependent on European markets for wool, meat, and part of its copper and nitrate.

Latin America has raised barriers in the path of foreign enterprises. Restrictions on the entry and activities of technicians, production managers, and others needed in raising the level of production have materially curtailed progress. In many cases, special skills and foreign techniques are said to be more important than the need for capital in Latin America.

In recent years many Latin American countries have displayed a strong tendency toward so-called self-sufficiency. This is in part a reaction against the one-crop or one-commodity specialization of the past, and in part it is the effect of war conditions, a period of scarcities. In all probability, a more balanced position will appear as world trading returns somewhat nearer to normal.

Looking forward. To maintain the expansion of Pan-American trade, each American nation should work toward a better understanding of production and marketing problems in the Western Hemisphere. Each country should not only reëxamine its own commercial affairs but also the trading policies and scope of the other Americas. The plan should include inter-American trade conferences and, in particular, actual field studies by competent specialists. Accurate field observations in representative regions are indispensable in the interpretation of the voluminous and often none-too-reliable trade statistics. When the businessman of the United States or any other American nation meets the businessman of the other Americas in his own land, then trade barriers will be removed or at least opened for discussion on a common ground of understanding.

Furthermore, we in the United States must face in the future an increasing amount of competition from other countries in Latin America, because no commercial nation free to trade in foreign lands will overlook the rich agricultural, forest, and mineral resources of the other Americas and their 159,000,000 inhabitants, regardless of their present deficiencies in available capital and their relatively low purchasing power.

SELECTED REFERENCES

Colby, C. C.: "Crisis in World Trade," *Journal of Geography,* Vol. 48, No. 3 (1949), pp. 89–99.

Heare, Gertrude E.: "Latin-American Republics' Trade Still Affected by War's Impact," *Foreign Commerce Weekly,* Vol. 35, No. 2 (1949), p. 10.

Horn, Paul V., and Bice, Hubert E.: *Latin-American Trade and Economics,* Prentice-Hall, Inc., New York, 1949.

Kramer, R. L.: "Our Foreign Commerce in Peace and War," *Annals of the American Academy of Political and Social Science,* September, 1940.

United States Department of Commerce, *World Trade Development in 1948,* Office of International Trade, Washington, D. C., 1949.

United States Tariff Commission, "Latin America as a Source of Strategic and Other Essential Materials," *Report No. 144, Second Series,* Washington, D.C., 1941.

Wythe, George: "Latin America's Vast Resources Spur Broadening Developments," *Foreign Commerce Weekly,* Vol. 35, No. 2 (1949).

CHAPTER XXXV

INTER-AMERICAN POLICY

American solidarity. The geographical continuity of the Americas has had much to do with the particular types of political relations existing among the republics of North and South America. Brought together as they are in one great hemisphere, isolated from immediate contacts with Europe by the Atlantic, and from intimate relations with Asia by the Pacific, they have had much in common. Geographical separatism permitted them to achieve independence of European political control and establish republican forms of government. The example of the United States, which first achieved political independence and wrought out a model constitution, inspired South America and Middle America to a struggle for the same political rights.

In general, political relations between the United States and Latin American republics are on a wholesome and pleasant basis. Differences of a political nature have been merely temporary. Many observers believe that the "good-neighbor policy" proclaimed by the United States in 1933 has completely eliminated any suspicion that Latin American nations may have had in regard to so-called "Yankee Imperialism." A clear definition or restatement of the Monroe Doctrine by United States official representatives has done much to bring about a more permanent attitude of warm friendship between the Americas. Also world affairs have conclusively satisfied Latin America that the Western Hemisphere must be free from European invasion, the very purpose of the Monroe Doctrine. We are all familiar with this fact—that the Monroe Doctrine was proclaimed in 1823, 40 years after the American Revolution and a year before the complete liberation of South America, in order to stem the possibility of a renewed political aggression in the New World on the part of the powers of the Holy Alliance. The abrogation of the Platt Amendment, except in so far as it concerns the United States naval base at Guantánamo, Cuba, was welcomed by Latin America. Other past events have made it easier for the other Americas to understand the United States, including particularly the assurance of the United States not to intervene in their internal affairs.

INTER-AMERICAN POLICIES

The world crisis of the past decade added further reality to the need for a strong political unity among the Americas. Again the possibility of a European invasion brought forth agreements in line with the purpose of the Monroe Doctrine. In 1936 the Inter-American Conference for the Maintenance of Peace held in Buenos Aires, previously referred to in this writing, stressed the necessity for establishing a procedure of consultation for the purpose of meeting any emergency that might befall the relations of the Americas and other nations. Two years later, at the Eighth International Conference of the American States in Lima, Peru, the procedure of consultation was again emphasized. The first of the war conferences of the Americas was held in Panama from September 23 to October 3, 1939. Another meeting of the American ministers of foreign affairs followed in July, 1940, at Habana. At this meeting the American nations declared in complete unity that the occupation or domination by the totalitarian powers of the present European possessions in the Western Hemisphere will be unacceptable to the American states and will be regarded as a menace to their safety. Resolutions were adopted pertaining to subversive activities of aliens in the Americas and providing for reciprocal assistance and coöperation in economic affairs among the Americas. The third, and by far the most significant of all inter-American war conferences to date, was held in Rio de Janeiro, Brazil, January 15–28, 1942. The American republics reaffirmed their previous declaration to consider "any act of aggression on the part of a non-American State against one of them as an act of aggression against all of them . . . their complete solidarity and their determination to coöperate jointly for their mutual protection. . . . "

In 1945 the Inter-American Conference on problems of war and peace was held at Chapultepec Castle, Mexico, D. F. Out of this session came the Act of Chapultepec which, in part, consisted of an authorization to use sanctions in order to prevent aggression by one American State against another. This authorization was effective for the duration of World War II. The Act, however, implied its continuance on a permanent basis after the war through the negotiation of a multi-lateral treaty. Later, in 1947, a conference was held in Petrópolis, Brazil, to prepare and sign a treaty that would give permanent force to the principle of hemispheric solidarity embodied in the Act of Chapultepec. The treaty became the first regional development under Article 51 of the United Nations Charter to recognize the right of individual or collective defense. The Ninth International Conference of American States was held in 1948 at Bogotá, Colombia.

CULTURAL RELATIONS

In Europe there are two well-known cultures, the one Nordic, the other Latin. The early colonization of the United States was effected from the Nordic stocks, especially that of the British Isles. The early colonization of Latin America originated in the Latinized nations of Spain and Portugal. Until 60 years ago these two parallel streams flowed constantly in the same directions: Nordic to the United States and Canada, Latin to South and Middle Americas. Our language became English; the language of the Latin American peoples became, mainly, Portuguese or Spanish. Our social, political, economic, and religious institutions are all colored by our Nordic inheritance. The institutions of the Latin American republics are colored by the corresponding inheritances of Latin Europe. Between the United States and the Latin American nations cultural divides developed.

The most serious barrier to cultural relations is the difference in language. Language affinities between the nations of Latin America and the homelands in Europe have been a basis for understanding. Both of the Latin American languages are immediately descended from the Latin. They have close affinities with Italian and French, but not with English or German. The cultured classes in all Latin American countries have made French their secondary language and have insisted that it be taught in their schools. Until a few years ago it was necessary to use some French textbooks in South American schools, particularly in Brazil. There were no suitable books in Portuguese at the time. English was almost impossible because of the difficulty involved in reading, but every advanced student could read French fluently. It is so easy for these Latin Americans to learn French; it is so difficult for them to learn English.

In like manner, because of the language affinity, we in the United States have given considerable attention to German and French, and, until comparatively recently, made little effort to offer Spanish and Portuguese in our schools. Spanish began to be recognized in small measure after the war for Cuban independence in 1898, but we did not begin to consider it seriously until World War I forced German temporarily from the high schools.

These affinities are perfectly understandable. As a result of our attitudes in ignoring in the past the languages of Latin America, and of their ignoring our language, a culture barrier has arisen between the two continents that is very difficult to surmount. English is being taught more extensively in Latin America because of its commercial importance, and Spanish is now being seriously taught among us for the same reason. But Portuguese, which is the language of nearly half of the population of

South America, is persistently ignored in our public schools. There is some hope that this language barrier will become less serious in the future.

Another barrier that separates the United States culturally from Latin America lies in the home ties which bind the people of the respective continents to Europe. When funds are available for travel, North and South Americans have visited Europe rather than each other. Because of this perfectly normal trend, hundreds of passenger ships make trips across the Atlantic between the ports of the old world and the new, but hardly a score of passenger steamers ply between the ports of North and South America. Capitalizing on the dominant trend, the transportation companies have listed exceedingly favorable rates to European ports. They have established the most attractive types of service possible to Europe, and with the widest range of rates. The expense of travelling between the two Americas has consistently remained higher than that between America and Europe. Travellers between North and South America have been compelled to take either first-class passage, paying high fares, or third-class steerage. On most steamers there is no such thing as second-class passage or the "tourist third" in which so many visitors to Europe travel. Only within recent years have steamship companies developed an attractive service from New York to South American ports. And still more recently has attractive service been arranged between the United States and the ports on the Caribbean Sea. The completion of the Pan-American Highway should greatly stimulate inter-American travel.

The ancestral home of both North and South Americans is in Europe. There their blood relatives live, and all the ties of kinship operate to draw travellers to the old home country. Sentimental attachments have grown up, and therefore when a Brazilian wants to go abroad, his first thought is to visit his ancestral home in Portugal and the province from which his ancestors came. In like manner, the North American of Irish descent thinks longingly of visiting his beloved Emerald Isle.

Europe has for many years realized the enormous revenues to be derived from the development of an American tourist trade and has consistently advertised her mountains, lakes, and seas and her places of historic or poetic interest. It has built hotels and intriguing places by the hundreds, always with American tourists in mind. Its factories have long been occupied in making gadgets for tourists to purchase, from the perfumes of Paris to the polished olive-wood souvenirs from the Holy Land (usually "made in Germany").

Latin America has never realized her latent potentialities in this regard and has let the remunerative tourist trade pass her by. The magnificent harbor of Rio de Janeiro, the gorgeous beauty of the Chilean chain of lakes, the mountain majesties of the Andes, the waterfalls and river trips and shorelines, the wonders of the Amazon and the island-studded estuary of the Plata, or the myriad surprises of the tortuous passage through the Strait of Magellan, the pyramids in Mexico—these have never been effectively advertised in the United States. The splendid hotel service to be had in all the larger centers, the quaint customs of the interior, the intricate yet simple beauty of the hand-made lace, and the hundreds of other attractive purchases that could be made by tourists with a little free cash—these have never been adequately exploited. When they are, another barrier will be broken down, and Americans abroad will visit Latin America and will marvel.

Other hindrances to a perfect understanding between the people of the north and south have arisen. They are personality complexes. Particularly significant has been the gradual growth of a spirit of misunderstanding: "All North Americans are imperialistic and money-mad!" "All Latin Americans are unintelligent and backward!" Many Latin Americans have learned to fear us, and some have learned to dislike us. Nordics and Latins are different in many ways, and strong bonds of friendship are not so easily cemented between them.

Since the Spanish-American War, and in very recent times, Spain has made great efforts to recapture the sympathy and friendship of South America. Recently a group of leading citizens of both continents proposed the organization of a Spanish-American cultural union, with Spain its center. They believe that natural sympathies lie in that direction rather than toward a Pan-American cultural union.

The cementing of cultural bonds with Europe has proceeded along many lines. Noted European scientists who speak Spanish, Portuguese, or French make frequent visits to the Latin American universities—not on "good will tours" or to "interpret Europe to Latin America." They simply offer the results of their discoveries to the service and cultural advantage of southern audiences. Operatic troupes from the great European capitals regularly visit Rio de Janeiro, São Paulo, Montevideo, Buenos Aires, and Santiago, and offer to appreciative audiences the best of European music. Press services bring news from European centers, and this news is the daily diet of millions. Bookstores in all the principal Latin American cities are abundantly supplied with recent importations from Spain, Portugal, Italy, and France—but relatively little appears in the English language.

And so with other influences. Our tourists are usually worthy representatives of the United States, but not always so. In general our citizens abroad have larger resources of cash than the people among whom they visit. They "demand the best" and willingly pay for it. They sometimes draw vocal conclusions, comparing Latin American customs, culture, and progress with those of the United States—and the comparisons are not always complimentary. Representatives of North American business houses are better paid by far than the run of Latin American business-men. The idea that "all North Americans are rich and seeking to become richer" is difficult to disprove. American workers in Latin America, paid as they are very small salaries in terms of United States gold, receive several times the sum each month that native workers receive. This inevitably compels the drawing of a contrast in the popular mind between the opulence of the United States and the poverty of Latin America.

The greatest culture barrier of all, however, has been the complacency with which we have remained ignorant of Latin America and with which those lands have remained ignorant of us. The false impressions we have concerning them would fill libraries; and the untrue conceptions of Latin Americans concerning Uncle Sam and his "dissipated children" and his "murderous and lawless youth"—as seen in the movies shown there—are enough to bring blushes of angry shame and resentment to honest Americans.

The growth of inter-American culture contacts is impeded, then, by these four types of barriers: First, there is a positive and natural affinity of the United States for Nordic Europe, and of Latin America for Latin Europe. Second, there is a corresponding lack of rapport between the United States and Latin America. Third, there is the difficulty of an alien tongue. Fourth, there are positive misunderstandings on the part of all the Americas that have arisen from a lack of information or interpretation of geographic conditions and culture in general.

EFFORTS TOWARD MUTUAL UNDERSTANDING

Friendship among nations, as among persons, is based upon *mutual* understanding, cultural knowledge, and appreciation. Inter-American culture contacts depend upon a mutually sympathetic approach. Someone said on his return from Latin America, "My most persistently recurring thought was that above all one must approach Latin America with a flexible mind; a mind that can leap lightly from one apparent contradiction to another and yet see understandingly what lies between, for it is a land of striking contrasts." There is only one method by which the Americas may come to know and appreciate each other more adequately: by personal contacts. When citizens of the United States visit Latin American lands, learn of them, and form friendships with their people; and when citizens of the Latin American nations visit the United States, learn of us, and form friendships with our people—then, and only then, will culture contacts become meaningful. "The intimacy of real acquaintance" is the only basis for mutual culture.

What, now, are some of the ways these visits have been made, and these friendships formed?

Not long ago the people of the United States and those of Latin

America, particularly South America, had little basis upon which to form a judgment of each other. There was little communication between the two continents. At the present time, cables join New York with the West Indies. One continues down the eastern coast of the southern continent. Others extend west to Panama, where they separate, serving Central America, the northern coast of the continent, and the west coast. By means of the national telegraph system which connects with the cable lines, it is now possible to reach nearly every city of importance in Latin America from any city in the United States.

The language barrier, however, and the element of cost prevent these agencies from becoming extensively used as instruments for uniting the two continents. Radio broadcasting, which is particularly effective in the transmission of music and speech, has become an important medium of inter-American culture. Correspondence, which formerly required two weeks or more to reach South American points, now may be transmitted by air and in a few days answers may be received. And so communication is constantly opening the way to understanding.

The Pan American Union is one of the important instruments in inter-American affairs. Established some 62 years ago, in 1889, as the Bureau of American Republics, it was later renamed the Pan American Union. It has consistently sought to develop an atmosphere of good will and a spirit of mutual service among the republics of the Western Hemisphere. Under the impulse of the Union, the idea of international solidarity has made remarkable progress, and has overcome much of the earlier misunderstanding that existed. The Pan American Union is an entirely voluntary association of the republics for cultural purposes. The governing board of the Union is composed of the diplomatic representatives of each of the 21 nations that compose the Union. The representative of the United States is our Secretary of State. The headquarters of the Union are in Washington, where its beautiful building has become a meeting place for all inter-American interests.

Someone referred to the Pan American Union as a glorified tourist bureau because of its consistent praise of Latin Americans and their countries, and its corresponding lack of a critical attitude toward their mistakes and shortcomings. *In this very attitude of praise lies its strength.* The Union has sought to discover and emphasize the aspects of inter-American life that are most worthy. In so doing it has succeeded in developing friendships that otherwise would never have been formed. In this connection a former director of the Union wrote: "The difficulty is that we still conceive of international relations in terms of international differences rather than in those of international coöperation."

The plan and functions of the Union were stated more fully in 1948 at the Ninth International Conference of American States, held at Bogotá, Colombia. The name "The Organization of American States" was bestowed upon the network of official conferences and institutions, including the Pan American Union, that had been referred to collectively as the Inter-American System.

The main purposes of the Organization are to seek solutions to inter-American political, juridical, and economic problems and to promote coöperative activities that will lead to economic, social, and cultural development in the member states.

Effective action also has been taken by the United States Government to improve inter-American relations. In 1940 an order of the Council of National Defense, approved by the President, established an office for the Coordination of Commercial and Cultural Relations between the United States and the other American Republics. This office was succeeded by the Office of the Coordinator of Inter-American Affairs, later renamed the Office of Inter-American Affairs. With the termination of the Office of Inter-American Affairs in 1946, the Institute of Inter-American Affairs was established. The management of the Institute is vested in a Board of Directors, each member of which is appointed by the Secretary of State.

The Institute is responsible for furthering the general welfare of, and for strengthening friendship and understanding among, the peoples of the American republics through collaboration with governments and governmental agencies of those republics in planning, initiating, assisting, financing, administering, and executing technical programs and projects, especially in the fields of public health, sanitation, agriculture, and education. The Institute has directed, in cooperation with the other Americas, demonstration farms, food marketing systems, agricultural extension services, health and sanitation projects, and educational programs. Its educational activities warrant special attention. Educational specialists have been sent from the United States to work with leaders in the other Americas, and in exchange distinguished educators, supervisors, and teachers have come to the United States to lecture, study, and participate in educational affairs. Millions of Latin Americans have benefited as a result of the Institute health and sanitation projects. Someone summarized the purpose of the Institute with the well-chosen words, "We do not deplete our knowledge and experience by sharing it—we often enrich it." [1]

---

[1] The present Institute of Inter-American Affairs was chartered for a period of three years as a wholly-owned government corporation in an act approved by Congress on August 5, 1947. The charter was extended to June 30, 1955 by Public Law 283, 81st Congress, September 3, 1949. For detailed information, read "The Program of the Institute of Inter-American Affairs," Department of State, Washington, D. C.

For information about federal offices, see United States Government Organization, *Federal Register,* National Archives establishment, Washington, D. C.

Other government offices emphasizing American and inter-American affairs are: Office of American Republic Affairs, Department of State; Division of Territories and

Another project of inter-American significance takes the form of cultural centers. The program is administered by the Division of Libraries and Institutes, Department of State. The purpose of the cultural centers is to establish channels for scientific and cultural interchange between the peoples of the United States and the other American republics. They are meeting places where Americans from both the north and the south can get better acquainted. Through their library service, the centers have made available the latest and best American publications, phonograph records, reproductions of American art, and numerous other expressions of American life. The centers are active in sponsoring distinguished lecturers and promoting classes for instruction in English, Spanish, Portuguese, and French. Americans traveling in Latin America find the centers an important source of information. The centers are supported, financially, by appropriations from the United States, subsidies from the host government, fees from classes, and contributions from local business firms and individuals.[2]

Among the private enterprises of the United States that are active in serving the other Americas and promoting better understanding and coöperation among all nations are the International Basic Economy Corporation (I.B.E.C.) and its affiliate, the Venezuela Basic Economy Corporation (V.B.E.C.), and the American International Association for Economic Development (A.I.A.). The founder of these organizations is Nelson A. Rockefeller, a distinguished American business executive, a student of foreign relations, and the Coordinator of Inter-American Affairs during the war. The International Basic Economy Corporation is described as a financing development company with the policy to promote a constructive pattern of joint enterprises with the other Americas; to determine economic bottlenecks in Latin America; to establish joint business enterprises; to train nationals for technical and managerial positions; to introduce new projects; and to develop affairs that will aid in the improvement of living standards.

The I.B.E.C. and the A.I.A. are in action in Brazil and Venezuela, and recent reports indicate that establishments will soon be in force in other Latin American countries. In Brazil a mechanized agricultural service company was organized to introduce the most modern methods of land clearing, terracing, planting, cultivating, and harvesting. Corn is one of

---

Island Possessions, Department of the Interior; Office of Education, Federal Security Agency; Division of Geography, Department of the Interior; Office of Foreign Agricultural Relations, Department of Agriculture; Office of International Trade, Department of Commerce; Office of International Labor Affairs, Department of Labor; Bureau of Mines, Department of the Interior.

[2] In April, 1950, there were 30 cultural centers in the other Americas. For a description of the cultural centers, see *Cultural Centers in the Other American Republics* and *Cooperation with Cultural Centers in the Other American Republics,* Department of State publications.

Brazil's basic foods and it is the fourth largest corn producing country in the world. However, Brazil had no available hybrid seed and had poor storage facilities. Consequently, a hybrid seed company was established and methods of storage were introduced. These illustrations are only a few of the many ways in which the international organizations are extending service for the improvement of the economy of the other Americas.

Every feasible method of communication is being employed to disseminate accurate and representative information about the United States in Latin America through news agencies, books, radio, motion pictures, music, and many other forms.

Special emphasis is placed on the importance of students pursuing work in the Americas. In 1941, more than 100 Latin American students attended a special session of the University of North Carolina. This was the first time that a university in the United States sponsored a session devoted to courses and work of specific interest to students from the other American nations.

This interest in education abroad continues, and during the past eight years the number of students in the United States from Latin America increased from 15 during the academic year 1933–1934 to approximately 1,400 in 1940–1941, and 6,069 in 1949–1950. The total international student population in the United States in 1949–1950 was 26,433.[3]

The gains of international education are set forth in a report by the Institute of International Education as follows: "There is no guarantee that international education will save the world, but it offers a practical, inexpensive means of bringing about better understanding, achieving long-range results out of all proportion to the money and effort invested. . . . If enough people are able to participate, perhaps eventually reason, understanding, and planning, rather than fear, may be the determining factors shaping the course of world events." International education is a two-way project, and applies not only to the residence of students from other lands in the United States but also to the residence of our students in foreign countries.

A PRINCIPLE OF DEMOCRACY

The Americas, the United States and the Latin Americas, merit the right to preserve their own traditions, to pursue their own policies, and to develop their own way of life. Each American nation deserves the respect of all other nations and should be thought of, not as a subordinate, but as a collaborator in world affairs.

---

[3] The census does not include students below college level or specialists and trainees who are not enrolled in regular courses at an institution on the United States Attorney General's approved list.

SELECTED REFERENCES

"An Appraisal of the Inter-American System—A Symposium," *Inter-American Economic Affairs,* Vol. II, No. 4 (1949), pp. 45–95.

Bemis, Samuel Flagg: *An Historical Interpretation of the Latin American Policy of the United States,* Harcourt, Brace, New York, 1943.

Brand, Donald D.: "United States–Mexican Scientific and Cultural Relations," *The Annals of the American Academy of Political and Social Science,* January, 1948.

Dozer, D. M.: "Roots of Revolution in Latin America," *Foreign Affairs,* Vol. 27, No. 2 (1949), pp. 274–288.

Fenwick, C. G.: *The Inter-American Regional System,* The Declan X. McMullen Co., Inc., New York, 1949.

Fitzgibbon, R. H.: *The Constitution of the Americas,* University of Chicago Press, Chicago, 1948.

Harris, A. R.: "The Institute of Inter-American Affairs," *The New International Yearbook,* Funk and Wagnalls Co., N. Y., 1948.

History of the Office of the Coordinator of Inter-American Affairs, United States Government Printing Office, Washington, D. C., 1947.

Kirkpatrick, F. A.: *Latin America—A Brief History,* Cambridge University Press, Cambridge, England, 1939.

Laski, Harold J.: *The American Democracy,* Viking Press, New York, 1948.

MacDonald, A. F.: *Latin American Politics and Government,* Crowell, New York, 1949.

Manager, William: *Inter-American Highlights, 1890–1940,* United States Government Printing Office, Washington, D. C., 1940.

Mosk, S. A.: "Latin America and the World Economy—1850–1914," *Inter-American Economic Affairs,* Vol. 2, No. 3 (1948), pp. 52–82.

Pearcy, G. Etzel and Associates: *World Political Geography,* Crowell, New York, 1949.

Perkins, D.: *Hands Off: A History of the Monroe Doctrine,* Little, Brown and Co., Boston, 1941.

Rockefeller, Nelson A.: *Partners in Progress.* A report to the President by the International Advisory Board, United States Government Printing Office, Washington, D. C., 1951.

United States Government Organization Manual, United States Government Printing Office, Washington, D. C.

Welles, Sumner: *Where Are We Heading?,* Harper & Bros., New York, 1946.

Whitaker, Arthur P.: *The United States and South America, The Northern Republics,* Harvard University Press, Cambridge, 1948.

Whitaker, Arthur P.: *Inter-American Affairs,* Columbia University Press, New York, 1942–45.

APPENDICES

APPENDIX I

PRONUNCIATION KEY AND SELECTED PLACES[1]

Before presenting the student with a guide for the pronunciation of place names, we shall offer some notes on the general principles of pronunciation of Spanish and Portuguese.

Since with minor exceptions all the names in the following index are either Spanish or Portuguese, the notes are restricted to these two languages. The pronunciation of the few French, Italian, and Dutch names is given in the modified phonetic symbols that are shown in the table. Those names which consist of familiar English words remain in their normal orthography in the index.

In these, as in all tongues foreign to us, it must be realized that pronunciation is a function of the ear rather than the eye or the imagination, and the difficulties of reproducing with precision and accuracy

[1] The orthography of Portuguese has been in a state of flux in recent years. The situation at present is a considerable improvement over the quasi-anarchy that existed before 1911 and the works of Gonçalves Viana.

Although much alleviated, the problems involved in the reduction of double consonants, the interchange of i and y both as vowels and semi-consonants, the appearance of h within words, and the rôle of the accent marks are still very much with us. Many authors in Brazil today feel free to foster or ignore certain aspects of traditional spelling, and it is not unusual to find the same word spelled in different ways in the same work.

In the light of a situation such as this, it is impossible to indicate a given spelling as "correct" or "standard" as opposed to another spelling. Bahia, Baia, Curityba, Curitiba, Itajai, Itajahy are but a few of the variants involved. For decisions on names in Brazil, see *Cumulative Decision List No. 5004,* United States Board on Geographic Names, Department of the Interior, Washington, D. C., June, 1950.

For the purpose of consistency and as an aid in pronunciation, those place names that bear an accent mark in their original Spanish or Portuguese forms are reproduced with that accent mark even when these names appear in an English context, e.g. Paraná River.

A few place names of foreign countries have, however, by virtue of the frequency of their use and the effective standardization of their English pronunciation become part and parcel of English vocabulary. Names of this type, such as Mexico, Panama, and Peru are reproduced in an English context as English words and as such bear no accent mark. In a Spanish context these names are considered Spanish words and retain their accent mark, e.g. Ciudad de México.

(Prepared by Doctor Stanley M. Sapon, Department of Romance Languages, Ohio State University.)

sounds that have not been heard, but only described, are manifold. They become more apparent when we take into account the fact that the descriptions of the sounds are based on *analogy* with the sounds of our native tongue. Analogy is never exact equivalence, but tends rather to render an approximation that will not offend the native ear.

To begin with the basic elements of Spanish pronunciation, the point of widest divergence from English speech sounds will be dealt with first. The vowels in Spanish—*a, e, i, o, u* and *y*—are noted above all for their consistency and unvarying values, regardless of their relation to the stress. The vowels in an unstressed syllable in English tend to be muted, to lose their distinguishing characteristics. For example, the *e* in open and the last *o* in cotton sound alike in normal speech. In Spanish, however, the vowels never lose their value in unstressed position. Both a's in the word *casa* (KÄ-sä) sound alike.

For the sounds in English that approximate the values of the Spanish vowels, their normal orthographic representation, and their symbols, see the table that follows.

Of further significance is the regularity of the orthographic representation of Spanish vowels, *i.e.*, the letter *a* must be considered for general purposes to represent the same vowel sound in all positions.

The consonant series in Spanish contains a number of sounds that are very close to those represented by the same letters in English; these are: *f, l, m, n, p, s,* and *t.*

The pronunciation of the remaining consonants is explained in the table.

The rules for stress of Spanish words are simple:

1. If a word ends in a vowel, *n,* or *s,* the stress falls on the next to the last syllable.
2. If a word ends in any consonant other than *n* or *s,* the stress falls on the last syllable.
3. If a word is pronounced in any way contrary to the above rules, the syllable that must receive the stress is marked with a written accent (′).

A syllable in Spanish begins with a consonant, or a consonant plus *l* or *r,* or a strong vowel (*e, a, o*). The weak vowels *i* and *u* can have syllabic value only if marked with an accent (′). Two strong vowels coming together are separated into two syllables. Any combination of a strong and a weak, or two weak vowels, forms a diphthong. The vowels of a diphthong are pronounced as they would be if each stood alone, but they are run into one syllable. Once formed, a diphthong may have syllabic value.

The pronunciation of Brazilian Portuguese presents more complexities than Spanish, and a very simplified description of its principles of pronunciation must be given here. The vowels in Brazilian Portuguese are similar to those in Spanish in their uniformity of value, with the exception of unstressed final vowels.

The most striking of these is the pronunciation of unstressed final *o* like the *oo* in moon. In many parts of Brazil the unaccented final *e* is pronounced like the *i* in either s*i*t or pol*i*ce.

Conspicuous in Portuguese are the nasal vowels, written with a *til* (˜) over them, as are the nasal diphthongs, both elements of which are nasalized, although only the first bears the til: *são*.

In Portuguese the distinction between open and closed vowels may serve to distinguish different words, and is therefore a most important aspect of the vowels. For the pronunciation of geographic place names, however, it has been considered sufficient to indicate the proper values in the guide and thus avoid a lengthy and involved description here.

The consonant series in Brazilian Portuguese offers less difficulties for speakers of English than does Spanish. The consonant sounds represented by the same letters in both English and Portuguese are as follows: *b, d, f, l, m, n, p, s, t, v, z.*

The single *s* between vowels and at the end of a word is pronounced like the *s* in ro*s*e. The double *ss* is always pronounced like *s* in *s*nake.

The letter *c* followed by *e* or *i* is pronounced like a hissing *s;* followed by *a, o,* or *u, c* is hard, as in the English word *c*ake.

The remaining consonants and their orthographic symbols are given in the table.

Portuguese has a system of stress very similar to that used in Spanish:

1. Words ending in *a, e, o, m, n, ns* or *as, es, os,* are stressed on the next to the last syllable.
2. The last syllable is stressed in words ending in any consonant other than those mentioned above; in words ending in *i, is, u, us;* in words ending in a nasal vowel (or nasal vowel plus *s*).
3. If a word is pronounced contrary to the above rules, a written accent is employed (ˆ or ´).

The syllable in Portuguese may be considered, for general purposes, as obeying the rules given for the Spanish syllable, with one important exception the weak vowels *i* and *u* have syllabic value in Portuguese in the combinations *ia, ias, io, ios, ie, ies, ua, uas, uo, uos, ue, ues* when they are found as final elements in a word, and therefore need no written accent (see Rio de Janeiro).

GUIDE TO PRONUNCIATION

Letter	Symbol	
a	ä	farm, art.
ã [2]	ã	a nasalized vowel, muted, with a value between the a in English bad, idea.
Port. ei	ā	mate, take.
Eng. a	å	mute, as in capital.
e	ẹ	closed e, compares to English a in may, but without the final ee sound of the English word.
e	e̜	open e, compares to English in let, get.
i, y	ị	closed i, compares to English in machine, police.
i	i̜	open i, compares to English in bit, sit.
Port. ou	ō	note, coke.
o	ọ	closed o, compares to the first element of English o in open, hope, but without the final oo sound of the English.
o	o̜	open o—compare English north.
u	ụ	closed u, very much like the oo in moon, spoon.
b, v	b	compare English boy, bat, but without the puff of air that follows the opening of the lips.
b, v	ƀ	a sound peculiar to Spanish, produced like b, but the lips barely touch.
d	d	like English d in do, Adam, but made with the tip of the tongue against the back of the upper teeth.
d	đ	similar to th in English either, these or that, but not as forceful.
f	f	English fine, first.
g	g	cf. English get, gift, ghost.
ch	ĉ	as in china, champ.
Port. j, ge, gi	zh	azure, vision.
l	l	cf. English like, alone.
Sp. ll Port. lh	l̬	cf. million.
m	m	cf. English many.

[2] The til can be applied over other vowels to give them nasal quality.

n	n	cf. English **none.**
n	ŋ	as in si**n**k, thi**n**g.
Sp. ñ Port. nh	n̬	cf. English o**n**ion, ca**n**yon.
p	p	cf. English **P**eter, ha**pp**en, without the accompanying puff of air.
ca, co, cu	k	as in English **c**at, loo**k.**
	Kw	as in **qu**iet, **qu**ick, **qu**ack.
r	r	as in British pronunciation of "very." Compares somewhat to the **d** in the rapid pronunciation of "He**d**y," "ca**dd**y."
rr	r̄	no similar sound exists in English. Actually a double trilled r as above. Heard in the sound of the familiar Irish "Begorrah."
ce, ci, s, z	s	as in English **s**nake, **s**it, a**s**k. Never as in President!
Port. ch	ŝ	as in **sh**ip, **sh**op.
t	t	as in **t**ake, **t**om, but pronounced with the tip of the tongue against the back of the upper front teeth.
Port. v	v	as in **v**ery, **v**ictory, e**v**en.
y	y	as in English **y**oung, **y**ankee.
Port. z	z	as in English **z**ipper, ha**z**ard.
Sp. ge, gi, j	χ	non-English sound, as in German a**ch**, Scottish lo**ch.**

A PRONOUNCING LIST OF SELECTED PLACE NAMES [1]

A

Aconcagua	ä-kọŋ-KÄ-gwä
Aguascalientes	ä-gwäs-kä-LYEN-tẹs
Alagôas	ä-lä-GỌ-äs
Amazonas	ä-mä-ZỌ-näs
Andes, Los	lọ-SÄN-dẹs
Antigua	än-TỊ-gwä
Antioquia	än-tị-Ọ-kyä
Antofagasta	än-tọ-fä-GÄS-tä
Apure	ä-PỤ-rẹ
Araguaia	ä-rä-GWÄ-yä
Arequipa	ä-rẹ-KỊ-pä

[1] The syllable to be accented is shown in capital letters.

Argentina .... är-χẹn-TỊ-nä
Asunción .... ä-sụn-SYỌN
Atacama .... ä-tä-KÄ-mä
Atrato .... ä-TRÄ-tọ
Ayacucho .... ä-yä-KỤ-ĉọ

B

Bahama .... Sp. bä-Ä-mä Eng. bä-HÄ-mä
Bahia .... bä-Ị-yä
Bahía Blanca .... bä-Ị-yä BLÄŋ-kä
Barbados .... bär-ƀÄ-đọs
Barbuda .... bär-ƀụ-đä
Barquisimeto .... bär-kị-sị-MẸ-tọ
Barranquilla .... bä-r̄äŋ-KỊ-l̬ä
Belém .... bẹ-LẼ(ŋ)
Belize .... bẹ-LỊ-zẹ
Belo Horizonte .... BẸ-lụ ọ-rị-ZỌN-tẹ
Bío-Bío .... BỊ-ọ BỊ-ọ
Bogotá .... bọ-gọ-TÄ
Bolívar .... bọ-LỊ-ƀär
Bolivia .... bọ-LỊ-ƀyä
Boyacá .... bọ-yä-KÄ
Brazil .... (conventional), Brazil (Portuguese) brä-ZỊL
British Guiana .... ——— gị-YÄ-nä
British Honduras .... see Honduras
Bucaramanga .... bụ-kä-rä-MÄŋ-gä
Buenaventura .... bwẹ-nä-ƀẹn-TỤ-rä
Buenos Aires .... bwẹ-nọ-SÄỊ-rẹs

C

Caldas .... KÄL-däs
Cali .... KÄ-lị
Callao .... kä-L̬Ä-ọ
Camagüey .... kä-mä-GWẸỊ
Campeche .... käm-PẸ-ĉẹ
Campinas .... käm-PỊ-näs
Caracas .... kä-RÄ-käs
Cárdenas .... KÄR-đẹ-näs
Cartagena .... kär-tä-XẸ-nä
Cartago .... kär-TÄ-gọ
Cauca .... KÄỤ-kä
Cayenne .... kä-YẸN
Ceará .... sẹ-ä-RÄ
Chile .... ĈỊ-lẹ

Chiloé . . . . ĉị-lọ-Ẹ
Chocó . . . . ĉọ-KỌ
Chubut . . . . ĉụ-BỤT
Cienfuegos . . . . syęn-FWẸ-gǫs
Coahuila . . . . kọ-ä-WỊ-lä
Cochabamba . . . . kọ-ĉä-ƀÄM-bä
Colima . . . . kọ-LỊ-mä
Colombia . . . . kọ-LǪM-byä
Colón . . . . kọ-LǪN
Comayagua . . . . kọ-mäị-YÄ-gwä
Concepción . . . . kǫn-sęp-SYǪN
Coquimbo . . . . kọ-KỊM-bọ
Córdoba . . . . KǪR-đọ-ƀä
Corrientes . . . . kọ-R̄ỊẸN-tẹs
Corumbá . . . . kọ-rụm-BÄ
Costa Rica . . . . KǪS tä RỊ-kä
Cotopaxi . . . . kọ-tọ-PÄ-χị
Cuba . . . . KỤ-ƀä
Cucutá . . . . kụ-kụ-TÄ
Cuenca . . . . KWẸŋ-kä
Cumaná . . . . kụ-mä-NÄ
Cundinamarca . . . . kụn-dị-nä-MÄR-kä
Curitiba . . . . kụ-rị-TỊ-bä
Cuzco . . . . KỤS-kọ
Cuiabá . . . . kụ-yä-BÄ

D

Diamantina . . . . dị-ä-män-TỊ-nä
Dominica . . . . dọ-MỊ-nị-kä
Durango . . . . dụ-RÄŋ-gọ

E

Ecuador . . . . ẹ-kwä-đǪR
El Salvador . . . . ęl-säl-ƀä-đǪR
Entre Ríos . . . . ẸN-trẹ RỊ-ọs
Espírito Santo . . . . ęs-PỊ-rị-tọ SÄN-tọ

F

Flores . . . . FLỌ-rẹs
Florianópolis . . . . flọ-rị-ä-NỌ-pọ-lịs
Fortaleza . . . . fǫr-tä-LẸ-zä

G

Goias . . . . GǪỊ-äz
Granada . . . . grä-NÄ-đä

Guadalajara . . . . gwä-đä-lä-XÄ-rä
Guadeloupe . . . . gwä-då-LỤP
Guaira, La: See La Guaira
Guanajuato . . . . gwä-nä-XWÄ-tọ
Guatemala . . . . gwä-tẹ-MÄ-lä
Guayaquil . . . . gwä-yä-KỊL
Guerrero . . . . gẹ-R̄Ẹ-rọ
Guiana . . . . gị-YÄ-nä

H

Haiti . . . . Fr. ẹ-TỊ, Eng. HĀ-tị
Hidalgo . . . . ị-đÄL-gọ
Honduras . . . . Sp. ọn-DỤ-räs, Eng. họn-DỤ-rås
Huancayo . . . . wäŋ-KÄ-yọ
Humuya . . . . ụ-MỤ-yä

I

Ibagué . . . . ị-ƀä-GẸ
Ilo . . . . Ị-lọ
Iquique . . . . ị-KỊ-kẹ
Iquitos . . . . ị-KỊ-tọs
Itajai . . . . ị-tä-ZHÄỊ
Ixtaccíhuatl . . . . ịs-täk-SỊ-wä-tål

J

Jalapa . . . . χä-LÄ-pä
Jamaica . . . . Sp. Xä-MÄỊ-kä Eng. jå-MĀ-kå
Japurá . . . . zhä-pụ-RÄ
Juan Fernández . . . . Xwän fẹr-NÄN-dẹs

L

La Ceiba . . . . lä SẸỊ-ƀa
La Guaira . . . . lä GWÄỊ-rä
La Paz . . . . lä PÄS
La Plata . . . . lä PLÄ-tä
León . . . . lẹ-ỌN
Limón . . . . lị-MỌN
Linares . . . . lị-NÄ-rẹs

M

Maceió . . . . mä-sā-YỌ
Madeira . . . . mä-dā-rä

Magallanes	mä-gä-LÄ-nẹs
Magdalena	mäg-dä-LẸ-nä
Managua	mä-NÄ-gwä
Manaus	mä-NÄ-ụs
Manizales	mä-nị-ZÄ-lẹs
Maracaibo	mä-rä-KÄỊ-ƀọ
Maranhão	mä-rä-N̬ÃU
Martinique	mär-tị-NỊK
Matagalpa	mä-tä-GÄL-pä
Matanzas	mä-TÄN-säs
Mato Grosso	MÄ-tụ GRO-sụ
Mazatlán	mä-sä-TLÄN
Medellín	mẹ-đẹ-L̬ỊN
Mendoza	mẹn-DỌ-sä
Mercedes	mẹr-SẸ-đẹs
Mérida	MẸ-rị-đa
Meta	MẸ-tä
México	Sp. MẸ-xị-kọ Eng. MĘK-sį-kō
Michoacán	mị-ĉọ-ä-KÄN
Minas Gerais	MỊ-näz zhę-RÄ-ịs
Miranda	mị-RÄN-dä
Mollendo	mọ-L̬ẸN-dọ
Monterrey	mọn-tę-R̄ẸỊ
Montevideo	mọn-tẹ-ƀị-đẸ-ọ
Montserrat	mọn-sę-R̄ÄT
Morelia	mọ-RẸ-lyä
Morelos	mọ-RẸ-lọs

N

Nariño	nä-RỊ-ṉo
Natal	nä-TÄL
Nayarit	nä-yä-RỊT
Nicaragua	nị-kä-RÄ-gwä
Niterói	nị-tẹ-RỌỊ
Norte de Santander	NỌR-tẹ dẹ sän-tän-DẸR
Nuevo León	NWẸ-ƀo lẹ-ỌN

O

Oaxaca	ọ-wä-XÄ-kä
O'Higgins	Sp. ọ-Ị-xịns
Oriente	ọ-rị-ẸN-tẹ
Orinoco	ọ-rị-NỌ-kọ
Oruro	ọ-RỤ-rọ

P

Pacaraima . . . . . . pä-kä-RÄ̆I-mä
Pachuca . . . . . . pä-ĈỤ-kä
Paita . . . . . . PÄ̆Ị-tä
Panamá (without accent, conventional) . . . . . . pä-nä-MÄ̆
Pará . . . . . . pä-RÄ̆
Paraguay . . . . . . pä-rä-GWÄ̆Ị
Paraíba . . . . . . pä-rä-Ị-bä
Paramaribo . . . . . . pä-rä-mä-RỊ-ƀọ
Paraná . . . . . . pä-rä-NÄ̆
Paranaguá . . . . . . pä-rä-nä-GWÄ̆
Paranaíba . . . . . . pär-ä-nä-Ị-bä
Paysandú . . . . . . päị-sän-DỤ
Pelotas . . . . . . pẹ-LỌ-täs
Pernambuco . . . . . . pęr-näm-BỤ-kụ
Perú (without accent, conventional) . . . . . . pẹ-RỤ
Piauí . . . . . . pị-ä-WỊ
Pilcomayo . . . . . . pịl-kọ-MÄ̆-yọ
Pinar del Rio . . . . . . pị-NÄ̆R đęl RỊ-ọ
Pirapora . . . . . . pị-rä-PỌ-rä
Pisco . . . . . . PỊS-kọ
Piura . . . . . . PYỤ-rä
Popocatépetl . . . . . . pọ-pọ-cä-TẸ-pẹ-tål
Port Antonio . . . . . . pǫr-tän-TỌ-nyọ
Port-au-Prince . . . . . . Fr. pǫr-tọ-prăns (ă as in English can't)
Pôrto Alegre . . . . . . pọr-tụ ä-lę-grẹ
Potosí . . . . . . pọ-tọ-SỊ
Puebla . . . . . . PWẸ-ƀlä
Puerto Plata . . . . . . PWẸR-tọ PLÄ̆-tä
Puntarenas . . . . . . pụn-tä-RẸ-näs
Putumayo . . . . . . pụ-tụ-MÄ̆-yọ

Q

Querétaro . . . . . . kẹ-RẸ-tä-rọ
Quetzaltenango . . . . . . kęt-säl-tẹ-näŋ-gọ
Quintana Roo . . . . . . kịn-TÄ̆-nä RỌ-ọ
Quito . . . . . . KỊ-tọ

R

Recife . . . . . . rẹ-SỊ-fẹ
Riobamba . . . . . . rị-ọ-ƀÄ̆M-bä

Rio de Janeiro	RI̥-u̥-de̥-zhä-NĀ-ru̥
Río Grande [2]	RI̥-o̥ GRÄN-de̥
Rio Grande do Norte	RI̥-u GRÄN-de̥ du̥ NO̥R-te̥
Rio Grande do Sul	RI̥-u̥ GRÄN-de̥ du̥ SU̥L
Río Negro	RI̥-o̥ NE̥-gro̥
Rosario	ro̥-sä-ryo̥

S

St. Lucia	Sp. SÄN-tä lu̥-SI̥-ä, Eng. sānt lu̥-ČI̥-å
Salado	sä-LÄ-đo̥
Salaverry	sä-lä-ƀE̥-r̄i̥
Salta	SÄL-tä
Saltillo	säl-TI̥-l̥o̥
Salto	SÄL-to̥
Salvador	säl-ƀä-đO̥R
San Cristóbal	säŋ-kri̥s-to̥-ƀÄL
San Fernando	sän fe̥r-NÄN-do̥
San José	säŋ χo̥-SE̥
San Juan	säŋ XWÄN
San Luis Potosí	sän lu̥-I̥S po̥-to̥-SI̥
San Miguel	säm mi̥-GE̥L
San Salvador	sän säl-ƀä-đO̥R
Santa Catarina	SÄN-tä kä-tä-RI̥-nä
Santa Cruz	SÄN-tä KRU̥S
Santa Fé	SÄN-tä FE̥
Santander	sän-tan-DE̥R
Santarém	sän-tä-RẼ(ŋ)
Santiago	sän-ti̥-Ä-go̥
Santo Domingo	SÄN-to̥ đo̥-MI̥ŋ-go̥
Santos	SÄN-tu̥s
São Francisco	SÃU̥ frän-SI̥S-ku
São Luis	SÃU̥ lu̥-I̥Z
São Paulo	SÃU̥ PÄU̥-lu̥
São Vicente	SÃU̥ vi̥-SE̥N-te̥
Segovia	se̥-GO̥-ƀyä
Sergipe	se̥r-ZHI̥-pe̥
Sinaloa	si̥-nä-LO̥-ä
Sucre	SU̥-kre̥
Surinam(e)	su̥-ri̥-NÄM

[2] The Spanish system of orthography requires the use of the accent mark on the weak vowel i to give it syllabic value, whereas the Portuguese does not demand such accentuation. Cf. Spanish Bahía and Portuguese Bahia.

T

Tabasco . . . . tä-ƀÄS-kọ
Táchira . . . . TÄ-ĉị-rä
Tacna . . . . TÄK-nä
Tacubaya . . . . tä-kụ-ƀÄ-yä
Talara . . . . tä-LÄ-rä
Talca . . . . TÄL-kä
Tamaulipas . . . . tä-mäụ-LỊ-päs
Tampico . . . . täm-PỊ-kọ
Tapajós . . . . tä-pä-ZHǪZ
Tarapacá . . . . tä-rä-pä-KÄ
Tegucigalpa . . . . tẹ-gụ-sị-GÄL-pä
Temuco . . . . tẹ-MỤ-kọ
Tierra del Fuego . . . . TYĘ-r̄ä đęl FWẸ-gọ
Titicaca . . . . tị-tị-KÄ-kä
Tlaxcala . . . . tläs-KÄ-lä
Tobago . . . . tọ-ƀÄ-gọ
Tocantins . . . . tọ-kän-TỊNS
Tolima . . . . tọ-LỊ-mä
Toluca . . . . tọ-LỤ-kä
Torreón . . . . tǫ-r̄ę-ǪN
Trinidad . . . . trị-nị-đÄđ
Trujillo . . . . trụ-χỊ-l̬ọ
Tucumán . . . . tụ-kụ-MÄN
Tumuc-Humac . . . . tụ-MỤ-kụ-MÄK

U

Ucayali . . . . ụ-kä-YÄ-lị
Ulúa . . . . ụ-LỤ-ä
Uruguay . . . . ụ-rụ-GWÄỊ

V

Valdivia . . . . bäl-DỊ-ƀyä
Valencia . . . . bä-LẸN-syä
Valle . . . . BA-l̬ẹ
Valparaíso . . . . bäl-pä-rä-Ị-sọ
Venezuela . . . . bẹ-nẹ-SWẸ-lä
Veracruz . . . . bẹ-rä-KRỤS
Vitória . . . . vị-TǪ-ryä
Viña del Mar . . . . BỊ-n̬ä đęl MÄR

X

Xingú . . . . ŝịŋ-GỤ

Y

Yaracuy .... yä-rä-KỤ-ị
Yucatán .... yụ-kä-TÄN

Z

Zacapa .... sä-KÄ-pä
Zacatecas .... sä-kä-TẸ-käs
Zulia .... SỤ-lyä

APPENDIX II

A. REPUBLICS IN LATIN AMERICA

South America	*Year of Country's Own Official Estimate*	*Area*	*Population*
Argentina	1950	1,079,965	18,000,000
Bolivia	1948	416,000	3,787,800
Brazil	1950	3,286,170	52,000,000
Chile	1947	286,396	5,537,881
Colombia	1946	439,828	10,350,000
Ecuador	1946	100,000	3,350,000
Paraguay	1946	157,000	1,165,000
Peru	1946	500,000	7,860,000
Uruguay	1946	72,153	2,295,000
Venezuela	1946	352,170	4,299,638
TOTAL		6,689,682	108,645,319
Mexico			
Mexico	1948	758,258	24,447,649
Central America			
Costa Rica	1948	23,000	825,000
El Salvador	1946	13,176	2,015,000
Guatemala	1946	48,290	3,706,205
Honduras	1946	46,322	1,230,000
Nicaragua	1946	57,143	1,110,000
Panama	1946	34,169	710,000
TOTAL		222,100	9,596,205
West Indies—Republics			
Cuba	1946	44,164	5,052,000
Dominican Republic	1949	19,325	2,245,000
Haiti	1946	10,700	3,500,000
TOTAL		74,189	10,797,000

B. PRINCIPAL POSSESSIONS IN LATIN AMERICA

British Commonwealth			
Anguilla	1946	34	5,035
Antigua	1946	108	41,826
Bahamas	1943	4,375	68,846
Barbados	1946	166	192,841
Barbuda		62	900
British Guiana		83,000	376,000
British Honduras	1946	8,867	59,149
British Virgin Islands		67	6,500
Dominica	1946	305	47,682
Falkland Islands [1]		4,618	2,400

[1] Falkland Islands, with a total area of 4,618 square miles, lie 300 miles east of the entrance to the Strait of Magellan. Stanley on East Falkland is the community center, with a population of 1,250. Wool, tallow, hides and skins are the chief exports.

British Commonwealth (Cont.)	*Year of Country's Own Official Estimate*	*Area*	*Population*
Grenada	1946	133	72,374
Grenadines		22	22
Jamaica	1943	4,411	1,237,391
Montserrat	1946	32	14,322
Nevis	1946	50	11,331
St. Christopher (St. Kitts)	1946	68	30,000
St. Lucia	1946	233	69,955
St. Vincent and Lesser Grenadines	1946	150	61,660
Tobago	1946	116	27,679
Trinidad	1950	1,862	568,000
TOTAL		108,679	2,893,913
Netherlands			
Aruba	1943	70	40,000
Bonaire		95	5,796
Curaçao		210	75,176
Saba		5	1,200
St. Eustatius		12	1,000
St. Martin (Part of)		13	2,200
Surinam		54,300	181,000
TOTAL		54,705	306,372
France			
Desirade	1946	14	1,500
La Guyane française		37,740	35,000
Guadeloupe and Grande-Terre		583	304,200
Les Saintes		5	1,700
Marie-Galante		58	15,000
Martinique		385	265,000
Petite-Terre		1	
St. Barthelemy		0	2,500
St. Martin (Part of)		20	4,300
TOTAL		35,814	629,200
United States			
Panama Canal Zone		549	52,000
Puerto Rico	1950	3,421	2,205,398
Virgin Islands:			
St. Croix		84	12,096
St. John		20	747
St. Thomas		28	13,811
TOTAL		4,102	2,284,052
GRAND TOTAL—ALL LATIN AMERICA		7,947,529	159,599,710

APPENDIX III

SELECTED INDEXES, YEARBOOKS AND ADDITIONAL REFERENCES

INDEXES

Handbook of Latin American Studies. Harvard University Press, Cambridge, Mass.

Books Abroad. An International Literary Quarterly. University of Oklahoma Press, Norman, Oklahoma.

Current Geographical Publications. Additions to the *Research Catalogue* of The American Geographical Society.

Cumulative Book Index.

International Index to Periodicals.

Latin America. A Selected Guide to Publications in English. Royal Institute of International Affairs. London and New York.

LEA (*Librarians Editors Authors*). Pan American Union, Washington, D. C.

Public Affairs Information Service.

Readers' Guide to Periodical Literature.

United Nations Documents Index.

United States Government Publications. Monthly Catalog of United States Public Documents.

YEARBOOKS

The American Yearbook. Thomas Nelson and Sons, New York.

The Statesman's Yearbook. The Macmillan Co., New York.

The South American Handbook. Trade and Travel Publication, Ltd. London (H. W. Wilson Co., Agents in the United States).

The Yearbook of The West Indies and Countries of The Caribbean—including The Bermudas, The Bahamas and The Guianas. Thomas Skinner and Company, Ltd., New York.

United Nations. Food and Agriculture Organization of the United Nations. *Yearbook of Food and Agricultural Statistics.* Vol. I Production, Vol. II Trade—Commerce.

United Nations. Food and Agriculture Organization of the United Nations. *Yearbook of Forest Products Statistics.*

United Nations. Statistical Office. *Statistical Yearbook.*

United Nations. Statistical Office of the United Nations in collaboration with the Department of Social Affairs. *Demographic Yearbook.*

United Nations. *Year Book of the United Nations.* Columbia University Press in cooperation with the United Nations, New York.

United States. Bureau of The Census. *Statistical Abstract of The United States.*

United States. Bureau of Foreign and Domestic Commerce. *The Foreign Commerce and Navigation of The United States.*

United States. Bureau of Mines. *Minerals Yearbook.*

United States. Department of Agriculture. *Agricultural Statistics.*

United States. Department of Agriculture. *The Yearbook of Agriculture.*

United States. Department of Commerce. Office of International Trade. *Foreign Commerce Yearbook.*

ADDITIONAL REFERENCES

United Nations. Department of Economic Affairs. *Economic Survey of Latin America.*

United States. Department of Agriculture. Office of Foreign Agricultural Relations. *Foreign Agriculture,* and *Foreign Crops and Markets.*

United States. Department of Commerce. Office of International Trade. *Foreign Commerce Weekly; International Reference Service;* and *World Trade in Commodities.*

United States Tariff Commission. *Reports.*

United States Government Organization Manual. United States Government Printing Office, Washington, D. C.

INDEX

INDEX

D

E

N

U

V

W

Y